S0-BZR-057

GOVERNORS STATE UNIVERSITY LIBRARY
3 1611 00312 0398

A General Model for Multivariate Analysis

INTERNATIONAL SERIES IN DECISION PROCESSES

INGRAM OLKIN, Consulting Editor

Statistical Theory of Reliability and Life Testing: Probability Models, R. E. Barlow and F. Proschan
Probability Theory and Elements of Measure Theory, H. Bauer
Time Series, R. Brillinger
Decision Analysis for Business, R. Brown
Probability and Statistics for Decision Making, Ya-lun Chow
A Guide to Probability Theory and Application, C. Derman, L. J. Gleser, and I. Olkin
Introduction to Statistics and Probability, E. Dudewicz
A General Model for Multivariate Analysis, J. D. Finn
Statistics: Probability, Inference, and Decision, 2d ed., W. L. Hays and R. L. Winkler
Statistics: Probability, Inference, and Decision, Volumes I and II and Combined ed., W. L. Hays and R. L. Winkler
Introduction to Statistics, R. A. Hultquist
Introductory Statistics with FORTRAN, A. Kirch
Reliability Handbook, B. A. Kozlov and I. A. Ushakov (edited by J. T. Rosenblatt and L. H. Koopmans)
An Introduction to Probability, Decision, and Inference, I. H. LaValle
Elements of Probability and Statistics, S. A. Lippman
Modern Mathematical Methods for Economics and Business, R. E. Miller
Applied Multivariate Analysis, S. J. Press
Fundamental Research Statistics for the Behavioral Sciences, J. T. Roscoe
Applied Probability, W. A. Thompson, Jr.
Quantitative Methods and Operations Research for Business, R. E. Trueman
Elementary Statistical Methods, 3d ed., H. M. Walker and J. Lev
An Introduction to Bayesian Inference and Decision, R. L. Winkler

FORTHCOMING TITLES

A Basic Course in Statistics with Sociological Applications, 3d ed., T. R. Anderson and M. Zelditch, Jr.
Fundamentals of Decision Analysis, I. H. LaValle

A General Model for Multivariate Analysis

JEREMY D. FINN
State University of New York at Buffalo

HOLT, RINEHART AND WINSTON, INC.
New York Chicago San Francisco Atlanta
Dallas Montreal Toronto London Sydney

Library of Congress Cataloging in Publication Data

Finn, Jeremy D.
A general model for multivariate analysis.

(International series in decision processes)
Bibliography: p. 410
1. Multivariate analysis. 2. Analysis of variance.
I. Title.
QA278.F56 519.5'3 74-8629
ISBN 0-03-083239-X

Printed in the United States of America
4 5 6 7 038 9 8 7 6 5 4 3 2 1

To J, K, and L

Preface

Scientists faced with the task of analyzing and understanding human behavior are in constant need of models by which they may test hypotheses involving a greater quantity and complexity of behavioral variables. In response to this need, multivariate models for the application of such techniques as analysis of variance, regression analysis, and analysis of covariance are gaining in accessibility and usage.

Multivariate analysis may be conceptualized in two ways. First, it is a means of analyzing behavioral phenomena. It is based upon the realization that hardly any form of human behavior worthy of study has only a single facet; that behind any measurable trait are components that covary only partially; that a "better" scientific description of any behavior is derived through some degree of finer analysis. Further, no observable behavior results from a single antecedent. The "principle of multiple causes" is one we confront in all except the smallest analytic units (for example, the "one-gene, one-enzyme theory" of genetic action).

The second conceptualization of multivariate analysis is fitting a set of algebraic models to situations with multiple random variables, usually criterion or outcome variables, which are measures of the same sample(s) of subjects. Behavioral data are often of this form. Intelligence is measured in terms of at least a quantitative and a verbal ability. Following Guilford (1959), creativity is measured by the administration of at least six separate scales. Often two achievement scores, one for speed and one for power, are assigned to a test respondent. The class of experimental designs known as "repeated measures" designs denotes a multivariate situation. In this case each subject is measured on a given scale at two or more points in time or under differing experimental conditions. The evaluation of the attainment of course objectives in either experimental or traditional instructional settings is likely to require multivariate analysis procedures. With multivariate models, the simultaneous consideration of the attainment of several cognitive levels or of both cognitive and non-cognitive instructional outcomes is facilitated.

In each instance, the analysis of a single summary measure—for example, a total or average score—will result in the loss of the information conveyed by the individual scales. Statistical analysis of each of a series of measures separately will result in redundancy, which in turn will threaten the validity of the interpretations drawn from the data. Use of the appropriate multivariate model will allow the researcher to retain the multiple scores and to treat them simultaneously, giving appropriate consideration to the correlations among them.

Multivariate techniques comprise two related methodologies, each with its own objectives. The first of these is concerned with the discovery of an underlying structure of response data that have been collected, or of the behaviors they represent. Factor analysis is employed in the attempt to locate and isolate sets of measures with the properties that the tests or scales within the set have relatively high intercorrelations with each other, and that scales of one set have small or zero intercorrelations with those of another set. If sets of variables that contribute very little to discrimination among subjects can be identified, they are often ignored or eliminated. In this sense, factor analysis or a simpler technique, component analysis, is used as a data-reduction device. Recent contributions by Bock and Bargmann (1966) and by Jöreskog (1969) allow the researcher to hypothesize, from psychological theory or from prior analysis, a given latent structure underlying a set of measures, and to apply statistical criteria to test the fit of the observed outcomes to the hypothesis.

A second set of multivariate procedures, which constitutes the primary focus of this book, includes multivariate extensions of such commonly used estimation and hypothesis-testing procedures as analysis of variance, analysis of covariance, and regression analysis. Through these methods questions may be answered about the contribution of structured and identifiable independent variables to the explanation of between-individual or between-group variation in one or more criterion measures. Examples of such questions in multivariate form might include: "Does intelligence predict these four achievement measures?" "Are there significant differences between control and experimental groups on speed as well as accuracy of learning, or on four body dimensions?" "Does the mean growth curve of the group administered an experimental drug differ from that of a placebo group?" The dependent or criterion variables generally have nonzero intercorrelations.

The model implied by each question is of a form familiar to most behavioral scientists. A primary purpose of this book is to describe the multiple-criterion form of these models, and to provide the computational tools which facilitate data analysis under that form.

A general model for multivariate analysis describes the analysis of quantitative data through application of a "general linear model." Linear estimation and tests of hypotheses are discussed, which are univariate and multivariate forms of the following techniques:

The summary of raw and transformed multivariable data
Multiple correlation and regression
Canonical correlation
Principal components
Analysis of variance, with equal or unequal subclass frequencies
Analysis of covariance
Discriminant analysis
Step-down analysis

To provide sequence with other statistical materials, the univariate multiple regression model is introduced first, and is discussed in greatest mathematical detail. Multivariate regression and univariate and multivariate analysis of variance are presented as extensions of that basic model. The analysis-of-variance presentation is less detailed and contains more exemplary material. The remaining techniques are viewed as by-products of the formulation of the regression and variance analysis models. Particular emphasis is given to topics that have been inadequately described in current journals and texts in the social sciences. For example, lengthy discussion is devoted to reparameterization in the analysis of variance and to the estimation of parameters in linear models.

Five sample problems are introduced in the first chapter and are described throughout the text as the appropriate analysis techniques are encountered. These are relatively large problems. Hand computation in multivariate analysis is not feasible for any but the most trivial examples. The sample problems were selected instead to exemplify a variety of real design and analysis problems. The analyses for the five samples were originally performed on the MULTIVARIANCE program (Finn, 1972d). The computer input-output listings are provided as an appendix to the text (separately numbered C.1 through C.166), along with a brief version of the MULTIVARIANCE user's manual. The statistical results are transcribed to the earlier chapters as they are discussed.

This book is addressed to users and potential users of multivariate statistical techniques. Readers should have familiarity with univariate statistical theory, to a degree provided by, say, a good one-year course in applied statistical methods. Topics that are especially requisite are estimation and significance testing in fixed-effects analysis of variance; the design and estimation of planned contrasts in analysis-of-variance models; simple univariate regression models and analysis; and the basic concepts of covariance and correlation. The book relies entirely on the statement and formulation of linear models, and some facility with these skills is essential. Knowledge of the algebra of matrices is desirable but not necessary. Those aspects of linear algebra employed in the book are discussed briefly in Chapter 2.

This book may be read in several ways. As a text in multivariate analysis, the organization provides sequence for detailed study of the general linear model and its applications. Supplementary material on matrix algebra plus computer routines for class exercises are recommended. As a reference, the examples may be studied by themselves as illustrations of (a) the data for which multivariate models are appropriate and (b) the presentation and interpretation of the outcomes. Toward this end, study of the computer runs and the respective problem discussions is likely to be especially useful.

This book has been in preparation a long time. In that time there have been many people who have helped in one way or another. I wish to thank them all.

In particular, I owe a great deal to Professor Darell Bock of The University of Chicago. Without his teachings this book, and more, would not have been possible. I wish to thank Professor Ingram Olkin, who has been continually supportive. His reviews and comments have had a major impact on the form of the book. Two students, Kathleen VanEvery and Nancy Breland, have provided useful reviews and suggestions for improvements.

Also there are those who have lent their data as examples and are acknowledged in the first chapter, those who have helped in the development of the MULTIVARIANCE program, and many who have made individual suggestions which are incorporated in the book. Thank you. Computer time and assistance in running the examples were provided by the Computing Center of the State University of New York at Buffalo.

In the preparation of the manuscript, Jeanette Ninas Johnson and the staff at Holt, Rinehart and Winston spent many difficult hours with the material. The manuscript was typed by Jacqueline Rance and Diana Webster. I am glad it is they who have their jobs. I am especially grateful to my wife, Joyce, who sat up many evenings reading and re-reading galley proofs with me. Although her knowledge of statistics increased only a little, her knowledge of Greek has grown immensely.

Stockholm, Sweden
June 1974

Jeremy D. Finn

Contents

A General Model for Multivariate Analysis

Section 1

Introduction

CHAPTER 1

Multivariate Analysis

1.1 PERSPECTIVE

This book describes the application of one general statistical model to behavioral data. The model frequently has high appeal. It is general; it is simple; there are available computer programs; and almost any behavioral data can be analyzed according to one form or another of the model. This same appeal function also requires that we be cautious. For we must ask whether this model is the correct one for our particular research assumptions and hypotheses.

It is not always clear whether mathematical models that contain estimable parameters, and that reflect the behavioral models we assume, actually exist. Frequently they do not, and models must be constructed for specific cases. Often enough, these endeavors culminate in formulations that have a more general applicability. Statistical journals publicize large numbers of such cases. In the discipline of psychology, no instance is more outstanding than Thurstone's attempts to discover processes basic to the then-held concept of general intelligence. The by-product of these endeavors was the development and dissemination of a widely used technique, multiple factor analysis.

Multivariate linear models are not always applicable to the specific problems at hand. And indeed the subset of multivariate procedures presented in this book represents only a small portion of those conceivable. Yet the procedures discussed in this book under the rubric "multivariate analysis techniques" share a resemblance to models of behavior in their very representation of behavior as having *multiple antecedents* and experimental outcomes as having *multiple facets*.

Students of human behavior, with frames of reference from the extremes of atomism to those of holism, find themselves with multiple observations of each subject. For the atomist, this may involve tracing the development of a specific trait over time, or of its variants with specific imposed or natural stimulation. Bloom (1964) has summarized more than a thousand longitudinal studies of the development of physical characteristics, cognitive achievement, interests and attitudes, and personality measures through the childhood years. Each characteristic is represented by responses to the same or parallel tests, at different ages, by the same individuals. The data are of a naturally multivariate form, and various multivariate growth models are useful for describing the trends over time. Similarly, traits from a variety of disciplines are studied over time or under varying experimental conditions: the effectiveness of drugs with given diseases, over time or after repeated administrations; the change in value of certain preferred stocks over time or with modifications in the company's and competitors' products; the gradual consumption of the nation's natural resources; changes in national birth rates; and so on.

For the holist there are problems of a different multivariate nature. Here the outcome of an experiment or comparative study, at a single point in time, is completely represented only by multiple measurement scales. This may occur when the construct of interest is composed of well-defined but conceptually smaller units *or* when there is some lack of certainty about the definition of the construct, and a subsequent need to measure it in several ways. Generally the multiple measures are moderately to highly intercorrelated, as aspects of the same behavioral phenomena.

Examples of such cases abound. All useful theories of personality attribute behavior to a multiplicity of underlying components. Murray (1938) has postulated a series of idiosyncratic "needs" as the driving forces in observed human behavior. For example, with respect to the seeking, giving, or withholding of affection, the individual will respond in a manner determined largely by his needs for affiliation, rejection, nurturance, and succorance. Thus the individual's capacity to exhibit a given degree of affection is reflected in four measurements on these partial constructs. They may in turn be analyzed simultaneously for between-individual or between-group variation.

Academic achievement is best described in terms of behaviors of progressively greater complexity. Both *The Conditions of Learning* (Gagné, 1966) and *The Taxonomy of Educational Objectives* (Bloom, 1956; Krathwohl, Bloom, and Masia, 1964) define categories of intellectual achievement. They are ordered according to the ability of an individual to achieve a given level of content mastery, only after having mastered the behaviors of lower or simpler levels. The *Taxonomy* pertaining to cognitive achievements lists six general levels of content mastery: knowledge, comprehension, application, analysis, synthesis, and evaluation. Each level is defined further in terms of subcategories. For example, comprehension includes the abilities to translate materials from one form of communication to another; to interpret, explain, or summarize a communication; and to extrapolate trends or sequences beyond given data to determine implications and consequences. Although an individual may achieve at one level in the hierarchy only after having mastered prior levels, the progression is far from absolute. As a result, a person's achievement with respect to any curriculum is adequately described only by providing estimates of achievement at every level. For analysis, the resulting data are both multivariate and naturally ordered by complexity.

There are additional situations in which multivariate analysis is particularly useful. A tester may be interested in the simultaneous reliability of a series of items or tests, which may not be independent or equally intercorrelated. Variable-reducing analyses, such as component or discriminant analysis, are of practical value for placing individuals into homogeneous groupings, from multiple behavioral measures. Multivariate procedures may be applied to sets of measures that have been identified through cluster or factor analysis to have common components. This may be accomplished without the necessity of forming arbitrary linear composites of the measures, such as the summation of scores on scales having high intercorrelations with a particular "factor." Finally, since most computer programs for multivariate methods also provide results for each of the criterion measures separately, their use facilitates the simultaneous performance of a number of univariate analyses. This feature is of value, for example, in the comparison of results from raw and transformed data (see Pruzek and Kleinke, 1967).

In every case, it is critical that the variables of any set share a *common conceptual meaning*, in order for the multivariate results to be valid. It is an easy matter to abuse, say, an extensive computer program to perform analyses on sets of variables which bear no "real-life" counterpart as a group. Likewise, an extensive program, such as MULTIVARIANCE, may be used to produce tests of significance that are quantitatively correct but do not conform to assumed probability statements. This may be due either to the quantity of nonindependent results, or to their exploratory nature. When research yields multiple response measures, the employment of rigorous scientific methodology resting on strong design formulations is more important than ever.

One of the most concise treatments of the design and conduct of quantitative evaluation of behavioral data is provided by Federer in the introductory chapter of *Experimental Design* (Macmillan, 1955). Federer's brief but important chapter is recommended reading for anyone concerned with problems in the behavioral sciences. The evaluation process may be conceptualized as having six aspects:

1. Discovery of a behavioral problem.
2. Searching for existing solutions to the problem.
3. Selection of an approach to the study of the unknowns and the statement of expectations.
4. Formulation of the technical methodology to be employed in the evaluation.
5. Execution of the technical formulations.
6. Interpretation of the research outcomes.

Quantitative analysis forms only a small portion of evaluation methodology, and we might be chagrined at the disproportionate quantity of reference material we have for this one aspect. However, quantitative thinking modes can form a basis for formulation of all phases of the evaluation process.

Unresolved research problems are subjected to evaluation through the principles of scientific method. The hypothetico-deductive approach to empirical investigation has been well described by Ellis (1952). The primary assumption is the existence of a research hypothesis, or expected solution to the problem, prior to the collection of quantitative data. Although unexpected findings have often been generated for verification by hypothesis-seeking approaches to data analysis, the validation of such findings through replication is essential. Testing hypotheses drawn from earlier studies and from behavioral theory has the advantage of providing two sets of confirmatory data, one logical and one empirical. When the two agree, the conclusions form a firm base and are likely to replicate. If one has a large set of data, dividing it into two parts—one for generating hypotheses and the other for confirmation—can maintain this confirmatory power.

Researchers often disavow any prior knowledge from which to draw hypotheses. Yet in informal discussion, the same individuals may admit that they really believe the new approach to be superior to the old or that their results will be essentially the same as another investigator's, in a different situation. These are hypotheses. That is, they are informed best guesses as to the experimental outcomes. Frequently a problem yields competing hypotheses, each of which would suggest a different outcome. These too should be stated and tested, as competing explanations. Nothing is lost, for no amount of exploration or estimation is precluded by testing prior beliefs.

1.2 THE MULTIVARIATE GENERAL LINEAR MODEL*

A *model* of an object or event is any attempt at representing that object or event other than the original occurrence or representation. The general linear model is a very specific sort of model, involving the algebraic representation of relationships among observable human characteristics. In most studies the symbolic representation of such relationships is the second model applied to the observed behavior. The first is the modeling of behavioral constructs through algebraic or quantitative representation. This occurs in the process of *measurement*. In contrast, we will restrict ourselves here to the analysis of the already quantified responses. If the measurements are objective, reliable, and valid, we will be willing to assume that such quantitative indicators correspond in important ways to the constructs of interest and will yield insight into their behavior.

Let us denote as y_i the quantified response of subject i to a single outcome or criterion measure y. Subject i may have been assigned to, or selected from, a population of observations identified by sharing common attributes on one or more exactly observable traits. In addition to the y_i then, subject i is identified by having values on a set of antecedent or independent variables x_j, hypothesized to be related in some way to y. The x_j may be categorical variables defining the population, or measured variables having ordinal, interval, or ratio scales, or both. x_{ji} is the value on variable x_j for subject i.

The process of fitting a linear model to data is one of determining a set of coefficients, a_j, that multiply the x_{ji} in order to reproduce y_i as closely as possible for a set of observations. The model may be written as

$$\begin{aligned} y_i &= \textstyle\sum_j a_j x_{ji} + \epsilon_i \\ &= a_1 x_{1i} + a_2 x_{2i} + \cdots + a_j x_{ji} + \epsilon_i \end{aligned} \qquad (1.2.1)$$

ϵ_i represents the extent to which y_i cannot be reproduced by the weighted function for the particular subject. If y is a random variable and x_{ji} represents a fixed

*For a more extensive discussion of linear statistical models, Chapter 5 of *Introduction to Linear Statistical Models, Volume 1* (Graybill, 1961) is highly recommended.

value of x_j, then ϵ will also be a random variable. It represents both the extent to which the model is incompletely specified and the measurement error in y.

To state that "the model fits the data" implies that the ϵ_i are small, and that y_i can be known from knowledge of the x_{ji}. Researchers in the behavioral sciences are perhaps more accustomed to asking, "Is there a significant difference between means?" or "Is a significant amount of variation in the dependent variable attributable to the predictors?" than "Does the model fit the data?" Yet when the components of the linear model are clearly specified and understood, it will be seen that the two sets of questions are in fact the same.

Equation 1.2.1 is a model in two senses. First, the equation specifies the components into which the observation is partitioned—that is, some function of the particular x_{ji} and all else. The original event y_i is represented as the sum of two components, one being itself a function of $j=1, 2, \ldots, J$ additional events chosen in advance by the researcher. Second, the relationship between the additional events x_j and the rest of the model is *linear*; that is, all weights a_j are to unit power only.

In still another sense, however, Eq. 1.2.1 is not truly a model. The sum of the right-hand components of 1.2.1 is exactly y_i, and not some other representation of it. Thus, for consistency, we will refer to the portion of 1.2.1 exclusive of ϵ_i as the linear model. Indeed, the most important modeling in behavioral research is the representation of the outcome y_i, by other selected and weighted measures, x_j. ϵ_i is commonly relegated the function of depicting unknown factors, hypothesized to be of a random and/or trivial nature in influencing y_i, at least when compared to the purposefully selected antecedent measures.

The variables x_j may be of several types. When the x_j are entirely categorical measurements and have values 0 and 1, the linear model is usually referred to as the analysis-of-variance model. The question of fit to sample data—that is, of the relative contributions of $\Sigma_j a_j x_{ji}$ and ϵ_i in yielding information about y_i—is most commonly phrased as "Are there significant differences among means of the J populations represented by the samples?" When x_j are scores on J measured variables, the model is that of regression. The question asked most often is one of the percentage of variation in y attributable to one or more of the x_j. Finally, the analysis-of-covariance model is the form of Eq. 1.2.1 when some of the x_j are categorical and others are measured.

The variables x_j may themselves be nonunit powers or cross products without destroying the linearity of the model. The variables x_j in unpowered form comprise the *additive* portion of the model. Any x_j that are nonunit powers of a measure, or the cross products of two or more other x_j, comprise the *nonadditive* or *interactive* portion of the model. Thus the general linear model as represented by 1.2.1 will suffice for a variety of polynomial analyses, as well as all linear analyses of variance, including interaction terms.

Model 1.2.1 is *multivariate* when y is a vector variable having more than a single outcome measure. A separate set of weights a_j is necessary for each outcome measure; that is, each element of y. The only restriction we shall impose is that all elements of y must have the same antecedents x_j.

Application

The most significant research in education assumes both multiple sources of influence and multiple outcomes of educational process. An essential condition in such research is the explicitly utilized assumption that the educational enterprise has *both* a manifest and latent curriculum and yields *both* intended outcomes, as well as others that co-occur and may not be anticipated. The multiple-input, multiple-outcome assumption is frequently formulated as a model depicting an educational setting.

For example, antecedent measures may be home and school variables (Coleman, 1966), time needed and time spent in learning (Carroll, 1963), environmental process variables (Wolf, 1965), educational opportunity and educational press (Finn, 1972c), or pupil entry behavior, affective entry characteristics, and instructional quality (Bloom, 1971). Outcome measures may be classified as cognitive and affective (Bloom, 1956; Krathwohl, Bloom, and Masia, 1964), higher and lower-level cognitive processes (Bloom, 1956), or in other categories (Finn, 1972a).

When a linear model in the form of Eq. 1.2.1 is employed with educational data, the independent variables are usually assumed fixed and known. The outcome measures comprise random variables or *variates*. Thus *multivariate* models are usually appropriate when a study contains multiple outcome, or dependent, or criterion measures. They frequently constitute the most realistic statistical models for behavioral data, especially when the research evolves from a multiple-input multiple-outcome paradigm.

The multivariate techniques described in this book are generalizations of well-known analysis-of-variance and regression procedures to the case of multiple dependent variables. For example, with several groups of subjects we may wish to test that group means are equal, not on a single outcome variable but on two or more intercorrelated variables simultaneously. For this a multivariate extension of the usual F test may be employed. Or we may wish to predict achievement in a literature course, from one or more instructional variables. Achievement may be measured by both an indicator of cognitive performance, as well as an index of the pupils' attitudes toward reading literary material. For this, a multivariate extension (here bivariate) of the multiple linear regression model is appropriate. We may test for the prediction of the two intercorrelated outcomes, which jointly describe the results of the course or unit.

In each case the multivariate approach attends to the data as a whole, rather than to a few isolated or transient aspects. The analysis of a single summary measure (such as a total or average score) will result in the loss of information conveyed by the individual scales. The results will have dubitable meaning. Analyses of each of the measures separately results in redundancy to the extent that the measures are nonindependent. Statistical error rates may be multiplied manyfold, and the replicability of the study is reduced. The appropriate multivariate model retains the multiple scores as a set of interrelated traits. It is essential that the set be conceptually meaningful!

The number of dependent variables determines whether the form of the model is univariate (1), bivariate (2), or multivariate (generally). In every instance, the multivariate results simplify to the familiar univariate form when the number of criteria is reduced to one. The dependent variables are assumed to be measured—that is, having a numerical scale with at least ordinal properties.

There is often some confusion of terms in referring to linear models, especially when the number of independent variables is considered. We shall assume the following conventions. When the independent variables are measured (regression model), the number of independent variables or predictors determines whether the model is simple regression (one predictor), or multiple regression (generally). Thus the regression model with one predictor and one criterion is the univariate simple regression model; with one predictor and multiple criteria, the multivariate simple regression model; with many predictors and many outcomes, the multivariate multiple regression model; and so on.

When the independent variables are categorical and subjects are classified by group membership, the model is that of analysis of variance. A one-factor design with each subject having many outcome measures requires a one-way multivariate analysis-of-variance model; a two-way or many-way design with multiple outcome variables requires a many-way multivariate analysis-of-variance model; and so on. Whenever each subject has only a single outcome measure, the model is univariate, regardless of the complexity of the sampling design. The only exception of course, is in random or mixed-effects models, which include random independent variables.

The independent variables in analysis-of-variance designs may reflect *either* experimental or naturally occurring groups. Computationally, there is no distinction, and means may be declared significantly different or not, in either case. However, causal inferences may be drawn only if subjects have been randomly assigned to treatment groups, and introduction of the experimental condition is controlled by the researcher. In this case the study may be designated as an *experiment*; in the comparison of naturally occurring or intact groups the research may be termed a *comparative study*. Both are included among the research examples that follow.

In multiple regression there is no necessary restriction upon the correlations of the predictor variables. Also, in analysis of variance the independent variables may be correlated. Specifically, this implies that valid and exact analyses of variance may be conducted with unequal subclass frequencies, and with contrast parameters that are not orthogonal. A special case, simplified only for textbook presentation, is the univariate equal-N analysis-of-variance model. Under the more general model presented here, it is not necessary to impose these artificial restrictions in order to fit the data to known analysis techniques.

As exemplified by Eq. 1.2.1, there is a direct parallel between regression and analysis-of-variance models. It is shown in later chapters that in general the two are identical and may be solved by a single estimation algorithm. The only distinction between them is the nature of the independent variables—measured or categorical. The common linear model with one or more intercorrelated independent variables of either sort, and one or more intercorrelated criteria, is the *multivariate general linear model.* All analysis-of-variance and regression problems may be solved as special cases. Analysis-of-covariance situations, with *both* measured and group membership independent variables, are yet another specialization. Data-manipulation practices such as the dichotomization of measured variables are obviated when the general model can be fit to data as they occur.

Multivariate models yield test statistics that are simple extensions of their univariate counterparts; for example, a single *F*-ratio to test H_0: $\boldsymbol{\mu}_1 = \boldsymbol{\mu}_2$, but for $\boldsymbol{\mu}_1$ and $\boldsymbol{\mu}_2$ being vectors composed of several means. In addition, several uniquely multivariate functions may be obtained as part of an analysis under the general model. These are referred to as canonical analyses, two of which are canonical correlation analysis and discriminant function analysis. Both are procedures for identifying linear combinations of criterion measures that have specified optimum properties. In the multivariate multiple regression model, the canonical correlations are measures of association of the criteria and the measured predictors. Linear functions of both sets of variables are identified which are themselves maximally intercorrelated. In the multivariate analysis-of-variance model, linear functions of the criteria are identified that have maximal between-group variation. In both instances, weighted combinations of measured variables replace the original measures for analysis purposes. This substitution introduces complexities that are not usually offset by the gain in parsimony.

1.3 APPROACH TO THE GENERAL MULTIVARIATE MODEL

There are several emphases in this book that reflect a philosophy of social science research and should be explicated. First, it is assumed that a workable paradigm involves the testing of major research hypotheses for decisions about essential acceptance. When the model consists of multiple outcome variables, multivariate test statistics provide the primary decision-making information.

Emphasis is placed upon the statement, interpretation, and testing of planned contrasts in analysis-of-variance models. The majority of elementary statistics texts first presents the partitioning of sums of squares for main effects and interactions—that is, for "omnibus" hypotheses of the sort H_0: $\mu_1 = \mu_2 = \cdots = \mu_J$. Discussion of planned or *post hoc* contrasts is reserved for later sections. The approach here is the reverse. Both because planned comparisons are usually of interest to researchers and because of their superior inferential power, the estimation of single-degree-of-freedom effects is presented first and in greatest detail. Sums of squares and tests for omnibus effects are viewed as optional "pooled" functions of the more detailed partition.

Specific estimates and univariate test statistics are stressed for interpretation beyond the acceptance decision. These include the simple, partial, and multiple correlation coefficients, the point and interval estimates of regression coefficients, mean differences, predicted means and residuals, and so on. The magnitudes of multiple univariate test statistics may be compared. Although they are not independent for any one hypothesis, univariate statistics aid in identifying the variates most and least affected by their antecedent(s). In contrast, canonical correlation and discriminant function analyses, which depend upon complex functions of the original measures, yield only minimal interpretive data, and are given minor emphasis. The purposes of social science are best served by the simplest and most straightforward techniques that yield valid research answers.

Discussion of each model is separated into "estimation" and "hypothesis testing." Estimation in regression models involves finding "best" estimates of the partial regression coefficients and their standard errors, the correlations between criteria and predictors, scores predicted by the regression model, and residuals. Hypothesis testing involves decisions about the nullity of the regression or correlation coefficients or about variation in the criteria attributable to the independent variables.

Estimation in analysis of variance involves determining sample values for means, mean differences, their directions and standard errors, means predicted under the model, and residuals. Hypothesis testing involves decisions about the nullity of population mean differences, in specific or general patterns.

In a sense, the presentation of estimation and hypothesis testing is in reverse order. Obtaining estimates of effects is dependent upon the knowledge that the effects are meaningful and not random; that is, dependent upon the results of the significance tests. The reader is asked to excuse the use of this reverse order, since the discussion of estimation provides for a better initial description of the effects themselves. *Reestimation* of terms in a reduced model is presented for the situation where tests indicate that not all of the original estimates are necessary.

Finally, the emphasis in this book is computational. The similarities and distinctions of specific models become the most obvious at this level. To understand the computations being applied to behavioral data involves comprehension of where they are useful *and* where they are likely to misrepresent the information content.

Five studies, which require analysis through a variety of multivariate linear models, have been selected. Each is briefly described in Section 1.4. The studies are introduced into each chapter as the appropriate analysis techniques are encountered. In addition, an attempt has been made to exemplify the minimal complete and clear *presentation* of the outcomes. It is each researcher's responsibility to strive toward these criteria in his own presentations.

The MULTIVARIANCE program has been used extensively for the examples. However, computing flow and algorithms are not given here. The program may be obtained from National Educational Resources, Inc., 215 Kenwood Avenue, Ann Arbor, Michigan 48103. Flow diagrams and algorithms are given in Enslein, Ralston, and Wilf (in press).

1.4 FIVE SAMPLE PROBLEMS

Sample Problem 1 – Creativity and Achievement*

In recent years the concept of creativity as an ability to exhibit new and unique idiosyncratic behaviors has grown in importance in the minds of edu-

*The data for this problem are selected from a larger set collected by Dr. I. Leon Smith, Yeshiva University, New York, N.Y.

cators. Although creativity is conceptually different from general intelligence both in definition and in its effects upon various cognitive and noncognitive achievements, independently developed measures of creativity have shown little unique reliable variance. It is the purpose of this study to determine whether creativity can be shown to contribute to a class of cognitive achievements that require a high level of functioning—that is, those known as divergent achievements.

Divergent achievement within an educational setting involves situations in which the individual is expected to create new and unique responses or organizations, where such responses were lacking in the stimulus situation, and where there is no single correct response. This definition necessitates additional criteria for evaluation. The levels of divergent achievement chosen for the study include the processes of *synthesis* and *evaluation*, as defined by Handbook I of the *Taxonomy of Educational Objectives* (Bloom, 1956). It is the assumption of the *Taxonomy* that achievement at lower levels (knowledge, comprehension, application, analysis) is necessary but not sufficient for achievement at the higher levels to be manifested. *Synthesis* is defined by the *Taxonomy* as "The putting together of elements and parts so as to form a whole. This involves the process of working with pieces, parts, elements, etc., and arranging and combining them in such a way as to constitute a pattern or structure not clearly there before" (p. 206). *Evaluation* involves "Quantitative and qualitative judgments about the extent to which material and methods satisfy criteria" (p. 207).*

The major research question is whether an individual's level of creativity is a determinant of divergent achievement, and further, whether this contribution represents an effect that cannot be more parsimoniously attributed to general intelligence. To answer these questions, 60 eleventh-grade students in a western New York metropolitan school were administered achievement tests developed by Kropp, Stoker, and Bashaw (1966), designed to provide a quantitative indicator of achievement at each level of the *Taxonomy*. The test items require the subject to read selected passages at varying levels of ease and familiarity and to respond to a variety of types of questions on each.

Data on creativity levels were obtained through administration of three subtests, designed by Guilford (1967) to measure levels of symbolic and semantic divergent production abilities. These tests are *consequences obvious*, which involves the ability of the subject to list direct consequences of a given hypothetical event, *consequences remote*, which involves identifying more remote or original consequences of similar situations, and *possible jobs*, which involves the ability to list a quantity of occupations that might be represented by a given emblem or symbol. Intelligence scores on the Lorge-Thorndike Multi-Level Intelligence Test, Level G, Form 1, were drawn from school records (Lorge, Thorndike, and Hagen, 1966).

Two major hypotheses are involved in the study. First, it is expected that the three tests of creativity and two of divergent achievement represent a homogeneous set of underlying thought processes. Thus, particular linear combinations of the five measures should account for large proportions of variation in the scales. Principal components of the correlation matrix among the measures are employed to provide evidence here.

Second, it is expected that levels of creativity do determine, to some extent, the individual's divergent achievement functioning. To test this hypothesis, multivariate multiple regression analysis is employed, with the two measures of divergent achievement as criteria. Independent (predictor) variables are intelligence and the creativity scores. Lorge-Thorndike scores are included as the first independent variable. Thus we may test whether the three creativity measures contribute to achievement above and beyond the established effect of general intelligence.

Torrence has postulated that creativity has a greater effect on the achievement of individuals having high intelligence than on individuals of low intelligence. Thus *interactions* of creativity and intelligence may function to determine an individual's level of divergent achievement. This postulate is evaluated by adding three predictors to the model, which are cross products of standardized intelligence scores and three standardized creativity measures. The complexity of the interaction terms suggests that they be placed last in the order of predictors. If they do not contribute to criterion variation above and beyond the simpler intelligence and creativity variables, the criterion of parsimony dictates that they be eliminated. All statistical tests are conducted through stepwise multivariate multiple regression techniques, with a fixed order of predictor variables.

Sample Problem 2—Word Memory Experiment*

It has long been held by psychologists that materials to be learned will be more easily internalized if their organization bears a resemblance to the internal organization imposed by human thought processes. In particular, Mandler and Stephens (1967) have suggested that if word lists to be memorized are presented to subjects arranged in common word-meaning categories, then memorizations of the words would be more accurately accomplished. Further, the facilitation is accentuated if the word categories follow a natural hierarchical ordering.

To test Mandler's hypotheses, four word lists having fifty words each were created. The first list (list A) contains ten words in each of the five major groupings: *recreation, inanimate materials, edible materials, plants,* and *animals*. Each grouping consists of five words in each of two subcategories. For example, *recreation* is considered to consist of subcategories *sports* and *dances*. The words included in category *sports* are *baseball, basketball, golf, hockey,* and *skiing*, and those in *dances* are *waltz*, *tango*, *mambo*, *cha-cha*, and *jitterbug*. The four remaining categories are similarly subdivided, as follows:

inanimate materials	into	*metals*	and	*precious stones*
edible materials	into	*vegetables*	and	*food flavorings*
plants	into	*flowers*	and	*trees*
animals	into	*insects*	and	*other animals*

*The data for this problem have been collected by Dr. Thomas J. Shuell, Department of Educational Psychology, State University of New York at Buffalo.

A second list (list B) having the same category structure and of equal overall difficulty was created to assure generalizability of results across a variety of specific words. The third list (list C) contains all ten words from lists A and B in each of the subcategories *sports, metals, vegetables, flowers,* and *insects.* It does not contain any built-in hierarchy of subcategories. A fourth list (list D) contains all ten words from lists A and B in the subcategories *dances, precious stones, food flavorings, trees,* and *other animals.* Each word contained in these lists was printed on an otherwise blank card. The cards for each list were shuffled. The lists were presented to a total of 48 college seniors, in four different manners.

1. Twelve subjects were told of the ten-category hierarchical structure, but not of the actual names of the categories. They were instructed to sort the cards into such a structure, using any groupings that they felt were meaningful. Six of the subjects were given list A and six list B.

2. Twelve subjects were presented with the lists (six each list A and B), and were instructed to sort the words into *ten* unique categories, without being informed of the hierarchical arrangement.

3. Twelve subjects were presented with the lists (six each list A and B), and were instructed to sort the words into *five* unique categories, without being informed of the hierarchical arrangement.

4. Twelve subjects were presented with the third and fourth lists (six each list C and D), and were instructed to sort the words into *five* unique categories.

At the end of the sorting, measurements were taken of the time the individual had spent in sorting, the number of words he could recall of the fifty, and the number of the original categories designed by the experimenter that were re-created by the subject. The latter was transformed to a proportion, based on the number of categories into which he was instructed to sort the words (ten for groups 1 and 2, five for groups 3 and 4). The entire procedure was repeated six times for each subject.

In order to test the hypotheses of the study, two achievement measures from the sixth trial are used as criterion measures in a one-factor (four-level) fixed-effects variance analysis. These are the number of words recalled and the proportion of the experimenter's categories that were re-created. Specific contrasts are established to provide data on subhypotheses. For the main hypothesis to be supported, the number of words recalled should decrease with an increase in the group's index number (that is, group 1 should have the highest recall score). The contrast of group 1 with 2 will be used to test the expectation that knowledge of a hierarchical structure of material will increase internalization. The comparison of groups 2 and 3 will provide an estimate of the extent to which smaller word categories improve internalization. That is, group 2 requires ten categories of five words each, and group 3 the reverse. Finally, the comparison of groups 3 and 4 will provide information on the extent to which any hierarchical structure of material, whether or not the subject is aware of its existence, will facilitate learning.

It is a plausible alternative hypothesis for any of the results, that time spent in sorting the words affects the degree of memorization. As a second analysis, the same outcome measures are considered, this time with the time measures from the second, fourth, and sixth trials as covariates. These three measures are assumed to represent the six time measures adequately. The exception may be time at trial 1, which is subject to additional extraneous sources of variation in beginning the experiment. A prior regression analysis is employed to determine the extent to which time does affect individual differences on the experimental outcomes.

Sample Problem 3 – Dental Calculus Reduction*

Producers of salable merchandise intended for consumer edification – be it educational material, such as textbooks or teaching programs, or consumable products, such as tobacco or petroleum products, foodstuffs, and medications – are in constant need of techniques for assessing their products' effects. Often the effects are measured simply in terms of sales volume. At other times, the more crucial effects are those of physiological or psychological changes in the consumers. Such is the case in the present example. The data represent a small portion of an ongoing program for the evaluation and improvement of agents for reducing the formation of dental calculus. Subjects for the study are random samples of male inmates in a large state prison.

The procedure for any experimental or control subject is as follows. The subject is randomly selected from prisoners who will be inmates for at least twelve months, and who are not missing any of the six anterior teeth of the lower mandible. The subjects are asked if they are willing to volunteer for the study. The majority of responses are positive. Demographic data are recorded for each volunteer, and all teeth in the mouth are given a complete scaling and prophylaxis. Experimentation is conducted over the following four three-month periods. During the first period, every subject is given toothpaste and mouth rinse, lacking the experimental agents. He is asked to use the products regularly, recording every use on a summary sheet. At the end of the three-month period, measurements are taken on the amount of calculus formation on each of the six lower front teeth. These early data provide an indication of normal calculus formation rates for the subjects, as well as an opportunity for some standardization of all subjects to a common beginning point.

The teeth are again cleansed and subjects are randomly assigned to control and experimental groups and provided with the same paste and rinse, or with the same products containing an anticalculus ingredient, respectively. For two three-month periods, the subjects use the paste and rinse provided, under a double-blind condition. At the end of each period, the calculus formation is measured and a prophylaxis given. All subjects return to the no-active-agent state for a final three-month period to determine the nature of any carryover effects that may exist. The first and final control periods are useful for eliminating the alternative explanation of observed effects as simply dental care or tooth-brushing effects. Many of the prisoners would otherwise ignore all dental care, and simple brushing is often the most effective dental health agent.

Three measures of calculus formation are taken from each of the six anter-

*The data for this problem are selected from a larger set collected by Dr. Stuart L. Fischman, School of Dentistry, State University of New York at Buffalo.

ior mandibular teeth in the manner described by Volpe, Manhold, and Hazen (1965). The three measures are obtained by placing a small rod, calibrated in millimeters, against the rear of the tooth in three positions, as illustrated in Figure 1.4.1. The experimenter compares the height of the calculus formation in each position to the calibrations, and records his readings. The three measures are summed for statistical analysis, providing a more reliable indicator

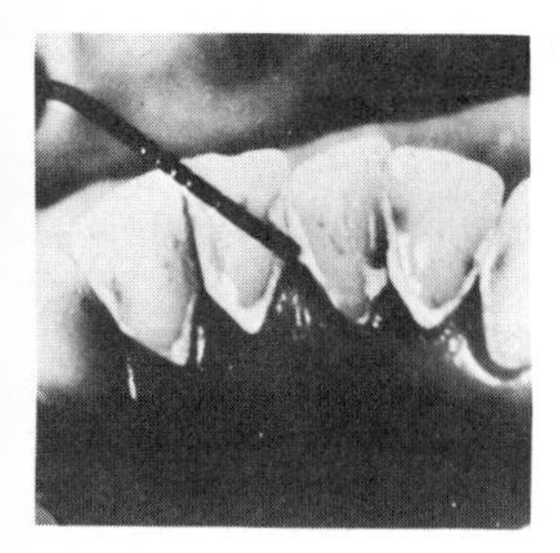
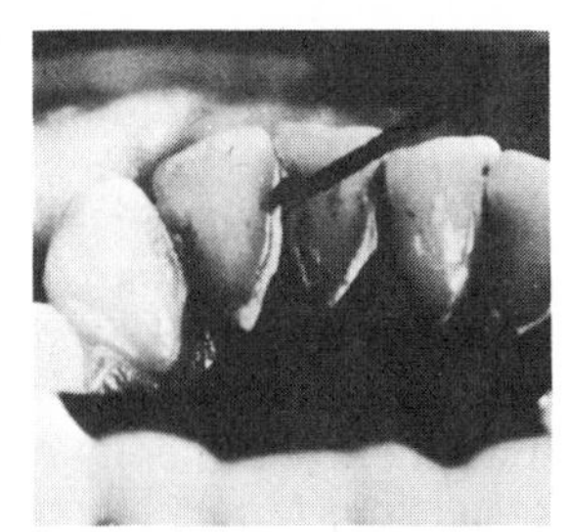
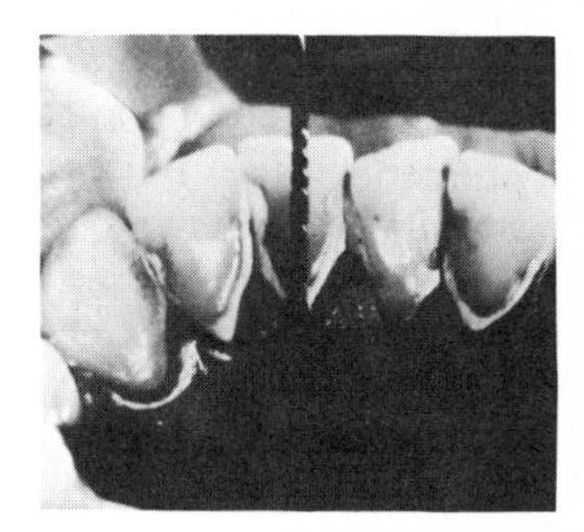

Figure 1.4.1 Placements of calibrated rod for measuring dental calculus formation.

than any one reading. The measurements from the six teeth at any one time period are considered as multiple dependent variables.

Experimental design considerations for product evaluation are often complex. Frequently, the numbers of subjects under the various experimental conditions are unequal, due to problems in subject accessibility or experimental mortality. Second, the expense factors involved demand that ineffective treatments be discontinued at the earliest possible time and that promising treatments be tested more extensively or in new quantities and forms. These problems are reflected in the present example, which draws from two consecutive years of testing the anticalculus agents.

During the first year, four treatment groups with 29 subjects were involved. Group 52 used only the unaltered paste and rinse for all periods. Group 54 used paste and rinse thought to contain an anticalculus agent. Group 56 used paste and rinse containing an active agent, and group 58 a second active ingredient. The experimental additive for group 54 was later discovered to be chemically inert and was not continued for a second year. For analysis purposes, the subjects involved are considered as control subjects, as long as their mean calculus scores are not significantly different from the other controls. The group 58 agent was discontinued due to high expense without a simultaneous large drop in calculus formation.

During the second year of experimentation, three larger experimental groups were used with a total sample size of 78. Group 67 received no additive and group 93 repeated the test of the first additive (used the previous year by group 56). Group 75 used paste and rinse containing a third additive, not tested the previous year but based upon the same principles as the more expensive additive of group 58. The arrangement of treatments is diagrammed in Table 1.4.1, with experimental group numbers.

Mean differences in calculus formation are tested through fitting a two-way fixed-effects analysis-of-variance model to the data. The six calculus measures

Table 1.4.1 Sampling Diagram for Dental Calculus Study

	Control	*Control*	*Active 1*	*Active 2*	*Active 3*
First Year, group	52	54	56	58	
Second Year, group	67		93		75

taken at the end of the third experimental period are simultaneous criterion variables. Planned contrasts are employed for information on the separate active agents and on the comparability of the two control groups. Some interactions are not estimable because of the irregular pattern of null subclasses.

Principal components of the covariance matrix among tooth measures are extracted and a discriminant analysis is performed to obtain further information on the development and retardation of dental calculus. Step-down analysis is employed to determine whether the experimental effects are concentrated in a subset of teeth having higher calculus formation rates.

Sample Problem 4 – Essay Grading Study*

Recent research on expectations (Rosenthal and Jacobson, 1968; Elashoff and Snow, 1971) suggests that teachers establish expectancies for pupil performance that are translated into teaching behaviors, and ultimately affect the learning achieved. Increases in learning as a function of expectancies can only be applauded. However, low or negative expectations can be harmful, especially if they are reinforced over several years' time (Finn, 1972b). It is important to identify the pupil and situational characteristics upon which teachers base their expectancies and to take educational and preventative measures where necessary.

Pupils' sex, race, and ability levels may be among the nonperformance determinants of teachers' expectations. If so, these factors would be reflected in teachers' evaluations of pupils, especially if the evaluations are subjective in nature. To test this hypothesis, a group of fifth-grade pupils was asked to write two essays each, on the topics "What I think about" and "My favorite school subject." Four essays were selected on each topic that were at about the center of the distribution of overall quality of writing. The essays chosen were typed, and averaged a little over half a page each in length. Each selected "What I think about" essay was paired with a single "My favorite school subject" essay, yielding four pairs. Though not randomly chosen, the four essays did represent differing writing styles and qualities.

Each pair of essays was sent to a fifth-grade teacher, accompanied by a cover letter providing him with systematic false information about the pupil who supposedly wrote both of the essays. The pupil was identified in terms of race (Negro–white), sex (male–female), and an achievement-ability rating that consisted of an IQ score and a report of the pupil's past achievement. The IQ scores were either high (115–120) or low (87–90), and the achievement rating

*The results of this research were reported in Finn (1970).

was "above average" for the high-IQ pupils and "below average" for the low-IQ pupils. Both the intelligence and achievement data were included to reinforce the concept that the child was generally bright or dull. Each essay was accompanied by a rating form consisting of a series of ten-point scales from "very poor" to "very good" for the categories "spelling and punctuation, grammar, sentence structure, organization, neatness, relevance of ideas, appropriate word usage, clarity, creativity and imagination," and "completeness of thought." The scales were not defined further, and no definition was provided for the ten scale points, other than to label the end points to clarify direction. The teachers were asked to evaluate the two essays on the rating scales, and were told to put any comments on the essays or rating forms that they cared to.

Subjects were 112 volunteer fifth-grade teachers in a large integrated urban school district in the northeastern part of the United States. The subjects represented every subclass of the 32-group experimental design, obtained by the crossing of pupil sex, pupil race, pupil ability, and the four different essay pairs. About half of the teachers did not respond to the "neatness" scale, since the essays were in typewritten form. The other nine scales are summed to provide a total score for each essay, yielding two totals for every teacher-subject. The possible range of scores on each scale is from 9 to 90 points. The two totals are treated as simultaneous criterion variables. Subclass means are compared through a four-way fixed-effects unequal-*N* variance analysis, with two criterion measures. For comparison purposes, the same analysis is repeated with the sum of the two totals as a single criterion measure. The expectation is that mean ratings will vary systematically as a function of the assumed characteristics of the pupil-authors.

Sample Problem 5 – Programmed Instruction Effects*

High absenteeism rates in schools attended by underprivileged pupils can counteract educational benefits that might otherwise accrue. In order to attempt to reduce the effects of absenteeism, a large eastern city in the United States has developed a set of programmed materials to parallel normal instruction in seventh-grade mathematics. The materials can be presented to the pupils, upon return to school, via individual computer consoles. If the students are able to learn the material by themselves, they are thus given the opportunity to compensate for learning not attained during their absence.

To test the remedial program, a random sample of nineteen seventh-grade classes was drawn from a large school district in the city's core area. The program consoles were installed at the rear of each room. The teachers were instructed to allow the students who had been absent to utilize the consoles for the appropriate missed lessons, and to provide instructions for the consoles' use. A second random sample of 18 classes was used as control with no

*These data were collected under the direction of Dr. Chester Kiser and Dr. Austin Swanson, Professors of Education at the State University of New York at Buffalo. The study was financed by a grant under Title I of the Elementary and Secondary Education Act during the fiscal year 1968, to Baltimore City Public Schools, Dr. Orlando F. Furno, Assistant Superintendant for Research and Development.

particular compensation for absences. All students were tested at the end of the school year on:

1. Cooperative Mathematics Test, Form A (Educational Testing Service)
2. Stanford Modern Mathematics Concepts Test (Harcourt, 1965)
3. City Junior High School Mathematics Test, Grade 7

In addition, the number of days of the school year each student was absent was recorded.

Since students may be assigned to classes in nonrandom fashion, and since students within classes do not function independently, class means are the unit of analysis. Prior studies have indicated sex differences both in achievement levels in mathematics and in absenteeism rates. Thus the data for statistical analysis are means on the four measures, for members of one sex group in each class. The sampling arrangement is diagrammed in Figure 1.4.2, with each of the subclasses containing a single mean observation.

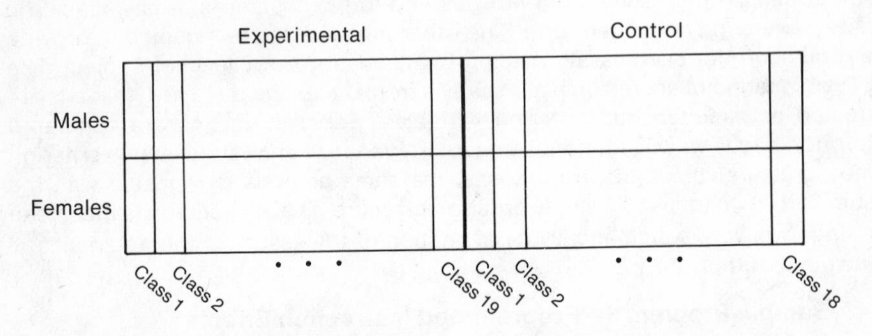

Figure 1.4.2 Sampling design for programmed instruction study.

To test for higher mean achievement in the experimental classes, a mixed-effects variance analysis is employed. Sex and experimental condition are fixed effects; classes are random, nested within experimental conditions and crossed with sex. Outcome measures are the three achievement scores. To control for differential absenteeism rates among classes within experimental conditions, a covariance analysis is performed. Total class absenteeism is the concomitant variable (covariate).

CHAPTER 

The Algebra of Matrices

Rectangular arrays of numbers are the basic data and algebraic representations for statistical analysis. Even in univariate problems, the data form a list of scores, which may be ordered by subject index number or sorted into groups. The list of scores for all subjects on a single measure is an *observational vector*. Or for one subject we may have multiple outcome measures. The list of scores for a single observation is termed a *vector observation*. Most commonly data from an experiment are ordered in a table that has a row for each subject of the study, and a column for each test administered. For example, we might place scores for N subjects on three tests in the form of Table 2.0.1. In this table X_{ij}

Table 2.0.1 Data Array for *N* observations, Each Having 3 Test Scores

		Test 1	*Test 2*	*Test 3*
Subject	1	X_{11}	X_{12}	X_{13}
	2	X_{21}	X_{22}	X_{23}
	⋮	⋮	⋮	⋮
	N	X_{N1}	X_{N2}	X_{N3}

represents the test score for subject i on test j. The complete array of scores is the *data matrix*, having three observational vectors as columns and N vector observations as rows.

Consider summarizing the data of Table 2.0.1. Minimal summary information would consist of the means for the three tests, which themselves may be placed in an array. If there are multiple groups of subjects, several arrays of means are necessary. The variances of the tests and the covariances of pairs of tests can be naturally ordered into a table that has as many rows and columns as tests, as in Table 2.0.2. s_{jk} is the *covariance* of test j with test k. The covariance of a test with itself, s_{jj}, is the *variance* of the test, and is represented s_j^2. The variances of the three tests appear as the diagonal entries in the table. Without such a table the representation and ordering of variances and covariances becomes complex, especially if the number of tests is large.

The distributional assumptions of analysis of variance require a table similar to Table 2.0.2 to be completely depicted. The usual assertion is that errors ϵ_{ij} are

Table 2.0.2 Variances and Covariances of Three Tests

	Test 1	*Test 2*	*Test 3*
Test 1	s_1^2	s_{12}	s_{13}
Test 2	s_{21}	s_2^2	s_{23}
Test 3	s_{31}	s_{32}	s_3^2

normal and independent, with common variance σ^2. Restated, this stipulates that the variances of errors for, say, three observations can be displayed in a table such as Table 2.0.2 with $s_1^2=s_2^2=s_3^2$ and all $s_{ij}=0$ $(i \neq j)$. With any reasonable number of observations, constructing the entire table is prohibitive and unnecessary. Just as in scalar algebra, we may use a condensed matrix form of the assumptions, to represent the entire array given in Table 2.0.2.

In univariate analysis, we can sometimes circumvent operations on arrays of numbers, since the basic datum for computations (for example, sums or sums of squares) is an individual score. Even then, in complex models array representations are a necessity as well as a convenience. In multivariate models the basic datum is the vector observation. Representations of multivariate models, as well as the simplest statistical operations, require an ability to operate with arrays. Otherwise the computations are intractable.

The notation of matrices forms a system for data analysis that is not only convenient, but often necessary. Matrix operations parallel the algebra employed in statistical analysis. Simple matrix algebra is used extensively throughout this book. The following sections provide a brief introduction to those aspects that are employed in later chapters. More extensive presentations may be found in Hohn (1964), Noble (1969), Searle (1966), and Graybill (1969). The exercises of Section 2.7 illustrate the application of these operations to simple problems.

2.1 NOTATION

A *matrix* is any rectangular array of real numbers or of symbols representing such numbers. In contrast, a single constant or symbol is termed a *scalar*. For example, the constant 6, and the variable representation *y*, which may take on a variety of values, are scalars. Matrices have more than a single element, either as additional rows, or additional columns, or both. For example, a matrix is

$$\mathbf{Y}=\begin{bmatrix}96 & 110\\ 44 & 58\\ 81 & 80\end{bmatrix}$$

Y has 3 rows and 2 columns. Matrices are symbolically represented by boldface uppercase Greek or Arabic letters, and are surrounded by brackets. The elements of a matrix are represented by the same symbol in lowercase form, followed by a row and column subscript. The element y_{11} is the element in the first row and first column of **Y**, or the number 96; y_{12} is 110, and so on.

The size of a matrix is its *order*. If matrix **Y** has 3 rows and 2 columns, we may denote the matrix as **Y** (3×2). In general, a matrix with m rows and n columns may be written as **Y** ($m \times n$) and depicted as

$$\mathbf{Y} = \begin{bmatrix} y_{11} & y_{12} & \cdots & y_{1n} \\ y_{21} & y_{22} & \cdots & y_{2n} \\ \vdots & & & \vdots \\ y_{m1} & y_{m2} & \cdots & y_{mn} \end{bmatrix}$$

A general element of **Y** in row i and column j is y_{ij} or $[y_{ij}]$.

A matrix having only a single row or a single column is a *vector.* Vectors are denoted by a boldface lowercase symbol, such as **a**, $\boldsymbol{\mu}$, **y**. For example, *column vector* **v** is

$$\mathbf{v} = \begin{bmatrix} 1.7 \\ 2.2 \\ -.8 \\ .2 \end{bmatrix}$$

v has scalar components $[v_1] = 1.7$, $[v_2] = 2.2$, $[v_3] = -.8$, and $[v_4] = .2$. A vector represented horizontally is a *row vector.* Matrices are sometimes represented by their vector components. For example, matrix **Y** has two column vectors,

$$\mathbf{y}_1 = \begin{bmatrix} 96 \\ 44 \\ 81 \end{bmatrix} \quad \text{and} \quad \mathbf{y}_2 = \begin{bmatrix} 110 \\ 58 \\ 80 \end{bmatrix}$$

Thus **Y** may also be represented as $\mathbf{Y} = [\mathbf{y}_1, \mathbf{y}_2]$. **Y** also consists of three row vectors.

Certain matrices arise in statistical applications which have particular unique forms. These include the *null matrix* or *null vector* of all zeros. We represent these by $\mathbf{0}$ and **0**, respectively. The *unit vector*, represented **1**, contains all unities. For example,

$$\mathbf{1}_3 = \begin{bmatrix} 1 \\ 1 \\ 1 \end{bmatrix}$$

The subscript on **1** is used to denote its order.

A *triangular matrix* is a square matrix containing all zeros to one side of the principal diagonal, and general elements elsewhere. For example,

$$\mathbf{T} = \begin{bmatrix} t_{11} & 0 & 0 & \cdots & 0 \\ t_{21} & t_{22} & 0 & \cdots & 0 \\ \vdots & & & & \vdots \\ \vdots & & & & 0 \\ t_{n1} & t_{n2} & t_{n3} & \cdots & t_{nn} \end{bmatrix}$$

A 4×4 triangular matrix is

$$\mathbf{T} = \begin{bmatrix} 1 & 0 & 0 & 0 \\ 4 & 3 & 0 & 0 \\ 6 & 6 & -2 & 0 \\ 7 & 1 & 0 & 4 \end{bmatrix} = \begin{bmatrix} 1 & & & \text{(Zero)} \\ 4 & 3 & & \\ 6 & 6 & -2 & \\ 7 & 1 & 0 & 4 \end{bmatrix}$$

T is a *lower triangular matrix*, with nonzero elements on or *below* the diagonal. An *upper triangular matrix* has nonzero elements on or *above* the diagonal.

A *diagonal matrix* is square with zeros in all positions except the principal diagonal; for example,

$$\mathbf{D} = \begin{bmatrix} 16 & 0 & 0 \\ 0 & 15 & 0 \\ 0 & 0 & 11 \end{bmatrix}$$

has diagonal elements $[d_{ii}] \neq 0$, and off-diagonal elements $[d_{ij}] = 0$ $(i \neq j)$. For simplicity, a diagonal matrix may be written in terms of only the diagonal elements; for example,

$$\mathbf{D} = \text{diag}\,(16, 15, 11)$$

or

$$\mathbf{D} = \text{diag}\,(d_{11}, d_{22}, \ldots, d_{nn})$$

A diagonal matrix with unities as the diagonal elements is the *identity matrix*, and is denoted **I**; for example,

$$\mathbf{I}_4 = \begin{bmatrix} 1 & 0 & 0 & 0 \\ 0 & 1 & 0 & 0 \\ 0 & 0 & 1 & 0 \\ 0 & 0 & 0 & 1 \end{bmatrix}$$

The subscript on **I** is used to denote its row and column order.

A *symmetric matrix* is any square array in which the elements above and below the principal diagonal, element for element, are identical. That is, the first row is identical to the first column, the second row is identical to the second column, and so on. For example,

$$\mathbf{S} = \begin{bmatrix} 13 & 102 & -6 & 4 \\ 102 & 12 & 17 & -4 \\ -6 & 17 & 0 & 0 \\ 4 & -4 & 0 & -8 \end{bmatrix}$$

Each element $[s_{ij}]$ is identical to corresponding element $[s_{ji}]$. For simplicity, only the lower symmetric half of a symmetric matrix is written explicitly. **S** may be represented as

$$\mathbf{S} = \begin{bmatrix} 13 & & \text{(Symmetric)} & \\ 102 & 12 & & \\ -6 & 17 & 0 & \\ 4 & -4 & 0 & -8 \end{bmatrix}$$

At times, two matrices are juxtaposed and treated as a single matrix. For example, let matrix **X** be

$$\mathbf{X} = \begin{bmatrix} 1 & 1 & 0 \\ 2 & 2 & 1 \\ 3 & 0 & 2 \end{bmatrix}$$

If we extend matrix **Y** by juxtaposing **X** to it, the result is a matrix having 3 rows and 5 columns. **V** is matrix **Y** *augmented* by **X**, or

$$\mathbf{V} = [\mathbf{Y}, \mathbf{X}] = \begin{bmatrix} 96 & 110 & 1 & 1 & 0 \\ 44 & 58 & 2 & 2 & 1 \\ 81 & 80 & 3 & 0 & 2 \end{bmatrix}$$

2.2 SIMPLE MATRIX OPERATIONS

Transposition

The transpose of the $m \times n$ matrix **A**, is the $n \times m$ matrix $\mathbf{A}'$, resulting from interchanging the rows and columns of **A**. For example, the transpose of

$$\mathbf{Y} = \begin{bmatrix} 96 & 110 \\ 44 & 58 \\ 81 & 80 \end{bmatrix}$$

is

$$\mathbf{Y}' = \begin{bmatrix} 96 & 44 & 81 \\ 110 & 58 & 80 \end{bmatrix}$$

Transposition is rewriting every $[ij]$ element of **A**, as the $[ji]$ element of $\mathbf{A}'$.

It is easy to see that the transpose of any symmetric matrix is the matrix itself. The transpose of an upper triangular matrix is lower triangular, and vice versa. The lower triangular form of such a matrix will be considered the normal or untransposed form. The transpose of an $n \times 1$ column vector $\mathbf{y}$ is the $1 \times n$ row vector $\mathbf{y}'$. Similarly the transpose of a row vector is a column vector having the same elements. The column form of a vector will always be considered as the normal or untransposed form. That is, $\mathbf{v}'$ is always the row vector form of $\mathbf{v}$. The transpose of a transpose, such as $(\mathbf{A}')'$, is the original matrix, **A**.

The placement of the transpose symbol is sometimes important. For example if matrix **Y** has two columns, $\mathbf{y}_1$ and $\mathbf{y}_2$, then $\mathbf{Y}'$ has two rows $\mathbf{y}_1'$ and $\mathbf{y}_2'$. By comparison the *rows* of **Y** are two-element row vectors, denoted $(\mathbf{y}')_1$, $(\mathbf{y}')_2$, and $(\mathbf{y}')_3$. The vectors represented are named and described in cases where this may be confusing.

Addition, Subtraction

Two matrices are *conformable* for addition or subtraction if they are of the same order. The sum or difference of two $m \times n$ matrices is the $m \times n$ matrix of sums or differences of each of the elements. That is $\mathbf{C} = \mathbf{A} \pm \mathbf{B}$ implies that, for each element, $[c_{ij}] = [a_{ij}] \pm [b_{ij}]$. For example,

$$\begin{bmatrix} 1 & 1 & 6 \\ 2 & 3 & 2 \\ 3 & 0 & 4 \end{bmatrix} + \begin{bmatrix} 2 & 9 & 4 \\ 2 & 2 & 3 \\ 6 & 5 & 7 \end{bmatrix} = \begin{bmatrix} 3 & 10 & 10 \\ 4 & 5 & 5 \\ 9 & 5 & 11 \end{bmatrix}$$

The operation of matrix addition is commutative $(\mathbf{A}+\mathbf{B}) = (\mathbf{B}+\mathbf{A})$, and associative $[\mathbf{A}+(\mathbf{B}+\mathbf{C}) = (\mathbf{A}+\mathbf{B})+\mathbf{C}]$.

It can be seen that sums or differences of two or more symmetric matrices are also symmetric. A row and a column vector are by definition not conformable for addition unless one is transposed. If $\mathbf{y}_i$ ($i=1, 2, \ldots, N$) are N column vectors, then the sum of the N vectors is the vector of element-by-element sums. For example, let

$$\mathbf{y}_1=\begin{bmatrix}1\\16\\4\\10\end{bmatrix} \qquad \mathbf{y}_2=\begin{bmatrix}3\\-10\\2\\8\end{bmatrix} \qquad \mathbf{y}_3=\begin{bmatrix}-1\\2\\1\\-6\end{bmatrix}$$

Then

$$\sum_{i=1}^{3} \mathbf{y}_i=\begin{bmatrix}1+\ 3-1\\16-10+2\\4+\ 2+1\\10+\ 8-6\end{bmatrix}=\begin{bmatrix}3\\8\\7\\12\end{bmatrix}$$

Multiplication

1. There are several forms of matrix products we shall consider. The simplest is the *scalar product* of a scalar and a matrix. The product of the scalar c and the matrix $\mathbf{A}$, written $c\mathbf{A}$, is the matrix formed by multiplying every element of $\mathbf{A}$ by the scalar c. That is, each $[ca_{ij}] = c[a_{ij}]$, for all i and j. For example, let $c=1/2$ and

$$\mathbf{y}'=[110 \quad 58 \quad 80]$$

Then

$$c\mathbf{y}'=1/2\mathbf{y}'=[55 \quad 29 \quad 40]$$

2. The most common vector product is the *inner product* of a *row* and a *column* vector, respectively. Computation of the inner product of two vectors, $\mathbf{v}'$ and $\mathbf{w}$, requires that the vectors be of the same order; that is, the two vectors must have the same number of elements to be conformable.

The inner product of two n-element vectors, $\mathbf{v}'$ and $\mathbf{w}$, is the scalar that results from summing the cross products of each element in $\mathbf{v}$ and the corresponding element in $\mathbf{w}$. That is, if $c=\mathbf{v}'\mathbf{w}$, then

$$c=\sum_{i=1}^{n} v_i w_i$$

For example, let

$$\mathbf{y}'=[1/2 \quad 1/6 \quad 2/3] \qquad \text{and} \qquad \mathbf{z}=\begin{bmatrix}4\\0\\12\end{bmatrix}$$

Then

$$c=\mathbf{y}'\mathbf{z}=(1/2\times 4)+(1/6\times 0)+(2/3\times 12)=10$$

It is obvious that multiplication of vectors in this manner is commutative; that is,

$\mathbf{v}'\mathbf{w}=\mathbf{w}'\mathbf{v}$. Two vectors whose inner product is zero are said to be *orthogonal*. If vectors are plotted geometrically, orthogonal vectors are at right angles to one another.

Just as $\mathbf{v}'\mathbf{w}$ is the *sum of cross products* of the elements of vectors **v** and **w**, the product of a row vector and its own transpose is the *sum of squares* of its elements. That is,

$$\mathbf{v}'\mathbf{v}=\sum_{i=1}^{n} v_i v_i=\sum_{i=1}^{n} v_i^2$$

With **z** from above,

$$\mathbf{z}'\mathbf{z}=[4 \quad 0 \quad 12]\begin{bmatrix} 4 \\ 0 \\ 12 \end{bmatrix}=(4\times4)+(0\times0)+(12\times12)$$
$$=160$$

The inner product of a vector **v** and its own transpose, $\mathbf{v}'\mathbf{v}$, is the *square length* of **v**, written $|\mathbf{v}|^2$. The square root of the product, or $|\mathbf{v}|$, is the *length* of vector **v**. A vector of length unity is said to be *normalized*. Any vector **v** can be transformed to a normalized vector, $\mathbf{v}^*$, by scalar multiplication,

$$\mathbf{v}^*=\frac{1}{|\mathbf{v}|}\mathbf{v}$$

For example, let

$$\mathbf{y}=\begin{bmatrix} 1 \\ 1 \\ -1 \\ -1 \end{bmatrix}$$

The length of **y** is $\sqrt{\mathbf{y}'\mathbf{y}}=\sqrt{4}=2$. The product $1/2\mathbf{y}$ is

$$\mathbf{y}^* = 1/2\mathbf{y} = \begin{bmatrix} .5 \\ .5 \\ -.5 \\ -.5 \end{bmatrix}$$

The length of $\mathbf{y}^*$ is 1, and $\mathbf{y}^*$ is the normalized vector.

If **v** and **w** are both normalized *and* are orthogonal, the two vectors are *orthonormal*; that is, if $|\mathbf{v}|=|\mathbf{w}|=1$ and $\mathbf{v}'\mathbf{w}=0$. If **w** is not orthogonal to **v**, it may be *orthogonalized* by

$$\mathbf{w}^{\perp} = \mathbf{w}-(\mathbf{v}'\mathbf{w})\mathbf{v}$$

For example, let

$$\mathbf{v}=\begin{bmatrix} .5 \\ .5 \\ .5 \\ .5 \end{bmatrix} \quad \text{and} \quad \mathbf{w}=\begin{bmatrix} .5 \\ .5 \\ .5 \\ -.5 \end{bmatrix}$$

Thus $\mathbf{v}'\mathbf{w} = .5$ and the two are not orthogonal (both are normalized). Then

$$\mathbf{w}^{\perp} = \begin{bmatrix} .5 \\ .5 \\ .5 \\ -.5 \end{bmatrix} - .5 \begin{bmatrix} .5 \\ .5 \\ .5 \\ .5 \end{bmatrix}$$

$$= \begin{bmatrix} .25 \\ .25 \\ .25 \\ -.75 \end{bmatrix}$$

Vector $\mathbf{w}^{\perp}$ is orthogonal to $\mathbf{v}$. It represents a *residual* vector, or just that portion of $\mathbf{w}$ which is at right angles to $\mathbf{v}$. $\mathbf{w}^{\perp}$ is not necessarily normalized, and renormalization may be required. Orthogonalization is order-specific; $\mathbf{v}^{\perp}$ and $\mathbf{w}$ are also orthogonal vectors, but $\mathbf{v}^{\perp}$ is the residual $\mathbf{v}$-vector from $\mathbf{w}$. The two are not the same as $\mathbf{v}$ and $\mathbf{w}^{\perp}$, although both pairs are at right angles on the same dimension graph.

Vector products can produce results that are usually represented in scalar algebra. The reader may wish to demonstrate for himself that the product of the $1 \times n$ unit vector $\mathbf{1}'$ and a conformable column vector $\mathbf{y}$ is simply the sum of the elements of $\mathbf{y}$. The square length of an n-element unit vector is n. Thus the mean of the elements of vector $\mathbf{y}$, is

$$y. = \frac{1}{\mathbf{1}'\mathbf{1}} \mathbf{1}'\mathbf{y}$$

The vector of mean deviation scores is

$$\mathbf{y}_d = \begin{bmatrix} y_1 - y. \\ y_2 - y. \\ \vdots \\ y_N - y. \end{bmatrix}$$

$$= \mathbf{y} - y.\mathbf{1}$$

The variance of the elements of $\mathbf{y}$ is

$$s_y^2 = \frac{1}{n-1} \sum_{i=1}^{n} (y_i - y.)^2$$

$$= \frac{1}{n-1} \mathbf{y}_d'\mathbf{y}_d$$

Substituting for $\mathbf{y}_d$, multiplying and combining like terms,

$$s_y^2 = \frac{1}{n-1} (\mathbf{y}'\mathbf{y} - ny.^2)$$

Since $\mathbf{y}'\mathbf{y} = \Sigma_i y_i^2$, this is the common computational form for the sample variance, but derived through vector operations.

3. The product of two matrices, **A** and **B**, is the matrix of inner products of each row vector of **A** and each column vector of **B**. The result has as many rows as **A** and as many columns as **B**. For **A** and **B** to be conformable for multiplication, the row vectors of **A** must be conformable for multiplication with the column vectors of **B**; that is, matrix **A** must have as many columns as **B** has rows.

If **A** is of the order $m \times n$ and **B** is $n \times p$, then the product $\mathbf{C}=\mathbf{AB}$ is $m \times p$. Each $[c_{ij}]$ is the inner product of the ith row of **A** and the jth column of **B**. That is,

$$[c_{ij}] = \sum_{k=1}^{n} a_{ik} b_{kj}$$

As an example, let

$$\mathbf{A} = \begin{bmatrix} 2 & 2 & 1 & 3 \\ 4 & 0 & 6 & 0 \end{bmatrix} \quad \text{and} \quad \mathbf{B} = \begin{bmatrix} 1 & 2 & 1 \\ 0 & 0 & 3 \\ 4 & 1 & 1 \\ 2 & 1 & 3 \end{bmatrix}$$

Then $\mathbf{C} = \mathbf{AB}$

$$= \begin{bmatrix} (2\times1+2\times0+1\times4+3\times2) & (2\times2+2\times0+1\times1+3\times1) & (2\times1+2\times3+1\times1+3\times3) \\ (4\times1+0\times0+6\times4+0\times2) & (4\times2+0\times0+6\times1+0\times1) & (4\times1+0\times3+6\times1+0\times3) \end{bmatrix}$$

$$= \begin{bmatrix} 12 & 8 & 18 \\ 28 & 14 & 10 \end{bmatrix}$$

Matrix multiplication is not generally commutative. In the example the product **BA** is not defined, since **B** has three columns and **A** two rows. $\mathbf{B}'\mathbf{A}'$ is possible, however; the result is $\mathbf{C}'$. In this case the same vectors are being multiplied as in forming **AB**, but in a transposed order. This is a general rule of matrix multiplication: The transpose of a product of two or more matrices is equal to the product of their separate transposes, multiplied in reverse order. Matrix multiplication is associative $[(\mathbf{AB})\mathbf{C}=\mathbf{A}(\mathbf{BC})]$ and distributive $[\mathbf{A}(\mathbf{B}\pm\mathbf{C})= \mathbf{AB}\pm\mathbf{AC}]$.

Certain matrix products recur frequently in statistical computation. Premultiplication of **A** by a diagonal matrix, **DA**, has the effect of multiplying every element in the ith *row* of **A** by $[d_{ii}]$. Postmultiplication by a diagonal matrix analogously affects the *columns* of the original matrix. Pre- or postmultiplication by the identity matrix leaves the original matrix unaltered.

An m-element *column* vector **v** and an n-element *row* vector $\mathbf{w}'$ are always conformable for multiplication (unlike the situation where $\mathbf{v}'$ is a row and **w** is a column). The column vector has one column and the row vector one row, assuring conformability of the two as general matrices. The product $\mathbf{vw}'$ is the $m \times n$ matrix of scalar products of each element in **v** and every element of $\mathbf{w}'$. As an example, let

$$\mathbf{y}' = [1 \quad 2 \quad 3]$$

Then

$$\mathbf{yy}' = \begin{bmatrix} 1 \\ 2 \\ 3 \end{bmatrix} [1 \quad 2 \quad 3]$$

$$= \begin{bmatrix} 1 & 2 & 3 \\ 2 & 4 & 6 \\ 3 & 6 & 9 \end{bmatrix}$$

$\mathbf{yy}'$ is the symmetric matrix of squares and cross products of the elements of $\mathbf{y}$.

The product of any matrix $\mathbf{A}$ and its own transpose, taken in either direction ($\mathbf{A}'\mathbf{A}$ or $\mathbf{AA}'$) is symmetric. Let $\mathbf{A}$ have n columns, $\mathbf{a}_i$ ($i=1, 2, \ldots, n$). Then $\mathbf{A}'$ has row vectors $\mathbf{a}_i'$. The product is

$$\mathbf{S} = \mathbf{A}'\mathbf{A} = \begin{bmatrix} \mathbf{a}_1' \\ \mathbf{a}_2' \\ \vdots \\ \mathbf{a}_n' \end{bmatrix} [\mathbf{a}_1 \quad \mathbf{a}_2 \qquad \mathbf{a}_n]$$

Multiplying each row of $\mathbf{A}'$ by each column of $\mathbf{A}$, we have

$$\mathbf{S} = \begin{bmatrix} \mathbf{a}_1'\mathbf{a}_1 & \mathbf{a}_1'\mathbf{a}_2 & \cdots & \mathbf{a}_1'\mathbf{a}_n \\ \mathbf{a}_2'\mathbf{a}_1 & \mathbf{a}_2'\mathbf{a}_2 & \cdots & \mathbf{a}_2'\mathbf{a}_n \\ \vdots & & & \vdots \\ \mathbf{a}_n'\mathbf{a}_1 & \mathbf{a}_n'\mathbf{a}_2 & \cdots & \mathbf{a}_n'\mathbf{a}_n \end{bmatrix}$$

$\mathbf{S}$ is symmetric, since $\mathbf{a}_i'\mathbf{a}_j = \mathbf{a}_j'\mathbf{a}_i$ for any two vectors $\mathbf{a}_j$ and $\mathbf{a}_i$.

As an example, let

$$\mathbf{B} = \begin{bmatrix} 1 & 2 & 1 \\ 0 & 0 & 3 \\ 4 & 1 & 1 \\ 2 & 1 & 3 \end{bmatrix}$$

$$= [\mathbf{b}_1 \quad \mathbf{b}_2 \quad \mathbf{b}_3]$$

Then

$$\mathbf{B}'\mathbf{B} = \begin{bmatrix} 1 & 0 & 4 & 2 \\ 2 & 0 & 1 & 1 \\ 1 & 3 & 1 & 3 \end{bmatrix} \begin{bmatrix} 1 & 2 & 1 \\ 0 & 0 & 3 \\ 4 & 1 & 1 \\ 2 & 1 & 3 \end{bmatrix}$$

$$= \begin{bmatrix} 21 & 8 & 11 \\ 8 & 6 & 6 \\ 11 & 6 & 20 \end{bmatrix}$$

The diagonal elements are the square lengths of the column vectors of $\mathbf{B}$; for example, $|\mathbf{b}_1|^2 = 21$. The off-diagonal elements are the cross products of every pair of vectors; for example, $\mathbf{b}_1'\mathbf{b}_2 = \mathbf{b}_2'\mathbf{b}_1 = 8$. $\mathbf{B}'\mathbf{B}$ is the matrix of *sums of squares and cross products* of the columns of $\mathbf{B}$. Similarly, $\mathbf{BB}'$ is the 4×4 matrix of sums of squares and cross products of the *rows* of $\mathbf{B}$. When $\mathbf{B}$ is a "subjects$\times$ tests" data matrix, $\mathbf{B}'\mathbf{B}$ is the first result in the computation of the matrix of variances and covariances or of correlations.

Let $\mathbf{b}'_i$ be the *i*th *row* vector of $\mathbf{B}$; that is, $\mathbf{b}'_1 = [1 \quad 2 \quad 1]$, and so on. It should be noted that $\mathbf{B}'\mathbf{B}$, the sum of squares and cross products of columns of $\mathbf{B}$, is equivalently $\Sigma_i \mathbf{b}_i \mathbf{b}'_i$. The result is obtained by computing a squares and products matrix for each row vector and summing. The same operations are performed, but in different sequence. That is,

$$\mathbf{B}'\mathbf{B} = \begin{bmatrix} 1 \\ 2 \\ 1 \end{bmatrix} [1 \quad 2 \quad 1] + \begin{bmatrix} 0 \\ 0 \\ 3 \end{bmatrix} [0 \quad 0 \quad 3] + \begin{bmatrix} 4 \\ 1 \\ 1 \end{bmatrix} [4 \quad 1 \quad 1] + \begin{bmatrix} 2 \\ 1 \\ 3 \end{bmatrix} [2 \quad 1 \quad 3]$$

If $\mathbf{A}'\mathbf{A}$ is diagonal, $\mathbf{A}$ is said to be *columnwise orthogonal*; the inner products of every pair of columns of $\mathbf{A}$ is zero. If $\mathbf{AA}'$ is diagonal, $\mathbf{A}$ is *row-wise orthogonal*. If, in addition, the diagonal elements of $\mathbf{A}'\mathbf{A}$ or $\mathbf{AA}'$ are unity, $\mathbf{A}$ is said to be *orthonormal*; each vector is normalized to unit length. For example, let

$$\mathbf{A} = \begin{bmatrix} .5 & .5 & .5 \\ .5 & -.5 & -.5 \\ .5 & -.5 & .5 \\ .5 & .5 & -.5 \end{bmatrix}$$

$\mathbf{A}$ is columnwise orthonormal. Every column $\mathbf{a}_i$ has zero inner product with $\mathbf{a}_j$ $(j \neq i)$, and unit length, $\mathbf{a}_i'\mathbf{a}_i = 1$. As a result, $\mathbf{A}'\mathbf{A} = \mathbf{I}$. However, it is not the case that $\mathbf{AA}' = \mathbf{I}$, since the rows of $\mathbf{A}$ in the example are neither orthogonal nor normalized.

Triple products of the form $\mathbf{A}'\mathbf{QA}$ or $\mathbf{AQA}'$ are also symmetric, if $\mathbf{Q}$ is symmetric. If $\mathbf{A}'\mathbf{QA}$ or $\mathbf{AQA}'$ is diagonal, $\mathbf{A}$ is said to be *orthogonal with respect to the metric* $\mathbf{Q}$. The products $\mathbf{A}'\mathbf{A}$, $\mathbf{AA}'$, $\mathbf{A}'\mathbf{QA}$, and $\mathbf{AQA}'$ are termed the *gramians* of matrix $\mathbf{A}$.

4. The final matrix product we shall consider is the *Kronecker product* of two matrices. $\mathbf{C} = \mathbf{A}\otimes\mathbf{B}$ is the matrix formed by juxtaposing scalar products of every element of $\mathbf{A}$ with the entire array $\mathbf{B}$. That is, if $\mathbf{A}$ is $m\times n$ and $\mathbf{B}$ is $k\times l$, $\mathbf{C}$ is the $mk\times nl$ matrix having matrices as elements, of the form $[a_{ij}]\mathbf{B}$. That is,

$$\mathbf{C} = \mathbf{A}\otimes\mathbf{B} = \begin{bmatrix} a_{11} & a_{12} & \cdots & a_{1n} \\ a_{21} & a_{22} & \cdots & a_{2n} \\ \vdots & & & \vdots \\ a_{m1} & a_{m2} & \cdots & a_{mn} \end{bmatrix} \otimes \mathbf{B}$$

$$= \left[\begin{array}{c|c|c|c} a_{11}\mathbf{B} & a_{12}\mathbf{B} & \cdots & a_{1n}\mathbf{B} \\ \hline a_{21}\mathbf{B} & a_{22}\mathbf{B} & \cdots & a_{2n}\mathbf{B} \\ \hline \vdots & & & \vdots \\ \hline a_{m1}\mathbf{B} & a_{m2}\mathbf{B} & \cdots & a_{mn}\mathbf{B} \end{array}\right]$$

Let

$$\mathbf{A}=\begin{bmatrix}6 & 4 & 1\\ 0 & 9 & -2\end{bmatrix} \quad \text{and} \quad \mathbf{B}=\begin{bmatrix}-1 & 0\\ -1 & 2\end{bmatrix}$$

Then

$$\mathbf{C}=\mathbf{A}\otimes\mathbf{B}=\left[\begin{array}{cc|cc|cc}-6 & 0 & -4 & 0 & -1 & 0\\ -6 & 12 & -4 & 8 & -1 & 2\\ \hline 0 & 0 & -9 & 0 & 2 & 0\\ 0 & 0 & -9 & 18 & 2 & -4\end{array}\right]$$

There is no restriction upon the sizes of the factors. It can be seen that $\mathbf{A}\otimes\mathbf{B}$ and $\mathbf{B}\otimes\mathbf{A}$ contain the same elements but in differing orders. The definition defines the order of elements, with the first matrix containing the scalar factors. In a product of the form $\mathbf{C}(\mathbf{A}\otimes\mathbf{B})\mathbf{D}$ where $\mathbf{C}$ and $\mathbf{D}$ are conformable for multiplication with $\mathbf{A}$, $\mathbf{B}$ becomes the postfactor; that is, $\mathbf{C}(\mathbf{A}\otimes\mathbf{B})\mathbf{D}=(\mathbf{CAD})\otimes\mathbf{B}$. The Kronecker product is distributive; that is, $(\mathbf{A}\otimes\mathbf{B})(\mathbf{C}\otimes\mathbf{B})=\mathbf{AC}\otimes\mathbf{B}$.

Kronecker products are used in constructing contrast matrices for factorial analysis-of-variance designs. Assume a main-effect contrast vector is

$$\mathbf{a}=\begin{bmatrix}1\\ 0\\ -1\end{bmatrix}\begin{matrix}y_{\cdot 1\cdot}\\ y_{\cdot 2\cdot}\\ y_{\cdot 3\cdot}\end{matrix}$$

and a contrast vector for a second, crossed factor, is

$$\mathbf{b}=\begin{bmatrix}1\\ -1\end{bmatrix}\begin{matrix}y_{\cdot\cdot 1}\\ y_{\cdot\cdot 2}\end{matrix}$$

The weights for the six subclass means for the interaction of the two contrasts is the Kronecker product:

$$\mathbf{a}\otimes\mathbf{b}=\begin{bmatrix}1\\ -1\\ 0\\ 0\\ -1\\ 1\end{bmatrix}\begin{matrix}y_{\cdot 11}\\ y_{\cdot 12}\\ y_{\cdot 21}\\ y_{\cdot 22}\\ y_{\cdot 31}\\ y_{\cdot 32}\end{matrix}$$

This application is discussed extensively in later chapters.

2.3 SCALAR FUNCTIONS OF MATRICES

Rank

The *rank* of an $m\times n$ matrix $\mathbf{A}$, is the number of columns (or rows) of the matrix that cannot be exactly obtained as linear composites of other columns (or rows). A column vector $\mathbf{a}_i$, is expressible as a linear composite of other columns $\mathbf{a}_j$ $(j\neq i)$, if

$$\mathbf{a}_i=\sum_{j=1}^{i-1} c_j\mathbf{a}_j+\sum_{j=i+1}^{n} c_j\mathbf{a}_j$$

The c_j are any real constants. The rank by columns is always identical to the rank by rows.

The rank of a matrix can never exceed the smaller of its two dimensions. That is, let $r(\mathbf{A})$ be the rank of matrix **A**. Then

$$r(\mathbf{A}) \leqslant \min(m, n)$$

If $r(\mathbf{A}) = \min(m, n)$, then **A** is said to be of *full rank*. If $r(\mathbf{A}) < \min(m, n)$, then **A** is of *deficient rank*.

As an example, let

$$\mathbf{A} = \begin{bmatrix} 1 & 2 & 2 \\ 1 & 3 & 0 \\ 1 & 2 & 1 \end{bmatrix}$$

The rank of **A** is 3 since no column can be expressed as a linear combination of other columns. By comparison, let

$$\mathbf{A}^* = \begin{bmatrix} 1 & 2 & 1 \\ 1 & 3 & 2 \\ 1 & 2 & 1 \end{bmatrix}$$

The third column $\mathbf{a}_3^*$ is exactly $\mathbf{a}_2^* - \mathbf{a}_1^*$. The rank of $\mathbf{A}^*$ is 2, and $\mathbf{A}^*$ is of deficient rank. $\mathbf{a}_3^*$ is said to be *linearly dependent* upon a_1^* and a_2^*; if no vector is expressible as a linear function of others, the vectors are *linearly independent*.

If matrix **B** is

$$\mathbf{B} = \begin{bmatrix} 1 & 2 & 2 \\ 1 & 3 & 0 \end{bmatrix}$$

the rank of **B** cannot exceed $m = 2$; the third column is necessarily linearly dependent upon the first two (can you find the c_j?). The matrix is of full rank 2, as long as the second column (or row) is not a linear function of the first.

The rank of a product of matrices never exceeds the smaller of their separate ranks:

$$r(\mathbf{AB}) \leqslant \min[r(\mathbf{A}), r(\mathbf{B})]$$

Further, if **A** is $m \times n$ and **B** is $n \times l$, and both are of rank n, then $r(\mathbf{AB}) = n$. If n is less than m and l, the product is of deficient rank; otherwise it is of full rank. If **B** is square and full rank, the rank of **AB** is always equal to the rank of **A**.

The rank of gramians $\mathbf{A}'\mathbf{A}$ and $\mathbf{AA}'$ are equal to the rank of **A**. Thus if **A** is square and of full rank, $\mathbf{A}'\mathbf{A}$ and $\mathbf{AA}'$ are of full rank. If **A** is rectangular with $m < n$, and of full rank m, then $\mathbf{AA}'$ $(m \times m)$ is of full rank, whereas $\mathbf{A}'\mathbf{A}$ $(n \times n)$ is of deficient rank. When **A** is of deficient rank, so are all gramians of **A**.

The rank of a matrix is one sort of information measure—that is, an indication of how much nonredundant information the matrix contains. A subjects× tests matrix or an $N \times p$ data matrix is usually of full rank. It is of deficient rank if any of the test scores are linear combinations of others; for example, if subtest scores plus a total test score are included, or if the scores are percentages that total 100 for each subject. The resulting matrix of means and the $p \times p$ matrix of variances and covariances will then also be of deficient rank. If there are fewer subjects than tests $(N < p)$ the data matrix may still be of full rank N. However, the $p \times p$ variance–covariance matrix is necessarily of deficient rank.

The condition of full rank is prerequisite to matrix factoring and inversion. In multivariate statistical analysis, the variance–covariance matrix of the tests is often factored. To preserve full rank, two conditions must be met: (a) no test can be linearly dependent upon other tests and (b) the number of observations must exceed the number of scores per subject.

Determinant

The *determinant* of a *square* matrix **A**, written |**A**|, is a unique scalar associated with **A**, which serves as a summary measure with respect to its vectors.† The determinant of a matrix represents the volume of the parallelpiped generated by its column vectors. In two dimensions, the determinant is the area of the parallelogram generated by the two vectors. In a single dimension, it is the length of the vector described.

Consider the 1×1 matrix $\mathbf{A} = [a_1]$. **A** may be depicted as a single vector, **a**, of length |**a**| in a single dimension, or drawn on a single axis, as follows:

$$a_1$$

The length of **a** is $\sqrt{\mathbf{a}'\mathbf{a}}$, or a_1 itself; also, then, |**A**|.

For two dimensions, first consider **A** diagonal. For example, let

$$\mathbf{A} = \begin{bmatrix} 5 & 0 \\ 0 & 3 \end{bmatrix}$$
$$= [\mathbf{a}_1 \quad \mathbf{a}_2]$$

In a unit Cartesian coordinate system of two dimensions, we may draw the col umn vectors of **A** as in Figure 2.3.1. The area of the rectangle formed by complet ing the parallelogram from the end points of the vectors is $|\mathbf{a}_1||\mathbf{a}_2|$, or $5 \cdot 3 = 15$ This result can also be obtained directly by multiplying the diagonal elements o **A**.

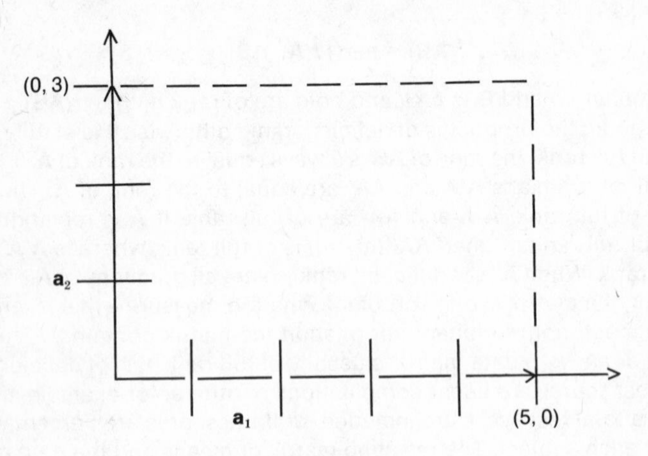

Figure 2.3.1

†The vertical lines are used in two ways. When the enclosed array is a matrix, such as |**A**|, the denote the determinant. When the array is a vector, such as |**v**|, they denote its length. In the case of 1×1 matrix or a 1-element vector, the two are equal.

In the nondiagonal case, the angle between $\mathbf{a}_1$ and $\mathbf{a}_2$ is of consequence. Consider

$$\mathbf{A} = \begin{bmatrix} 5 & 2 \\ 1 & 3 \end{bmatrix}$$

which may be represented as a parallelogram, completed by drawing the additional parallel sides; see Figure 2.3.2.

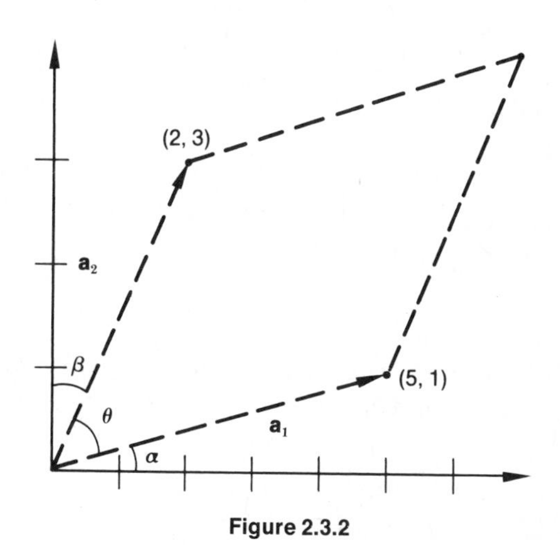

Figure 2.3.2

The area of the parallelogram may now be computed as $|\mathbf{a}_1|\,|\mathbf{a}_2| \sin\theta$. To evaluate, note that

$$\theta = \frac{\pi}{2} - (\alpha + \beta)$$

and

$$\begin{aligned} \sin\theta &= \sin\left[\frac{\pi}{2} - (\alpha+\beta)\right] \\ &= \cos(\alpha+\beta) \\ &= \cos\alpha\cos\beta - \sin\alpha\sin\beta \end{aligned}$$

Further,

$$\cos\alpha = \frac{5}{\sqrt{26}} \qquad \cos\beta = \frac{3}{\sqrt{13}} \qquad \sin\alpha = \frac{1}{\sqrt{26}} \qquad \sin\beta = \frac{2}{\sqrt{13}}$$

and

$$\begin{aligned} |\mathbf{A}| &= \sqrt{26}\sqrt{13}\left(\frac{5}{\sqrt{26}}\frac{3}{\sqrt{13}} - \frac{1}{\sqrt{26}}\frac{2}{\sqrt{13}}\right) \\ &= 15 - 2 = 13 \end{aligned}$$

Again the result may be obtained directly from **A**, as the difference of products $a_{11}a_{22} - a_{12}a_{21}$. Higher-order determinants are more difficult to depict graphically, although their conceptual basis is the same as the simpler cases presented here.

Generally, the determinant of any $n \times n$ matrix **A** is defined by

$$|\mathbf{A}| = \sum_i (-1)^i a_{1j} a_{2k} \cdots a_{nr}$$

summed over all permutations of the second subscript from the natural order 1, 2, 3, 4, and so on. The total sum is across $n!$ terms, each term being the product of n elements.

The resulting products form certain patterns. The determinant when $n=2$ is $a_{11}a_{22} - a_{12}a_{21}$, or the product of the diagonal elements minus the product of the off-diagonal elements:

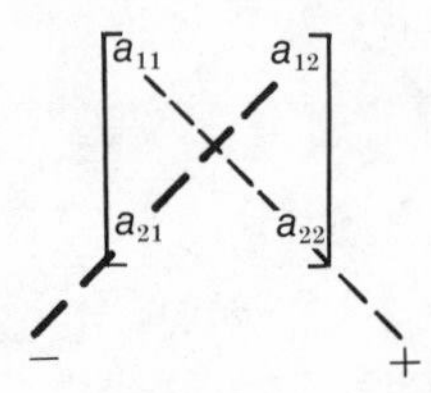

For $n=3$, the products are across one element from each row; that is,

$$a_{11}a_{22}a_{33} + a_{12}a_{23}a_{31} + a_{13}a_{21}a_{32} - a_{13}a_{22}a_{31} - a_{23}a_{32}a_{11} - a_{33}a_{12}a_{21}$$

or

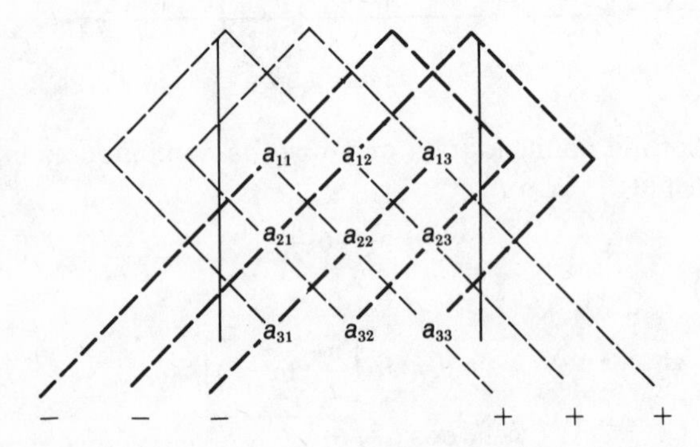

When $n \geqslant 4$, the pattern is more complex, and $|\mathbf{A}|$ may be evaluated by *expansion by minors*. The *minor* of any element $[a_{ij}]$, represented $|\mathbf{M}_{ij}|$, is the determinant of the $(n-1) \times (n-1)$ matrix that remains when column i and row j of **A** are deleted. The determinant of **A** is found from its minors by

$$|\mathbf{A}| = \sum_j a_{ij} (-1)^{i+j} |\mathbf{M}_{ij}|$$

This is the product of elements in *any one* row of **A**, each times 1 or −1, times the corresponding minor.

For example, let

$$\mathbf{A} = \begin{bmatrix} 2 & -3 & 2 & 5 \\ 1 & -1 & 1 & 2 \\ 3 & 2 & 2 & 1 \\ 1 & 1 & -3 & -1 \end{bmatrix}$$

Summing across the first row,

$$|\mathbf{A}| = 2(-1)^2 \left| \begin{bmatrix} -1 & 1 & 2 \\ 2 & 2 & 1 \\ 1 & -3 & -1 \end{bmatrix} \right| -3(-1)^3 \left| \begin{bmatrix} 1 & 1 & 2 \\ 3 & 2 & 1 \\ 1 & -3 & -1 \end{bmatrix} \right|$$

$$+2(-1)^4 \left| \begin{bmatrix} 1 & -1 & 2 \\ 3 & 2 & 1 \\ 1 & 1 & -1 \end{bmatrix} \right| +5(-1)^5 \left| \begin{bmatrix} 1 & -1 & 1 \\ 3 & 2 & 2 \\ 1 & 1 & -3 \end{bmatrix} \right|$$

Each of the smaller determinants may be evaluated by minor expansion, or by summing diagonal products as in the 3×3 example. Then

$$|\mathbf{A}| = 2(-14) + 3(-17) + 2(-5) - 5(-18) = 1$$

Multiplying matrix $\mathbf{A}$ by a scalar c, has the effect of multiplying the determinant by c^n. That is,

$$|c\mathbf{A}| = c^n |\mathbf{A}|$$

The determinant of a product of matrices is the product of their separate determinants.

$$|\mathbf{AB}| = |\mathbf{A}|\,|\mathbf{B}|$$

From this it follows that interchanging two rows or columns of $\mathbf{A}$ multiplies the determinant by -1. For example, let $\mathbf{A}$ be 3×3, with columns $[\mathbf{a}_1, \mathbf{a}_2, \mathbf{a}_3]$, and

$$\mathbf{B} = \begin{bmatrix} 0 & 1 & 0 \\ 1 & 0 & 0 \\ 0 & 0 & 1 \end{bmatrix}$$

Then $\mathbf{AB}$ has columns $[\mathbf{a}_2, \mathbf{a}_1, \mathbf{a}_3]$ and determinant

$$\begin{aligned} |\mathbf{AB}| &= |\mathbf{A}|\,|\mathbf{B}| \\ &= -1|\mathbf{A}| \end{aligned}$$

If matrix $\mathbf{A}$ is $m \times n$ and $\mathbf{B}$ is $n \times m$, then

$$|\mathbf{I}_m + \mathbf{AB}| = |\mathbf{I}_n + \mathbf{BA}|$$

Specifically, this property is used for $\mathbf{a}$ and $\mathbf{b}$ vectors. Then

$$|\mathbf{I} + \mathbf{ab}'| = 1 + \mathbf{b}'\mathbf{a}$$

From the expansion by minors, it can be seen that the determinant of a triangular matrix is the product of its diagonal elements. All coefficients a_{ij} except a_{11} are zero, and all terms but the first vanish from the summation. Thus, if $\mathbf{T}$ is (upper or lower) triangular,

$$|\mathbf{T}| = \prod_{i=1}^{n} t_{ii}$$

If $|\mathbf{A}| = 0$, then $\mathbf{A}$ is said to be *singular*; if $|\mathbf{A}| \neq 0$, then $\mathbf{A}$ is a *nonsingular* matrix. A square matrix can be nonsingular only if none of its rows or columns is expressible as a linear combination of others; that is, if it is of full rank. Any matrix of deficient rank and all products and gramians of it are singular. If two square matrices are nonsingular, their product is also nonsingular.

The matrix of variances and covariances is a function of a gramian of the data matrix. For it to be nonsingular there must be at least as many subjects as tests, and no variable can be exactly a linear combination of other test scores. The determinant of the variance–covariance matrix is called the *generalized variance* of the tests, since it comprises a p-dimensional volume or dispersion measure for the set.

Trace

The *trace* of a square matrix **A**, written tr (**A**), is the sum of the diagonal elements of the matrix; that is, $\Sigma_i a_{ii}$. The trace is encountered in statistical applications when only diagonal matrix elements are of concern, and the remaining matrix elements are ignored. For example, if

$$\mathbf{A} = \begin{bmatrix} 1 & 2 & 8 \\ 2 & 4 & 17 \\ 3 & 6 & -2 \end{bmatrix}$$

then

$$\text{tr}\,(\mathbf{A}) = 1+4-2 = 3$$

Although the trace is a simple matrix function, it has several properties that are important.

1. If c is a scalar, then $\text{tr}\,(c\mathbf{A}) = c \cdot \text{tr}\,(\mathbf{A})$
2. $\text{tr}\,(\mathbf{A}\pm\mathbf{B}) = \text{tr}\,(\mathbf{A}) \pm \text{tr}\,(\mathbf{B})$
3. $\text{tr}\,(\mathbf{CB}) = \text{tr}\,(\mathbf{BC})$
4. The trace of gramians $\mathbf{C}'\mathbf{C}$ and $\mathbf{CC}'$ are both the sum of the squares of all of the elements of **C**; that is, $\text{tr}\,(\mathbf{C}'\mathbf{C}) = \text{tr}\,(\mathbf{CC}') = \Sigma_i \Sigma_j c_{ij}^2$.

It follows from property 3 that if **b** is a vector, $\text{tr}\,(\mathbf{b}'\mathbf{Cb}) = \text{tr}\,(\mathbf{Cbb}')$. Since $\mathbf{b}'\mathbf{Cb}$ is a scalar, its trace is identically the same scalar value. If further $\mathbf{b}'_i$ ($i = 1, 2, \ldots, n$) is the ith row vector of matrix **B**, then

$$\begin{aligned} \textstyle\sum_i \mathbf{b}'_i \mathbf{Cb}_i &= \textstyle\sum_i \text{tr}\,(\mathbf{Cb}_i\mathbf{b}'_i) \\ &= \text{tr} \textstyle\sum_i (\mathbf{Cb}_i\mathbf{b}'_i) \\ &= \text{tr}\,(\mathbf{CB}'\mathbf{B}) \end{aligned}$$

The result follows since $\sum_i (\mathbf{Cb}_i\mathbf{b}'_i) = \mathbf{C}\sum_i \mathbf{b}_i\mathbf{b}'_i = \mathbf{CB}'\mathbf{B}$.

2.4 MATRIX FACTORING AND INVERSION

There are two types of factorizations of matrices that have repeated application in statistical methods. The first is the factoring of a gramian matrix into triangular factors, which are the transposes of one another. Triangular factoring is presented here as a first step in matrix inversion. The second and closely related technique involves factoring a rectangular matrix into components, of which one is an orthonormal rectangular matrix of the same order. For further information on both procedures, see Golub (1969).

Triangular Factorization

An $n \times n$ symmetric matrix **A** can be factored into the product of a triangular matrix and its transpose. We will represent this decomposition as

$$\mathbf{A} = \mathbf{TT}'$$

The form of the decomposition may be represented pictorially as

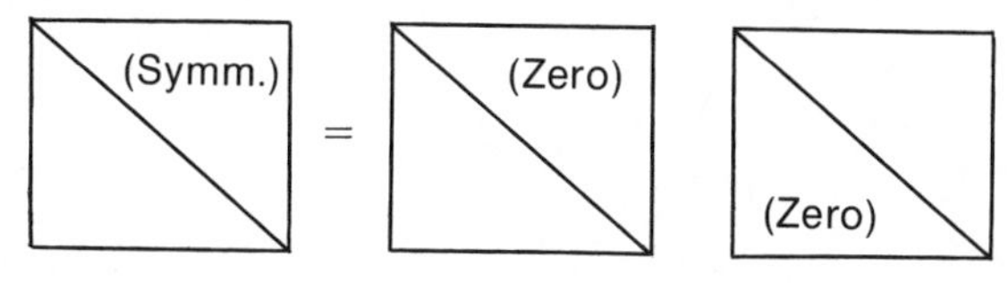

The condition for factoring **A** is that $|\mathbf{A}_{[k]}|$ is greater than zero, where

$$\mathbf{A}_{[k]} = \begin{bmatrix} a_{11} & \cdots & a_{1k} \\ \vdots & & \vdots \\ a_{k1} & \cdots & a_{kk} \end{bmatrix}$$

for $k = 1, 2, \ldots, n$. Most sum-of-cross-product and variance–covariance matrices meet this condition.

The method of decomposition is that of Cholesky or, equivalently, *square-root factoring*. Other factoring techniques are available, although comparisons presented by Fox (1965) indicate that the Cholesky method is both efficient and accurate.

The Cholesky factors of a diagonal matrix **D**, are easily obtained. Let the matrix to be factored be

$$\mathbf{D} = \begin{bmatrix} d_{11} & & & \text{(Zero)} \\ & d_{22} & & \\ & & \ddots & \\ \text{(Zero)} & & & d_{nn} \end{bmatrix}$$

The Cholesky factor is the diagonal matrix of the square roots of the $[d_{ii}]$. That is,

$$\mathbf{T} = \begin{bmatrix} \sqrt{d_{11}} & & & \text{(Zero)} \\ & \sqrt{d_{22}} & & \\ & & \ddots & \\ \text{(Zero)} & & & \sqrt{d_{nn}} \end{bmatrix}$$

It can easily be seen that $\mathbf{TT}' = \mathbf{D}$.

For a general $n \times n$ symmetric matrix **A**, the computations are more complex. We shall begin by allowing for a check on computational accuracy. To accomplish this, extend each column of **A** by adding an element

$$a_{n+1,j} = -\sum_{i=1}^{n} a_{ij}$$

to the column. All computations upon column j are extended to operate upon this additional element.

For the first column of triangular factor **T**,

$$t_{11} = \sqrt{a_{11}}$$

$$t_{i1} = \frac{a_{i1}}{t_{11}} \qquad i = 2, 3, \ldots, n+1$$

For the jth column of **T** $(j = 2, 3, \ldots, n)$

$$t_{ij} = 0 \qquad i = 1, 2, \ldots, j-1$$

$$t_{jj} = \sqrt{a_{jj} - \sum_{k=1}^{j-1} t_{jk}^2} \qquad \text{(Pivotal elements)}$$

$$t_{ij} = \frac{a_{ij} - \sum_{k=1}^{j-1} t_{ik} t_{jk}}{t_{jj}} \qquad i = j+1, j+2, \ldots, n+1$$

With the check row included, columns of **T** will sum to zero, within rounding error. The diagonal elements of **T** (that is, t_{jj}) are the *pivotal elements* of the factorization.

As an example, let **B** be the first three columns of the matrix of powers,

$$\mathbf{B} = \begin{bmatrix} 1 & 1 & 1 \\ 1 & 2 & 4 \\ 1 & 3 & 9 \\ 1 & 4 & 16 \end{bmatrix}$$

The gramian **B′B** is symmetric and of full rank 3. That is,

$$\mathbf{A} = \mathbf{B}'\mathbf{B} = \begin{bmatrix} 4 & 10 & 30 \\ 10 & 30 & 100 \\ 30 & 100 & 354 \\ \hline -44 & -140 & -484 \end{bmatrix}$$

The check row is affixed.

For the first column $(j = 1)$

$$t_{11} = \sqrt{4} = 2 \qquad t_{21} = \frac{10}{2} = 5 \qquad t_{31} = \frac{30}{2} = 15 \qquad t_{41} = \frac{-44}{2} = -22$$

For $j = 2$,

$$t_{12} = 0 \qquad t_{22} = \sqrt{30 - 5^2} = \sqrt{5}$$

$$t_{32} = \frac{100 - (15)(5)}{\sqrt{5}} = 5\sqrt{5} \qquad t_{42} = \frac{-140 - (-22)(5)}{\sqrt{5}} = -6\sqrt{5}$$

For $j=3$,

$$t_{13}=0 \qquad t_{23}=0$$

$$t_{33}=\sqrt{354-(15^2+\{5\sqrt{5}\}^2)}=2$$

$$t_{43}=\frac{-484-(-22)(15)-(6\sqrt{5})(5\sqrt{5})}{2}=-2$$

The following array is formed:

$$\mathbf{T}=\left[\begin{array}{ccc} 2 & 0 & 0 \\ 5 & \sqrt{5} & 0 \\ 15 & 5\sqrt{5} & 2 \\ \hline -22 & -6\sqrt{5} & -2 \end{array}\right]$$

It is easily verified that the columns of **T** sum to zero, and that $\mathbf{TT}'=\mathbf{A}$, for the first three rows of both matrices.

Had any column of **B** been linearly dependent upon other columns, or had **B** contained more columns that rows, both **B** and **A** would be of deficient rank. The effect upon **T** is that a pivotal element t_{jj} becomes zero when the corresponding column is encountered. Further computation is not possible unless the dependency is eliminated. Some computer algorithms, such as those in MULTIVARIANCE (Finn, 1972d), will ignore the dependent column so that any further dependencies may also be discovered.

The Cholesky factorization can facilitate computing the determinant of symmetric matrices, especially if they are of high order. According to the rule for determinants of products, $|\mathbf{A}|=|\mathbf{T}||\mathbf{T}|=|\mathbf{T}|^2$. The determinant of **T** is simply the product of its diagonal elements; that is,

$$|\mathbf{A}|=|\mathbf{T}|^2$$

$$=\prod_{j=1}^{n} t_{jj}^2$$

Conveniently, t_{jj}^2 is computed prior to t_{jj} in the Cholesky algorithm. The log determinant, frequently of use in multivariate analysis, is

$$\log|\mathbf{A}|=\log\prod_{j=1}^{n} t_{jj}^2$$

$$=2\textstyle\sum_j \log\,[t_{jj}]$$

The log provides further accuracy for large matrices.

For the example,

$$|\mathbf{A}|=(2\times\sqrt{5}\times 2)^2=80$$

$$\log_e|\mathbf{A}|=1.3863+1.6094+1.3863=4.3820$$

If **A** had been of deficient rank, at least one of the t_{jj} would have been zero, requiring that $|\mathbf{A}|=0$ as well.

Assume that **A** is a matrix of variances and covariances for two tests, y_1 and y_2. $s_{21}=s_{12}$ is the covariance of y_1 and y_2, while $s_{11}=s_1^2$ and $s_{22}=s_2^2$ are the respective variances.

$$\mathbf{A}=\begin{bmatrix} s_1^2 & s_{12} \\ s_{21} & s_2^2 \end{bmatrix}$$

The resulting Cholesky factor is

$$\mathbf{T}=\begin{bmatrix} s_1 & 0 \\ s_{21}/s_1 & \sqrt{s_2^2-(s_{12}^2/s_1^2)} \end{bmatrix}$$

We recognize t_{22} as the conditional standard deviation of y_2 *given*, or *holding constant*, y_1; t_{22}^2 is the conditional variance $s_{2|1}^2$.

This property holds for all variance–covariance matrices. The Cholesky factor contains the conditional standard deviations, holding constant *all* prior variables, on the diagonal. The off-diagonal elements are the conditional covariances, given preceding variables. Thus triangular factorization is of significant use in all stepwise or ordered analyses, when we wish to examine the effect of some variables independent of those preceding.

For example, with three variates the variance–covariance matrix is

$$\mathbf{A}=\begin{bmatrix} s_1^2 & s_{12} & s_{13} \\ s_{21} & s_2^2 & s_{23} \\ s_{31} & s_{32} & s_3^2 \end{bmatrix}$$

The Cholesky factor is

$$\mathbf{T}=\begin{bmatrix} s_1 & 0 & 0 \\ s_{21}/s_1 & s_{2|1} & 0 \\ s_{31}/s_1 & s_{32|1} & s_{3|12} \end{bmatrix}.$$

$s_{2|1}$ and $s_{32|1}$ are the standard deviation of y_2 and covariance of y_2 and y_3, respectively, holding constant y_1; $s_{3|12}$ is the standard deviation of y_3, holding constant both y_1 and y_2.

Inversion

The *inverse* of square nonsingular matrix **A** is the matrix $\mathbf{A}^{-1}$, such that

$$\mathbf{A}\mathbf{A}^{-1}=\mathbf{I}=\mathbf{A}^{-1}\mathbf{A}$$

We need not discuss matrix inversion generally. For in most statistical computations we are concerned with inverses of symmetric or gramian matrices; their inverses are simpler to find than for general nonsymmetric matrices.

Inversion for diagonal matrices is straightforward. $\mathbf{D}^{-1}$ is the diagonal matrix for reciprocals of the nonzero elements of **D**; that is,

$$[d^{-1}]_{ii}=\frac{1}{[d_{ii}]}$$

For example, let

$$\mathbf{D}=\begin{bmatrix} 4 & 0 & 0 \\ 0 & 10 & 0 \\ 0 & 0 & 50 \end{bmatrix}$$

Then

$$\mathbf{D}^{-1}=\begin{bmatrix} .25 & 0 & 0 \\ 0 & .10 & 0 \\ 0 & 0 & .02 \end{bmatrix}$$

and $\mathbf{D}^{-1}\mathbf{D} = \mathbf{D}\mathbf{D}^{-1} = \mathbf{I}$.

The inverse of a small square matrix (for example, of order 2, 3, or 4) may be found from its determinant and minors. For $n \times n$ matrix $\mathbf{A}$, the inverse is

$$\mathbf{A}^{-1}=\frac{1}{|\mathbf{A}|}\mathbf{B}'$$

$\mathbf{B}$ has elements

$$[b_{ij}]=(-1)^{i+j}\,|\mathbf{M}_{ij}|$$

and $|\mathbf{M}_{ij}|$ is the minor of $[b_{ij}]$.

Let

$$\mathbf{A}=\begin{bmatrix} 4 & 10 & 30 \\ 10 & 30 & 100 \\ 30 & 100 & 354 \end{bmatrix}$$

with determinant $|\mathbf{A}| = 80$. The inverse elements are 1/80 times $\mathbf{B}'$, where

$$b_{11}=(-1)^2\begin{vmatrix} 30 & 100 \\ 100 & 354 \end{vmatrix}=620$$

$$b_{12}=b_{21}=(-1)^3\begin{vmatrix} 10 & 100 \\ 30 & 354 \end{vmatrix}=-540$$

$$b_{13}=b_{31}=(-1)^4\begin{vmatrix} 10 & 30 \\ 30 & 100 \end{vmatrix}=100$$

$$b_{22}=(-1)^4\begin{vmatrix} 4 & 30 \\ 30 & 354 \end{vmatrix}=516$$

$$b_{23}=b_{32}=(-1)^5\begin{vmatrix} 4 & 10 \\ 30 & 100 \end{vmatrix}=-100$$

$$b_{33}=(-1)^6\begin{vmatrix} 4 & 10 \\ 10 & 30 \end{vmatrix}=20$$

The inverse matrix is

$$\mathbf{A}^{-1}=\frac{1}{80}\mathbf{B}'$$

$$=\begin{bmatrix} 7.75 & -6.75 & 1.25 \\ -6.75 & 6.45 & -1.25 \\ 1.25 & -1.25 & .25 \end{bmatrix}$$

It is easily verified that $\mathbf{A}^{-1}\mathbf{A} = \mathbf{I}$.

In the case of a symmetric matrix, $|\mathbf{M}_{ij}| = |\mathbf{M}_{ji}|$ and the inverse is also symmetric. For larger matrices, or matrices with fractional elements, inversion by determinants is neither accurate nor practical. Thus we shall make use of two inverse relationships. First, for any matrix $\mathbf{A}$, which may be expressed as a product **BC**, the inverse of **A** is equal to the product of the inverses of **B** and **C** in the reverse order; that is, if $\mathbf{A} = \mathbf{BC}$, then $\mathbf{A}^{-1} = \mathbf{C}^{-1}\mathbf{B}^{-1}$. Second, the inverse of a triangular matrix is easily determined. Thus, for symmetric **A** we may utilize the Cholesky factorization, $\mathbf{A} = \mathbf{TT}'$, and determine $\mathbf{A}^{-1}$ as $(\mathbf{T}^{-1})'\mathbf{T}^{-1}$.

In the previous section, we discussed the triangular factorization of **A** to the product $\mathbf{TT}'$. $\mathbf{T}^{-1}$ is computed as follows. Maintain the $n \times n$ matrix **T**, plus the check row as obtained from factoring **A**, with elements

$$t_{n+1,j} = \sum_{i=1}^{n} t_{ij}$$

For the ith diagonal element of $\mathbf{T}^{-1}$ $(i = 1, 2, \ldots, n)$

$$(t^{-1})_{ii} = \frac{1}{t_{ii}}$$

For the ith row of T^{-1} $(i = 2, 3, \ldots, n)$

$$(t^{-1})_{ij} = -\frac{\sum_{k=j}^{i-1} t_{ik}[t^{-1}]_{kj}}{t_{ii}} \qquad j = 1, 2, \ldots, i-1$$

$$(t^{-1})_{ij} = 0 \qquad j = i+1, i+2, \ldots, n$$

For the $(n+1)$th row,

$$(t^{-1})_{n+1,j} = \sum_{k=j}^{n} t_{n+1,k}(t^{-1})_{kj} \qquad j = 1, 2, \ldots, n$$

Elements of the check row should equal unity, within rounding error.

As an example, let us recall **T**, the Cholesky factor of **A**,

$$\mathbf{A} = \begin{bmatrix} 4 & 10 & 30 \\ 10 & 30 & 100 \\ 30 & 100 & 354 \end{bmatrix}$$

Including the check row,

$$\mathbf{T} = \begin{bmatrix} 2 & 0 & 0 \\ 5 & \sqrt{5} & 0 \\ 15 & 5\sqrt{5} & 2 \\ \hline -22 & -6\sqrt{5} & -2 \end{bmatrix}$$

The diagonal elements of $\mathbf{T}^{-1}$ are $(t^{-1})_{11} = 1/2$, $(t^{-1})_{22} = \sqrt{5}/5$, and $(t^{-1})_{33} = 1/2$. For the first row $(i = 1)$

$$(t^{-1})_{12} = 0 \qquad (t^{-1})_{13} = 0$$

For $i=2$,

$$(t^{-1})_{21}=-\frac{5(1/2)}{\sqrt{5}}=-\frac{\sqrt{5}}{2}$$

$$(t^{-1})_{23}=0$$

For $i=3$,

$$(t^{-1})_{31}=-\frac{15(1/2)+(5\sqrt{5})(-\sqrt{5}/2)}{2}=\frac{5}{2}$$

$$(t^{-1})_{32}=-\frac{(5\sqrt{5})(\sqrt{5}/5)}{2}=-\frac{5}{2}$$

For the check row,

$$(t^{-1})_{41}=-[-22(1/2)+(-6\sqrt{5})(-\sqrt{5}/2)+(-2)(5/2)]=1$$

$$(t^{-1})_{42}=-[(-6\sqrt{5})(\sqrt{5}/5)+(-2)(-5/2)]=1$$

$$(t^{-1})_{43}=-(-2)(1/2)=1$$

Forming the array,

$$\mathbf{T}^{-1}=\begin{bmatrix} 1/2 & 0 & 0 \\ -\sqrt{5}/2 & \sqrt{5}/5 & 0 \\ 5/2 & -5/2 & 1/2 \end{bmatrix}$$

It is easily verified that $\mathbf{TT}^{-1}=\mathbf{T}^{-1}\mathbf{T}=\mathbf{I}$.

Returning to $\mathbf{A}$,

$$\mathbf{A}^{-1}=(\mathbf{T}^{-1})'\mathbf{T}^{-1}$$

$$=\begin{bmatrix} 31/4 & -27/4 & 5/4 \\ -27/4 & 129/20 & -5/4 \\ 5/4 & -5/4 & 1/4 \end{bmatrix}$$

It may now also be verified that $\mathbf{AA}^{-1}=\mathbf{A}^{-1}\mathbf{A}=\mathbf{I}$. It can be seen that the inverse of $\mathbf{A}$ agrees with that obtained by the method of determinants.

If matrix $\mathbf{A}$ had been singular, one of the diagonal elements $[t_{ii}]$ would be zero. In this case the inverse diagonal element cannot be found and the inverse matrix is not defined. A *generalized inverse* (see Searle, 1966, Chapter 6) for $\mathbf{A}$ may be obtained, by ignoring rows that have dependencies. We shall restrict ourselves here to symmetric matrices with nonzero determinants.

We have noted that the inverse of a symmetric matrix is itself symmetric. Also, if $\mathbf{A}=\mathbf{BC}$, then $\mathbf{C}^{-1}\mathbf{B}^{-1}=\mathbf{A}^{-1}$. For all square matrices, the inverse of the transpose is the transpose of the inverse matrix; that is,

$$(\mathbf{A}^{-1})'=(\mathbf{A}')^{-1}$$

This follows since

$$\mathbf{AA}^{-1}=\mathbf{I} \qquad \text{and} \qquad (\mathbf{A}^{-1})'\mathbf{A}'=\mathbf{I}'$$

Since $\mathbf{I}'=\mathbf{I}$, $(\mathbf{A}^{-1})'$ is the inverse of $\mathbf{A}'$ and must be identical to $(\mathbf{A}')^{-1}$. The left inverse matrix is also the right inverse, $\mathbf{A}^{-1}\mathbf{A}=\mathbf{I}=\mathbf{AA}^{-1}$. Thus if $\mathbf{K}$ is square and orthonormal by columns ($\mathbf{K}'\mathbf{K}=\mathbf{I}$), it must also be orthonormal by rows ($\mathbf{K}\mathbf{K}'=\mathbf{I}$), since $\mathbf{K}'=\mathbf{K}^{-1}$.

The determinant of the inverse matrix is the inverse of the original determinant,

$$|\mathbf{A}^{-1}|=\frac{1}{|\mathbf{A}|}$$

In the preceding example, $|\mathbf{A}|=80$. Then

$$\begin{aligned}|\mathbf{A}^{-1}|&=|\mathbf{T}^{-1}|^2\\&=\left(\frac{1}{2}\times\frac{\sqrt{5}}{5}\times\frac{1}{2}\right)^2=\frac{1}{80}\end{aligned}$$

Let an $n\times n$ matrix $\mathbf{A}$ be expressed in partitioned form, with sections having n_1 and n_2 rows and columns, respectively, with $n_1+n_2=n$.

$$\mathbf{A}=\left[\begin{array}{c|c}\mathbf{A}_{11} & \mathbf{A}_{12}\\\hline \mathbf{A}_{21} & \mathbf{A}_{22}\end{array}\right]\begin{array}{l}n_1 \text{ rows}\\ n_2 \text{ rows}\end{array}$$

$$\begin{array}{cc}n_1 & n_2\\ \text{columns} & \text{columns}\end{array}$$

The determinant of $\mathbf{A}$ can be expressed as a function of the determinants of the separate portions. Specifically,

$$\begin{aligned}|\mathbf{A}|&=|\mathbf{A}_{11}||\mathbf{A}_{22}-\mathbf{A}_{21}\mathbf{A}_{11}{}^{-1}\mathbf{A}_{12}|\\&=|\mathbf{A}_{22}||\mathbf{A}_{11}-\mathbf{A}_{12}\mathbf{A}_{22}{}^{-1}\mathbf{A}_{21}|\end{aligned}$$

It is necessary that $\mathbf{A}_{11}$ or $\mathbf{A}_{22}$ be nonsingular. Note that in utilizing these relationships, it is normally preferable to invert the smaller of the two matrices, $\mathbf{A}_{11}$ or $\mathbf{A}_{22}$.

The computation of the Cholesky factor or inverse matrix requires computer routines for both speed and accuracy. Good subroutines for these functions are contained in the Chicago package (Bock and Repp, 1970). The MULTIVARIANCE program (Finn, 1972d), contains a single routine with three entry and exit points, respectively, for one, two, or all steps:

$$\begin{array}{ll}(1) & \mathbf{A}=\mathbf{T}\mathbf{T}'\\(2) & \mathbf{T}\Rightarrow\mathbf{T}^{-1}\\(3) & (\mathbf{T}^{-1})'\mathbf{T}^{-1}=\mathbf{A}^{-1}\end{array}$$

Orthonormalization

Suppose that $\mathbf{X}$ is an $m\times n$ rectangular matrix of full rank n. Then $\mathbf{X}'\mathbf{X}$ is of full rank and is symmetric. Factoring $\mathbf{X}'\mathbf{X}$ by the method of Cholesky, we have

$$\mathbf{X}'\mathbf{X}=\mathbf{T}\mathbf{T}'$$

and

$$(\mathbf{X}'\mathbf{X})^{-1}=(\mathbf{T}^{-1})'\mathbf{T}^{-1}$$

Let us examine the product

$$\mathbf{X}^* = \mathbf{X}(\mathbf{T}^{-1})'$$

First, $\mathbf{X}^*$ has the same order as $\mathbf{X}$ but is columnwise orthonormal; that is,

$$\begin{aligned}[\mathbf{X}^*]'\mathbf{X}^* &= \mathbf{T}^{-1}(\mathbf{X}'\mathbf{X})(\mathbf{T}^{-1})' \\ &= \mathbf{T}^{-1}\mathbf{T}\mathbf{T}'(\mathbf{T}^{-1})' \\ &= \mathbf{I}\end{aligned}$$

Second, columns of $\mathbf{X}^*$ are linear composites of columns of $\mathbf{X}$, as defined by $(\mathbf{T}^{-1})'$. Specifically, $\mathbf{x}_1^*$ is simply $\mathbf{x}_1$ normalized; $\mathbf{x}_2^*$ is a linear function of $\mathbf{x}_1$ and $\mathbf{x}_2$ such that $\mathbf{x}_2^*$ is orthogonal to $\mathbf{x}_1$ and is normalized; $\mathbf{x}_3^*$ is a linear function of $\mathbf{x}_1$, $\mathbf{x}_2$, and $\mathbf{x}_3$ such that $\mathbf{x}_3^*$ is orthogonal to $\mathbf{x}_1$ and $\mathbf{x}_2$ and is normalized; and so on.

The *orthonormalization* of $\mathbf{X}$ to $\mathbf{X}^*$ is equivalent to factoring $\mathbf{X}$ into the product of $\mathbf{X}^*$ and $\mathbf{T}'$. The superscript (*) on $\mathbf{X}$ is used to denote that the matrix is orthonormal, that is, $(\mathbf{X}^*)'\mathbf{X}^* = \mathbf{I}$. In general any $m \times n$ rectangular matrix of full rank n, may be factored into the product of an $m \times n$ columnwise orthonormal matrix and an $n \times n$ upper triangular matrix. The decomposition can be represented as

$$\mathbf{X} = \mathbf{X}^*\mathbf{T}'$$

This may be depicted as

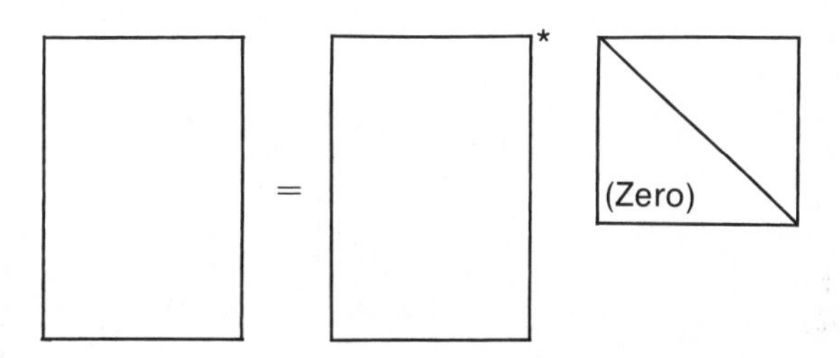

The method of decomposition is the Gram–Schmidt technique, which does not require computation of $\mathbf{X}'\mathbf{X}$ or the Cholesky factor from $\mathbf{X}'\mathbf{X}$. A modification of the Gram–Schmidt procedure (Björk, 1967) and other methods, such as that of Householder (1964), are more accurate and should be employed for large problems. The Gram–Schmidt method operates by successively computing columns of $\mathbf{X}$ that are orthogonal to preceding columns, at each stage normalizing the newly computed vector. Björk's modification postpones normalization until all orthogonal vectors are computed.

It is also possible to produce a factorization which is orthogonal with respect to an $m \times m$ diagonal matrix metric $\mathbf{D}$. The outcome is a matrix $\mathbf{X}^*$, such that $(\mathbf{X}^*)'\mathbf{D}\mathbf{X}^* = \mathbf{I}$. The computations involved in using $\mathbf{D}$ reduce to those of the simpler case if $\mathbf{D}$ is an identity matrix. Therefore the general algorithm is presented here.

Assume that we wish to factor matrix $\mathbf{X}$ with columns $\mathbf{x}_i$ $\quad (i = 1, 2, \ldots, n)$.

For the first column of **X**,

$$[t']_{11} = \sqrt{\mathbf{x}_1'\mathbf{D}\mathbf{x}_1} \qquad \mathbf{x}_1^* = \frac{1}{t_{11}}\mathbf{x}_1 \qquad \text{(Normalization)}$$

For the jth column of **X** $(j = 2, 3, \ldots, n)$

$$[t']_{ij} = \mathbf{x}_j'\mathbf{D}\mathbf{x}_i^* \qquad i = 1, 2, \ldots, j-1$$

$$\mathbf{x}_j^{\perp} = \mathbf{x}_j - \sum_{i=1}^{j-1} [t']_{ij}\mathbf{x}_i^* \qquad \text{(Intermediate orthogonal result)}$$

$$[t']_{jj} = \sqrt{(\mathbf{x}_j^{\perp})'\mathbf{D}\mathbf{x}_j^{\perp}} \qquad \text{(Normalizing constant)}$$

$$\mathbf{x}_j^* = \frac{1}{[t']_{jj}}\mathbf{x}_j^{\perp} \qquad \text{(Normalization)}$$

Let **B** be the first three columns of the order-four matrix of powers, as in the Cholesky example; define **D** to be an order-four identity matrix.

$$\mathbf{B} = \begin{bmatrix} 1 & 1 & 1 \\ 1 & 2 & 4 \\ 1 & 3 & 9 \\ 1 & 4 & 16 \end{bmatrix}$$

For the first column,

$$[t']_{11} = \sqrt{4} = 2 \qquad \mathbf{b}_1^* = 1/2 \begin{bmatrix} 1 \\ 1 \\ 1 \\ 1 \end{bmatrix} = \begin{bmatrix} .5 \\ .5 \\ .5 \\ .5 \end{bmatrix}$$

For $j = 2$,

$$[t']_{12} = 5 \qquad \mathbf{b}_2^{\perp} = \begin{bmatrix} 1 \\ 2 \\ 3 \\ 4 \end{bmatrix} - 5 \begin{bmatrix} .5 \\ .5 \\ .5 \\ .5 \end{bmatrix} = \begin{bmatrix} -1.5 \\ -.5 \\ .5 \\ 1.5 \end{bmatrix}$$

$$[t']_{22} = \sqrt{5} \qquad \mathbf{b}_2^* = \begin{bmatrix} -3\sqrt{5}/10 \\ -\sqrt{5}/10 \\ \sqrt{5}/10 \\ 3\sqrt{5}/10 \end{bmatrix}$$

For $j = 3$,

$$[t']_{13} = 15 \qquad [t']_{23} = 5\sqrt{5}$$

$$\mathbf{b}_3^{\perp} = \begin{bmatrix} 1 \\ 4 \\ 9 \\ 16 \end{bmatrix} - 15 \begin{bmatrix} .5 \\ .5 \\ .5 \\ .5 \end{bmatrix} - 5\sqrt{5} \begin{bmatrix} -3\sqrt{5}/10 \\ -\sqrt{5}/10 \\ \sqrt{5}/10 \\ 3\sqrt{5}/10 \end{bmatrix} = \begin{bmatrix} 1 \\ -1 \\ -1 \\ 1 \end{bmatrix}$$

$$[t']_{33} = \sqrt{4} = 2 \qquad \mathbf{b}_3^* = \begin{bmatrix} .5 \\ -.5 \\ -.5 \\ .5 \end{bmatrix}$$

Forming the entire arrays,

$$\mathbf{B}^* = \begin{bmatrix} .5 & -3\sqrt{5}/10 & .5 \\ .5 & -\sqrt{5}/10 & -.5 \\ .5 & \sqrt{5}/10 & -.5 \\ .5 & 3\sqrt{5}/10 & .5 \end{bmatrix} \quad \text{and} \quad \mathbf{T}' = \begin{bmatrix} 2 & 5 & 15 \\ 0 & \sqrt{5} & 5\sqrt{5} \\ 0 & 0 & 2 \end{bmatrix}$$

It is easily verified that $(\mathbf{B}^*)'\mathbf{B}^* = \mathbf{I}$ and that $\mathbf{T}'$ is identically the Cholesky factor of $\mathbf{B}'\mathbf{B}$, obtained earlier. $\mathbf{B}^*$ is termed an *orthonormal basis* for the columns of $\mathbf{B}$. Again, if the rank of $\mathbf{B}$ is less than n, one or more of the diagonal elements of $\mathbf{T}$ will be null. These are the normalizing constants (lengths) for the orthogonal vectors. The column of $\mathbf{B}$ that is dependent upon preceding columns will go to zero in $\mathbf{B}^\perp$, and would have zero length. This can occur either by columns of $\mathbf{B}$ being direct linear combinations of one another or by $\mathbf{B}$ having more columns than rows.

While the Cholesky factor contains the conditional standard deviations and covariances for each column given preceding columns, $\mathbf{B}^\perp$ contains the conditional variables themselves. That is $\mathbf{b}_2^\perp$ is the part of $\mathbf{b}_2$ that is independent of (given) $\mathbf{b}_1$; $\mathbf{b}_3^\perp$ is the residual $\mathbf{b}_3$ that is independent of the variables in $\mathbf{b}_1$ and $\mathbf{b}_2$; and so on. Readers may recognize $\mathbf{B}^*$ as containing the first three normalized orthogonal polynomial contrasts of common use.

2.5 MATRIX DERIVATIVES

The calculus of matrices is a complex topic, but fortunately we do not require more than a few operations. The needed rules are presented here. The reader should be able to see a close resemblance of these rules to those of scalar algebra.

The partial derivative of a function of a vector with respect to the individual elements is the vector of partial derivatives taken with respect to each element separately. Let the $n \times 1$ vector variable be

$$\mathbf{v} = \begin{bmatrix} v_1 \\ v_2 \\ \vdots \\ v_n \end{bmatrix}$$

Let $\mathbf{w}$ be an $n \times 1$ vector of constants.

Rule 1:

$$\frac{\partial w_i}{\partial \mathbf{v}} = \mathbf{0}$$

Rule 2:

$$\frac{\partial \mathbf{w}'\mathbf{v}}{\partial \mathbf{v}} = \frac{\partial \mathbf{v}'\mathbf{w}}{\partial \mathbf{v}} = \mathbf{w}$$

Rule 3:

$$\frac{\partial \mathbf{v}'\mathbf{A}\mathbf{v}}{\partial \mathbf{v}} = 2\mathbf{A}\mathbf{v} \qquad \text{if } \mathbf{A} \text{ is an } n\times n \text{ symmetric matrix.}$$

Corollary 3.1: If $\mathbf{A} = \mathbf{I}$, then $\mathbf{v}'\mathbf{A}\mathbf{v} = \mathbf{v}'\mathbf{v}$ and $\partial\mathbf{v}'\mathbf{v}/\partial\mathbf{v} = 2\mathbf{v}$.

2.6 CHARACTERISTIC ROOTS AND VECTORS

Frequently in statistical applications it becomes necessary to find a vector $\mathbf{x}$ in order to define a linear combination of variables y_i that has maximum variance. That is, if we let $\mathbf{y}$ be the vector variable with elements y_i ($i=1, 2, \ldots, n$), the problem is one of finding $\mathbf{x}$ such that $\mathscr{V}(\mathbf{x}'\mathbf{y})$ is maximal. It will be shown in the next chapter that if the variance–covariance matrix of the y_i is $n\times n$ matrix $\mathbf{A}$, then the variance of the linear combination $\mathbf{x}'\mathbf{y}$ is the scalar $\mathbf{x}'\mathbf{A}\mathbf{x}$. Even without this understanding, the matrix problem is one of general interest: to find $\mathbf{x}$ that maximizes $\mathbf{x}'\mathbf{A}\mathbf{x}$, where $\mathbf{A}$ is any symmetric matrix of order n and rank m ($\leq n$).

Since the maximum value of $\mathbf{x}'\mathbf{A}\mathbf{x}$ can become infinite, $\mathbf{x}$ is frequently restricted to having unit length; that is, $\mathbf{x}'\mathbf{x}=1$. Let us introduce λ to represent the maximum value of the variance:

$$\lambda = \max(\mathbf{x}'\mathbf{A}\mathbf{x}) \tag{2.6.1}$$

The maximum value λ may be obtained by maximizing $\mathbf{x}'\mathbf{A}\mathbf{x}$ or, more conveniently, by maximizing the equivalent expression

$$g = \mathbf{x}'\mathbf{A}\mathbf{x} - \lambda(\mathbf{x}'\mathbf{x} - 1)$$

Setting the first derivative with respect to $\mathbf{x}$ at zero

$$\frac{\partial g}{\partial \mathbf{x}} = 2\mathbf{A}\mathbf{x} - 2\lambda\mathbf{x}$$

and

$$\mathbf{A}\mathbf{x} = \lambda\mathbf{x}$$

This may be reexpressed as the set of n homogeneous equations

$$(\mathbf{A} - \lambda\mathbf{I})\mathbf{x} = \mathbf{0} \tag{2.6.2}$$

The maximum λ and corresponding vector $\mathbf{x}$ are the non-null solutions of these equations. $\mathbf{I}$ is an identity matrix of order n.

In order for there to be a non-null $\mathbf{x}$, it is necessary that

$$|\mathbf{A} - \lambda\mathbf{I}| = 0 \tag{2.6.3}$$

If $|\mathbf{A}-\lambda\mathbf{I}|$ were *not* equal to zero, we could invert $\mathbf{A}-\lambda\mathbf{I}$ and solve for $\mathbf{x}$ by premultiplying both sides of Eq. 2.6.2 by $(\mathbf{A}-\lambda\mathbf{I})^{-1}$. The only solution for $\mathbf{x}$ would then be $\mathbf{x}=\mathbf{0}$. This is not the only solution when $\mathbf{A}-\lambda\mathbf{I}$ is singular and cannot be inverted.

The solution λ of Eq. 2.6.2 is the *characteristic root*, or *eigenvalue*, of $\mathbf{A}$; $\mathbf{x}$ is the associated *characteristic vector*, or *eigenvector*. To solve Eq. 2.6.3 we subtract $\mathbf{A}-\lambda\mathbf{I}$ and write the expression for the determinant in terms of the resulting elements. The result is a polynomial in λ of degree n. This *characteristic equation* of $\mathbf{A}$ has as many roots above zero as the rank of $\mathbf{A}$. The remaining $n-m$ roots and vectors, if they exist, will be null.

For example, let

$$\mathbf{A}=\begin{bmatrix} 4 & 10 \\ 10 & 30 \end{bmatrix}$$

Then

$$\mathbf{A}-\lambda\mathbf{I}=\begin{bmatrix} 4-\lambda & 10 \\ 10 & 30-\lambda \end{bmatrix}$$

The determinant of $\mathbf{A}-\lambda\mathbf{I}$ is

$$|\mathbf{A}-\lambda\mathbf{I}|=\lambda^2-34\lambda+20$$

Setting the determinant to zero, we find that the characteristic equation is

$$\lambda^2-34\lambda+20=0$$

We note that the polynomial is of degree two, and has two real roots. Solving for the two roots,

$$\lambda_1=33.40 \qquad \text{and} \qquad \lambda_2=.60$$

Associated with each root or eigenvalue is an n-element eigenvector $\mathbf{x}$. The vector corresponding to λ_1 is $\mathbf{x}_1$, with elements x_{11} and x_{21}. Substituting λ_1 in Eq. 2.6.2,

$$\mathbf{A}-\lambda_1\mathbf{I}=\begin{bmatrix} -29.4 & 10.0 \\ 10.0 & -3.4 \end{bmatrix}$$

From either row, the ratio of x_{11} to x_{12} is .34 to 1. Taking these values as the initial vector, we may normalize so that $\mathbf{x}_1'\mathbf{x}_1 = 1$. That is,

$$\left\|\begin{bmatrix} .34 \\ 1.00 \end{bmatrix}\right\|=\sqrt{1.1156}=1.06$$

$$\mathbf{x}_1=\frac{1}{1.06}\begin{bmatrix} .34 \\ 1.00 \end{bmatrix}=\begin{bmatrix} .32 \\ .94 \end{bmatrix}$$

$\mathbf{x}_1$ is the first normalized eigenvector. Its components are the weights that produce the maximum value $\lambda_1 = \mathbf{x}_1'\mathbf{A}\mathbf{x}_1$, subject only to the restriction of unit length.

There is a second solution to Eq. 2.6.2, with $\lambda_2=.60$. Substituting in 2.6.2 and solving for $\mathbf{x}_2$, the normalized vector is

$$\mathbf{x}_2=\begin{bmatrix} .94 \\ -.32 \end{bmatrix}$$

$\mathbf{x}_2$ is the second eigenvector of $\mathbf{A}$, and maximizes Eq. 2.6.1 to give λ_2. In addition to unit length, $\mathbf{x}_2$ is subject to the condition that it is *orthogonal* to $\mathbf{x}_1$. In the example, the characteristic equation is of degree two, and there are no further solutions.

It is convenient to form an $n\times n$ diagonal matrix of characteristic roots, $\mathbf{\Lambda}$, and an $n \times m$ matrix $\mathbf{X}$, having the characteristic vectors as columns. $\mathbf{\Lambda}$ and $\mathbf{X}$ have the following properties:

1. $\mathbf{X}'\mathbf{X} = \mathbf{I}_m$; that is, nonzero eigenvectors are orthonormal if $\mathbf{A}$ is symmetric.
2. $\mathbf{AX} = \mathbf{X\Lambda}$; $\mathbf{X}'\mathbf{AX} = \mathbf{\Lambda}$; $\mathbf{X\Lambda X}' = \mathbf{A}$.
3. $|\mathbf{A}| = |\mathbf{X\Lambda X}'| = |\mathbf{\Lambda}| = \prod_{i=1}^{n} \lambda_{ii}$.
4. $\text{tr}\,[\mathbf{A}] = \text{tr}\,[\mathbf{X\Lambda X}'] = \text{tr}\,[\mathbf{\Lambda}] = \sum_{i=1}^{n} \lambda_{ii}$.

It can be seen from property 3 that at least one of the eigenvalues of a singular matrix will be zero. A matrix having all eigenvalues greater than zero is said to be *positive definite*. If some of the values are null and others are greater than zero, the matrix is said to be *positive semidefinite*.

At times in statistical applications the problem is more complex and maxima are required of the ratio of two quadratic expressions. Here,

$$\lambda = \max \left\{ \frac{\mathbf{x}'\mathbf{Ax}}{\mathbf{x}'\mathbf{Bx}} \right\}$$

If $\mathbf{B}$ is positive definite and symmetric, it may be factored into triangular components, $\mathbf{B} = \mathbf{TT}'$, by the Cholesky algorithm. Letting $\mathbf{v} = \mathbf{T}'\mathbf{x}$ and $\mathbf{x} = (\mathbf{T}^{-1})'\mathbf{v}$,

$$\lambda = \max \left\{ \frac{\mathbf{x}'\mathbf{Ax}}{\mathbf{v}'(\mathbf{T}^{-1})\mathbf{TT}'(\mathbf{T}^{-1})'\mathbf{v}} \right\}$$

$$= \max \left\{ \frac{\mathbf{v}'(\mathbf{T}^{-1})\mathbf{A}(\mathbf{T}^{-1})'\mathbf{v}}{\mathbf{v}'\mathbf{v}} \right\}$$

If we now restrict $\mathbf{v}$ to unit length so that $\mathbf{v}'\mathbf{v} = 1$, the problem reduces to the simpler one of computing eigenvalues and vectors, λ and $\mathbf{v}$, of the single matrix $(\mathbf{T}^{-1})\mathbf{A}(\mathbf{T}^{-1})'$. The $\mathbf{x}_i$ may be obtained as a second step, through $\mathbf{x} = (\mathbf{T}^{-1})'\mathbf{v}$.

The computation of eigenvalues and vectors, even for small matrices, is formidable. Algorithms have been forwarded by Householder (1964), Ortega (1960), and Wilkinson (1965), and have been summarized for programming in Ralston and Wilf (1965, 1967). Since eigen solutions constitute a minor role in this book, these methods are not discussed here. The MULTIVARIANCE program utilizes a subroutine written according to the Householder specifications (Bock and Repp, 1970).

2.7 EXERCISES

Understanding the components of the matrix expressions in the following chapters is necessary to understanding the statistical methodology. The following matrix exercises provide examples of the important aspects of matrix computation, and are recommended to readers without matrix algebra preparation. Answers to the problems are given in the Appendix.

Matrices

$$\mathbf{A}=\begin{bmatrix}1 & 2 & 1\\3 & -1 & -1\\0 & 2 & 3\\1 & 0 & 0\end{bmatrix}\qquad \mathbf{B}=\begin{bmatrix}1 & 1 & 1 & 1\\0 & 1 & 2 & 1\\-1 & -1 & 0 & 0\end{bmatrix}\qquad \mathbf{C}=\begin{bmatrix}23 & 0 & -3\\0 & 30 & 32\\-3 & 32 & 41\end{bmatrix}$$

$$\mathbf{D}=\begin{bmatrix}3 & 0 & 0 & 0\\0 & 2 & 0 & 0\\0 & 0 & 4 & 0\\0 & 0 & 0 & 2\end{bmatrix}\qquad \mathbf{e}=\begin{bmatrix}1.0\\1.5\\1.0\\2.5\end{bmatrix}\qquad \mathbf{f}=\begin{bmatrix}28\\44\\10\end{bmatrix}\qquad \mathbf{v}=\begin{bmatrix}-2\\-1\\1\\1\end{bmatrix}$$

$$\mathbf{H}=\begin{bmatrix}4 & 4 & -2 & 2\\4 & 8 & -2 & 4\\-2 & -2 & 17 & -1\\2 & 4 & -1 & 3\end{bmatrix}\qquad \mathbf{K}=\begin{bmatrix}\sqrt{3}/3 & -\sqrt{2}/2 & \sqrt{6}/6\\\sqrt{3}/3 & 0 & -\sqrt{6}/3\\\sqrt{3}/3 & \sqrt{2}/2 & \sqrt{6}/6\end{bmatrix}$$

$$\mathbf{T}=\begin{bmatrix}3 & 0 & 0\\4 & 1 & 0\\6 & -1 & 2\end{bmatrix}\qquad \mathbf{U}=\begin{bmatrix}.5 & 0 & 0\\1 & 1 & 0\\-1 & 2 & 2\end{bmatrix}\qquad \mathbf{G}=\begin{bmatrix}1 & 0 & 0 & 0\\0 & 0 & 0 & 1\\0 & 0 & 1 & 0\\0 & 1 & 0 & 0\end{bmatrix}$$

Problems

1. *Elements:* What is the value of a_{22}? of $\mathbf{c}_2$?
2. *Definitions:* Write $\mathbf{I}_3$; $\mathbf{1}_3$.
3. *Transposition:* Write $\mathbf{A}'$; $\mathbf{e}'$; $\mathbf{H}'$.
4. *Addition:* Compute $\mathbf{C}+\mathbf{T}$; $(\mathbf{e}+\mathbf{v})'$; $\mathbf{D}-\mathbf{H}$.
5. *Scalar multiplication:* Compute $(1/10)\mathbf{A}$; $4\mathbf{v}$.
6. *Vector multiplication:*

   Compute $\mathbf{e}'\mathbf{v}$; $\mathbf{v}'\mathbf{e}$. What property do $\mathbf{v}$ and $\mathbf{e}$ have with respect to one another?
   Compute $\mathbf{e}\mathbf{f}'$; $\mathbf{e}'\mathbf{f}$; $\mathbf{1}_4'\mathbf{v}$.
   Compute $\mathbf{1}_4'\mathbf{1}_4$; $\mathbf{e}'\mathbf{e}$; $\mathbf{v}'\mathbf{v}$. What is this function of the respective vectors?
   Find $|\mathbf{e}|$, the length of $\mathbf{e}$; $|\mathbf{v}|$, the length of $\mathbf{v}$.
   Normalize $\mathbf{v}$; that is, find $\mathbf{v}^* = (1/|\mathbf{v}|)\mathbf{v}$.
   What is $|\mathbf{v}^*|$, the length of $\mathbf{v}^*$?
7. *Matrix multiplication:*

   Compute $\mathbf{AI}$; $\mathbf{IA}$.
   The transpose of a matrix product is the product of their transposes multiplied in the reverse order. Find $\mathbf{AB}$; $(\mathbf{AB})'$; $\mathbf{A}'\mathbf{B}$; $\mathbf{B}'\mathbf{A}$; $\mathbf{B}'\mathbf{A}'$.
   Compute $\mathbf{DA}$, $\mathbf{BD}$. What are the effects of pre- and postmultiplication by diagonal matrices?
   Compute $\mathbf{T}+\mathbf{U}$; $\mathbf{TU}$. In what way do these two results resemble $\mathbf{T}$ and $\mathbf{U}$?
   Compute $\mathbf{KK}'$; $\mathbf{K}'\mathbf{K}$. What is the nature of $\mathbf{K}$?
   Compute $\mathbf{A}'\mathbf{A}$; $\mathbf{B}'\mathbf{B}$; $\mathbf{AA}'$; $\mathbf{BB}'$. Note that $\mathbf{A}'\mathbf{A}$ and $\mathbf{B}'\mathbf{B}$ are the sums of squares and cross products of the columns of $\mathbf{A}$ and $\mathbf{B}$, respectively. $\mathbf{AA}'$ and $\mathbf{BB}'$ are the sums of squares and cross products of the rows of $\mathbf{A}$ and $\mathbf{B}$, respectively.
   Compute $\mathbf{A}'\mathbf{DA}$; $\mathbf{BHB}'$. Note that the gramian symmetry is preserved even when the product is taken with a third symmetric matrix as a metric.
   Compute $\mathbf{D}\otimes\mathbf{T}$; $\mathbf{f}\otimes\mathbf{v}$.
   Compute $e. = (1/\{\mathbf{1}_4'\mathbf{1}_4\})\mathbf{e}'\mathbf{1}$; $\mathbf{e}-e.\mathbf{1}$. What are these?
   Compute $\mathbf{GA}$. How is the product related to $\mathbf{A}$?

8. *Factorization:*
   Find the Cholesky factor of $\mathbf{C}$; that is, find $\mathbf{W}$, where $\mathbf{C}=\mathbf{W}\mathbf{W}'$ and $\mathbf{W}$ is lower triangular. Verify that $\mathbf{C}=\mathbf{W}\mathbf{W}'$.
   What is the determinant of $\mathbf{W}$? of $\mathbf{C}$?
   Find the inverse of $\mathbf{W}$. What is its determinant?
   Verify that $\mathbf{W}^{-1}\mathbf{W}=\mathbf{W}\mathbf{W}^{-1}=\mathbf{I}$.
   Find $\mathbf{C}^{-1}=(\mathbf{W}^{-1})'\mathbf{W}^{-1}$. What is the determinant of $\mathbf{C}^{-1}$? Verify that $\mathbf{C}^{-1}\mathbf{C}=\mathbf{C}\mathbf{C}^{-1}=\mathbf{I}$.
   Find $\mathbf{A}^*$, orthonormalized by columns with respect to the metric $\mathbf{D}$. Call the corresponding triangular factor $\mathbf{R}$. What is $\mathbf{A}(\mathbf{R}^{-1})'$? Verify that $(\mathbf{A}^*)'\mathbf{D}\mathbf{A}^*=\mathbf{I}$.
9. *Rank and determinants:*
   What is the rank of $\mathbf{A}$? of $\mathbf{A}'\mathbf{A}$? of $\mathbf{A}\mathbf{A}'$? of $\mathbf{D}$?
   What is $|\mathbf{A}'\mathbf{A}|$? $|\mathbf{A}\mathbf{A}'|$? $|\mathbf{D}|$? $|\mathbf{A}\mathbf{A}'\mathbf{D}|$? $|\mathbf{G}|$? $|\mathbf{G}\mathbf{D}|$?
10. *Trace:* What is $\mathrm{tr}\,(\mathbf{T}\mathbf{T}')$?

Section 2

Method

CHAPTER 3

Summary of Multivariate Data

3.1 VECTOR EXPECTATIONS

A basic concept of multivariate statistics is a *vector variable.* When each member of a population is represented by more than a single outcome measure, the measures may be juxtaposed to yield a vector; to summarize data in this form, we may use matrix operations and develop conventions for the simultaneous treatment of multiple variables.

A *vector random variable* or *random vector* is a vector comprised of p (≥ 1) distinct random variables; each variable or element may be described by its own univariate density function. Let

$$\mathbf{x} = \begin{bmatrix} x_1 \\ x_2 \\ \vdots \\ x_p \end{bmatrix}$$

be a vector random variable. Each x_i is itself a random variable with *expectation*

$$\mathscr{E}(x_i) = \mu_i \tag{3.1.1}$$

and *variance*

$$\begin{aligned} \mathscr{V}(x_i) &= \mathscr{E}(x_i - \mu_i)^2 \\ &= \sigma_{ii} \end{aligned} \tag{3.1.2}$$

The variance σ_{ii} is represented as σ_i^2, to agree with elementary statistics presentations. The standard deviation is the square root σ_i.

Let σ_{ij} be the *covariance* of random variables x_i and x_j; that is,

$$\begin{aligned} \mathscr{V}(x_i, x_j) &= \mathscr{E}(x_i - \mu_i)(x_j - \mu_j) \\ &= \sigma_{ij} \end{aligned} \tag{3.1.3}$$

The covariance of x_i and itself is the variance of x_i. That is, when $i = j$, $\sigma_{ij} = \sigma_{ii} = \sigma_i^2$. Further the covariance is always symmetric so that $\sigma_{ij} = \sigma_{ji}$.

From univariate theory, we have the following results. For c constant,

$$\mathscr{E}(cx_i) = c\mu_i \tag{3.1.4}$$

$$\mathscr{E}(x_i + c) = \mu_i + c \tag{3.1.5}$$

$$\mathscr{V}(cx_i) = c^2\sigma_i^2 \tag{3.1.6}$$

$$\mathscr{V}(x_i + c) = \mathscr{V}(x_i) = \sigma_i^2 \tag{3.1.7}$$

For two variables x_i and x_j,

$$\mathscr{E}(x_i + x_j) = \mu_i + \mu_j \tag{3.1.8}$$

$$\mathscr{V}(x_i + x_j) = \sigma_i^2 + \sigma_j^2 + 2\sigma_{ij} \tag{3.1.9}$$

Like the variance, adding a constant to x_i or x_j does not alter the covariance. Multiplication of either variable by a constant multiplies the covariance by the same quantity. That is, with c and d constants,

$$\mathscr{V}(x_i + c, x_j + d) = \mathscr{V}(x_i, x_j) = \sigma_{ij} \tag{3.1.10}$$

$$\mathscr{V}(cx_i, dx_j) = cd\,\mathscr{V}(x_i, x_j) = cd\sigma_{ij} \tag{3.1.11}$$

If we *standardize* x_i and x_j to obtain z_i and z_j, respectively, we have

$$z_i = \frac{x_i - \mu_i}{\sigma_i} \quad \text{and} \quad z_j = \frac{x_j - \mu_j}{\sigma_j} \tag{3.1.12}$$

Then

$$\mathscr{E}(z_i) = \mathscr{E}(z_j) = 0 \tag{3.1.13}$$

and

$$\mathscr{V}(z_i) = \mathscr{V}(z_j) = 1 \tag{3.1.14}$$

The covariance of z_i and z_j is

$$\begin{aligned} \mathscr{V}(z_i, z_j) &= \frac{1}{\sigma_i\sigma_j}\mathscr{V}(x_i, x_j) \\ &= \frac{\sigma_{ij}}{\sigma_i\sigma_j} \\ &= \rho_{ij} \end{aligned} \tag{3.1.15}$$

ρ_{ij} is the *correlation* of x_i and x_j and has limits -1 and 1.

Let us proceed to the entire vector $\mathbf{x}$. The expectation of a vector variable is the vector of separate expectations.

$$\mathscr{E}(\mathbf{x}) = \mathscr{E}\begin{bmatrix} x_1 \\ x_2 \\ \vdots \\ x_p \end{bmatrix} = \begin{bmatrix} \mathscr{E}(x_1) \\ \mathscr{E}(x_2) \\ \vdots \\ \mathscr{E}(x_p) \end{bmatrix} = \begin{bmatrix} \mu_1 \\ \mu_2 \\ \vdots \\ \mu_p \end{bmatrix} = \boldsymbol{\mu} \tag{3.1.16}$$

The variance of any vector variable is the *matrix* of variances of each of the variates, and covariances of each pair of variables. That is,

$$\begin{aligned} \mathscr{V}(\mathbf{x}) &= \mathscr{E}[\mathbf{x} - \mathscr{E}(\mathbf{x})][\mathbf{x} - \mathscr{E}(\mathbf{x})]' \\ &= \mathscr{E}(\mathbf{x} - \boldsymbol{\mu})(\mathbf{x} - \boldsymbol{\mu})' \\ &= \mathscr{E}(\mathbf{x}\mathbf{x}') - \boldsymbol{\mu}\boldsymbol{\mu}' \\ &= \boldsymbol{\Sigma} \end{aligned} \tag{3.1.17}$$

$\boldsymbol{\Sigma}$ is the $p \times p$ *variance–covariance matrix* of the variables:

$$\boldsymbol{\Sigma} = \begin{bmatrix} \sigma_1^2 & \sigma_{12} & \cdots & \sigma_{1p} \\ \sigma_{21} & \sigma_2^2 & \cdots & \sigma_{2p} \\ \sigma_{31} & \sigma_{32} & \cdots & \sigma_{3p} \\ \vdots & & & \vdots \\ \sigma_{p1} & \sigma_{p2} & \cdots & \sigma_p^2 \end{bmatrix} \tag{3.1.17a}$$

The expectation and variance–covariance matrix of *any* vector variable (observed scores, errors, linear combination of scores) are the basic summary measures which parallel μ and σ^2 in univariate theory. In fact, when $p=1$, $\boldsymbol{\mu}=\mu$ and $\boldsymbol{\Sigma}=\sigma^2$. When $p>1$, $\boldsymbol{\Sigma}$ has the separate variances of the p variates as diagonal elements, and the covariance of x_i and x_j as the ij off-diagonal element. Since $\sigma_{ij}=\sigma_{ji}$, $\boldsymbol{\Sigma}$ is symmetric. The covariance of each variable with itself is the variance, or diagonal element, $\sigma_{ii}=\sigma_i^2$; the standard deviations are $\sqrt{\sigma_{ii}}=\sigma_i$.

The algebra of expectations and variance for vector variables parallels that for scalars. Let c be any given scalar and $\mathbf{c}'$ be a vector of constants; that is, $\mathbf{c}'=[c_1, c_2, \ldots, c_p]$. We have the following results:

$$\mathscr{E}(c\mathbf{x}) = c\boldsymbol{\mu} \tag{3.1.18}$$

$$\mathscr{E}(\mathbf{x}+\mathbf{c}) = \boldsymbol{\mu}+\mathbf{c} \tag{3.1.19}$$

$$\mathscr{V}(c\mathbf{x}) = c^2\boldsymbol{\Sigma} \tag{3.1.20}$$

$$\mathscr{V}(\mathbf{x}+\mathbf{c}) = \mathscr{V}(\mathbf{x}) = \boldsymbol{\Sigma} \tag{3.1.21}$$

As an example, assume that we have two random variables x_1 and x_2. Let $\mu_1=10$, $\mu_2=11$, $\sigma_1^2=100$, $\sigma_2^2=64$, and $\sigma_{12}=\sigma_{21}=40$. Then

$$\boldsymbol{\mu}' = [10 \quad 11] \qquad \text{and} \qquad \boldsymbol{\Sigma} = \begin{bmatrix} 100 & 40 \\ 40 & 64 \end{bmatrix}$$

Suppose further that $c=1/2$. Then

$$\mathscr{E}(c\mathbf{x}') = (1/2)\boldsymbol{\mu}' = [5.0 \quad 5.5]$$

and

$$\mathscr{V}(c\mathbf{x}) = (1/2)^2\boldsymbol{\Sigma} = \begin{bmatrix} 25 & 10 \\ 10 & 16 \end{bmatrix}$$

Thus if every score on both variables is divided in half, the resulting scores have 1/4 the original variances and covariance.

Assume instead that 3 is added to every score on x_1, and 2 subtracted from x_2. Then

$$\mathbf{c}' = [3 \quad -2]$$

$$\mathscr{E}(\mathbf{x}+\mathbf{c})' = \boldsymbol{\mu}'+\mathbf{c}' = [13 \quad 9]$$

$$\mathscr{V}(\mathbf{x}+\mathbf{c}) = \begin{bmatrix} 100 & 40 \\ 40 & 64 \end{bmatrix}$$

The expectation of a sum or any linear combination of the random variables of $\mathbf{x}$ can be formulated in matrix notation. For example, with $p=2$ and $\mathbf{1}'=[1 \quad 1]$, we may apply Eq. 3.1.8:

$$\mathscr{E}(x_1+x_2)=\mathscr{E}(\mathbf{1}'\mathbf{x})=\mu_1+\mu_2=\mathbf{1}'\boldsymbol{\mu}$$

Generally, if $\mathbf{c}$ is any vector defining a weighted linear combination of the x_i, the expectation of the linear function $y=c_1x_1+c_2x_2+\cdots+c_px_p$ is

$$\begin{aligned}\mathscr{E}(y)&=\mathscr{E}(\mathbf{c}'\mathbf{x})\\&=\mathbf{c}'\boldsymbol{\mu}\end{aligned} \tag{3.1.22}$$

The variance of the sum x_1+x_2, according to Eq. 3.1.9, is $\sigma_1{}^2+\sigma_2{}^2+2\sigma_{12}$. This is also obtained through vector manipulation. Note that $\mathscr{V}(x_1+x_2)=\mathscr{V}(\mathbf{1}'\mathbf{x})$. Expression 3.1.9 is equivalent to $\mathbf{1}'\boldsymbol{\Sigma}\mathbf{1}$, since

$$\begin{aligned}\mathscr{V}(\mathbf{1}'\mathbf{x})&=\mathbf{1}'\boldsymbol{\Sigma}\mathbf{1}\\&=[1 \quad 1]\begin{bmatrix}\sigma_1{}^2 & \sigma_{12}\\ \sigma_{21} & \sigma_2{}^2\end{bmatrix}\begin{bmatrix}1\\1\end{bmatrix}\\&=\sigma_1{}^2+\sigma_2{}^2+2\sigma_{12}\end{aligned}$$

Further, if $\boldsymbol{\Sigma}$ is diagonal with $\sigma_{12}=0$, then $\mathbf{1}'\boldsymbol{\Sigma}\mathbf{1}=\sigma_1{}^2+\sigma_2{}^2$. That is, the variance of the sum of independent random variables is the sum of their separate variances.

For a general set of weights $\mathbf{c}$, the variance of the linear function $y=\mathbf{c}'\mathbf{x}$ is

$$\begin{aligned}\mathscr{V}(y)&=\mathscr{E}(\mathbf{c}'\mathbf{x}-\mathbf{c}'\boldsymbol{\mu})^2\\&=\textstyle\sum_i\sum_j c_ic_j\sigma_{ij}\\&=\mathbf{c}'\mathscr{V}(\mathbf{x})\mathbf{c}\\&=\mathbf{c}'\boldsymbol{\Sigma}\mathbf{c}\end{aligned} \tag{3.1.23}$$

If $y_1=\mathbf{c}'\mathbf{x}$ and $y_2=\mathbf{d}'\mathbf{x}$ are both linear combinations of the x_i, the covariance of y_1 and y_2 is

$$\begin{aligned}\mathscr{V}(y_1, y_2)&=\mathscr{E}[(\mathbf{c}'\mathbf{x}-\mathbf{c}'\boldsymbol{\mu})(\mathbf{d}'\mathbf{x}-\mathbf{d}'\boldsymbol{\mu})]\\&=\sum_{i=1}^{p}\sum_{j=1}^{p} c_id_j\sigma_{ij}\\&=\mathbf{c}'\mathscr{V}(\mathbf{x})\mathbf{d}\\&=\mathbf{c}'\boldsymbol{\Sigma}\mathbf{d}\end{aligned} \tag{3.1.24}$$

Results 3.1.22 to 3.1.24 can be formulated in a more general way. Suppose that we have a vector variable $\mathbf{x}$ with p elements. Let $\boldsymbol{\mu}$ and $\boldsymbol{\Sigma}$ be the expectation and variance–covariance matrix of $\mathbf{x}$. To form q ($\geqslant 1$) linear combinations of $\mathbf{x}$, we may construct a $q\times p$ *transformation matrix* $\mathbf{C}$, with each row containing the weights for a single linear function. The vector of transformed variables is

$$\mathbf{y}=\mathbf{C}\mathbf{x} \tag{3.1.25}$$

$\mathbf{x}$ is the $p\times 1$ untransformed vector; $\mathbf{y}$ is the $q\times 1$ vector of linear combinations.

The vector of expectations for the y-variables is $q \times 1$; that is,

$$\begin{aligned} \boldsymbol{\mu}_y &= \mathscr{E}(\mathbf{Cx}) \\ &= \mathbf{C}\boldsymbol{\mu} \end{aligned} \tag{3.1.26}$$

The variances and covariances of the y-variables form the $q \times q$ matrix:

$$\begin{aligned} \boldsymbol{\Sigma}_y &= \mathscr{E}(\mathbf{y}-\boldsymbol{\mu}_y)(\mathbf{y}-\boldsymbol{\mu}_y)' \\ &= \mathscr{E}(\mathbf{Cxx'C'} - \mathbf{C}\boldsymbol{\mu}\boldsymbol{\mu}'\mathbf{C}') \\ &= \mathbf{C}\mathscr{V}(\mathbf{x})\mathbf{C}' \\ &= \mathbf{C}\boldsymbol{\Sigma}\mathbf{C}' \end{aligned} \tag{3.1.27}$$

For example, let

$$\mathbf{x} = \begin{bmatrix} x_1 \\ x_2 \\ x_3 \end{bmatrix}$$

with

$$\mathscr{E}(\mathbf{x}) = \boldsymbol{\mu} = \begin{bmatrix} 10 \\ 11 \\ 9 \end{bmatrix}$$

and

$$\mathscr{V}(\mathbf{x}) = \boldsymbol{\Sigma} = \begin{bmatrix} 100 & 40 & 0 \\ 40 & 64 & -24 \\ 0 & -24 & 144 \end{bmatrix}$$

Suppose we wish to form two new variables $y_1 = \Sigma_i x_i$ and $y_2 = x_3 - (1/2)x_1$. The transformation matrix is

$$\mathbf{C} = \begin{bmatrix} 1 & 1 & 1 \\ -1/2 & 0 & 1 \end{bmatrix}$$

The two linear functions are

$$\mathbf{y} = \begin{bmatrix} x_1 + x_2 + x_3 \\ x_3 - (1/2)x_1 \end{bmatrix}$$

The expectation of **y** is

$$\boldsymbol{\mu}_y = \begin{bmatrix} 10+11+9 \\ 9-1/2(10) \end{bmatrix} = \begin{bmatrix} 30 \\ 4 \end{bmatrix}$$

The covariance matrix of y_1 and y_2 is

$$\boldsymbol{\Sigma}_y = \mathbf{C}\boldsymbol{\Sigma}\mathbf{C}' = \begin{bmatrix} 340 & 50 \\ 50 & 169 \end{bmatrix}$$

These are identically the results from 3.1.23 and 3.1.24 for the two linear combinations simultaneously. That is, if we let

$$\mathbf{c}' = [1 \quad 1 \quad 1] \qquad \text{and} \qquad \mathbf{d}' = [-1/2 \quad 0 \quad 1]$$

then

$$\boldsymbol{\Sigma}_y = \mathbf{C}\boldsymbol{\Sigma}\mathbf{C}' = \begin{bmatrix} \mathbf{c}'\boldsymbol{\Sigma}\mathbf{c} & \mathbf{c}'\boldsymbol{\Sigma}\mathbf{d} \\ \mathbf{d}'\boldsymbol{\Sigma}\mathbf{c} & \mathbf{d}'\boldsymbol{\Sigma}\mathbf{d} \end{bmatrix}$$

These results for linear functions of measured variables are particularly useful in statistical analysis. The sample results are identical to those given here except that sample values $\mathbf{y}.$ and $\mathbf{V}$ substitute for $\boldsymbol{\mu}$ and $\boldsymbol{\Sigma}$, respectively.

Let us consider some cases of special interest. First, in general, *two linear combinations of correlated variables have nonzero covariance.* This is the case even when the weight vectors are orthogonal. For example, consider the orthogonal vectors

$$\mathbf{c} = \begin{bmatrix} 1 \\ 1 \\ 1 \end{bmatrix} \quad \text{and} \quad \mathbf{d} = \begin{bmatrix} 1 \\ 0 \\ -1 \end{bmatrix}$$

The covariance of $\mathbf{c}'\mathbf{x}$ and $\mathbf{d}'\mathbf{x}$ is

$$\mathbf{c}'\boldsymbol{\Sigma}\mathbf{d} = \sigma_1^2 + \sigma_{21} - \sigma_{23} - \sigma_3^2$$

This sum will only be null under a particular equality of variance components.

Should the original variates be uncorrelated, with $\sigma_{21} = \sigma_{23} = 0$, the covariance of the linear composites may still be nonzero, if $\sigma_1^2 \neq \sigma_3^2$. Thus, *two linear combinations of variables having differing variances will generally be intercorrelated.*

Third, *nonorthogonal linear combinations of variables will generally have nonzero intercorrelations.* For example, consider

$$\mathbf{c} = \begin{bmatrix} 1 \\ -1 \\ 0 \end{bmatrix} \quad \text{and} \quad \mathbf{d} = \begin{bmatrix} 1 \\ 0 \\ -1 \end{bmatrix}$$

$\mathbf{c}$ and $\mathbf{d}$ have unit inner product. The covariance of $\mathbf{c}'\mathbf{x}$ and $\mathbf{d}'\mathbf{x}$ is

$$\mathbf{c}'\boldsymbol{\Sigma}\mathbf{d} = \sigma_1^2 - \sigma_{21} - \sigma_{13} + \sigma_{23}$$

This expression is not generally null, even when all $\sigma_{ij} = 0$ ($i \neq j$). In each of the cases above, it is possible to construct weight vectors for either correlated or uncorrelated variables such that the linear composites do have zero intercorrelation.

Standardization

The random variables of $\mathbf{x}$ may be simultaneously standardized through matrix operations. Represent as $\boldsymbol{\Delta}$ the diagonal matrix consisting of only the diagonal elements of $\boldsymbol{\Sigma}$. That is, let

$$\begin{aligned} \boldsymbol{\Delta} &= \text{diag}\,(\boldsymbol{\Sigma}) \\ &= \text{diag}\,(\sigma_1^2,\ \sigma_2^2, \ldots, \sigma_p^2) \end{aligned}$$

Then $\boldsymbol{\Delta}^{-1/2}$ is the matrix of inverse standard deviations, with diagonal elements $(\sigma_j^2)^{-1/2} = 1/\sigma_j$.

$$\mathbf{\Delta}^{-1/2} = \text{diag}\,(1/\sigma_1,\ 1/\sigma_2, \ldots, 1/\sigma_p)$$

Then

$$\mathbf{z} = \mathbf{\Delta}^{-1/2}(\mathbf{x} - \boldsymbol{\mu}) \tag{3.1.28}$$

z is the vector of standardized random variables, expressed as linear functions of the original x_i:

$$\mathbf{z} = \begin{bmatrix} \dfrac{x_1 - \mu_1}{\sigma_1} \\ \dfrac{x_2 - \mu_2}{\sigma_2} \\ \vdots \\ \dfrac{x_p - \mu_p}{\sigma_p} \end{bmatrix} = \begin{bmatrix} z_1 \\ z_2 \\ \vdots \\ z_p \end{bmatrix}$$

The expectation and covariance matrix of **z** are

$$\mathscr{E}(\mathbf{z}) = \mathscr{E}[\mathbf{\Delta}^{-1/2}(\mathbf{x} - \boldsymbol{\mu})] = \mathbf{\Delta}^{-1/2}[\mathscr{E}\mathbf{x} - \mathscr{E}\mathbf{x}] = \mathbf{0} \tag{3.1.29}$$

and

$$\begin{aligned} \mathscr{V}(\mathbf{z}) &= \mathbf{\Delta}^{-1/2}\mathscr{V}(\mathbf{x} - \boldsymbol{\mu})\mathbf{\Delta}^{-1/2} \\ &= \mathbf{\Delta}^{-1/2}\mathscr{V}(\mathbf{x})\mathbf{\Delta}^{-1/2} \\ &= \mathbf{\Delta}^{-1/2}\mathbf{\Sigma}\mathbf{\Delta}^{-1/2} \\ &= \mathscr{R} \end{aligned} \tag{3.1.30}$$

The expectation of each standardized variable is zero. The covariance matrix of standardized variables is the $p \times p$ symmetric *correlation matrix* of **x**. The elements are the correlations of each pair of measures x_i and x_j; that is,

$$\rho_{ij} = \frac{\sigma_{ij}}{\sigma_i \sigma_j} \tag{3.1.30a}$$

ρ_{ij} has limits $(-1 \leqslant \rho_{ij} \leqslant 1)$. The correlation of each variable with itself is unity, since $\rho_{ii} = \sigma_i^2/(\sigma_i \sigma_i) = 1$. $\mathscr{R}$ has the form

$$\mathscr{R} = \begin{bmatrix} 1 & \rho_{12} & \rho_{13} & \cdots & \rho_{1p} \\ \rho_{21} & 1 & \rho_{23} & \cdots & \rho_{2p} \\ \rho_{31} & \rho_{32} & 1 & \cdots & \rho_{3p} \\ \vdots & & & \ddots & \vdots \\ \rho_{p1} & \rho_{p2} & \cdots & \rho_{p,p-1} & 1 \end{bmatrix}$$

The covariance matrix $\mathbf{\Sigma}$ is transformed to correlational form by dividing each element in row i by $[\sigma_i]$, and each element of column j by $[\sigma_j]$. This is accomplished as the pre- and postmultiplication of $\mathbf{\Sigma}$ by the diagonal matrix in Eq. 3.1.30.

As an example, let **x** be the three-element vector with

$$\boldsymbol{\mu}' = [10 \quad 11 \quad 9]$$

and

$$\boldsymbol{\Sigma}=\begin{bmatrix}100 & 40 & 0\\ 40 & 64 & -24\\ 0 & -24 & 144\end{bmatrix}$$

The diagonal matrix of variances is

$$\boldsymbol{\Delta}=\text{diag}\ (100, 64, 144)$$

and the standard deviations are

$$\boldsymbol{\Delta}^{1/2}=\text{diag}\ (10, 8, 12)$$

Let $\mathbf{z}=\boldsymbol{\Delta}^{-1/2}\ (\mathbf{x}-\boldsymbol{\mu})$. Then

$$\mathscr{E}(\mathbf{z})'=[0 \quad 0 \quad 0]$$

and

$$\mathscr{V}(\mathbf{z})=\boldsymbol{\Delta}^{-1/2}\boldsymbol{\Sigma}\boldsymbol{\Delta}^{-1/2}=\begin{bmatrix}\dfrac{100}{10\cdot 10} & \dfrac{40}{10\cdot 8} & \dfrac{0}{10\cdot 12}\\[2ex] \dfrac{40}{10\cdot 8} & \dfrac{64}{8\cdot 8} & \dfrac{-24}{8\cdot 12}\\[2ex] \dfrac{0}{12\cdot 10} & \dfrac{-24}{12\cdot 8} & \dfrac{144}{12\cdot 12}\end{bmatrix}$$

$$=\begin{bmatrix}1.00 & .50 & 0\\ .50 & 1.00 & -.25\\ 0 & -.25 & 1.00\end{bmatrix}$$

The correlation of x_1 and x_2 is $\rho_{12}=.50$.

3.2 THE MULTIVARIATE NORMAL DISTRIBUTION

The probability distribution assumed for statistical tests in this book is a multivariate extension of the normal distribution. The density function of a p-variate normal vector $\mathbf{x}$ is

$$\phi(\mathbf{x})=(2\pi)^{-p/2}|\boldsymbol{\Sigma}|^{-1/2}\exp\left[\frac{-(\mathbf{x}-\boldsymbol{\mu})'\boldsymbol{\Sigma}^{-1}(\mathbf{x}-\boldsymbol{\mu})}{2}\right] \tag{3.2.1}$$

For standardized vector $\mathbf{z}=\boldsymbol{\Delta}^{-1/2}(\mathbf{x}-\boldsymbol{\mu})$, the density becomes

$$\phi(\mathbf{z})=(2\pi)^{-p/2}|\mathscr{R}|^{-1/2}\exp\left[\frac{-\mathbf{z}'\mathscr{R}^{-1}\mathbf{z}}{2}\right] \tag{3.2.2}$$

Expressions 3.2.1 and 3.2.2 are complex, but they can be seen to parallel the usual univariate normal density, with $\mathbf{x}$, $\boldsymbol{\mu}$, and $\boldsymbol{\Sigma}$ replacing x, μ, and σ^2, respectively.

For exemplary purposes, Figure 3.2.1 presents an overhead view of the two-variate or bivariate normal distribution. We may specify that x_1 and x_2 have a

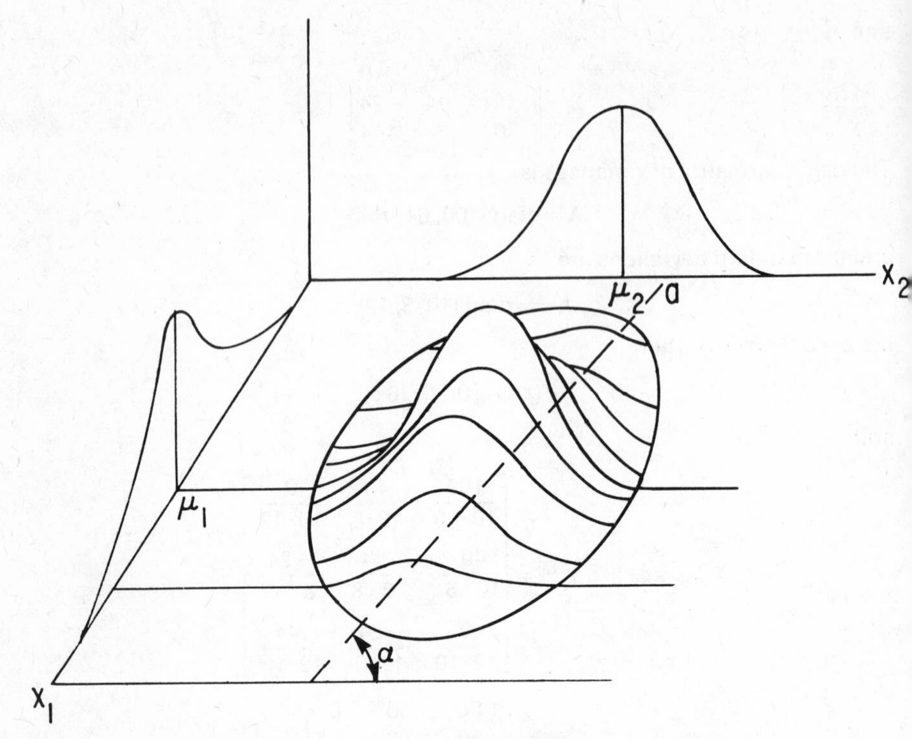

Figure 3.2.1 Bivariate normal distribution of x_1 and x_2.

joint normal distribution, with $\mathscr{E}(\mathbf{x}) = \boldsymbol{\mu}$ and $\mathscr{V}(\mathbf{x}) = \boldsymbol{\Sigma}$, by writing

$$\begin{bmatrix} x_1 \\ x_2 \end{bmatrix} \sim \mathscr{N}\left[\begin{pmatrix} \mu_1 \\ \mu_2 \end{pmatrix}, \begin{pmatrix} \sigma_1{}^2 & \sigma_{12} \\ \sigma_{21} & \sigma_2{}^2 \end{pmatrix}\right]$$

or

$$\mathbf{x} \sim \mathscr{N}_2(\boldsymbol{\mu}, \boldsymbol{\Sigma})$$

The subscript on $\mathscr{N}$ (that is, 2) gives the dimensionality of **x** and of the corresponding normal distribution.

Perhaps the most useful aspect of multivariate normality of p variables x_i is that all linear combinations of the x_i also have multivariate normal distributions (Dempster, 1969, p. 277). Let random vector **x** have a p-variate normal distribution with expectation $\boldsymbol{\mu}$ and covariance matrix $\boldsymbol{\Sigma}$; that is,

$$\mathbf{x} \sim \mathscr{N}_p(\boldsymbol{\mu}, \boldsymbol{\Sigma}) \tag{3.2.3}$$

x and $\boldsymbol{\mu}$ are $p \times 1$; $\boldsymbol{\Sigma}$ is $p \times p$.

Then any q ($\geqslant 1$) linear functions $\mathbf{y} = \mathbf{Cx} + \mathbf{d}$, where **d** is a $q \times 1$ vector of constants, have distribution

$$\mathbf{y} \sim \mathscr{N}_q(\mathbf{C}\boldsymbol{\mu} + \mathbf{d}, \mathbf{C}\boldsymbol{\Sigma}\mathbf{C}') \tag{3.2.4}$$

C is the $q \times p$ transformation matrix defining q linear functions of the x_i. **y** is the

$q \times 1$ vector of transformed variables; $\mathbf{C}\boldsymbol{\mu}+\mathbf{d}$ is its $q \times 1$ vector expectation, and $\mathbf{C}\boldsymbol{\Sigma}\mathbf{C}'$ its $q \times q$ variance–covariance matrix. The result for $\mathscr{E}(\mathbf{y})$ follows from 3.1.19 and 3.1.26; $\mathscr{V}(\mathbf{y})$ follows from 3.1.21 and 3.1.27.

From this theorem, we may observe the properties of subsets of variables forming the p-variate set. That is we shall examine the *marginal distribution* of some of the variates out of context, or ignoring the others. For example, assume that $\mathbf{x}$ is a p-variate normal vector composed of p_1 variates $\mathbf{x}_1$ ($p_1 \geq 1$) and p_2 variates $\mathbf{x}_2$ ($p_2 \geq 1$); that is, $\mathbf{x}' = [\mathbf{x}_1', \mathbf{x}_2']$. The moments of the total distribution may be represented as

$$\begin{bmatrix} \boldsymbol{\mu}_1 \\ \boldsymbol{\mu}_2 \end{bmatrix} \quad \text{and} \quad \begin{bmatrix} \boldsymbol{\Sigma}_{11} & \boldsymbol{\Sigma}_{12} \\ \boldsymbol{\Sigma}_{21} & \boldsymbol{\Sigma}_{22} \end{bmatrix} \tag{3.2.5}$$

respectively, where

$p = p_1 + p_2$
$\boldsymbol{\mu}_1$ is the $p_1 \times 1$ vector mean of the vector variable $\mathbf{x}_1$
$\boldsymbol{\mu}_2$ is the $p_2 \times 1$ vector mean of $\mathbf{x}_2$
$\boldsymbol{\Sigma}_{11}$ is the $p_1 \times p_1$ covariance matrix of $\mathbf{x}_1$
$\boldsymbol{\Sigma}_{22}$ is the $p_2 \times p_2$ covariance matrix of $\mathbf{x}_2$
$\boldsymbol{\Sigma}_{12} = \boldsymbol{\Sigma}_{21}'$ is the $p_1 \times p_2$ matrix of covariances of each variable in $\mathbf{x}_1$ and each variate in $\mathbf{x}_2$

We may inspect the distribution of $\mathbf{x}_1$ alone by applying 3.2.4 with $\mathbf{d} = \mathbf{0}$, and

$$\mathbf{C} = [\underset{\substack{p_1 \times p_1 \text{ identity} \\ \text{matrix}}}{\mathbf{I}_{p_1}} \;\vdots\; \underset{\substack{p_1 \times p_2 \text{ null} \\ \text{matrix}}}{\mathbf{0}}]$$

The effect of this transformation is only to delete the $\mathbf{x}_2$ variables. $\mathbf{y} = \mathbf{C}\mathbf{x} + \mathbf{d}$ retains only the $\mathbf{x}_1$ set. According to 3.2.4, the $\mathbf{y}$ (or $\mathbf{x}_1$) variables have a p_1-variate normal distribution, with

$$\mathscr{E}(\mathbf{x}_1) = \boldsymbol{\mu}_1 \qquad \text{and} \qquad \mathscr{V}(\mathbf{x}_1) = \boldsymbol{\Sigma}_{11}$$

By letting $\mathbf{C} = [\mathbf{0}' \;\vdots\; \mathbf{I}_{p_2}]$, we may ignore $\mathbf{x}_1$ and observe that

$$\mathbf{x}_2 \sim \mathscr{N}_{p_2}(\boldsymbol{\mu}_2, \boldsymbol{\Sigma}_{22})$$

The marginal distribution of any subset of multivariate normal variates is (univariate or multivariate) normal, and retains the same expectation, variances, and covariances as in the higher-order multivariate distribution. In Figure 3.2.1, x_1 alone is univariate $\mathscr{N}(\mu_1, \sigma_1^2)$ and x_2 is univariate $\mathscr{N}(\mu_2, \sigma_2^2)$. In each case, other variables in the set are simply ignored.

The *conditional distribution* of x_2 given x_1 is the distribution of x_2 values at any particular x_1 value. This is often termed the distribution of x_2 *given* x_1, *removing the effects of* x_1 or *holding* x_1 *constant*. The conditional distributions for x_2 are indicated by the horizontal cross-cut lines in Figure 3.2.1. The conditional variate is represented $x_2|x_1$.

In the bivariate normal distribution the conditional distributions of x_2 have the following properties: (1) All of the conditional distributions are normal. (2)

The center (expectation) of each lies on the straight *regression line*, a, of x_2 on x_1. (3) The variance of each conditional x_2 distribution is the same, regardless of the x_1 value.

These results are most easily represented if we first standardize x_1 and x_2. Let

$$z_1 = \frac{x_1 - \mu_1}{\sigma_1} \quad \text{and} \quad z_2 = \frac{x_2 - \mu_2}{\sigma_2}$$

Then

$$\begin{bmatrix} z_1 \\ z_2 \end{bmatrix} \sim \mathcal{N}\left[\begin{pmatrix} 0 \\ 0 \end{pmatrix}, \begin{pmatrix} 1 & \rho_{12} \\ \rho_{21} & 1 \end{pmatrix}\right]$$

The covariance of z_1 and z_2 is ρ_{12}. In Figure 3.2.1 there is a concentration of points in the first and third quadrants, reflecting a positive covariance.

The conditional variate after standardizing is z_2 given z_1 or $z_2|z_1$. The mean of z_2 at a particular z_1 value depends upon z_1 and the angle, α, which the regression line makes with the z_2 axis. The equation relating the mean to the z_1 value is

$$\mathcal{E}(z_2|z_1) = \rho_{12} z_1$$

ρ_{12} is the slope of the regression line after standardization, or the tangent of angle α. The variance of $z_2|z_1$ is $1-\rho_{12}^2$, regardless of z_1.

These results may be extended to the unstandardized x_i. The equation of the line connecting the means of the conditional distributions is given above. Substituting raw-score forms for ρ_{12}, z_1 and z_2, we obtain

$$\mathcal{E}\left(\frac{x_2 - \mu_2}{\sigma_2}\middle| x_1\right) = \frac{\sigma_{12}}{\sigma_1 \sigma_2}\left(\frac{x_1 - \mu_1}{\sigma_1}\right)$$

Solving for x_2,

$$\mathcal{E}(x_2|x_1) = \frac{\sigma_{12}}{\sigma_1^2}(x_1 - \mu_1) + \mu_2 \tag{3.2.6}$$

Expression 3.2.6 is the mean of the conditional distribution of x_2 at particular values of x_1.

The variance of x_2 is $\sigma_2^2 \mathcal{V}(z_2) = \sigma_2^2$. The variance of x_2 given x_1 is

$$\begin{aligned} \sigma_2^2 \mathcal{V}(z_2|z_1) &= \sigma_2^2(1-\rho_{12}^2) \\ &= \sigma_2^2 - \frac{\sigma_{12}^2}{\sigma_1^2} \\ &= \sigma_{2|1}^2 \end{aligned} \tag{3.2.7}$$

The variance does not depend on the value of x_1. Summarizing then, the distribution of x_2 given x_1 is

$$x_2|x_1 \sim \mathcal{N}_{p_2}\left\{\frac{\sigma_{12}}{\sigma_1^2}(x_1 - \mu_1) + \mu_2, \quad \sigma_2^2 - \frac{\sigma_{12}^2}{\sigma_1^2}\right\}. \tag{3.2.8}$$

These expressions may be extended to the general (p_1+p_2)-variate form. If p variates are partitioned into sets of p_1 variables $\mathbf{x}_1$, and p_2 variables $\mathbf{x}_2$, as in

3.2.5, the expectation of $\mathbf{x}_2$ given $\mathbf{x}_1$ is the $p_2 \times 1$ vector,

$$\mathscr{E}(\mathbf{x}_2|\mathbf{x}_1) = \boldsymbol{\Sigma}_{21}\boldsymbol{\Sigma}_{11}^{-1}(\mathbf{x}_1 - \boldsymbol{\mu}_1) + \boldsymbol{\mu}_2 \tag{3.2.9}$$

The variance–covariance matrix of $\mathbf{x}_2$ at any given set of values $\mathbf{x}_1$ is $p_2 \times p_2$.

$$\begin{aligned}\mathscr{V}(\mathbf{x}_2|\mathbf{x}_1) &= \boldsymbol{\Sigma}_{22} - \boldsymbol{\Sigma}_{21}\boldsymbol{\Sigma}_{11}^{-1}\boldsymbol{\Sigma}_{12} \\ &= \boldsymbol{\Sigma}_{22|1}\end{aligned} \tag{3.2.10}$$

Like its univariate counterpart, $\boldsymbol{\Sigma}_{22|1}$ does not depend on the particular $\mathbf{x}_1$ values. The covariance matrix of the conditional distribution remains unchanged regardless of where the $\mathbf{x}_1$ variables are fixed.

It is easily seen that when $p_1 = p_2 = 1$, Eqs. 3.2.9 and 3.2.10 simplify to yield 3.2.6 and 3.2.7, respectively. When p_1 is greater than unity, the inversion of $\boldsymbol{\Sigma}_{11}$ is complex, and algebraic parallels to the operation are difficult to follow.

If $\mathbf{x}_1$ and $\mathbf{x}_2$ are jointly (p_1+p_2)-variate normal, then $\mathbf{x}_2$ is p_2-variate normal at all values of $\mathbf{x}_1$. Also, $\mathbf{x}_2$ given $\mathbf{x}_1$ is uncorrelated with $\mathbf{x}_1$. Assuming normality, the two sets are statistically independent; that is,

$$\mathscr{V}(\mathbf{x}_1, \ \mathbf{x}_2|\mathbf{x}_1) = \mathbf{0} \tag{3.2.11}$$

$\mathbf{0}$ is a $p_1 \times p_2$ null matrix.

$\boldsymbol{\Sigma}_{22|1}$ may be standardized to yield the $p_2 \times p_2$ correlation matrix among the $\mathbf{x}_2$ variables, eliminating $\mathbf{x}_1$. Let

$$\boldsymbol{\Delta}_{22|1} = \text{diag}\,(\boldsymbol{\Sigma}_{22|1})$$

be the diagonal matrix of conditional variances. $\boldsymbol{\Delta}_{22|1}^{-1/2}$ is the matrix of inverse standard deviations. Then

$$\mathscr{R}_{22|1} = \boldsymbol{\Delta}_{22|1}^{-1/2}\boldsymbol{\Sigma}_{22|1}\boldsymbol{\Delta}_{22|1}^{-1/2}$$

$\mathscr{R}_{22|1}$ is the $p_2 \times p_2$ matrix of *partial correlations* among the $\mathbf{x}_2$ variables, holding constant the $\mathbf{x}_1$ measures.

We may also examine the moments of successive univariate conditional distributions. For example, we may require the variance of y_2 given y_1, of y_3 given y_1 and y_2, of y_4 given y_1, y_2, and y_3, and so on to y_p, eliminating all others. These results are obtained directly from the Cholesky factor of the total variance–covariance matrix.

For example, let $p = 2$ and

$$\boldsymbol{\Sigma} = \begin{bmatrix} \sigma_1^2 & \sigma_{12} \\ \sigma_{21} & \sigma_2^2 \end{bmatrix}$$

Operating upon the elements of $\boldsymbol{\Sigma}$ yields the Cholesky factor

$$\mathbf{T} = \begin{bmatrix} \sigma_1 & 0 \\ \sigma_{21}/\sigma_1 & \sqrt{\sigma_2^2 - \sigma_{12}^2/\sigma_1^2} \end{bmatrix}$$

The second diagonal element is the square root of the variance of x_2 given x_1 – that is, the conditional standard deviation, or $\sqrt{\mathscr{V}(x_2|x_1)}$. Let us represent this as $\sigma_{2|1}$. Should the original matrix be larger, the factor would contain the conditional covariances and standard deviation of each variable, given all preceding. That is,

$$\mathbf{T}=\begin{bmatrix} \sigma_1 & & & & \text{(Zero)} \\ \sigma_{21}/\sigma_1 & \sigma_{2|1} & & & \\ \sigma_{31}/\sigma_1 & \sigma_{32|1} & \sigma_{3|12} & & \\ \vdots & & & \ddots & \\ \sigma_{p1}/\sigma_1 & \sigma_{p2|1} & \sigma_{p3|12} & \cdots & \sigma_{p|12\ldots(p-1)} \end{bmatrix} \quad (3.2.12)$$

$\sigma_{ij|kl}$ is the conditional covariance of x_i and x_j, given x_k and x_l. $\sigma_{i|kl}$ is the conditional standard deviation. This procedure of successively eliminating ordered variates is termed the *stepwise* procedure, and has frequent application in statistical problems.

3.3 SAMPLES OF MULTIVARIATE DATA

One Sample

Let us represent the observed scores for one observation i on p variates, as the $1\times p$ row vector $\mathbf{y}_i'$:

$$\mathbf{y}_i'=[y_{i1} \quad y_{i2} \quad \cdots \quad y_{ip}]$$

$\mathbf{y}_i$ is a single *vector observation*. Its elements may consist of raw scores on p measured variates, or may have resulted from linear or nonlinear transformations of a prior set of p' original measures. For example, the creativity-intelligence problem (Sample Problem 1) requires that the product of standardized variates be formed, to yield interaction terms for regression analysis. The category-reproduction measure of Sample Problem 2 must be converted to a proportion in order to make results comparable across experimental conditions. Or transformations may be employed to cause the variates under study to approximate more nearly the properties of multivariate normal variates (see Kirk, 1968, pp. 63–67).

The vector observations for N subjects may be juxtaposed to produce the complete $N\times p$ *data matrix* for the group:

$$\mathbf{Y}=\begin{bmatrix} y_{11} & y_{12} & \cdots & y_{1p} \\ y_{21} & y_{22} & \cdots & y_{2p} \\ \vdots & & & \vdots \\ y_{N1} & y_{N2} & \cdots & y_{Np} \end{bmatrix}$$

$$=\begin{bmatrix} \mathbf{y}_1' \\ \mathbf{y}_2' \\ \vdots \\ \mathbf{y}_N' \end{bmatrix} \quad (3.3.1)$$

Each column, consisting of scores for all subjects on a single variate, is the *observational vector*. The data matrix contains all the information necessary for describing the sample. If the sample is representative of a defined population, **Y** is also sufficient for estimating the parameters of the population from which it was drawn. If the data are drawn from a normal distribution, then sufficient summary statistics are the vector of means for the p variables, and the $p \times p$ variance–covariance matrix.

The sum of the N observations' scores on each of the variates may be presented in vector form, as

$$\mathbf{y}'_{+} = \sum_{i=1}^{N} \mathbf{y}'_i$$

$$= \mathbf{1}'\mathbf{Y} \tag{3.3.2}$$

1 is an N-element unit vector. The number of subjects in the sample may be computed from the unit vector as the scalar product $\mathbf{1}'\mathbf{1}$. From these results, the *vector mean* of the p variates is a $1 \times p$ row vector

$$\mathbf{y}'_{.} = \frac{1}{N} \sum_{i=1}^{N} \mathbf{y}'_i$$

$$= \frac{1}{\mathbf{1}'\mathbf{1}} \mathbf{1}'\mathbf{Y} \tag{3.3.3}$$

Example

Fifteen students were randomly sampled from the freshman class at a large midwestern university. Each student yielded five measures: y_1, grade average for required courses taken; y_2, grade average for elective courses taken; x_1, high-school general knowledge test, taken previous year; x_2, IQ score from previous year; x_3, educational motivation score from previous year. The scores are reported in Table 3.3.1.

Table 3.3.1 Scores for Fifteen College Freshmen on Five Educational Measures

Observation	y_1	y_2	x_1	x_2	x_3
1	.8	2.0	72	114	17.3
2	2.2	2.2	78	117	17.6
3	1.6	2.0	84	117	15.0
4	2.6	3.7	95	120	18.0
5	2.7	3.2	88	117	18.7
6	2.1	3.2	83	123	17.9
7	3.1	3.7	92	118	17.3
8	3.0	3.1	86	114	18.1
9	3.2	2.6	88	114	16.0
10	2.6	3.2	80	115	16.4
11	2.7	2.8	87	114	17.6
12	3.0	2.4	94	112	19.5
13	1.6	1.4	73	115	12.7
14	.9	1.0	80	111	17.0
15	1.9	1.2	83	112	16.1

Each row of Table 3.3.1 is a single vector observation. The portion of the table enclosed in dashed lines is the 15×5 data matrix **Y**. If we let **1** be a 15-element unit vector, then the sums for the five measures are

$$\mathbf{y}'_{+} = [34.0 \quad 37.7 \quad 1263 \quad 1733 \quad 255.3]$$

The means are

$$\mathbf{y}'_{\cdot} = \frac{1}{15}\mathbf{y}'_{+} = [2.27 \quad 2.51 \quad 84.2 \quad 115.5 \quad 17.02]$$

In most behavioral science applications the origins of the measurement scales are arbitrary. Thus, we may wish to express each vector observation as a row vector of mean deviations, $\mathbf{y}'_i - \mathbf{y}'_{\cdot}$. Each element is the deviation of the score for subject *i* on variate *j* from the variable mean, or $y_{ij} - y_{\cdot j}$. The data matrix of mean deviations is the $N \times p$ matrix having mean-deviation vectors as rows:

$$\mathbf{Y} - \mathbf{1}\mathbf{y}'_{\cdot} = \begin{bmatrix} \mathbf{y}'_1 - \mathbf{y}'_{\cdot} \\ \mathbf{y}'_2 - \mathbf{y}'_{\cdot} \\ \vdots \\ \mathbf{y}'_N - \mathbf{y}'_{\cdot} \end{bmatrix}$$

1 is an $N \times 1$ unit vector.

The data of Table 3.3.1 can be expressed in this form. The first row of $\mathbf{Y} - \mathbf{1}\mathbf{y}'_{\cdot}$ is

$$[.8 \quad 2.0 \quad 72 \quad 114 \quad 17.3] - [2.27 \quad 2.51 \quad 84.2 \quad 115.5 \quad 17.02]$$
$$= [-1.47 \quad -.51 \quad -12.2 \quad -1.5 \quad .28]$$

It can be seen that the sum or mean of the mean-deviation vectors is null, since

$$\begin{aligned} \mathbf{1}'(\mathbf{Y} - \mathbf{1}\mathbf{y}'_{\cdot}) &= \mathbf{1}'\mathbf{Y} - \mathbf{1}'\mathbf{1}\mathbf{y}'_{\cdot} \\ &= \mathbf{1}'\mathbf{Y} - \mathbf{1}'\mathbf{1}\left(\frac{1}{\mathbf{1}'\mathbf{1}}\right)\mathbf{1}'\mathbf{Y} \\ &= \mathbf{0}' \end{aligned}$$

The basic data for the variance–covariance matrix are the sum of squared scores for each variable, and the sums of cross products for pairs of variables, across all subjects. The matrix product of each vector observation $\mathbf{y}_i$ and its transpose is the $p \times p$ symmetric matrix of squares and cross products of each of the elements:

$$\mathbf{y}_i\mathbf{y}'_i = \begin{bmatrix} y_{i1}^2 & y_{i1}y_{i2} & \cdots & y_{i1}y_{ip} \\ y_{i2}y_{i1} & y_{i2}^2 & \cdots & y_{i2}y_{ip} \\ \vdots & & & \vdots \\ y_{ip}y_{i1} & y_{ip}y_{i2} & \cdots & y_{ip}^2 \end{bmatrix}$$

Summing these matrices across all *N* subjects yields the *total sum-of-squares and cross-products* matrix

$$\mathbf{S}_T = \sum_{i=1}^{N} \mathbf{y}_i \mathbf{y}_i'$$

$$= \mathbf{Y}'\mathbf{Y} \qquad (3.3.4)$$

The matrix, abbreviated *total sum of products*, contains $\Sigma_i y_{ij}^2$, the sum of squared scores on the jth variate in the jj diagonal position. $\Sigma_i y_{ij} y_{ik}$, the sum of cross products of variables y_j and y_k is in the jk off-diagonal position, for all N subjects. $\mathbf{S}_T$ is also symmetric, and of order $p \times p$.

For a single variable y_j, the sum of squared mean deviations is

$$\Sigma_i (y_{ij} - y_{\cdot j})^2 = \Sigma_i y_{ij}^2 - N y_{\cdot j}^2 \qquad (3.3.5)$$

The sum of cross products of mean deviations on y_j and y_k is

$$\Sigma_i (y_{ij} - y_{\cdot j})(y_{ik} - y_{\cdot k}) = \Sigma_i y_{ij} y_{ik} - N y_{\cdot j} y_{\cdot k} \qquad (3.3.6)$$

In the multiple-variable case we may adjust all sums of squares and cross products simultaneously. Let $\mathbf{S}_w$ represent the $p \times p$ sum of squares and cross products of mean deviations; that is,

$$\mathbf{S}_w = \sum_{i=1}^{N} (\mathbf{y}_i - \mathbf{y}.)(\mathbf{y}_i - \mathbf{y}.)'$$

$$= \sum_{i=1}^{N} \mathbf{y}_i \mathbf{y}_i' - N\mathbf{y}.\mathbf{y}.'$$

$$= \mathbf{S}_T - N\mathbf{y}.\mathbf{y}.' \qquad (3.3.7)$$

since $\Sigma \mathbf{y}_i \mathbf{y}.' = \Sigma \mathbf{y}.\mathbf{y}_i' = N\mathbf{y}.\mathbf{y}.'$.

In Eq. 3.3.7, $N y_{\cdot j} y_{\cdot k}$ is subtracted from the jk element of $\mathbf{S}_T$. The reader may wish to demonstrate for himself that the diagonal elements of $\mathbf{S}_w$ contain exactly the mean-adjusted sums of squares that would be obtained for that variable alone by Eq. 3.3.5. The off-diagonal elements identically reproduce Eq. 3.3.6 for each pair of measures. $\mathbf{S}_w$ is the *sum of products adjusted to the group vector mean*, or the *within-group sum of products*.

The variances and covariances of the p variables may be obtained from $\mathbf{S}_w$ by dividing each element by the associated degrees of freedom, $N-1$. The sample *variance–covariance matrix* is

$$\mathbf{V}_w = \frac{1}{N-1} \mathbf{S}_w$$

$$= \frac{1}{N-1} \sum_{i=1}^{N} (\mathbf{y}_i - \mathbf{y}.)(\mathbf{y}_i - \mathbf{y}.)' \qquad (3.3.8)$$

$\mathbf{V}_w$ has the sample variance (s_j^2) of each of the variables on the diagonal, and the sample covariance (s_{jk}) of variates y_j and y_k in the jk off-diagonal position.

That is,

$$[v_w]_{jk} = \frac{1}{N-1} \sum_i (y_{ij} - y_{\cdot j})(y_{ik} - y_{\cdot k})$$

$$= s_{jk}$$

for ($j, k = 1, 2, \ldots, p$). This is the common form, $1/(N-1)$ times Eq. 3.3.5 or 3.3.6. The standard deviation of variable y_j is the square root of the jj diagonal element of $\mathbf{V}_w$, $[v_w]_{jj}^{1/2} = s_j$.

Example

Represent the data of Table 3.3.1 as the 15×5 matrix **Y**. The total sum of products for the five measures is

$$\mathbf{S}_T = \mathbf{Y}'\mathbf{Y} = \begin{bmatrix} 85.38 & & & & \text{(Symmetric)} \\ 92.21 & 105.31 & & & \\ 2918.70 & 3225.10 & 107009 & & \\ 3934.10 & 4380.20 & 145976 & 200363.00 & \\ 585.70 & 651.79 & 21585 & 29503.90 & 4383.13 \end{bmatrix}$$

The sum of squared scores are on the diagonal—for example, $.8^2 + 2.2^2 + \cdots + 1.9^2 = 85.38$. The sums of cross products are the off-diagonal elements—for example, $.8 \times 2.0 + 2.2 \times 2.2 + \cdots + 1.9 \times 1.2 = 92.21$. The within-group sum of products is $\mathbf{S}_w = \mathbf{S}_T - 15\mathbf{y}.\mathbf{y}.'$; that is,

$$15\mathbf{y}.\mathbf{y}.' = \begin{bmatrix} 77.07 & & & & \text{(Symmetric)} \\ 85.45 & 94.75 & & & \\ 2862.80 & 3174.34 & 106344.60 & & \\ 3928.13 & 4355.61 & 145918.60 & 200219.27 & \\ 578.68 & 641.65 & 21496.26 & 29495.66 & 4345.21 \end{bmatrix}$$

and therefore

$$\mathbf{S}_w = \begin{bmatrix} 8.31 & & & & \text{(Symmetric)} \\ 6.76 & 10.56 & & & \\ 55.90 & 50.76 & 664.40 & & \\ 5.97 & 24.59 & 57.40 & 143.73 & \\ 7.02 & 10.14 & 88.74 & 8.24 & 37.92 \end{bmatrix}$$

The variance–covariance matrix is

$$\mathbf{V}_w = \frac{1}{14}\mathbf{S}_w = \begin{bmatrix} .59 & & & & \text{(Symmetric)} \\ .48 & .75 & & & \\ 3.99 & 3.63 & 47.46 & & \\ .43 & 1.76 & 4.10 & 10.27 & \\ .50 & .72 & 6.34 & .59 & 2.71 \end{bmatrix} \begin{matrix} y_1 \\ y_2 \\ x_1 \\ x_2 \\ x_3 \end{matrix}$$

$$\qquad\qquad\qquad y_1 \quad y_2 \quad x_1 \quad x_2 \quad x_3$$

The standard deviations of the five measures are:

$$\begin{aligned} s_1 &= \sqrt{.59} = .77 \quad [y_1] \\ s_2 &= \sqrt{.75} = .87 \quad [y_2] \\ s_3 &= \sqrt{47.46} = 6.89 \quad [x_1] \\ s_4 &= \sqrt{10.27} = 3.20 \quad [x_2] \\ s_5 &= \sqrt{2.71} = 1.65 \quad [x_3] \end{aligned}$$

The reader may wish to verify that $\mathbf{V}_w$ contains the usual (marginal) variances and covariances of the five measures. These results would have been obtained by scalar algebra for any one or two of the measures removed from the set. The matrix operations facilitate computing multiple dispersion measures simultaneously.

The sample intercorrelations among the measures are obtained by substituting sample values in Eqs. 3.1.28 and 3.1.30. Let $\mathbf{D}_w$ be an order-p diagonal matrix of variances

$$\begin{aligned} \mathbf{D}_w &= \text{diag}\,(\mathbf{V}_w) \\ &= \text{diag}\,(s_1^2,\ s_2^2, \ldots, s_p^2) \end{aligned} \tag{3.3.9}$$

$\mathbf{D}_w^{1/2}$ is the diagonal matrix of standard deviations, and $\mathbf{D}_w^{-1/2}$ is the matrix of inverse standard deviations,

$$\mathbf{D}_w^{-1/2} = \text{diag}\,(1/s_1,\ 1/s_2, \ldots, 1/s_p)$$

The vector of standardized scores for observation i is

$$\mathbf{z}_i = \mathbf{D}_w^{-1/2}(\mathbf{y}_i - \mathbf{y}.) = \begin{bmatrix} (y_{i1} - y_{\cdot 1})/s_1 \\ (y_{i2} - y_{\cdot 2})/s_2 \\ \vdots \\ (y_{ip} - y_{\cdot p})/s_p \end{bmatrix} \tag{3.3.10}$$

The mean of all standardized vectors in the sample is $\mathbf{0}$. The variance–covariance matrix of standard scores is the *sample correlation matrix* among the variables.

$$\begin{aligned} \mathbf{R}_w &= \frac{1}{N-1} \sum_{i=1}^{N} [\mathbf{D}_w^{-1/2}(\mathbf{y}_i - \mathbf{y}.)\,(\mathbf{y}_i - \mathbf{y}.)'(\mathbf{D}_w^{-1/2})'] \\ &= \mathbf{D}_w^{-1/2}\mathbf{V}_w\mathbf{D}_w^{-1/2} \end{aligned} \tag{3.3.11}$$

The diagonal elements of $\mathbf{R}_w$ are the variances of the standardized variables, or unity. The jk off-diagonal element is r_{jk}, the sample correlation of y_j and y_k. The pre- and postmultiplication of $\mathbf{V}_w$ by the diagonal matrix yields elements

$$r_{jk} = \frac{s_{jk}}{s_j s_k}$$

The maximum possible absolute value of s_{jk} is $s_j s_k$. Thus r_{jk} has absolute limit 1, with the sign depending only upon the sign of the covariance s_{jk}.

Expression 3.3.11 is the matrix of common Pearson correlations among the p measures. The elements agree with the results which would be obtained if the variables were correlated two at a time, in isolation. However, if data consist of distinct subgroups of subjects having different means, separate covariance matrices, or else the pooled within-group covariance matrix must be used in place of $\mathbf{V}_w$ (3.3.8). The groups may be either natural (for example, sex, grade) or experimentally formed (for example, control, treatment 1, 2). Details are given in the next section and the "Note on within-group variances and correlations," p.81.

The general form of Eqs. 3.3.8 and 3.3.11 may be followed in reducing any sum of products of mean deviations **S** to covariance form **V** and to correlational form **R**. If we let ν be the degrees of freedom for **S**, then

$$\mathbf{V} = \frac{1}{\nu}\mathbf{S} \tag{3.3.12}$$

Letting $\mathbf{D} = \text{diag}(\mathbf{V})$, then

$$\mathbf{R} = \mathbf{D}^{-1/2}\mathbf{V}\mathbf{D}^{-1/2} \tag{3.3.13}$$

R is the symmetric matrix of intercorrelations, having unities on the principal diagonal. **S** may also be easily reconstructed from **R**, as $\mathbf{S} = \nu\mathbf{D}^{1/2}\mathbf{R}\mathbf{D}^{1/2}$. The value of ν is a function of the number of observations, N, and the number of subgroups, J, into which they are combined. In the preceding discussion there is only one group of observations and $\nu = N - J = N - 1$. If some subjects are missing scores on one or more tests, determination of **S** and ν is complex, with a number of possible solutions.

Example

The five variables of Table 3.3.1 give us variance–covariance matrix

$$\mathbf{V}_w = \begin{bmatrix} .59 & & & & \text{(Symmetric)} \\ .48 & .75 & & & \\ 3.99 & 3.63 & 47.46 & & \\ .43 & 1.76 & 4.10 & 10.27 & \\ .50 & .72 & 6.34 & .59 & 2.71 \end{bmatrix}$$

The variances alone are

$$\mathbf{D}_w = \text{diag}(.59, \quad .75, \quad 47.46, \quad 10.27, \quad 2.71)$$

The inverse standard deviations are

$$\mathbf{D}_w^{-1/2} = \text{diag}(1/.77, \quad 1/.87, \quad 1/6.89, \quad 1/3.20, \quad 1/1.65)$$

The correlations are

$$\mathbf{R}_w = \mathbf{D}_w^{-1/2}\mathbf{V}_w\mathbf{D}_w^{-1/2}$$

$$= \begin{bmatrix} \frac{.59}{.77(.77)} & & & & \text{(Symmetric)} \\ \frac{.48}{.77(.87)} & \frac{.75}{.87(.87)} & & & \\ \frac{3.99}{.77(6.89)} & \frac{3.63}{.87(6.89)} & \frac{47.46}{6.89(6.89)} & & \\ \frac{.43}{.77(3.20)} & \frac{1.76}{.87(3.20)} & \frac{4.10}{6.89(3.20)} & \frac{10.27}{3.20(3.20)} & \\ \frac{.50}{.77(1.65)} & \frac{.72}{.87(1.65)} & \frac{6.34}{6.89(1.65)} & \frac{.59}{3.20(1.65)} & \frac{2.71}{1.65(1.65)} \end{bmatrix}$$

$$= \begin{bmatrix} 1.00 & & & & \text{(Symmetric)} \\ .72 & 1.00 & & & \\ .75 & .61 & 1.00 & & \\ .17 & .63 & .19 & 1.00 & \\ .40 & .51 & .56 & .11 & 1.00 \end{bmatrix} \begin{matrix} y_1 \\ y_2 \\ x_1 \\ x_2 \\ x_3 \end{matrix}$$

$$\quad y_1 \quad\; y_2 \quad\; x_1 \quad\; x_2 \quad\; x_3$$

The variable having highest intercorrelation with y_1 is x_1; x_2 and x_3 have very little interrelationship. All measures have positive intercorrelations and so seem to be measuring aspects of the same general phenomenon, perhaps a general verbal ability.

More than One Sample

Often subjects have been sampled from or assigned to $J > 1$ populations. The number of populations may be a function of the crossing or nesting of a number of classification variables. In a completely crossed $A \times B \times C$ sampling design having a levels of factor A, b levels of B, and c levels of C, J is the product abc. Or J may be a function of the sample size, as in cases where the sampling design includes effects that are functions of the sampling unit, as in most randomized block designs. A nested sampling design having b_1 levels of B within A_1 and b_2 levels of B within A_2 has a maximum of $J = b_1 + b_2$ subclasses.

It is not necessary that all J groups or *subclasses* of subjects have observations. Some subclasses may be null either because of design considerations or such external factors as subject mortality. For general applications, we shall represent the number of subclasses having at least one analysis unit as J_0, so $J_0 \leq J$. It will be seen that the $J - J_0$ null subclasses do not contribute in any way to the summary data and may be eliminated from the computations.

The dimensionality of sampling designs may be too great to allow us to represent the data in multidimensional tables. Thus we will assign a unique number to each subclass of subjects so that the data array may be represented in a subjects-by-variates or groups-by-variates table. A convenient convention is to assign numerals from 1 to J according to the natural order of subclass identification numbers. For example, in the $A \times B \times C$ design, the group at the first level of A, B, and C, or group 1, 1, 1 is coded simply 1. Group 2 is at the first level of A and B, and the second level of C (that is, group 1, 1, 2), and so on. In a $2 \times 2 \times 3$ arrangement, the numerals 1 through 12 may be assigned to the groups, in the *natural ascending order* of the group identifications:

Group	*Assigned*
1, 1, 1	1
1, 1, 2	2
1, 1, 3	3
1, 2, 1	4
1, 2, 2	5
1, 2, 3	6
2, 1, 1	7
2, 1, 2	8
2, 1, 3	9
2, 2, 1	10
2, 2, 2	11
2, 2, 3	12

We shall assume this numbering system for designs considered in this text. The result is a single subclass identification code or subscript in all cases. Hierarchial arrangements with equal or unequal numbers of levels of nested factors may be represented notationally as crossed but possibly incomplete designs. The programmed instruction problem (Sample Problem 5) involves 19 experimental classes and 18 control classes, constituting a random nested effect. This may be considered a treatment×classes×sex ($2 \times 19 \times 2$) incomplete design, with $J=76$ and $J_0=74$. The nested effects of course must be identified in the computation of summary data.

For multiple groups of subjects the data matrix may be represented in partitioned form. Let N_j represent the number of subjects in subclass j ($j=1, 2, \ldots, J$). The N_j are not restricted to being equal or proportional to other N_j's. The total number of observations is $N=\Sigma_j N_j$.

Let $\mathbf{y}_{ij}$ be the $p \times 1$ vector observation for subject i in group j. The $N \times p$ array of data is

$$\mathbf{Y} = \begin{bmatrix} \mathbf{y}'_{11} \\ \mathbf{y}'_{21} \\ \vdots \\ \mathbf{y}'_{N_1 1} \\ \hline \mathbf{y}'_{12} \\ \mathbf{y}'_{22} \\ \vdots \\ \mathbf{y}'_{N_2 2} \\ \hline \vdots \\ \hline \mathbf{y}'_{1J} \\ \mathbf{y}'_{2J} \\ \vdots \\ \mathbf{y}'_{N_J J} \end{bmatrix} \begin{matrix} \\ \\ N_1 \text{ observations group 1} \\ \\ \\ \\ \\ N_2 \text{ observations group 2} \\ \\ \\ \\ \\ \\ \\ N_J \text{ observations group } J \\ \\ \end{matrix}$$

The $J \times p$ *matrix of subclass sums* is

$$\mathbf{Y}_+ = \begin{bmatrix} \sum_{i=1}^{N_1} \mathbf{y}'_{i1} \\ \sum_{i=1}^{N_2} \mathbf{y}'_{i2} \\ \vdots \\ \sum_{i=1}^{N_J} \mathbf{y}'_{iJ} \end{bmatrix} = \begin{bmatrix} \mathbf{y}'_{+1} \\ \mathbf{y}'_{+2} \\ \vdots \\ \mathbf{y}'_{+J} \end{bmatrix}$$

Each row contains simply the sum of all vector observations for the respective group or subclass.

The *matrix of subclass means* is formed by dividing the elements of each row in $\mathbf{Y}_+$ by the number of subjects in the subclass. That is

$$\mathbf{Y}_{\cdot} = \begin{bmatrix} \frac{1}{N_1} \mathbf{y}'_{+1} \\ \frac{1}{N_2} \mathbf{y}'_{+2} \\ \vdots \\ \frac{1}{N_J} \mathbf{y}'_{+J} \end{bmatrix} = \begin{bmatrix} \mathbf{y}'_{\cdot 1} \\ \mathbf{y}'_{\cdot 2} \\ \vdots \\ \mathbf{y}'_{\cdot J} \end{bmatrix}$$

$\mathbf{y}_{\cdot j}$ is the p-element vector mean for subclass j.

Y. may be derived from $\mathbf{Y}_+$ as a matrix product. Represent the numbers of subjects in the J subclasses as a diagonal matrix **D**,

$$\mathbf{D} = \text{diag}\,(N_1, N_2, \ldots, N_J)$$

The subclass means are the product

$$\mathbf{Y}. = \mathbf{D}^{-1}\mathbf{Y}_+ \qquad (3.3.14)$$

$\mathbf{D}^{-1}$ is the diagonal matrix with elements $[d^{-1}]_{jj} = 1/N_j$. Should any of the N_j be zero, computation of $\mathbf{D}^{-1}$ for that element may simply be bypassed. As an alternative, $\mathbf{Y}_+$ may be reduced in size to $(J_0 \times p)$ by omitting any rows corresponding to null subclasses. The analogous operation upon **D** will result in a $J_0 \times J_0$ diagonal matrix with all positive diagonal elements.

For interpretive purposes, *combined observed means and frequencies* are often required. Consider the $2 \times 2 \times 3$ $(A \times B \times C)$ arrangement introduced earlier. It may be desired, for example, to table means for each of the two levels of the A classification variable. The vector mean for all subjects sharing A_1 is the weighted average of the means for the first six groups; that is,

$$\frac{\mathbf{y}'_{+1} + \mathbf{y}'_{+2} + \mathbf{y}'_{+3} + \mathbf{y}'_{+4} + \mathbf{y}'_{+5} + \mathbf{y}'_{+6}}{N_1 + N_2 + N_3 + N_4 + N_5 + N_6} = \frac{\sum_{j=1}^{6} N_j \mathbf{y}'_{\cdot j}}{\sum_{j=1}^{6} N_j}$$

The associated total frequency is $\sum_{j=1}^{6} N_j$. In like fashion, the rows of **Y.** may be combined to yield means for the second or third classification variables, B or C. Further breakdowns to the means of combinations of effects may also be obtained. The mean of all subjects sharing attributes B_2 and C_2, for example, is

$$\frac{N_5 \mathbf{y}'_{\cdot 5} + N_{11} \mathbf{y}'_{\cdot 11}}{N_5 + N_{11}}$$

This is the mean of $N_5 + N_{11}$ observations.

Example

Random samples of students were drawn from the student body at a large midwestern university at the time of continued violent clashes between students and police. Students were classified according to (A) sex, and (B) whether or not they participated in confrontations with the police. Each student subject was scored on y_1, his attitude toward the university and its administration, prior to the violence; and y_2, his attitudes following the violent confrontations. A higher score on y_1 or y_2 indicates a higher negative attitude (dislike) toward the university. Due to difficulties in locating students after the confrontations, unequal numbers of subjects resulted in the four subgroups. The data are presented in Table 3.3.2.

Table 3.3.2 Attitude Scores for College Students before and after Violent Confrontations with City Police

Sex (A)	*Participation* (B)	*Group Number* (j)	*Observation* (i)	*Scores* y_1	y_2
Male (A_1)	No (B_1)	1	1	0	0
			2	0	0
			3	2	2
			4	0	1
	Yes (B_2)	2	1	2	3
			2	4	4
			3	3	4
			4	4	4
			5	4	4
			6	2	3
Female (A_2)	No (B_1)	3	1	2	2
			2	1	1
			3	3	3
			4	4	4
			5	1	2
	Yes (B_2)	4	1	3	4
			2	3	3
			3	4	4
			4	3	3
			5	3	3
			6	4	4
			7	4	4

The sums for the four groups are the J (=4) rows of $\mathbf{Y}_+$.

$$\mathbf{Y}_+ = \begin{bmatrix} 2.0 & 3.0 \\ 19.0 & 22.0 \\ 11.0 & 12.0 \\ 24.0 & 25.0 \end{bmatrix} \begin{matrix} \mathbf{y}'_{+1} \\ \mathbf{y}'_{+2} \\ \mathbf{y}'_{+3} \\ \mathbf{y}'_{+4} \end{matrix}$$

The cell frequencies are

$$\mathbf{D} = \text{diag}\,(4, 6, 5, 7)$$

The total N is 22. The means for the four groups are $\mathbf{Y}_. = \mathbf{D}^{-1}\mathbf{Y}_+$ where

$$\mathbf{D}^{-1} = \text{diag}\,(1/4, 1/6, 1/5, 1/7)$$

Then

$$\mathbf{Y}_. = \begin{bmatrix} .50 & .75 \\ 3.17 & 3.67 \\ 2.20 & 2.40 \\ 3.43 & 3.57 \end{bmatrix} \begin{matrix} \mathbf{y}'_{\cdot 1} \\ \mathbf{y}'_{\cdot 2} \\ \mathbf{y}'_{\cdot 3} \\ \mathbf{y}'_{\cdot 4} \end{matrix}$$

The mean attitude scores for nonparticipants (B_1) are

$$\frac{\mathbf{y}'_{+1}+\mathbf{y}'_{+3}}{N_1+N_3}=[1.44 \quad 1.67]$$

with 4+5=9 observations. Mean scores for participants (B_2) are

$$\frac{\mathbf{y}'_{+2}+\mathbf{y}'_{+4}}{N_2+N_4}=[3.31 \quad 3.62]$$

with 13 observations. It appears that participants have more negative attitudes toward the university.

Whenever there is more than one group of subjects, variances and covariances must be expressed in terms of deviations from the separate group mean vectors. Let $\mathbf{S}_{T_j}$ ($j=1, 2, \ldots, J$) represent the total sum of products for observations in group j alone. That is,

$$\mathbf{S}_{T_j}=\sum_{i=1}^{N_j} \mathbf{y}_{ij}\mathbf{y}'_{ij} \tag{3.3.15}$$

The $p \times p$ symmetric total sum of squares and cross products for *all* subjects is

$$\begin{aligned}\mathbf{S}_T&=\textstyle\sum_j \mathbf{S}_{T_j}\\ &=\mathbf{Y}'\mathbf{Y}\end{aligned} \tag{3.3.16}$$

This form is equivalent to Eq. 3.3.4, but summed across multiple groups.

Since subclasses generally have different mean vectors, within-group sums of products are computed separately for *each group*. They may then be pooled for a common estimate. The sum of products of mean deviation scores in a single subclass j is identical to the matrix for one group in Eq. 3.3.7.

$$\begin{aligned}\mathbf{S}_{w_j}&=\sum_{i=1}^{N_j} (\mathbf{y}_{ij}-\mathbf{y}_{\cdot j})(\mathbf{y}_{ij}-\mathbf{y}_{\cdot j})'\\ &=\mathbf{S}_{T_j}-N_j\mathbf{y}_{\cdot j}\mathbf{y}'_{\cdot j}\end{aligned} \tag{3.3.17}$$

The additional subscript indicates the particular group of observations, with N_j-1 degrees of freedom.

The variance–covariance matrix for the group is

$$\mathbf{V}_{w_j}=\frac{1}{N_j-1}\mathbf{S}_{w_j} \tag{3.3.18}$$

The variances and correlations for the group are

$$\mathbf{D}_{w_j}=\text{diag}\,(\mathbf{V}_{w_j}) \tag{3.3.19}$$

and

$$\mathbf{R}_{w_j}=\mathbf{D}_{w_j}^{-1/2}\mathbf{V}_{w_j}\mathbf{D}_{w_j}^{-1/2} \tag{3.3.20}$$

respectively, following Eq. 3.3.11.

To obtain a single common estimate of the variance–covariance or correla tion matrix, we may pool the $\mathbf{S}_{w_j}$. The *pooled within-group sum of products* is

$$\begin{aligned}\mathbf{S}_W &= \textstyle\sum_j \mathbf{S}_{w_j} \\ &= \textstyle\sum_j (\mathbf{S}_{T_j} - N_j \mathbf{y}_{\cdot j} \mathbf{y}'_{\cdot j}) \\ &= \mathbf{S}_T - \textstyle\sum_j N_j \mathbf{y}_{\cdot j} \mathbf{y}'_{\cdot j} \\ &= \mathbf{Y}'\mathbf{Y} - \mathbf{Y}'_{\cdot}\mathbf{D}\mathbf{Y}.\end{aligned} \qquad (3.3.21)$$

$\mathbf{S}_W$ is $p \times p$ symmetric, and has the usual within-group sum of squares for y_i in the *ii* diagonal position. The *ij* off-diagonal element of $\mathbf{S}_W$ is the sum of cross products for y_i and y_j, adjusted to the J variable means. Each $\mathbf{S}_{w_j}$ has $N_j - 1$ degrees of freedom; $\mathbf{S}_W$ has $\sum_j(N_j - 1) = N - J$ degrees of freedom.

From expression 3.3.12, the *pooled within-group variance–covariance matrix* is

$$\mathbf{V}_W = \frac{1}{N-J}\mathbf{S}_W \qquad (3.3.22)$$

Let

$$\mathbf{D}_W = \text{diag}\,(\mathbf{V}_W) \qquad (3.3.23)$$

be the diagonal matrix of variances. Then the pooled within-group standard deviations and correlations are $\mathbf{D}_W{}^{1/2}$ and

$$\mathbf{R}_W = \mathbf{D}_W{}^{-1/2}\mathbf{V}_W\mathbf{D}_W{}^{-1/2} \qquad (3.3.24)$$

respectively.

Example

The total sum of products for group 1 in Table 3.3.2 is

$$\mathbf{S}_{T_1} = \begin{bmatrix} 4 & 4 \\ 4 & 5 \end{bmatrix}$$

Adjusting to the group mean vector, $\mathbf{S}_{w_1} = \mathbf{S}_{T_1} - N_1 \mathbf{y}_{\cdot 1}\mathbf{y}'_{\cdot 1}$, where

$$N_1 \mathbf{y}_{\cdot 1}\mathbf{y}'_{\cdot 1} = 4\begin{bmatrix} .50 \\ .75 \end{bmatrix}[.50 \quad .75] = \begin{bmatrix} 1.00 & 1.50 \\ 1.50 & 2.25 \end{bmatrix}$$

Then

$$\mathbf{S}_{w_1} = \begin{bmatrix} 3.00 & 2.50 \\ 2.50 & 2.75 \end{bmatrix}$$

The variance–covariance matrix is

$$\mathbf{V}_{w_1} = (1/3)\mathbf{S}_{w_1} = \begin{bmatrix} 1.00 & .83 \\ .83 & .92 \end{bmatrix}$$

The inverse standard deviations are

$$\mathbf{D}_{w_1}{}^{-1/2} = \begin{bmatrix} 1/\sqrt{1.00} & 0 \\ 0 & 1/\sqrt{.92} \end{bmatrix}$$

and the correlations are

$$\mathbf{R}_{w_1} = \begin{bmatrix} 1.00 & .87 \\ .87 & 1.00 \end{bmatrix} \begin{matrix} y_1 \\ y_2 \end{matrix}$$
$$\begin{matrix} y_1 & y_2 \end{matrix}$$

In like fashion,

$$\mathbf{S}_{w_2} = \begin{bmatrix} 4.83 & 2.33 \\ 2.33 & 1.33 \end{bmatrix} \qquad \mathbf{R}_{w_2} = \begin{bmatrix} 1.00 & .92 \\ .92 & 1.00 \end{bmatrix}$$

$$\mathbf{S}_{w_3} = \begin{bmatrix} 6.80 & 5.60 \\ 5.60 & 5.20 \end{bmatrix} \qquad \mathbf{R}_{w_3} = \begin{bmatrix} 1.00 & .94 \\ .94 & 1.00 \end{bmatrix}$$

$$\mathbf{S}_{w_4} = \begin{bmatrix} 1.71 & 1.29 \\ 1.29 & 1.71 \end{bmatrix} \qquad \mathbf{R}_{w_4} = \begin{bmatrix} 1.00 & .75 \\ .75 & 1.00 \end{bmatrix}$$

The correlations for all groups are similar, and we may pool to obtain the common value. The total sum of products for all the data of Table 3.3.2 is

$$\mathbf{Y'Y} = \begin{bmatrix} 184 & 195 \\ 195 & 212 \end{bmatrix}$$

The mean corrections form the product

$$\mathbf{Y.'DY.} = \begin{bmatrix} 167.65 & 183.18 \\ 183.18 & 201.00 \end{bmatrix}$$

The difference is

$$\mathbf{S}_W = \begin{bmatrix} 16.35 & 11.72 \\ 11.72 & 11.00 \end{bmatrix} \begin{matrix} y_1 \\ y_2 \end{matrix}$$
$$\begin{matrix} y_1 & y_2 \end{matrix}$$

The reader may wish to verify that this is equivalently

$$\mathbf{S}_W = \sum_{j=1}^{4} \mathbf{S}_{w_j}$$

The within-group degrees of freedom are $N-J=22-4=18$; the variance–covariance matrix is

$$\mathbf{V}_W = 1/18 \begin{bmatrix} 16.35 & 11.72 \\ 11.72 & 11.00 \end{bmatrix}$$

$$= \begin{bmatrix} .91 & .65 \\ .65 & .61 \end{bmatrix} \begin{matrix} y_1 \\ y_2 \end{matrix}$$
$$\begin{matrix} y_1 & y_2 \end{matrix}$$

The standard deviations are $s_1=\sqrt{.91}=.95$ and $s_2=\sqrt{.61}=.78$, respectively. The correlation matrix from $\mathbf{V}_W$ is

$$\mathbf{R}_W = \begin{bmatrix} 1.00 & .87 \\ .87 & 1.00 \end{bmatrix} \begin{matrix} y_1 \\ y_2 \end{matrix}$$
$$\begin{matrix} y_1 & y_2 \end{matrix}$$

All summary statistics necessary for representing data from multivariate normal populations can be obtained from the subclass sums, frequencies, and the total sum of products, $\mathbf{Y}_{+}$, $\mathbf{D}$, and $\mathbf{S}_T$. In general the complete data matrix $\mathbf{Y}$ is not required. Vector observations may be entered into computation one at a time, as when the analysis is performed by computer. The sums and frequencies may be sequentially accumulated, as may the sum of products

$$\mathbf{S}_T = \sum_j \mathbf{S}_{T_j} = \sum_j \sum_i \mathbf{y}_{ij}\mathbf{y}'_{ij}$$

At times researchers wish to reconstruct analyses from published sources. Usually provided are the means, frequencies, standard deviations, and within-group correlation coefficients. The missing matrix is the total sum of products, $\mathbf{S}_T$. However, $\mathbf{S}_T$ may be reconstructed by

$$\begin{aligned} \mathbf{S}_T &= \mathbf{S}_W + \mathbf{Y}'_{\cdot}\mathbf{D}\mathbf{Y}_{\cdot} \\ &= (N-J)\mathbf{V}_W + \mathbf{Y}'_{\cdot}\mathbf{D}\mathbf{Y}_{\cdot} \\ &= (N-J)\mathbf{D}_W{}^{1/2}\mathbf{R}_W\mathbf{D}_W{}^{1/2} + \sum_j N_j \mathbf{y}_{\cdot j}\mathbf{y}'_{\cdot j} \end{aligned} \tag{3.3.25}$$

$\mathbf{D}_W{}^{1/2}$ is a diagonal matrix of within-group standard deviations.

The matrices of sums and frequencies may be reduced in size if J_0 subclasses have observations, and the remaining $J-J_0$ do not. If the null rows are left intact in $\mathbf{D}$ and $\mathbf{Y}_{\cdot}$, the effect upon $\mathbf{S}_W$ can be seen to be nil. The groups without subjects do not make a contribution to either $\mathbf{Y}'\mathbf{Y}$, or to $\mathbf{Y}'_{\cdot}\mathbf{D}\mathbf{Y}_{\cdot}$, since $\mathbf{y}_{+j}$ is also null. Thus collapsing rows of $\mathbf{Y}_{\cdot}$ and $\mathbf{D}$ does not affect the correct computation of $\mathbf{S}_W$. Since the number of subclass mean adjustments is J_0 instead of J, the degrees of freedom associated with $\mathbf{S}_W$ is $N-J_0$ rather than $N-J$. The covariance matrix is

$$\mathbf{V}_W = \frac{1}{N-J_0}\mathbf{S}_W \tag{3.3.26}$$

Note on Within-group Variances and Correlations

The pooled within-group variances, covariances, and correlations will generally differ from those computed without adjusting to separate subgroup means. Common formulas for Pearson product-moment correlations contain only a single mean adjustment. These correlations are *not* correct when there are subgroups of subjects in the data that have different means.

Suppose that we have two independent groups of observations with $N_1 = N_2 = 11$. Each subject is measured on two variables y_1 and y_2. The mean vectors for the two groups are

$$\begin{aligned} \mathbf{y}'_{\cdot 1} &= [20 \quad 20] \\ \mathbf{y}'_{\cdot 2} &= [40 \quad 40] \end{aligned}$$

Assume further that both groups have identical covariance matrices. The variances of the two measures in either group are $s_1{}^2 = s_2{}^2 = 100$ and the covariance is $s_{12} = 50$. Then

$$\mathbf{V}_{w_1} = \mathbf{V}_{w_2} = \begin{bmatrix} 100 & 50 \\ 50 & 100 \end{bmatrix}$$

Reducing $\mathbf{V}_{w_1}$ or $\mathbf{V}_{w_2}$ to correlational form, the correlation is $50/\sqrt{100 \cdot 100}$ and

$$\mathbf{R}_{w_1} = \mathbf{R}_{w_2} = \begin{bmatrix} 1.00 & .50 \\ .50 & 1.00 \end{bmatrix}$$

The actual correlation of y_1 and y_2 for any group of subjects is .50.

The pooled within-group matrix will give this result correctly.

$$\mathbf{V}_W = \frac{1}{22-2}[10\mathbf{V}_{w_1} + 10\mathbf{V}_{w_2}]$$

$$= \begin{bmatrix} 100 & 50 \\ 50 & 100 \end{bmatrix}$$

Reducing $\mathbf{V}_W$ to correlational form, r_{12} is again .50.

The common within-group matrix is a weighted average of the variances and covariances for the separate groups of observations. If subgroup matrices differ slightly, the pooled within-group matrix correctly averages the differences.

Suppose however that instead of computing the within-group matrix, we had simply computed the correlation for *all* 22 observations, ignoring subclass membership. The overall mean vector is

$$\mathbf{y}'_{..} = [30 \quad 30]$$

The all-subjects covariance matrix is

$$\mathbf{V} = \frac{1}{22-2}\left[\Sigma_i \Sigma_j \mathbf{y}_{ij}\mathbf{y}'_{ij} - N\mathbf{y}_{..}\mathbf{y}'_{..}\right]$$

We can find $\Sigma_i \Sigma_j \mathbf{y}_{ij}\mathbf{y}'_{ij}$ from the subclass means and covariance matrix:

$$\Sigma_i \Sigma_j \mathbf{y}_{ij}\mathbf{y}'_{ij} = \Sigma_j [(N_j - 1)\mathbf{V}_{w_j} + N_j \mathbf{y}_{.j}\mathbf{y}'_{.j}]$$

$$= \begin{bmatrix} 24{,}000 & 23{,}000 \\ 23{,}000 & 24{,}000 \end{bmatrix}$$

Then

$$\mathbf{V} = \begin{bmatrix} 200.00 & 152.38 \\ 152.38 & 200.00 \end{bmatrix}$$

From $\mathbf{V}$ the correlation is $r_{12} = 152.38/\sqrt{200^2} = .76$.

The correlation is clearly discrepant from the known .50. It results from our having doubled the value of the variance, while more than tripling the covariance, in going from pooled subclasses ($\mathbf{V}_W$) to total-group results ($\mathbf{V}$). This is because the mean deviations from the common $\mathbf{y}_{..}$ are larger than those from subgroup means $\mathbf{y}_{.j}$. The variances in $\mathbf{V}$ are artificially inflated by the fact that the two group means $\mathbf{y}_{.1}$ and $\mathbf{y}_{.2}$ are not the same, and not equal to $\mathbf{y}_{..}$; in other situations the covariances may be inflated to a greater extent than the variances resulting in unduly low correlation measures.

Whenever a data set contains results for several distinct groups of observations, valid dispersion measures cannot be obtained by treating the sample as a single group. Either separate subclass variances and covariances or the pooled within-group measures are necessary. Caution must be exercised in using computer programs to produce summary statistics which do not correctly reflect the subgroup structure in the data. The degree of bias in ignoring subgroup structure is a function of the differences among subgroup means, and should not be introduced into the summary statistics.

Linear Combinations of Variables

There are numerous situations in which linear combinations of an original set of p measures are required. We may wish to compute subtest and total scores from item responses, to create factor scores from test results, to select subsets of the measures, or to take differences and contrasts among the scores that reflect experimental effects of interest. This may be accomplished through the application of a *transformation matrix* to each vector observation. The sample results for linear transformations follow directly from population results, as given in Eqs. 3.1.25–3.1.27.

Assume that we wish to create q linear combinations of the p variables in vector $\mathbf{y}$. Let each set of weights define one row of the $q \times p$ transformation matrix $\mathbf{C}$. Represent the row as $\mathbf{c}'_i$ $(i=1, 2, \ldots, q)$. The transformed variable is $x_i = \mathbf{c}'_i\mathbf{y}$. The complete transformation matrix is

$$\mathbf{C} = \begin{bmatrix} \mathbf{c}'_1 \\ \mathbf{c}'_2 \\ \vdots \\ \mathbf{c}'_q \end{bmatrix}$$

The vector observation of q transformed scores for subject k in group j is

$$\mathbf{x}_{kj} = \mathbf{C}\mathbf{y}_{kj} \tag{3.3.27}$$

where $\mathbf{y}_{kj}$ is the untransformed vector for the same subject.

Let $\mathbf{Y}.$ be the $J \times p$ matrix of means for the J $(\geqslant 1)$ groups on the original measures; let $\mathbf{V}_W$ be the variance–covariance matrix. Then the means and variance–covariance matrix of the transformed variables are

$$\mathbf{X}. = \mathbf{Y}.\mathbf{C}' \tag{3.3.28}$$

and

$$\mathbf{V}_W^{(x)} = \mathbf{C}\mathbf{V}_W\mathbf{C}' \tag{3.3.29}$$

$\mathbf{X}.$ is $J \times q$; $\mathbf{V}_W^{(x)}$ is $q \times q$ symmetric. The same pre- and postmultiplication as in Eq. 3.3.29 may be applied to $\mathbf{S}_T$, $\mathbf{S}_W$, or a matrix for any specific subgroup (such as $\mathbf{S}_{w_j}$). Transformation of a correlation matrix $(\mathbf{R}_W)$ will not generally result in standardized measures, and requires restandardization by Eq. 3.3.13.

For analyses that require both the transformed measures and the original variables, the matrix of weights may be augmented by a $p \times p$ identity matrix; that is,

$$\mathbf{C} = \begin{bmatrix} \mathbf{c}'_1 \\ \mathbf{c}'_2 \\ \vdots \\ \mathbf{c}'_{q-p} \\ \hline \mathbf{I}_p \end{bmatrix} \begin{matrix} q-p \text{ rows} \\ \\ \\ \\ p \text{ rows} \end{matrix}$$

Altogether, $\mathbf{C}$ has q rows and p columns.

Example

The data of Table 3.3.2 contain pre- and postattitude scores. For additional analyses, the change or difference (post minus pre) is useful. The means for four groups and within-group variance–covariance matrix are

$$\mathbf{Y.} = \begin{bmatrix} .50 & .75 \\ 3.17 & 3.67 \\ 2.20 & 2.40 \\ 3.43 & 3.57 \end{bmatrix} \quad \mathbf{V}_W = \begin{bmatrix} .91 & .65 \\ .65 & .61 \end{bmatrix}$$

(columns y_1, y_2; rows of $\mathbf{V}_W$: y_1, y_2)

The change score ($x_1 = y_2 - y_1$) requires weight vector

$$\mathbf{c}'_1 = [-1 \quad 1]$$

In addition, let us preserve the original measures by adding an identity matrix to $\mathbf{C}$:

$$\mathbf{C} = \begin{bmatrix} -1 & 1 \\ 1 & 0 \\ 0 & 1 \end{bmatrix}$$

The three measures may be scored for each vector observation. Or the means and covariance matrix are found by Eqs. 3.3.28 and 3.3.29.

$$\mathbf{X.} = \begin{bmatrix} .25 & .50 & .75 \\ .50 & 3.17 & 3.67 \\ .20 & 2.20 & 2.40 \\ .14 & 3.43 & 3.57 \end{bmatrix}$$

(columns x_1, y_1, y_2)

$$\mathbf{V}_W^{(x)} = \begin{bmatrix} .22 & -.26 & -.04 \\ -.26 & .91 & .65 \\ -.04 & .65 & .61 \end{bmatrix}$$

(rows and columns x_1, y_1, y_2)

$\mathbf{V}_W^{(x)}$ may be reduced to correlational form in the usual manner:

$$\mathbf{R}_W^{(x)} = \begin{bmatrix} 1.00 & -.58 & -.11 \\ -.58 & 1.00 & .87 \\ -.11 & .87 & 1.00 \end{bmatrix}$$

The change score has a negative correlation with both pre- and post-measures. The more negative the original attitude, the less likely is change in a positive direction. The effect of the identity matrix in preserving the **y** variables among the **x** can be seen in **X.**, $\mathbf{V}_W^{(x)}$, and $\mathbf{R}_W^{(x)}$.

3.4 SAMPLE PROBLEMS

Sample Problem 1 – Creativity and Achievement

The complete data set for each of the sample problems is listed in Appendix C. The $N=60$ subjects of the example were measured on two tests of divergent achievement, three of creativity, and on an intelligence scale.*

Three additional variables were created, the products of standardized scores on each of the creativity measures and standardized values on the intelligence measure. For standardization, the sample means and standard deviations of the four measures were determined by prior analyses. Standardizing the four measures does not affect their relationships with the criteria. This adjustment is necessary however, for computation of the cross-product or interaction terms. In this manner, the dominance of the interaction by one or another variable due to scaling is avoided. The interaction terms themselves need not be standardized.

Each six-element vector observation $\mathbf{y}_i$ is transformed to a nine-element vector, in the following sequence of operations:

Transformation	*Variable*	
y_{i1} left intact	Synthesis	
y_{i2} left intact	Evaluation	
y_{i3} replaced by $\frac{y_{i3}-102.02}{14.83}$	Intelligence	
y_{i4} replaced by $\frac{y_{i4}-18.43}{6.80}$	Consequences obvious	Creativity
y_{i5} replaced by $\frac{y_{i5}-4.12}{3.27}$	Consequences remote	Creativity
y_{i6} replaced by $\frac{y_{i6}-14.52}{5.42}$	Possible jobs	Creativity
y_{i7} formed by $y_{i4}y_{i3}$	Consequences obvious $\times$ intelligence	
y_{i8} formed by $y_{i5}y_{i3}$	Consequences remote $\times$ intelligence	
y_{i9} formed by $y_{i6}y_{i3}$	Possible jobs $\times$ intelligence	

For the first observation with observed scores of 5, 1, 106, 20, 5, and 13, respectively, the nine-element transformed vector observation is

$$\mathbf{y}_1' = [5.0 \quad 1.0 \quad .27 \quad .23 \quad .27 \quad -.28 \quad .06 \quad .07 \quad -.08]$$

The complete 60×9 data matrix is formed by juxtaposing the $\mathbf{y}_i'$ ($i=1, 2, \ldots,$

*Intelligence scores are considered the first independent variable. On the punched and listed data cards, intelligence scores follow those for the three creativity measures. Thus the summary matrices presented here and in the following sections constitute a simple reordering of the elements of the same matrices as produced by the MULTIVARIANCE program.

60). The sample vector mean is

$$\mathbf{y}'_{\cdot} = \frac{1}{60} \sum_{i=1}^{60} \mathbf{y}'_i$$

$$= [2.55 \quad 1.38 \quad 0.0 \quad 0.0 \quad 0.0 \quad 0.0 \quad .09 \quad .40 \quad .46]$$

We note that the four variables that have been standardized in the sample do indeed have mean zero.

The mean intelligence score before standardization is about 102, with a standard deviation of approximately 15 points. The range of intelligence scores is from 67 to 143. Together, these findings indicate that the sample has a not-atypical mean and a wide range of values. The heterogeneity is desirable to avoid biasing effects of a truncated range in a situation that demands considering a large spectrum of score values.

The total sum of products for the $p=9$ variates is

$$\mathbf{S}_T = \begin{bmatrix} 569.00 & & & & & & & & \text{(Symmetric)} \\ 322.00 & 301.00 & & & & & & & \\ 65.79 & 56.69 & 59.00 & & & & & & \\ 21.29 & 17.66 & 5.55 & 59.00 & & & & & \\ 35.23 & 40.49 & 24.29 & 3.38 & 59.00 & & & & \\ 40.74 & 33.58 & 27.47 & 31.98 & 25.13 & 59.00 & & & \\ 18.73 & 27.90 & 5.56 & -3.06 & 18.56 & 1.19 & 43.86 & & \\ 107.31 & 73.77 & 28.65 & 18.56 & 38.66 & 24.42 & 24.52 & 114.53 & \\ 101.83 & 67.77 & 17.56 & 1.19 & 24.42 & 14.98 & 21.66 & 68.91 & 77.36 \end{bmatrix}$$

The reader may wish to verify that $[s_t]_{21}=322$, for example, is the total sum of cross products of scores on the first two variables, which are left untransformed.

The sum of products of all nine variates adjusted to the vector mean is

$$\mathbf{S}_w = \sum_{i=1}^{60} (\mathbf{y}_i - \mathbf{y}_{\cdot})(\mathbf{y}_i - \mathbf{y}_{\cdot})'$$

$$= \mathbf{S}_T - 60\mathbf{y}_{\cdot}\mathbf{y}'_{\cdot}$$

$$= \begin{bmatrix} 178.85 & & & & & & & & \text{(Symmetric)} \\ 110.35 & 186.18 & & & & & & & \\ 65.79 & 56.69 & 59.00 & & & & & & \\ 21.29 & 17.66 & 5.55 & 59.00 & & & & & \\ 35.23 & 40.49 & 24.29 & 3.38 & 59.00 & & & & \\ 40.74 & 33.58 & 27.47 & 31.98 & 25.13 & 59.00 & & & \\ 4.56 & 20.22 & 5.56 & -3.06 & 18.56 & 1.19 & 43.35 & & \\ 45.38 & 40.17 & 28.65 & 18.56 & 38.66 & 24.42 & 22.27 & 104.70 & \\ 31.79 & 29.77 & 17.56 & 1.19 & 24.42 & 14.98 & 19.12 & 57.79 & 64.79 \end{bmatrix}$$

$\mathbf{S}_w$ has 59 degrees of freedom. We note that columns three through six of $\mathbf{S}_T$ and $\mathbf{S}_w$ are identical, since the corresponding variates have been standardized.

The sample covariance matrix is

$$\mathbf{V}_w = \frac{1}{59}\mathbf{S}_w = \begin{bmatrix} 3.03 & & & & & & & & \text{(Symmetric)} \\ 1.87 & 3.16 & & & & & & & \\ 1.12 & .96 & 1.00 & & & & & & \\ .36 & .30 & .09 & 1.00 & & & & & \\ .60 & .69 & .41 & .06 & 1.00 & & & & \\ .69 & .57 & .47 & .54 & .43 & 1.00 & & & \\ .08 & .34 & .09 & -.05 & .31 & .02 & .73 & & \\ .77 & .68 & .49 & .31 & .66 & .41 & .38 & 1.77 & \\ .54 & .50 & .30 & .02 & .41 & .25 & .32 & .98 & 1.10 \end{bmatrix}$$

The diagonal elements of $\mathbf{V}_w$ are the variances of the nine variates. Those for the four standardized variables are, of course, unity. The off-diagonal elements are the covariances; for example, the sample covariance of the first two measures, evaluation and synthesis, is 1.87.

The diagonal matrix of standard deviations is

$$\mathbf{D}_w{}^{1/2} = \text{diag}\,(1.74,\ 1.78,\ 1.00,\ 1.00,\ 1.00,\ 1.00,\ .86,\ 1.33,\ 1.05)$$

Each nonzero element is the square root of the corresponding element of $\mathbf{V}_w$.

Taking the reciprocal of each principal element of $\mathbf{D}_w{}^{1/2}$ to obtain $\mathbf{D}_w{}^{-1/2}$, and multiplying, the matrix of intercorrelations is

$$\mathbf{R}_w = \mathbf{D}_w{}^{-1/2}\mathbf{V}_w\mathbf{D}_w{}^{-1/2}$$

$$= \begin{bmatrix} 1.00 & & & & & & & & \text{(Symmetric)} \\ .60 & 1.00 & & & & & & & \\ .64 & .54 & 1.00 & & & & & & \\ .21 & .17 & .09 & 1.00 & & & & & \\ .34 & .39 & .41 & .06 & 1.00 & & & & \\ .40 & .32 & .47 & .54 & .43 & 1.00 & & & \\ .05 & .23 & .11 & -.06 & .37 & .02 & 1.00 & & \\ .33 & .29 & .36 & .24 & .49 & .31 & .33 & 1.00 & \\ .30 & .27 & .28 & .02 & .39 & .24 & .36 & .70 & 1.00 \end{bmatrix} \begin{matrix} \text{Synthesis} \\ \text{Evaluation} \\ \text{Intelligence} \\ \text{Cons. obvious} \\ \text{Cons. remote} \\ \text{Possible jobs} \\ \text{Cons. ob.} \times \text{intell.} \\ \text{Cons. rem.} \times \text{intell.} \\ \text{Poss. jobs} \times \text{intell.} \end{matrix}$$

Synthesis, Evaluation, Intelligence, Consequences obvious, Consequences remote, Possible jobs, Cons. obvious × intelligence, Cons. remote × intelligence, Poss. jobs × intelligence

$\mathbf{R}_w$ presents a number of noteworthy patterns. The entire matrix appears to display a manifold of positive correlations, indicating that to some extent all tests are measuring a common (general ability) trait. The correlation of the two cognitive achievement measures is high ($r_{12} = .60$), as would be expected. Intelligence displays the expected high relationship with the two achievement measures. By contrast, the correlations of the creativity measures with achievement are lower (.17 to .40). With no further evidence, one might adopt a pessimistic attitude toward the possibility of finding creativity to be a factor in achievement, beyond the role played by intelligence. Creativity by itself may play a role in determining achievement, if the confounding with intelligence is ignored.

Sample Problem 3 – Dental Calculus Reduction

The subjects of the calculus study have been assigned to one of five dentifrice treatment groups, over a two-year period. The first year, treatment group five had no subjects. The second year of the study, treatments two and four were discontinued. The resulting subclass membership is as follows:

Year	*Treatment Group*	*Subclass Index* (j)	*Frequency* (N_j)
First (1)	1	1	8
First (1)	2	2	9
First (1)	3	3	7
First (1)	4	4	5
First (1)	5	–	0
Second (2)	1	5	28
Second (2)	2	–	0
Second (2)	3	6	24
Second (2)	4	–	0
Second (2)	5	7	26

The total N for the problem is

$$N=\sum_{j=1}^{7} N_j=107$$

Although the number of subclasses implied by the design is $J=2(5)=10$, three have no observations, leaving $J_0=7$ for computational purposes. It is only necessary to maintain the 7×7 matrix of frequencies, and a seven-row matrix of means.

The six measures involved in the problem are calculus accumulation measures for six anterior teeth of the lower mandible. The matrix of sample means for the seven groups is

$$\mathbf{Y.}=\begin{bmatrix} .75 & 2.25 & 3.75 & 4.13 & 2.25 & .88 \\ 1.33 & 1.78 & 3.11 & 3.33 & 2.56 & 1.56 \\ .43 & .86 & 1.29 & 1.57 & 1.00 & .43 \\ 1.00 & .80 & 2.00 & 1.20 & .60 & .00 \\ .68 & 1.57 & 2.71 & 2.75 & 1.57 & .71 \\ .54 & .79 & 2.08 & 1.71 & .96 & .67 \\ .23 & .42 & .77 & 1.31 & .65 & .19 \end{bmatrix}$$

Right canine, Right lateral incisor, Right central incisor, Left central incisor, Left lateral incisor, Left canine

Reading across the columns of **Y.**, it becomes apparent that the greatest calculus development is on the central teeth. In contrast, the teeth farther from the center in either direction show less calculus formation. Fewer than six tooth measurements may be adequate for product testing. The hypothesis that the end teeth do not contribute to between-group variability may be statistically tested through "step-down analysis."

It is more difficult to interpret the rows of **Y.**, both because of missing rows and the multiplicity of rows for some treatments. The observed means, combined across years for each level of the treatment factor, are more lucid. These are given in Table 3.4.1. Active agents 2 and 3 appear to produce the greatest reduction in dental calculus, although all three seem beneficial.

For further detail, Table 3.4.2 presents the distribution of raw calculus scores for each tooth. The table has results for all groups of subjects combined, and separately for group 1 (the primary control group) and group 5 (using active agent 3).

We may examine the effectiveness of the experimental dentifrice. One effect is the virtual elimination of extreme calculus scores and the concentration of low calculus levels in each of the teeth. Although the entire range of scores was observed in the control group, the range has been severely curtailed at the upper end in the experimental group. Further, the absence of *any* measurable calculus from the teeth is more prominent with the experimental subjects.

There are also intertooth differences of interest. The predominance of zero scores for the canines, and secondarily for the lateral incisors, reflects overall calculus formation differences in all groups. It would appear that the lateral and central incisors are more affected by the anticalculus agents. That is, there appears to be a regression effect, with teeth having higher calculus levels also showing the greatest reduction with treatment. We note also that the positive skew of the distributions may violate the assumption of normality necessary for statistical testing.

Table 3.4.1 Combined Observed Means for Treatment Factor of Anticalculus Agent Example

			Means					
Level	*Vectors*	*N*	R.C.	R.L.I.	R.C.I.	L.C.I.	L.L.I.	L.C.
1. Control	$\frac{8\mathbf{y}'_{\cdot 1}+28\mathbf{y}'_{\cdot 5}}{36}$	36	.69	1.72	2.94	3.06	1.72	.75
2. Control	$\mathbf{y}'_{\cdot 2}$	9	1.33	1.78	3.11	3.33	2.56	1.56
3. Anticalculus agent 1	$\frac{7\mathbf{y}'_{\cdot 3}+24\mathbf{y}'_{\cdot 6}}{31}$	31	.52	.81	1.90	1.68	.97	.61
4. Anticalculus agent 2	$\mathbf{y}'_{\cdot 4}$	5	1.00	.80	2.00	1.20	.60	.00
5. Anticalculus agent 3	$\mathbf{y}'_{\cdot 7}$	26	.23	.42	.77	1.31	.65	.19

Table 3.4.2 Distribution of Raw Calculus Scores for all Subjects ($N=107$) and for Experimental Groups 1 ($N=36$) and 5 ($N=26$)

		Score											
Tooth	*Occurrence*	0	1	2	3	4	5	6	7	8	9	10	11
Right Canine	Frequency in total sample	69	25	7	4	1					1		
	Percent control 1	63.9	22.2	11.1							2.8		
	Percent experimental 5	84.6	11.5	3.8									
Right Lateral Incisor	Frequency in total sample	51	33	9	5	1	4	1	2	1			
	Percent control 1	44.4	19.4	13.9	2.8	2.8	5.6	2.8	5.6	2.8			
	Percent experimental 5	69.2	23.1	3.8	3.8								
Right Central Incisor	Frequency in total sample	33	23	15	13	4	8	4	5	2			
	Percent control 1	19.4	22.2	8.3	11.1	8.3	11.1	5.6	11.1	2.8			
	Percent experimental 5	57.7	19.2	7.7									
Left Central Incisor	Frequency in total sample	43	14	11	11	9	7	4		6	1		1
	Percent control 1	30.6	11.1	11.1	5.6	11.1	11.1	5.6		8.3	2.8		2.8
	Percent experimental 5	53.8	7.7	7.7	19.2	7.7	3.8						
Left Lateral Incisor	Frequency in total sample	52	24	14	4	3	4	3	3				
	Percent control 1	44.4	13.9	22.2		2.8	5.6	2.8	8.3				
	Percent experimental 5	69.2	7.7	11.5	11.5								
Left Canine	Frequency in total sample	74	20	5	3	3			2				
	Percent control 1	66.7	19.4	8.3					5.6				
	Percent experimental 5	92.3	3.8			3.8							

To test hypotheses about mean effectiveness, information on the variances and covariances of the measures is also required. The pooled within-group sum of products is

$$\mathbf{S}_W = \sum_{j=1}^{7} \mathbf{S}_{w_j} = \mathbf{Y}'\mathbf{Y} - \mathbf{Y}_{\cdot}'\mathbf{D}\mathbf{Y}.$$

$$= \begin{bmatrix} 186 & & & & & (\text{Symmetric}) \\ 186 & 428 & & & & \\ 238 & 518 & 981 & & & \\ 265 & 570 & 995 & 1206 & & \\ 170 & 351 & 577 & 697 & 519 & \\ 140 & 190 & 277 & 299 & 226 & 213 \end{bmatrix}$$

$$- \begin{bmatrix} 48.10 & & & & & (\text{Symmetric}) \\ 84.09 & 166.13 & & & & \\ 156.96 & 300.47 & 557.02 & & & \\ 157.77 & 309.65 & 563.80 & 586.86 & & \\ 96.41 & 184.33 & 334.48 & 348.04 & 210.38 & \\ 48.59 & 89.42 & 165.13 & 169.13 & 104.56 & 55.10 \end{bmatrix}$$

$$
= \begin{bmatrix}
137.90 & & & & & \text{(Symmetric)} \\
101.91 & 261.87 & & & & \\
81.04 & 217.53 & 423.98 & & & \\
107.23 & 260.35 & 431.20 & 619.14 & & \\
73.59 & 166.67 & 242.52 & 348.96 & 308.62 & \\
91.41 & 100.58 & 111.87 & 129.87 & 121.44 & 157.90
\end{bmatrix}
$$

The variance–covariance matrix is

$$
\mathbf{V}_W = \frac{1}{107-7}\mathbf{S}_W = \begin{bmatrix}
1.38 & & & & & \text{(Symmetric)} \\
1.02 & 2.62 & & & & \\
.81 & 2.18 & 4.24 & & & \\
1.07 & 2.60 & 4.31 & 6.19 & & \\
.74 & 1.67 & 2.43 & 3.49 & 3.09 & \\
.91 & 1.01 & 1.12 & 1.30 & 1.21 & 1.58
\end{bmatrix}
$$

$\mathbf{V}_W$ has 100 degrees of freedom. The within-group standard deviations and correlations are

$$
\mathbf{D}_W^{1/2} = \text{diag}\,(1.17, 1.62, 2.06, 2.49, 1.76, 1.26)
$$

and

$$
\mathbf{R}_W = \begin{bmatrix}
1.00 & & & & & \text{(Symmetric)} \\
.54 & 1.00 & & & & \\
.34 & .65 & 1.00 & & & \\
.37 & .65 & .84 & 1.00 & & \\
.36 & .59 & .67 & .80 & 1.00 & \\
.62 & .49 & .43 & .42 & .55 & 1.00
\end{bmatrix}
\begin{matrix}
\text{Right canine} \\
\text{Right lateral incisor} \\
\text{Right central incisor} \\
\text{Left central incisor} \\
\text{Left lateral incisor} \\
\text{Left canine}
\end{matrix}
$$

Columns: Right canine, Right lateral incisor, Right central incisor, Left central incisor, Left lateral incisor, Left canine

Like the achievement measures of Sample Problem 1, the calculus measures exhibit a strong positive manifold of correlations. The structure underlying the present correlations is probably better determined, however. There appears to be two nonindependent components underlying the tooth intercorrelations. The first is a spatial pattern, with close teeth bearing a stronger relationship than more disparate teeth. Second, because of similar proximities to the salivary glands and to similar use in eating and brushing, the left and right canines tend to react alike, as do the left and right lateral incisors and the left and right central incisors. Thus we see high intercorrelations on the diagonal of $\mathbf{R}_W$, from the lower left to the upper right. Both structural components influence the correlation of measures taken from the two central incisors, which is the highest of the set (.84).

CHAPTER 4

Multiple Regression Analysis: Estimation

Multivariate multiple linear regression analysis is presented in this and the next chapter. Construction of the regression model, the point and interval estimation of regression coefficients, and the prediction of scores and residuals are the topics of Chapter 4. Chapter 5 presents the partitioning of sums of squares and cross products according to specified sources of variation, and tests of significance for individual and multiple independent variables. Measures of association or correlation between the independent and dependent variables are described separately in Chapter 6.

4.1 UNIVARIATE MULTIPLE REGRESSION MODEL

A regression model is applicable to data having one or more *measured* independent or *predictor variables* x_j. The x_j generally have scales with ordinal properties, although they may also comprise 0–1 dichotomous nominal measures. Let x_{ij} be the value of variable x_j for observation i ($i=1, 2, \ldots, N$). The x_{ij} are assumed to be exactly known constants. They may be, for example, specific values of random variable x_j, or they may represent specific values of experimental variables determined by the researcher.

Let y_i be the value of a random outcome y for observation i. The linear regression model relating the dependent variable y to q antecedents x_j is

$$\begin{aligned} y_i &= \alpha+\beta_1 x_{i1}+\beta_2 x_{i2}+\cdots+\beta_q x_{iq}+\epsilon_i \\ &= \alpha+\sum_{j=1}^{q} \beta_j x_{ij}+\epsilon_i \end{aligned} \tag{4.1.1}$$

The β_j are *partial regression coefficients*, or weights applied to the x_{ij} in the attempt to optimally predict y_i. The β_j are common to all N observations and are population constants to be estimated from the data. The regression model is *linear* as long as all β_j are to unit power, that is, are not multiplied, raised to powers, transformed to logarithms, and so on.

The constant α is included to assure equality of the left- and right-hand portions of Eq. 4.1.1; the term serves to absorb scaling differences in the y- and

x-variables. ϵ_i is the error, or difference between y_i and that portion of it predicted by the model. That is,

$$\epsilon_i = y_i - \left(\alpha + \sum_{j=1}^{q} \beta_j x_{ij}\right)$$

ϵ_i encompasses both measurement error in y_i and errors in the selection and weighted summing of predictors.

When there is only a single predictor variable ($q=1$), the model is the *simple regression* model; when $q>1$, the model is that of *multiple regression*. Since the multiple regression model subsumes the simple model as a specific instance, only the more general form is discussed in the following sections.

Models for N randomly chosen subjects may be written in array form:

$$\begin{aligned}
y_1 &= (1)\alpha + \beta_1 x_{11} + \beta_2 x_{12} + \cdots + \beta_q x_{1q} + \epsilon_1 \\
y_2 &= (1)\alpha + \beta_1 x_{21} + \beta_2 x_{22} + \cdots + \beta_q x_{2q} + \epsilon_2 \\
&\vdots \\
y_N &= (1)\alpha + \beta_1 x_{N1} + \beta_2 x_{N2} + \cdots + \beta_q x_{Nq} + \epsilon_N
\end{aligned}$$

The models may be represented in vector notation as the sum and product of matrices: Let $\mathbf{y}$ be the N-element vector of outcomes y_i and $\boldsymbol{\epsilon}$ the vector of errors. Then

$$\begin{bmatrix} y_1 \\ y_2 \\ \vdots \\ y_N \end{bmatrix} = \begin{bmatrix} 1 & x_{11} & x_{12} & \cdots & x_{1q} \\ 1 & x_{21} & x_{22} & \cdots & x_{2q} \\ \vdots & & & & \vdots \\ 1 & x_{N1} & x_{N2} & \cdots & x_{Nq} \end{bmatrix} \begin{bmatrix} \alpha \\ \beta_1 \\ \vdots \\ \beta_q \end{bmatrix} + \begin{bmatrix} \epsilon_1 \\ \epsilon_2 \\ \vdots \\ \epsilon_N \end{bmatrix}$$

or

$$\mathbf{y} = \mathbf{X}\boldsymbol{\beta} + \boldsymbol{\epsilon} \qquad (4.1.2)$$

$\mathbf{X}$ is the $N \times (q+1)$ regression *model matrix* consisting of a vector of unities corresponding to the constant term α, and of the N values on the q predictor variables. $\boldsymbol{\beta}$ is the $(q+1) \times 1$ vector of partial regression coefficients.

It can be seen that the model for any one observation comprises a single row of Eq. 4.1.2. Let $\mathbf{x}_i'$ be the vector of predictor values for observation i; that is, row i of the model matrix;

$$\mathbf{x}_i' = [1 \quad x_{i1} \quad x_{i2} \quad \cdots \quad x_{iq}]$$

Then Eq. 4.1.1 is identically

$$y_i = \mathbf{x}_i'\boldsymbol{\beta} + \boldsymbol{\epsilon}_i \qquad (4.1.3)$$

The analysis of data under Eqs. 4.1.1–4.1.3 rests upon determining "best" estimates of the regression weights. The weights are used to obtain predicted or estimated outcome scores under the model, which can be compared with the observed y_i. Hypotheses may be tested about the nullity of all or portions of $\boldsymbol{\beta}$. The results of the hypothesis tests determine whether the model fits the data or does not. The model is said to fit the data if variation of the ϵ_i in the sample is small relative to variation in y. When this is the case, the difference of the two variances is attributable to the remaining term $\mathbf{X}\boldsymbol{\beta}$; knowledge of an individual's

x-scores does in fact give some knowledge of the outcome y_i. When variation in y and ϵ are the same, the x-variables do not aid in knowing y, and elements of $\boldsymbol{\beta}$ are null. Correlation measures reflect the *extent* to which variation in y is attributable to the x-variables.

Frequently, the regression model is employed to provide estimates for some predictor variables and tests of significance for others. An initial model may include predictor variables that are *known* to be related to the criterion measure; for example, verbal and quantitative Scholastic Aptitude Test scores and high-school grades will certainly be included in any regression model predicting college freshman achievement. If we are employed by the college admissions office to derive a selection equation, our first and perhaps only purpose will be to obtain best estimates of the regression weights for these variables. The number of predictor variables for which regression coefficients alone are sought is the *rank of the model for estimation.*

In addition, however, there may be other variables that are *hypothesized* or suspected to contribute to criterion variation. We may believe that a new test of motivation will make an important contribution to predicting college success. Thus we may include the motivation variable with our predictors. Significance tests can be employed to determine whether motivation accounts for additional criterion variation beyond that attributable to the aptitude and achievement scores. If we decide from this that the motivation score is worthy of inclusion in the model, we shall then want best estimates of the regression weights for all four measures. For maximum external validity (Campbell and Stanley, 1966) these estimates should be derived from a separate sample of observations. If motivation does not contribute significantly to criterion variation, it is excluded from the final model. The *total* number of predictor variables for estimation or tests of significance is q, the *rank of the model for significance testing* ($q+1$ if the constant term is counted).

A variation of the regression model is the *polynomial model* of the form

$$y_i = \alpha + \sum_{j=1}^{q} \beta_j x_i^{\,j} + \epsilon_i.$$

The model matrix for N observations is

$$\mathbf{X} = \begin{bmatrix} x_1^0 & x_1^1 & x_1^2 & \cdots & x_1^q \\ x_2^0 & x_2^1 & x_2^2 & \cdots & x_2^q \\ \vdots & & & & \vdots \\ x_N^0 & x_N^1 & x_N^2 & \cdots & x_N^q \end{bmatrix}$$

with parameters α and β_j ($j=1, 2, \ldots, q$). x_i^1 is the value of the independent variable for subject i. Here interest is in the degree of polynomial in x that will optimally predict y. The powers of x differ from the x_{ij} of the Eq. 4.1.1 model in that the squares and higher powers of x are not directly observable. The purposes and modes of analysis directly follow those of the multiple regression model.

For example, a child's standing height should be predictable from his age. Since height has a decreasing acceleration with age, we might postulate the model

$$y_i = \alpha + \beta_1 x_i + \beta_2 x_i^2 + \epsilon_i \tag{4.1.4}$$

where y_i is measured height for subject i and x_i is his age. Although squared age is not observable, its inclusion in the model accurately predicts the deceleration, as long as β_2 is negative. To estimate α, β_1, and β_2, we might select a sample of children at various ages between birth and five years, and record the heights of each. The model matrix would consist of a vector of unities, a vector of ages, and a vector of squared ages. If we wish to test the fit of the model, we might also include the third power, age cubed, as an additional predictor variable. The corresponding β_3 will be nonzero if more complex growth trends occur. If the correct model is the simpler one of Eq. 4.1.4, tests of significance will reveal that β_3 is zero.

A further generalization of the regression model that fits the same analysis pattern is the *response surface model.* Here the independent variables are expressed both in their powers and cross products. For example, a complete model for a cubic "surface" in two predictors (x_1 and x_2) is

$$y_i = \alpha + \beta_1 x_{i1} + \beta_2 x_{i2} + \beta_3 x_{i1}^2 + \beta_4 x_{i2}^2 + \beta_5 x_{i1} x_{i2} + \beta_6 x_{i1} x_{i2}^2 + \beta_7 x_{i1}^2 x_{i2} + \beta_8 x_{i1}^3 + \beta_9 x_{i2}^3 + \epsilon_i$$

The model matrix is

$$\mathbf{X} = \begin{bmatrix} 1 & x_{11} & x_{12} & x_{11}^2 & x_{12}^2 & x_{11}x_{12} & x_{11}x_{12}^2 & x_{11}^2 x_{12} & x_{11}^3 & x_{12}^3 \\ 1 & x_{21} & x_{22} & x_{21}^2 & x_{22}^2 & x_{21}x_{22} & x_{21}x_{22}^2 & x_{21}^2 x_{22} & x_{21}^3 & x_{22}^3 \\ \vdots & & & & & \vdots & & & & \vdots \\ 1 & x_{N1} & x_{N2} & x_{N1}^2 & x_{N2}^2 & x_{N1}x_{N2} & x_{N1}x_{N2}^2 & x_{N1}^2 x_{N2} & x_{N1}^3 & x_{N2}^3 \end{bmatrix}$$

with parameters α and β_j ($j = 1, 2, \ldots, 9$).

As an example, consider Sample Problem 1, the creativity–achievement study. It is certain that general verbal intelligence plays a role in cognitive achievements such as "synthesis" and "evaluation." Thus the intelligence variable is included in the model as the first predictor x_1 (in addition to the constant term). Creativity is hypothesized to be related to divergent achievement in ways not attributable to intelligence. Three creativity variables have been measured, and these become predictors x_2, x_3, and x_4. Finally it is hypothesized that the effect of creativity upon divergent achievement is accentuated for individuals of high intelligence. That is, there is an interaction of creativity and intelligence in determining achievement scores. The higher the intelligence level, the more important creativity becomes.

To create predictor variables to reflect the hypothesized interaction, cross products of standardized intelligence scores and the three (standardized) creativity measures are taken. The four variables are standardized so that scaling factors in one measure do not obscure the contribution of the other measure to the product. If we assume that x_1 through x_4 are standardized, the cross-product terms are $x_5 = x_1 x_2$, $x_6 = x_1 x_3$, and $x_7 = x_1 x_4$.

The complete response model is

$$y_i = \alpha + \beta_1 x_{i1} + \beta_2 x_{i2} + \beta_3 x_{i3} + \beta_4 x_{i4} + \beta_5 x_{i1} x_{i2} + \beta_6 x_{i1} x_{i3} + \beta_7 x_{i1} x_{i4} + \epsilon_i$$

The model matrix has a column of unities, four columns with intelligence and creativity scores, and three columns of their respective cross products. Tests of significance will reveal that β_1 through β_4 are nonzero to the extent that intelligence and creativity are related to the outcome. β_5 through β_7 will be nonzero to the extent that the dependence of achievement upon creativity is greater at high intelligence levels. The rank of the model is eight.

Exercise

Examine the effects of interaction terms in a regression model, by assuming two standardized predictors z_1 and z_2. Let z_1 and z_2 have all interval values from −4 to +4. Obtain "predicted" y-scores by substituting in

$$y_i = 6 + .5z_{i1} + 1.25z_{i2} + .125z_{i1}z_{i2}$$

Graph y as height against z_1 and z_2. Note that height increases directly with both z_1 and z_2, but that it increases to a greater degree with z_2 at higher z_1 values.

4.2 ESTIMATION OF PARAMETERS: UNIVARIATE MODEL

The univariate regression model is given by Eq. 4.1.2 as $\mathbf{y} = \mathbf{X}\boldsymbol{\beta} + \boldsymbol{\epsilon}$. We shall want to sample observations and use the observed values of the vector variable $\mathbf{y}$ at the particular levels of the x_j to estimate $\boldsymbol{\beta}$. We shall assume that the elements of y constitute N independent observations drawn at random from a specified population.

Let $\hat{\boldsymbol{\beta}}$ represent the $(q+1) \times 1$ vector estimate of $\boldsymbol{\beta}$, to be computed from the sample. Then Eq. 4.1.2 can be rewritten in terms of the partition of effects in the sample. The *observational equation* is

$$\mathbf{y} = \mathbf{X}\hat{\boldsymbol{\beta}} + \mathbf{e} \tag{4.2.1}$$

$\mathbf{y}$ is the N-element vector of sample values on random variable y. $\mathbf{e} = \hat{\boldsymbol{\epsilon}}$ is the N-element random vector of sample errors, or residuals. $\mathbf{e}$ will differ from $\boldsymbol{\epsilon}$ for the sample to the extent that $\hat{\boldsymbol{\beta}}$ is not equal to the population value $\boldsymbol{\beta}$.

We shall employ the least-squares criterion to provide an estimate of $\boldsymbol{\beta}$. That is, $\hat{\boldsymbol{\beta}}$ is chosen in such a way as to minimize the sum of squared sample errors

$$c = \sum_{i=1}^{N} e_i^2$$

Equivalently,

$$\begin{aligned} c &= \mathbf{e}'\mathbf{e} \\ &= (\mathbf{y} - \mathbf{X}\hat{\boldsymbol{\beta}})'(\mathbf{y} - \mathbf{X}\hat{\boldsymbol{\beta}}) \\ &= \mathbf{y}'\mathbf{y} - \mathbf{y}'\mathbf{X}\hat{\boldsymbol{\beta}} - \hat{\boldsymbol{\beta}}'\mathbf{X}'\mathbf{y} + \hat{\boldsymbol{\beta}}'\mathbf{X}'\mathbf{X}\hat{\boldsymbol{\beta}} \\ &= \mathbf{y}'\mathbf{y} - 2\hat{\boldsymbol{\beta}}'\mathbf{X}'\mathbf{y} + \hat{\boldsymbol{\beta}}'\mathbf{X}'\mathbf{X}\hat{\boldsymbol{\beta}} \end{aligned} \tag{4.2.2}$$

c may be a minimum when the partial derivatives with respect to the $\hat{\beta}_j$ are zero. The vector derivative is

$$\frac{\partial c}{\partial \hat{\boldsymbol{\beta}}'} = -2\mathbf{X}'\mathbf{y} + 2\mathbf{X}'\mathbf{X}\hat{\boldsymbol{\beta}}$$

Setting the derivative equal to the null vector, we obtain the set of *normal equations*,

$$\mathbf{X}'\mathbf{X}\hat{\boldsymbol{\beta}} = \mathbf{X}'\mathbf{y} \tag{4.2.3}$$

To solve for the vector estimate of $\boldsymbol{\beta}$, both sides of Eq. 4.2.3 may be premultiplied by $(\mathbf{X}'\mathbf{X})^{-1}$. Then

$$(\mathbf{X}'\mathbf{X})^{-1}\mathbf{X}'\mathbf{X}\hat{\boldsymbol{\beta}} = (\mathbf{X}'\mathbf{X})^{-1}\mathbf{X}'\mathbf{y}$$

and

$$\hat{\boldsymbol{\beta}} = (\mathbf{X}'\mathbf{X})^{-1}\mathbf{X}'\mathbf{y} \tag{4.2.4}$$

$\hat{\boldsymbol{\beta}}$ is the "best" estimate of $\boldsymbol{\beta}$ in the sense that it yields the minimum sum of squared errors (c) in the sample. This can be seen without calculus. Let some *other* estimate of $\boldsymbol{\beta}$ be $\hat{\boldsymbol{\beta}}^*$. Since $\hat{\boldsymbol{\beta}}^*$ is not equal to $\hat{\boldsymbol{\beta}}$ but has the same number of elements, we may write

$$\hat{\boldsymbol{\beta}}^* = \hat{\boldsymbol{\beta}} + \mathbf{d}$$

The sum of squared errors with $\hat{\boldsymbol{\beta}}^*$ in place of $\hat{\boldsymbol{\beta}}$ is

$$\begin{aligned} c^* &= (\mathbf{y} - \mathbf{X}\hat{\boldsymbol{\beta}}^*)'(\mathbf{y} - \mathbf{X}\hat{\boldsymbol{\beta}}^*) \\ &= [(\mathbf{y} - \mathbf{X}\hat{\boldsymbol{\beta}}) - \mathbf{X}\mathbf{d}]'[(\mathbf{y} - \mathbf{X}\hat{\boldsymbol{\beta}}) - \mathbf{X}\mathbf{d}] \\ &= (\mathbf{y} - \mathbf{X}\hat{\boldsymbol{\beta}})'(\mathbf{y} - \mathbf{X}\hat{\boldsymbol{\beta}}) - 2\mathbf{d}'\mathbf{X}'(\mathbf{y} - \mathbf{X}\hat{\boldsymbol{\beta}}) + \mathbf{d}'\mathbf{X}'\mathbf{X}\mathbf{d} \end{aligned}$$

The first term is c; the second term is zero since

$$\mathbf{d}'\mathbf{X}'(\mathbf{y} - \mathbf{X}\hat{\boldsymbol{\beta}}) = \mathbf{d}'\mathbf{X}'\mathbf{y} - \mathbf{d}'\mathbf{X}'\mathbf{X}(\mathbf{X}'\mathbf{X})^{-1}\mathbf{X}'\mathbf{y} = 0$$

The final term, $\mathbf{d}'\mathbf{X}'\mathbf{X}\mathbf{d}$, is positive since it is the sum of squared elements of the vector $\mathbf{X}\mathbf{d}$. It will inflate c^* to be larger than c unless $\mathbf{d} = \mathbf{0}$. That is, any estimate other than $\hat{\boldsymbol{\beta}}$ (Eq. 4.2.4) will result in larger residual values.

Conditions for the Estimability of $\boldsymbol{\beta}$

One component in Eq. 4.2.4 is the inverse of the sum of squares and cross products of the columns or variables in $\mathbf{X}$. In order for a unique inverse to exist, $\mathbf{X}'\mathbf{X}$ must be of full rank $(q+1)$. This condition is met only if $N \geqslant q+1$, and no column of $\mathbf{X}$ can be exactly expressed as weighted linear combinations of other columns. That is, there must be more subjects than predictor variables. Also, the inclusion of both subtest and total test scores, or a set of scores that sum to the same constant for all subjects, will violate this requisite. Techniques have been developed for the computer to overlook the dependencies. However, the researcher should reconsider the meaning of his analysis if he finds himself in such a situation.

No further statistical conditions need be met to estimate $\boldsymbol{\beta}$. In particular, the patterns of intercorrelations among the predictors or between predictors and criterion is arbitrary.

In practice the number of subjects N is usually larger than $q+1$. When the two are equal, the regression model is trivial. This can be seen since $\mathbf{X}$ will be square and can itself be inverted. Then

$$\begin{aligned}\hat{\boldsymbol{\beta}} &= (\mathbf{X}'\mathbf{X})^{-1}\mathbf{X}'\mathbf{y} \\ &= \mathbf{X}^{-1}(\mathbf{X}')^{-1}\mathbf{X}'\mathbf{y} \\ &= \mathbf{X}^{-1}\mathbf{y}\end{aligned}$$

When substituted in Eq. 4.2.1, the equations simplify to

$$\begin{aligned}\mathbf{y} &= \mathbf{X}\hat{\boldsymbol{\beta}}+\mathbf{e} \\ &= \mathbf{X}\mathbf{X}^{-1}\mathbf{y}+\mathbf{e} \\ &= \mathbf{y}\end{aligned}$$

That is, the "modeling" of N observations through an equal number of predictor variables will not lead to parsimony or to understanding the trends in the data. The original N outcome scores are undoubtedly better understood by the researcher, than a linear combination of an equal number of predictor variables.

Properties of $\hat{\boldsymbol{\beta}}$

Examination of Eq. 4.2.4 will reveal some of the relationships among the elements estimating the regression weights. Altering the order of the independent variables will not affect the estimates, other than to reorder them in the same way. Addition or deletion of independent variables will affect all of the remaining estimates. This is the case since each estimate is a function of all predictor variables. The nature of the interrelationships among the $\hat{\beta}_j$ is complex and depends upon the interrelationships of the predictor variables. The set of partial regression coefficients is determined so as to maximize prediction under this particular model only. Each coefficient may be read as a coefficient of regression of y on x_j, "given" the values of the other predictors in the equation.

To estimate $\boldsymbol{\beta}$ no assumptions about the distribution of random variables y or ϵ are necessary. Let us now assume that over repeated samplings each of the ϵ_i is normally distributed with expectation zero and variance σ^2. Further, we shall assume that the covariance of ϵ_i with ϵ_j $(j \neq i)$ is zero. That is, the ϵ_i are independent and normal and have common variance σ^2. The distributional assumption may be written in matrix form as

$$\boldsymbol{\epsilon} \sim \mathcal{N}_N(\mathbf{0}, \sigma^2\mathbf{I}) \tag{4.2.5}$$

The expectation of the vector $\boldsymbol{\epsilon}$ is the null vector; the variance–covariance matrix is $N \times N$ diagonal:

$$\mathcal{V}(\boldsymbol{\epsilon}) = \sigma^2\mathbf{I} = \text{diag}\,(\sigma^2, \sigma^2, \ldots, \sigma^2)$$

From these assumptions, it follows that the distribution of $\mathbf{y}$ is also N-variate normal, since $\mathbf{X}$ and $\boldsymbol{\beta}$ are both matrices of constants. The expectation of **y** is

$$\mathscr{E}(\mathbf{y}) = \mathscr{E}(\mathbf{X}\boldsymbol{\beta}+\boldsymbol{\epsilon})$$
$$= \mathscr{E}(\mathbf{X}\boldsymbol{\beta})+\mathscr{E}(\boldsymbol{\epsilon})$$
$$= \mathbf{X}\boldsymbol{\beta} \qquad (4.2.6)$$

For any one observation

$$\mathscr{E}(y_i) = \mathbf{x}_i'\boldsymbol{\beta} \qquad (4.2.6a)$$

$\mathbf{x}_i'$ is the $1\times(q+1)$ vector of x-values.

The variance of **y** for the particular set of values in **X** is

$$\mathscr{V}(\mathbf{y}) = \mathscr{E}[\mathbf{y}-\mathscr{E}(\mathbf{y})][\mathbf{y}-\mathscr{E}(\mathbf{y})]'$$
$$= \mathscr{E}(\mathbf{y}-\mathbf{X}\boldsymbol{\beta})(\mathbf{y}-\mathbf{X}\boldsymbol{\beta})'$$
$$= \mathscr{E}(\boldsymbol{\epsilon}\boldsymbol{\epsilon}')$$
$$= \mathscr{V}(\boldsymbol{\epsilon})$$
$$= \sigma^2\mathbf{I} \qquad (4.2.7)$$

The y_i, like the ϵ_i, are independent and have common variance σ^2, at the particular values of the independent variables. This value is the *conditional variance* of y given the values of the independent variables x_j.

From Eqs. 4.2.6 and 4.2.7, we can deduce further properties of $\hat{\boldsymbol{\beta}}$ as an estimator of $\boldsymbol{\beta}$. First, it can be seen that $\hat{\boldsymbol{\beta}}$ is an unbiased estimator. The expectation of $\hat{\boldsymbol{\beta}}$ is

$$\mathscr{E}(\hat{\boldsymbol{\beta}}) = \mathscr{E}[(\mathbf{X}'\mathbf{X})^{-1}\mathbf{X}'\mathbf{y}]$$

Since **X** is a matrix of constants, $\mathbf{X}'\mathbf{X}$ is likewise fixed. $(\mathbf{X}'\mathbf{X})^{-1}\mathbf{X}'$ is a $(q+1)\times N$ matrix with rows defining linear combinations of the elements of **y**. Thus

$$\mathscr{E}(\hat{\boldsymbol{\beta}}) = (\mathbf{X}'\mathbf{X})^{-1}\mathbf{X}'\mathscr{E}(\mathbf{y})$$
$$= (\mathbf{X}'\mathbf{X})^{-1}\mathbf{X}'\mathbf{X}\boldsymbol{\beta}$$
$$= \boldsymbol{\beta} \qquad (4.2.8)$$

$\hat{\boldsymbol{\beta}}$ is also an efficient estimator; each element is the minimum-variance estimate of the corresponding population weight β_j. Over many samples we would obtain a range of estimates of each β_j. The degree of variation is described by the variance of each $\hat{\beta}_j$ and covariance of each pair of estimated weights. Together these form the variance–covariance matrix of the vector $\hat{\boldsymbol{\beta}}$. The matrix is $(q+1)\times(q+1)$ symmetric, and may be derived through the rules of expectation of Chapter 3:

$$\mathscr{V}(\hat{\boldsymbol{\beta}}) = \mathscr{V}[(\mathbf{X}'\mathbf{X})^{-1}\mathbf{X}'\mathbf{y}]$$
$$= (\mathbf{X}'\mathbf{X})^{-1}\mathbf{X}'\mathscr{V}(\mathbf{y})\mathbf{X}(\mathbf{X}'\mathbf{X})^{-1}$$

using the rule given by Eq. 3.1.27. Substituting $\mathscr{V}(\mathbf{y}) = \sigma^2\mathbf{I}$,

$$\mathscr{V}(\hat{\boldsymbol{\beta}}) = (\mathbf{X}'\mathbf{X})^{-1}\mathbf{X}'\sigma^2\mathbf{I}\mathbf{X}(\mathbf{X}'\mathbf{X})^{-1}$$
$$= \sigma^2(\mathbf{X}'\mathbf{X})^{-1}$$
$$= \sigma^2\mathbf{G} \qquad (4.2.9)$$

The partial result $\mathbf{G}=(\mathbf{X}'\mathbf{X})^{-1}$ is termed the matrix of *variance–covariance factors* of the estimates. Each diagonal element is proportional (by a factor of σ^2) to the variance of one of the $\hat{\beta}_j$; each off-diagonal element is proportional to the covariance of the two respective regression coefficients.

The *standard error* of regression weight $\hat{\beta}_j$ is the square root of the *jj* diagonal element of $\sigma^2\mathbf{G}$—that is, the square root of the variance of the element. The variance is

$$\sigma_{\hat{\beta}_j}{}^2 = \sigma^2[g_{jj}] \tag{4.2.10}$$

The standard error is

$$\sigma_{\hat{\beta}_j} = \sigma\sqrt{[g_{jj}]} \tag{4.2.11}$$

The variances and covariances of the $\hat{\beta}_j$ may be expressed in correlational form. The covariance matrix is $\sigma^2\mathbf{G}$. Following the usual procedures for correlations, let

$$\begin{aligned}\mathbf{D}_G &= \text{diag}\,(\sigma^2\mathbf{G})\\ &= \text{diag}\,(\sigma^2 g_{11},\quad \sigma^2 g_{22}, \ldots, \sigma^2 g_{q+1,q+1})\end{aligned}$$

$\mathbf{D}_G{}^{1/2}$ is the diagonal matrix of square roots of these elements, or the standard errors of the $\hat{\beta}_j$. The inverse $\mathbf{D}_G{}^{-1/2}$ is diagonal and has nonzero elements $1/\sigma\sqrt{[g_{jj}]}$. The matrix of intercorrelations is

$$\mathbf{R}_G = \mathbf{D}_G{}^{-1/2}\sigma^2\mathbf{G}\mathbf{D}_G{}^{-1/2} \tag{4.2.12}$$

Elements of $\mathbf{R}_G$ are of the form

$$[r_g]_{ij} = \frac{\sigma^2[g_{ij}]}{\sigma\sqrt{[g_{ii}]}\sigma\sqrt{[g_{jj}]}} = \frac{[g_{ij}]}{\sqrt{[g_{ii}][g_{jj}]}}$$

All multiplications by σ^2 may be omitted, so long as σ^2 is assumed common to all observations. The unstandardized covariance matrix $\sigma^2\mathbf{G}$ is generally of use in determining the precision of estimation. Correlational form 4.2.12 is easier to interpret and provides some indication of the interdependence of the estimates. The information is useful in describing the effect of deleting predictors from the regression equation.

Estimating Dispersions

From the N-observation sample, we may estimate σ^2, which in turn can be used for interval estimates and significance tests on $\boldsymbol{\beta}$. $\hat{\boldsymbol{\beta}}$ is obtained under the condition that the error sum of squares, $\mathbf{e}'\mathbf{e}=\Sigma e_i^2$, is minimal. This provides the conditions for estimating σ^2. $\mathbf{e}'\mathbf{e}=(\mathbf{y}-\mathbf{X}\hat{\boldsymbol{\beta}})'(\mathbf{y}-\mathbf{X}\hat{\boldsymbol{\beta}})$ is the residual sum of squares from the model. $\mathbf{y}$ has N independent observations; $q+1$ terms, which are linear functions of $\mathbf{y}$, have been subtracted. Thus $\mathbf{e}'\mathbf{e}$ is the sum of squares of $N-(q+1)$ independent random variables; $\mathbf{e}'\mathbf{e}$ has $N-(q+1)$ residual *degrees of freedom*.

An unbiased estimate of σ^2 is

$$\hat{\sigma}^2 = \frac{\mathbf{e}'\mathbf{e}}{N-(q+1)}$$

$$= \frac{(\mathbf{y}-\mathbf{X}\hat{\boldsymbol{\beta}})'(\mathbf{y}-\mathbf{X}\hat{\boldsymbol{\beta}})}{N-q-1}$$

$$= \frac{\mathbf{y}'\mathbf{y}-\hat{\boldsymbol{\beta}}'\mathbf{X}'\mathbf{y}}{N-q-1} \tag{4.2.13}$$

The reader will also recognize this as being the variance of the conditional distribution of y at particular values of x_j, when y and the x_j have a multivariate normal distribution. The estimate of σ^2 is the same whether the x_j are fixed or random variables. The estimated conditional standard deviation of y is $\sqrt{\hat{\sigma}^2}=\hat{\sigma}$.

$\hat{\sigma}$ may be substituted in Eq. 4.2.11 to estimate the standard error of each regression coefficient. The estimated standard error of $\hat{\beta}_j$ is

$$\hat{\sigma}_{\hat{\beta}_j} = \hat{\sigma}\sqrt{[g_{jj}]} \tag{4.2.14}$$

If $\mathbf{y}$ is normally distributed, then $\hat{\beta}_j$, a linear function of $\mathbf{y}$, is also distributed normally (with expectation β_j and variance $\sigma_{\hat{\beta}_j}{}^2$. Then

$$t = \frac{\hat{\beta}_j-\beta_j}{\hat{\sigma}_{\hat{\beta}_j}} \tag{4.2.15}$$

follows a t distribution with $N-q-1$ degrees of freedom. The $1-\alpha$ confidence interval on β_j is

$$\hat{\beta}_j - k\hat{\sigma}_{\hat{\beta}_j} \leqslant \beta_j \leqslant \hat{\beta}_j + k\hat{\sigma}_{\hat{\beta}_j} \tag{4.2.16}$$

Alternately, expression 4.2.16 may be written

$$\beta_j\text{:}\ \ \hat{\beta}_j \pm k\hat{\sigma}_{\hat{\beta}_j} \tag{4.2.16a}$$

k is the $100\alpha/2$ upper percentage point of the t distribution with $N-q-1$ degrees of freedom $(t_{N-q-1,\alpha/2})$.

We may test that β_j is equal to any fixed value β_j^* by using Eq. 4.2.15. The hypothesis is H_0: $\beta_j = \beta_j^*$ for the two-tailed test. H_0 is rejected if $|t| > k$; otherwise maintain H_0. For a one-tail test, the critical value is $k = t_{N-q-1,\alpha}$ and the sign on t_j must be in the proper direction.

Some Simple Cases

To understand the estimation of $\boldsymbol{\beta}$, it is useful to consider some simple cases algebraically. The simplest regression model is $y_i=\alpha+\epsilon_i$. The model matrix is an N-element unit vector, $\mathbf{X}=\mathbf{1}$. The estimate of $\boldsymbol{\beta}$ is

$$\begin{aligned}\hat{\boldsymbol{\beta}} &= \hat{\alpha}\\ &= (\mathbf{X}'\mathbf{X})^{-1}\mathbf{X}'\mathbf{y}\\ &= (\mathbf{1}'\mathbf{1})^{-1}\mathbf{1}'\mathbf{y}\\ &= \frac{1}{N}\sum_{i=1}^{N} y_i\\ &= y.\end{aligned}$$

With no predictor variables, the population constant is the sample mean. The standard error is $\sigma_{\hat{\alpha}} = \sigma^2(\mathbf{1}'\mathbf{1})^{-1} = \sigma^2/N$.

It can be seen that the function of the constant in the model, and the unit vector in **X**, is to preserve the equality $\mathbf{y}=\mathbf{X}\hat{\boldsymbol{\beta}}+\mathbf{e}$. By absorbing scaling factors, the estimation of other terms in $\boldsymbol{\beta}$ is not dependent upon the origins of the measurement scales. For this model the observational equation is $y_i=y.+e_i$. y_i is a simple function of the origin of the measurements in the sample.

If there is a single independent variable in addition to the unit vector, the model is $y_i=\alpha+\beta x_i+\epsilon_i$. The vectors of **X** are $\mathbf{x}_i'=[1 \quad x_i]$. The model matrix is

$$\mathbf{X}=\begin{bmatrix} 1 & x_1 \\ 1 & x_2 \\ \vdots & \vdots \\ 1 & x_N \end{bmatrix}$$

and

$$\mathbf{X}'\mathbf{X}=\begin{bmatrix} N & \sum x_i \\ \sum x_i & \sum x_i^2 \end{bmatrix}$$

Then

$$(\mathbf{X}'\mathbf{X})^{-1}=\frac{1}{N\sum(x_i-x.)^2}\begin{bmatrix} \sum x_i^2 & -\sum x_i \\ -\sum x_i & N \end{bmatrix}$$

$$\mathbf{X}'\mathbf{y}=\begin{bmatrix} \sum y_i \\ \sum x_i y_i \end{bmatrix}$$

and

$$\begin{aligned}\hat{\boldsymbol{\beta}}&=(\mathbf{X}'\mathbf{X})^{-1}\mathbf{X}'\mathbf{y}\\ &=\begin{bmatrix}\hat{\alpha}\\ \hat{\beta}\end{bmatrix}\\ &=\begin{bmatrix} y.-\hat{\beta}x. \\ \dfrac{\sum(x_i-x.)(y_i-y.)}{\sum(x_i-x.)^2}\end{bmatrix}\end{aligned}$$

Again we can see that the estimate of α preserves the model equality.

The observational equation is $y_i=\mathbf{x}_i'\hat{\boldsymbol{\beta}}+e_i$

or

$$y_i=y.-\hat{\beta}x.+\hat{\beta}x_i+e_i$$

and

$$y_i-y.=\hat{\beta}(x_i-x.)+e_i$$

$\hat{\beta}$ describes the relationship between y and x when both are expressed in mean deviation units. The estimate of β obtained through matrix operations is identical to the usual simple regression coefficient of y on x. When there is more than a single predictor, however, the expressions become complex and even intractable in scalar algebra.

Example

Employing the data of Table 3.3.1, assume that y_1 is a criterion measure we wish to predict from a linear combination of x_1, x_2, and x_3. The **y** observational vector has $N=15$ elements (.8, 2.2, . . . , 1.9). The regression model matrix has four columns: a unit vector, $\mathbf{x}_1$ (72, 78, . . . , 83), $\mathbf{x}_2$ (114, 117, . . . , 112), and $\mathbf{x}_3$ (17.3, 17.6, . . . , 16.1). The corresponding $q+1=4$ parameters are

$$\boldsymbol{\beta}' = [\alpha \quad \beta_1 \quad \beta_2 \quad \beta_3]$$

The model to be fit to the data is

$$y_i = \alpha + \beta_1 x_{i1} + \beta_2 x_{i2} + \beta_3 x_{i3} + \epsilon_i$$

The conditions for estimability of $\boldsymbol{\beta}$ are met: N exceeds q and no predictor is a linear function of other x-variables. The matrix of cross products for predictors is

$$\mathbf{X}'\mathbf{X} = \begin{bmatrix} 15.00 & & & \text{(Symmetric)} \\ 1263.00 & 107{,}009.00 & & \\ 1733.00 & 145{,}976.00 & 200{,}363.00 & \\ 255.30 & 21{,}585.00 & 29{,}503.90 & 4383.13 \end{bmatrix} \begin{matrix} \text{Constant} \\ x_1 \\ x_2 \\ x_3 \end{matrix}$$
$$\begin{matrix} \text{Constant} & x_1 & x_2 & x_3 \end{matrix}$$

Then

$$\mathbf{G} = (\mathbf{X}'\mathbf{X})^{-1} = (10^{-3}) \times \begin{bmatrix} 96{,}279.46 & & & \text{(Symmetric)} \\ -32.12 & 2.24 & & \\ -779.26 & -.60 & 7.21 & \\ -204.32 & -5.11 & -.16 & 38.36 \end{bmatrix} \begin{matrix} \text{Constant} \\ x_1 \\ x_2 \\ x_3 \end{matrix}$$
$$\begin{matrix} \text{Constant} & x_1 & x_2 & x_3 \end{matrix}$$

$$\mathbf{X}'\mathbf{y} = \begin{bmatrix} 34.00 \\ 2918.70 \\ 3934.10 \\ 585.70 \end{bmatrix} \begin{matrix} \text{Constant} \\ x_1 \\ x_2 \\ x_3 \end{matrix}$$

and

$$\hat{\boldsymbol{\beta}} = \begin{bmatrix} -5.613 \\ .086 \\ .008 \\ -.017 \end{bmatrix} \begin{matrix} \text{Constant} \\ x_1 \\ x_2 \\ x_3 \end{matrix}$$

The estimated variance is

$$\hat{\sigma}^2 = \frac{1}{15-4}(\mathbf{y}'\mathbf{y} - \hat{\boldsymbol{\beta}}'\mathbf{X}'\mathbf{y}) = \frac{1}{11}(85.38 - 81.79) = .33$$

The standard deviation is

$$\hat{\sigma} = \sqrt{.33} = .57$$

The standard errors of the regression coefficients are the square roots of the diagonal elements of $\hat{\sigma}^2\mathbf{G}$:

$$\begin{aligned}\hat{\sigma}_{\hat{\alpha}} &= .57\sqrt{96.28} = 5.608\\ \hat{\sigma}_{\hat{\beta}_1} &= .57\sqrt{.0022} = .027\\ \hat{\sigma}_{\hat{\beta}_2} &= .57\sqrt{.0072} = .049\\ \hat{\sigma}_{\hat{\beta}_3} &= .57\sqrt{.0384} = .112\end{aligned}$$

The .95 confidence interval on β_1 requires $t_{11,.025} = 2.201$. The interval is

$$.086 - 2.201(.027) \leq \beta_1 \leq .086 + 2.201(.027)$$

or

$$.027 \leq \beta_1 \leq .145$$

We reject H_0: $\beta_1 = 0$, and maintain predictor x_1 in the equation. The equation with all three predictors is

$$y_i = -5.613 + .086x_{i1} + .008x_{i2} - .017x_{i3} + e_i$$

Prediction

Having estimated $\boldsymbol{\beta}$, we may obtain the vector of scores on the outcome variable as predicted by the model. The vector of *predicted* or *estimated scores* is

$$\hat{\mathbf{y}} = \mathbf{X}\hat{\boldsymbol{\beta}} \tag{4.2.17}$$

or

$$\hat{y}_i = \hat{\alpha} + \hat{\beta}_1 x_{i1} + \hat{\beta}_2 x_{i2} + \cdots + \hat{\beta}_q x_{iq} \tag{4.2.17a}$$

Substituting Eq. 4.2.17 in the observational equation (4.2.1), we have

$$\mathbf{y} = \hat{\mathbf{y}} + \mathbf{e} \tag{4.2.18}$$

With the inclusion of the unit vector in $\mathbf{X}$, the mean of the predicted scores is the mean of the observed scores ($y_{\cdot}$). The expectation of $\hat{\mathbf{y}}$ is

$$\begin{aligned}\mathscr{E}(\hat{\mathbf{y}}) &= \mathscr{E}(\mathbf{X}\hat{\boldsymbol{\beta}})\\ &= \mathbf{X}\boldsymbol{\beta}\end{aligned} \tag{4.2.19}$$

The covariance matrix of the predicted scores is of use in applying Eq. 4.2.17 and in deriving interval estimates. That is,

$$\begin{aligned}\mathscr{V}(\hat{\mathbf{y}}) &= \mathscr{V}(\mathbf{X}\hat{\boldsymbol{\beta}})\\ &= \mathbf{X}\mathscr{V}(\hat{\boldsymbol{\beta}})\mathbf{X}'\\ &= \mathbf{X}\sigma^2(\mathbf{X}'\mathbf{X})^{-1}\mathbf{X}'\\ &= \sigma^2\mathbf{X}\mathbf{G}\mathbf{X}'\end{aligned} \tag{4.2.20}$$

Predicted *mean* y at a particular set of x-values is given by Eq. 4.2.17a. In vector notation,

$$\hat{y}_i = \mathbf{x}_i' \hat{\boldsymbol{\beta}} \tag{4.2.21}$$

$\mathbf{x}_i'$ is the vector of values on the x-variables, or one row of $\mathbf{X}$.

The variances of the N estimates are on the diagonal of Eq. 4.2.20, and the covariances are in the off-diagonal positions. The standard error of $\hat{y}_i$ is the square root of the variance, or the square root of the ii diagonal element of Eq. 4.2.20:

$$\sigma_{\hat{y}_i} = \sigma(\mathbf{x}_i' \mathbf{G} \mathbf{x}_i)^{1/2} \tag{4.2.22}$$

The sample value $\hat{\sigma}_{\hat{y}_i}$ may be obtained by substituting $\hat{\sigma}^2$ for σ^2. Unlike the original observations, the predicted scores generally have nonzero covariances.

Let us inspect the variance for a one-predictor situation. Let $\mathbf{x}_j' = [1 \quad x_j]$ be the jth row of $\mathbf{X}$ for one observation. Then $\hat{y}_j = \mathbf{x}_j' \hat{\boldsymbol{\beta}}$ and

$$\begin{aligned}
\sigma_{\hat{y}_j}^2 &= \sigma^2 \mathbf{x}_j' \mathbf{G} \mathbf{x}_j \\
&= \sigma^2 [1 \quad x_j] \begin{bmatrix} g_{11} & g_{12} \\ g_{21} & g_{22} \end{bmatrix} \begin{bmatrix} 1 \\ x_j \end{bmatrix} \\
&= \frac{\sigma^2}{N \sum (x_i - x.)^2} [1 \quad x_j] \begin{bmatrix} \sum x_i^2 & -\sum x_i \\ -\sum x_i & N \end{bmatrix} \begin{bmatrix} 1 \\ x_j \end{bmatrix} \\
&= \sigma^2 \left\{ \frac{\sum [(x_i - x.) + (x. - x_j)]^2}{N \sum (x_i - x.)^2} \right\} \\
&= \sigma^2 \left[\frac{1}{N} + \frac{(x_j - x.)^2}{\sum (x_i - x.)^2} \right]
\end{aligned}$$

It can be seen that the variance of the estimated mean of y is minimal (σ^2/N) when estimated at mean x ($x_j = x.$). The variance increases as x_j moves away from $x.$, and the precision of estimation decreases. When $x_j \neq x.$, the variance contains components relating to the precision of both $\hat{\alpha}$ and $\hat{\beta}$ in the regression equation; when $x_j = x.$, only $\hat{\alpha}$ need be considered.

The standard error may be used to obtain an interval estimate of mean y at the values $\mathbf{x}_i'$. The $1-\alpha$ interval is

$$y_i\text{: } \hat{y}_i \pm k \hat{\sigma}_{\hat{y}_i} \tag{4.2.23}$$

k is the $100\alpha/2$ upper percentage point of the t distribution with $N-q-1$ degrees of freedom ($t_{N-q-1, \alpha/2}$).

The prediction of values other than mean y for given $\mathbf{x}_i$ involves additional variation of the scores about their mean. The variance of y-scores about the mean is σ^2, which is the same at all sets of x-values. Thus if $\hat{y}_i$ is an estimate of a particular y-score instead of a mean, the error variance is increased by the addition of the σ^2 component. In this case

$$\sigma_{\hat{y}_i}^2 = \sigma^2 (1 + \mathbf{x}_i' \mathbf{G} \mathbf{x}_i) \tag{4.2.24}$$

which may be estimated by substituting $\hat{\sigma}^2$ for σ^2.

The vector of sample *residuals* is

$$\begin{aligned}\mathbf{e} &= \hat{\boldsymbol{\epsilon}} \\ &= \mathbf{y}-\hat{\mathbf{y}} \\ &= \mathbf{y}-\mathbf{X}\hat{\boldsymbol{\beta}}\end{aligned} \qquad (4.2.25)$$

The mean of the e_i is zero; the sample variance is $\hat{\sigma}^2$, with $N-q-1$ degrees of freedom. The residuals are useful in locating observations that do not follow the model and observations that do, and in isolating unmodeled trends in the data (Anscombe and Tukey, 1963; Draper and Smith, 1966).

The expectation of **e** is

$$\begin{aligned}\mathscr{E}(\mathbf{e}) &= \mathscr{E}(\mathbf{y}-\mathbf{X}\hat{\boldsymbol{\beta}}) \\ &= \mathbf{0}\end{aligned} \qquad (4.2.26)$$

The variance–covariance matrix is

$$\begin{aligned}\mathscr{V}(\mathbf{e}) &= \mathscr{V}(\mathbf{y}-\mathbf{X}\hat{\boldsymbol{\beta}}) \\ &= \mathscr{V}(\mathbf{y}-\mathbf{XGX}'\mathbf{y}) \\ &= \mathscr{V}[(\mathbf{I}-\mathbf{XGX}')\mathbf{y}] \\ &= (\mathbf{I}-\mathbf{XGX}')\mathscr{V}(\mathbf{y})(\mathbf{I}-\mathbf{XGX}')' \\ &= \sigma^2(\mathbf{I}-\mathbf{XGX}')\end{aligned} \qquad (4.2.27)$$

The standard error of the *i*th residual, σ_{e_i}, is the square root of the *ii* diagonal element of Eq. 4.2.27. That is,

$$\sigma_{e_i} = \sigma\sqrt{1-\mathbf{x}_i'\mathbf{G}\mathbf{x}_i} \qquad (4.2.28)$$

Substituting the estimated $\hat{\sigma}$, $e_i/\hat{\sigma}_{e_i}$ follows a *t* distribution with $N-q-1$ degrees of freedom. The $1-\alpha$ interval estimate of ϵ_i is

$$\epsilon_i\colon\ e_i \pm k\sigma_{e_i} \qquad (4.2.29)$$

k is the $100\alpha/2$ percentage point of the *t* distribution with $N-q-1$ degrees of freedom ($t_{N-q-1,\alpha/2}$).

Example

The predicted score for variable y_1 of Table 3.3.1 is obtained by

$$\hat{y}_i = -5.613 + .086x_{i1} + .008x_{i2} - .017x_{i3}$$

For the first set of predictor values,

$$\mathbf{x}_1' = [1 \quad 72 \quad 114 \quad 17.3]$$

and

$$\hat{y}_1 = \mathbf{x}_1'\hat{\boldsymbol{\beta}} = 1.20$$

The standard error of mean $\hat{y}_1$ at $\mathbf{x}_1$ is

$$\hat{\sigma}\sqrt{\mathbf{x}_1(\mathbf{X}'\mathbf{X})^{-1}\mathbf{x}_1} = .57\sqrt{.50} = .403$$

The .95 confidence interval, with $t_{11,.025} = 2.201$, is

$$1.20-2.201(.403) \leqslant \mu_{y_1|\mathbf{x}_1} \leqslant 1.20+2.201(.403)$$

or

$$.310 \leqslant \mu_{y_1|\mathbf{x}_1} \leqslant 2.084$$

The residual for $\mathbf{x}_1$ is

$$e_1 = y_1 - \hat{y}_1 = .80 - 1.20 = -.40$$

The standard error is

$$\hat{\sigma}_{e_1} = .57\sqrt{1-.50} = .40$$

The model overpredicts y_1 at $\mathbf{x}_1'$. If the first subject had followed the model exactly, he would have attained a score of 1.20; instead we observe only .80. The difference is the extent to which we cannot know the outcome from knowledge of the antecedent (x_j) variables.

The residuals for all observations are given in Table 4.2.1. The mean (within rounding error) is zero. Only one residual is outstanding in its value, $e_{14} = -.97$. Although $\mathbf{x}_{14}'$ is close to the mean vector, $y_{14} = 90$ is considerably below the group mean, leading to the large difference between the predicted and observed outcomes.

Table 4.2.1 Predicted Scores and Residuals

Observation (i)	*Observed* (y_i)	*Predicted* ($\hat{y}_i$)	*Residual* (e_i)
1	.80	1.20	−.40
2	2.20	1.73	.47
3	1.60	2.29	−.69
4	2.60	3.21	−.61
5	2.70	2.57	.13
6	2.10	2.20	−.10
7	3.10	2.95	.15
8	3.00	2.39	.61
9	3.20	2.60	.60
10	2.60	1.91	.69
11	2.70	2.48	.22
12	3.00	3.04	−.04
13	1.60	1.37	.23
14	.90	1.87	−.97
15	1.90	2.15	−.25

Summary

We may now inspect portions of the model, $\mathbf{y} = \mathbf{X}\boldsymbol{\beta} + \boldsymbol{\epsilon}$, in juxtaposition. The covariance matrix of $\boldsymbol{\epsilon}$ and $\mathbf{y}$ are both $\sigma^2\mathbf{I}$ (see Eq. 4.2.7). The product $\mathbf{X}\boldsymbol{\beta}$ has no variance in the population, since $\boldsymbol{\beta}$ is a vector constant that multiplies the model matrix of fixed values.

The estimate $\hat{\boldsymbol{\beta}}$ varies over repeated samplings, as do vectors $\mathbf{y}$ and $\hat{\boldsymbol{\epsilon}}=\mathbf{e}$. The covariance matrices of $\mathbf{y}$, $\mathbf{X}\hat{\boldsymbol{\beta}}$, and $\mathbf{e}$ are $\sigma^2\mathbf{I}$, $\sigma^2\mathbf{XGX}'$, and $\sigma^2(\mathbf{I}-\mathbf{XGX}')$, respectively.

We may note the following relationships:

1. $\mathscr{V}(\mathbf{y})=\mathscr{V}(\mathbf{X}\hat{\boldsymbol{\beta}})+\mathscr{V}(\hat{\boldsymbol{\epsilon}})$. The exact partition of variation and covariation of the observations follows from the normal equations, requiring $\mathbf{X}'\mathbf{y}-\mathbf{X}'\mathbf{X}\hat{\boldsymbol{\beta}}=\mathbf{0}$. Then $\hat{\boldsymbol{\beta}}'\mathbf{X}'\mathbf{y}-\hat{\boldsymbol{\beta}}'\mathbf{X}'\mathbf{X}\hat{\boldsymbol{\beta}}=0$ and $(\mathbf{X}\hat{\boldsymbol{\beta}})'(\mathbf{y}-\mathbf{X}\hat{\boldsymbol{\beta}})=(\mathbf{X}\hat{\boldsymbol{\beta}})'\mathbf{e}=0$. That is, $\mathbf{X}\hat{\boldsymbol{\beta}}$ and $\mathbf{e}$ are always orthogonal partitions of the observational vector, $\mathbf{y}$. It follows that $\mathbf{X}\hat{\boldsymbol{\beta}}$ and $\mathbf{e}$ are statistically independent, since $\mathscr{E}[(\mathbf{X}\hat{\boldsymbol{\beta}})'(\mathbf{y}-\mathbf{X}\hat{\boldsymbol{\beta}})]=0=\mathscr{E}(\mathbf{X}\hat{\boldsymbol{\beta}})'\mathscr{E}(\mathbf{y}-\mathbf{X}\hat{\boldsymbol{\beta}})$.

2. In general, as predictors are added to the model, σ^2 will decrease and the diagonal elements of $\mathbf{XGX}'$ will increase. At some value of q between zero and N there will be an optimum selection of predictor variables, beyond which the decrease in σ^2 by the addition of predictors will be exceeded by the increases in the diagonal of $\mathbf{XGX}'$. It is beyond this point that additional predictors are not contributing to predictive power, but are instead compounding error. At the same time, it can be seen that decreases in the variance terms of $\sigma^2\mathbf{XGX}'$ are accompanied by parallel increases in the variances of $\mathbf{e}$.

3. Individual observations y_i and errors ϵ_i are both independently distributed. This is seen through their diagonal covariance matrices. The predicted scores and sample residuals are not independent except in the (rare) situation in which $\mathbf{X}$ is columnwise orthogonal. In general this correlation presents little problem in the plotting and interpretation of the residuals, so long as the number of predictor variables is small relative to the sample size (Anscombe and Tukey, 1968).

4.3 MULTIVARIATE MULTIPLE REGRESSION MODEL

When more than a single outcome measure is to be considered, a multivariate form of the linear regression model is appropriate. Multivariate techniques are useful for obtaining multiple univariate results from a given sample. In addition, simultaneous confidence intervals and significance tests may be obtained. However, these are only as meaningful as the common trait being measured by the outcome variables!

Assume that observation i has been measured on p ($\geqslant 1$) random variables y_k. In addition, scores are obtained on q antecedents x_j, as for the univariate case. The linear model relating the two sets contains p separate univariate equations:

$$\begin{aligned}[y_{i1}\quad y_{i2}\quad \cdots\quad y_{ip}] = {} & [\alpha_1\quad \alpha_2\quad \cdots\quad \alpha_p]\\ & +x_{i1}[\beta_{11}\quad \beta_{12}\quad \cdots\quad \beta_{1p}]\\ & +x_{i2}[\beta_{21}\quad \beta_{22}\quad \cdots\quad \beta_{2p}]\\ & \quad\vdots\\ & +x_{iq}[\beta_{q1}\quad \beta_{q2}\quad \cdots\quad \beta_{qp}]\\ & +[\epsilon_{i1}\quad \epsilon_{i2}\quad \cdots\quad \epsilon_{ip}]\end{aligned} \tag{4.3.1}$$

y_{ik} is the response of the subject on criterion y_k; x_{ij} is his value on predictor x_j.

Any one term of the vectors of Eq. 4.3.1 reproduces univariate equation 4.1.1 exactly. A second subscript is added to y_i and ϵ_i to indicate the respective criterion measure. The constants α and β_j differ for each criterion measure. Thus these too have an additional subscript to correspond to the y-variate. α_k is the scaling constant for criterion y_k; β_{jk} is the partial regression coefficient relating y_k to predictor x_j. The same antecedents appear in the model for every outcome measure. Their differing importance is reflected in different β_{jk} values.

Expression 4.3.1 may be represented more succinctly in matrix form. Let $\mathbf{y}_i'$ be the p-element outcome vector

$$\mathbf{y}_i' = [y_{i1} \quad y_{i2} \quad \cdots \quad y_{ip}]$$

Then Eq. 4.3.1 is represented as

$$\mathbf{y}_i' = \mathbf{x}_i'\mathbf{B} + \boldsymbol{\epsilon}_i' \tag{4.3.2}$$

As in the univariate model, $\mathbf{x}_i$ contains the values of the predictor variables for observation i; that is,

$$\mathbf{x}_i' = [1 \quad x_{i1} \quad x_{i2} \quad \cdots \quad x_{iq}]$$

$\mathbf{B}$ is the $(q+1)\times p$ matrix of partial regression coefficients, for predicting each outcome measure from the independent variables:

$$\mathbf{B} = \begin{bmatrix} \alpha_1 & \alpha_2 & \cdots & \alpha_p \\ \beta_{11} & \beta_{12} & \cdots & \beta_{1p} \\ \vdots & & & \vdots \\ \beta_{q1} & \beta_{q2} & \cdots & \beta_{qp} \end{bmatrix}$$

$$= [\boldsymbol{\beta}_1 \quad \boldsymbol{\beta}_2 \quad \cdots \quad \boldsymbol{\beta}_p]$$

Each column $\boldsymbol{\beta}_k$ contains exactly the coefficients for predicting y_k alone, from the x_j. Thus α_k and β_{jk} for any outcome variable are not affected by the addition of other criterion measures. This is in contrast to the addition or deletion of independent variables, which will generally alter all the values.

We may also represent the models for N subjects in matrix form. Let us first juxtapose the N models:

$$\mathbf{y}_1' = \mathbf{x}_1'\mathbf{B} + \boldsymbol{\epsilon}_1'$$
$$\mathbf{y}_2' = \mathbf{x}_2'\mathbf{B} + \boldsymbol{\epsilon}_2'$$
$$\vdots$$
$$\mathbf{y}_N' = \mathbf{x}_N'\mathbf{B} + \boldsymbol{\epsilon}_N'$$

Since $\mathbf{B}$ is common to all observations, the models may be written in matrix form, as

$$\begin{bmatrix} \mathbf{y}_1' \\ \mathbf{y}_2' \\ \vdots \\ \mathbf{y}_N' \end{bmatrix} = \begin{bmatrix} \mathbf{x}_1' \\ \mathbf{x}_2' \\ \vdots \\ \mathbf{x}_N' \end{bmatrix} \mathbf{B} + \begin{bmatrix} \boldsymbol{\epsilon}_1' \\ \boldsymbol{\epsilon}_2' \\ \vdots \\ \boldsymbol{\epsilon}_N' \end{bmatrix}$$

or

$$\begin{bmatrix} y_{11} & y_{12} & \cdots & y_{1p} \\ y_{21} & y_{22} & \cdots & y_{2p} \\ \vdots & & & \vdots \\ y_{N1} & y_{N2} & \cdots & y_{Np} \end{bmatrix} = \begin{bmatrix} 1 & x_{11} & x_{12} & \cdots & x_{1q} \\ 1 & x_{21} & x_{22} & \cdots & x_{2q} \\ \vdots & & & & \vdots \\ 1 & x_{N1} & x_{N2} & \cdots & x_{Nq} \end{bmatrix} \begin{bmatrix} \alpha_1 & \alpha_2 & \cdots & \alpha_p \\ \beta_{11} & \beta_{12} & \cdots & \beta_{1p} \\ \beta_{21} & \beta_{22} & \cdots & \beta_{2p} \\ \vdots & & & \vdots \\ \beta_{q1} & \beta_{q2} & \cdots & \beta_{qp} \end{bmatrix}$$

$$+ \begin{bmatrix} \epsilon_{11} & \epsilon_{12} & \cdots & \epsilon_{1p} \\ \epsilon_{21} & \epsilon_{22} & \cdots & \epsilon_{2p} \\ \vdots & & & \vdots \\ \epsilon_{N1} & \epsilon_{N2} & \cdots & \epsilon_{Np} \end{bmatrix}$$

Let $\mathbf{Y}$ be the $N \times p$ observed matrix with elements y_{ik}, and $\mathbf{E}$ the $N \times p$ matrix of errors ϵ_{ik}. Then the equations may be represented as

$$\mathbf{Y} = \mathbf{XB} + \mathbf{E} \tag{4.3.3}$$

$\mathbf{X}$ is the $N \times (q+1)$ model matrix, exactly as in Eq. 4.1.2. Any of the model matrices described in Section 4.1 can also be substituted in the multivariate model. Each row of $\mathbf{Y}$, $\mathbf{X}$, and $\mathbf{E}$ corresponds to a single observation; each column of $\mathbf{Y}$ and $\mathbf{E}$ to a single criterion measure. $\mathbf{B}$ has p columns of weights for predicting each variable y_k from the q antecedents x_j.

The primary goals in the multivariate case are the same as for a single response measure. We shall draw a sample of N observations at random and use the observed data to derive point and interval estimates of the entire matrix $\mathbf{B}$. Tests of significance can be obtained for the regression weights for any one criterion measure, or jointly for all outcomes (that is, for one or more *rows* of $\mathbf{B}$). In this manner we determine whether the x-variables, alone or together predict the multiple-measure response.

4.4 ESTIMATION OF PARAMETERS: MULTIVARIATE MODEL

Let $\hat{\mathbf{B}}$ be the $(q+1) \times p$ estimate of $\mathbf{B}$ to be obtained from sample data. The observational equation for the multivariate situation is

$$\mathbf{Y} = \mathbf{X}\hat{\mathbf{B}} + \hat{\mathbf{E}} \tag{4.4.1}$$

$\hat{\mathbf{E}}$ is the $N \times p$ matrix of sample residuals or errors, with elements $\hat{\epsilon}_{ik} = e_{ik}$.

In order to estimate $\mathbf{B}$, we will minimize the squared sample residuals for *all* of the outcome measures. The sum of squared residuals for one outcome measure is one diagonal element of $\hat{\mathbf{E}}'\hat{\mathbf{E}}$. Their sum is the trace of $\hat{\mathbf{E}}'\hat{\mathbf{E}}$. Let

$$\begin{aligned} c &= \sum_{i,k} e_{ik}^2 \\ &= \operatorname{tr}(\hat{\mathbf{E}}'\hat{\mathbf{E}}) \\ &= \operatorname{tr}[(\mathbf{Y} - \mathbf{X}\hat{\mathbf{B}})'(\mathbf{Y} - \mathbf{X}\hat{\mathbf{B}})] \end{aligned}$$

To minimize c we set the partial derivatives with respect to the elements of $\hat{\mathbf{B}}$ to zero and solve. The resulting normal equations are

$$\mathbf{X}'\mathbf{X}\hat{\mathbf{B}} = \mathbf{X}'\mathbf{Y} \tag{4.4.2}$$

Premultiplying by $(\mathbf{X}'\mathbf{X})^{-1}$, the estimate of $\mathbf{B}$ is the $(q+1)\times p$ matrix

$$\begin{aligned}\hat{\mathbf{B}} &= (\mathbf{X}'\mathbf{X})^{-1}\mathbf{X}'\mathbf{Y} \\ &= \mathbf{G}\mathbf{X}'\mathbf{Y}\end{aligned} \tag{4.4.3}$$

Expression 4.4.3 shows obvious similarities to the univariate solution (4.2.4). In fact, each column of $\hat{\mathbf{B}}$ consists of exactly that set of regression coefficients for predicting a single outcome measure. The same result would have been obtained for the particular variate had it been considered alone for univariate estimates. The estimability criterion is also the same. For $\hat{\mathbf{B}}$ to have a unique solution, the number of subjects must exceed the number of predictor variables and no predictor can be expressible as an exact linear combination of other antecedents. When the conditions are met, $\mathbf{X}'\mathbf{X}$ is nonsingular and can be inverted. There is no restriction on the intercorrelations of the y-variables.

Properties of $\hat{\mathbf{B}}$

The effects of order in the matrix estimate are the same as in the univariate model. Interchanging either predictors or criterion measures will not alter the value of the regression weights, but will only interchange their order in the same manner. The addition or deletion of y-variables will not affect the remaining estimates, since the columns of $\hat{\mathbf{B}}$ are multiple univariate results. The addition or deletion of predictor variables, however, will generally affect the values of all coefficients. Each *row* of $\hat{\mathbf{B}}$ is the set of regression coefficients of vector $\mathbf{y}$ on predictor x_j, "given" the other predictor variables, or at the particular values of the other predictors.

Let us assume that the errors for observation i (elements of $\boldsymbol{\epsilon}_i'$) have a p-variate normal distribution with expectation $\mathbf{0}'$ and variance–covariance matrix $\boldsymbol{\Sigma}$, at any set of values $\mathbf{x}_i$:

$$\boldsymbol{\epsilon}_i' \sim \mathscr{N}_p(\mathbf{0}', \boldsymbol{\Sigma}) \tag{4.4.4}$$

Further, we shall assume that the errors are independent across observations.

Since $\boldsymbol{\epsilon}_i'$ is a row of $\mathbf{E}$, the expectation of $\mathbf{E}$ is an $N\times p$ null matrix. The assumption that $\mathscr{V}(\boldsymbol{\epsilon}_i') = \boldsymbol{\Sigma}$ simply asserts that there is a general interrelationship of the criterion measures. That is, $\boldsymbol{\Sigma}$ is the $p\times p$ covariance matrix *among* variates, or among elements of a row of $\mathbf{E}$:

$$\boldsymbol{\Sigma} = \begin{bmatrix} \sigma_1^2 & \sigma_{12} & \cdots & \sigma_{1p} \\ \sigma_{21} & \sigma_2^2 & \cdots & \sigma_{2p} \\ \vdots & & \ddots & \vdots \\ \sigma_{p1} & \sigma_{p2} & \cdots & \sigma_p^2 \end{bmatrix}$$

Since observations are independent, the matrix of covariances *between* the p elements in one row of $\mathbf{E}$ and the p terms of any other row is a $p\times p$ null matrix, $\mathscr{V}(\boldsymbol{\epsilon}_i', \boldsymbol{\epsilon}_{i'}) = \mathbf{0}$ for $i \neq i'$.

The assumptions may be represented in several ways. A column of $\mathbf{E}$ contains the errors for all observations on one outcome measure. The variance–covariance matrix of one column ($\boldsymbol{\epsilon}_k$) is $\sigma_k^2\mathbf{I}$. That is, the variance of each ϵ_{ik} is σ_k^2, the variance of the criterion measure; the covariances of errors across observations are all zero. Thus, the distribution of a single column is

$$\boldsymbol{\epsilon}_k \sim \mathcal{N}_N(\mathbf{0}, \sigma_k^2\mathbf{I}) \tag{4.4.5}$$

Since the column contains all the errors for one criterion measure, expression 4.4.5 is similar to the univariate form (4.2.5). The only distinction is that σ^2 requires a subscript to indicate which criterion measure the column represents.

Expressions 4.4.4 and 4.4.5 summarize the distributional information about $\mathbf{E}$.* To facilitate algebra involving $\mathbf{E}$, we may write the total covariance matrix of all elements. The result is an $Np \times Np$ matrix which consists of blocks, each block being a $p \times p$ matrix. On the diagonal of the large matrix is the matrix of variances and covariances of any one row of $\mathbf{E}$—that is, $\boldsymbol{\Sigma}$. The off-diagonal matrices are covariance matrices of pairs of rows of $\mathbf{E}$, that is, $\mathbf{0}$ ($p \times p$). The entire covariance matrix has the form,

$$\mathcal{V}(\mathbf{E}) = \text{diag}(\boldsymbol{\Sigma}, \boldsymbol{\Sigma}, \ldots, \boldsymbol{\Sigma})$$

$$= \left[\begin{array}{c|c|c|c} \boldsymbol{\Sigma} & \mathbf{0} & \cdots & \mathbf{0} \\ \hline \mathbf{0} & \boldsymbol{\Sigma} & \cdots & \mathbf{0} \\ \hline \vdots & & \ddots & \vdots \\ \hline \mathbf{0} & \mathbf{0} & \cdots & \boldsymbol{\Sigma} \end{array}\right] \begin{array}{l} \text{Row 1 of } \mathbf{E} \\ \text{Row 2 of } \mathbf{E} \\ \vdots \\ \text{Row } N \text{ of } \mathbf{E} \end{array}$$

$$\begin{array}{cccc} \text{Row 1} & \text{Row 2} & \cdots & \text{Row } N \end{array}$$

The total covariance matrix may be found as the Kronecker product of an order-N identity matrix, with $\boldsymbol{\Sigma}$. That is,

$$\mathcal{V}(\mathbf{E}) = \mathbf{I} \otimes \boldsymbol{\Sigma} \tag{4.4.6}$$

The distribution of matrix $\mathbf{E}$ is

$$\mathbf{E} \sim \mathcal{N}_{Np}(\mathbf{0}, \mathbf{I} \otimes \boldsymbol{\Sigma}) \tag{4.4.7}$$

$\mathbf{0}$ is an $N \times p$ null matrix.

The Kronecker product form (4.4.7) can be used to find the distribution of matrix $\mathbf{Y}$. $\mathbf{Y}$ is distributed in multivariate normal form with expectation

$$\begin{aligned} \mathscr{E}(\mathbf{Y}) &= \mathscr{E}(\mathbf{XB} + \mathbf{E}) \\ &= \mathbf{XB} \end{aligned} \tag{4.4.8}$$

For any one observation (one row of $\mathbf{Y}$),

$$\mathscr{E}(\mathbf{y}_i') = \mathbf{x}_i'\mathbf{B} \tag{4.4.8a}$$

*For readers not concerned with the derivation of the various variance–covariance matrices, this discussion may be bypassed, through expression 4.4.9.

The variance–covariance matrix of $\mathbf{Y}$ given $\mathbf{X}$, is

$$\begin{aligned}\mathscr{V}(\mathbf{Y}) &= \mathscr{E}[\mathbf{Y}-\mathscr{E}(\mathbf{Y})][\mathbf{Y}-\mathscr{E}(\mathbf{Y})]' \\ &= \mathscr{E}(\mathbf{Y}-\mathbf{XB})(\mathbf{Y}-\mathbf{XB})' \\ &= \mathscr{E}(\mathbf{EE}') \\ &= \mathscr{V}(\mathbf{E}) \\ &= \mathbf{I} \otimes \mathbf{\Sigma} \end{aligned} \tag{4.4.9}$$

The $\mathbf{y}_i'$ vectors for observations are independent of one another. The variates within the vector observations are generally related, with variance–covariance matrix $\mathbf{\Sigma}$. This is the covariance matrix of the y-variables at any particular $\mathbf{x}_i$ value, and is termed the *conditional variance–covariance matrix.* The variance of criterion y_k at particular x-values is the kk diagonal element, σ_k^2. In summary, the distribution of vector observations is

$$\mathbf{y}_i' \sim \mathscr{N}_p(\mathbf{x}_i'\mathbf{B}, \mathbf{\Sigma}) \tag{4.4.10}$$

$\mathbf{\Sigma}$ may also be expressed in standardized or correlational form in the usual manner. Let

$$\mathbf{\Delta} = \text{diag}\ (\mathbf{\Sigma})$$

be the diagonal matrix of variances from $\mathbf{\Sigma}$. $\mathbf{\Delta}^{1/2}$ is the matrix of standard deviations, at the particular values of the predictors. The *matrix of partial correlations* among the criterion variables is

$$\mathscr{R} = \mathbf{\Delta}^{-1/2}\mathbf{\Sigma}\,\mathbf{\Delta}^{-1/2} \tag{4.4.11}$$

with elements $-1 \leqslant \rho_{ij} \leqslant 1$.

Adjusting the variances or correlations to particular x-values is sometimes termed "holding the x_j constant" or "removing the effects of $\mathbf{X}$." Both the covariance and the variances involved in ρ_{ij} have been adjusted for the x-variables. Thus ρ_{ij} is termed a partial correlation.

The estimate $\hat{\mathbf{B}}$, like its univariate counterpart, is unbiased and minimum variance. The expectation and variance–covariance matrix of $\hat{\mathbf{B}}$ are

$$\begin{aligned}\mathscr{E}(\hat{\mathbf{B}}) &= \mathscr{E}[(\mathbf{X}'\mathbf{X})^{-1}\mathbf{X}'\mathbf{Y}] \\ &= (\mathbf{X}'\mathbf{X})^{-1}\mathbf{X}'\mathscr{E}(\mathbf{Y}) \\ &= (\mathbf{X}'\mathbf{X})^{-1}\mathbf{X}'\mathbf{XB} \\ &= \mathbf{B} \end{aligned} \tag{4.4.12}$$

and

$$\begin{aligned}\mathscr{V}(\hat{\mathbf{B}}) &= \mathscr{V}[(\mathbf{X}'\mathbf{X})^{-1}\mathbf{X}'\mathbf{Y}] \\ &= (\mathbf{X}'\mathbf{X})^{-1}\mathbf{X}'\mathscr{V}(\mathbf{Y})\mathbf{X}(\mathbf{X}'\mathbf{X})^{-1} \\ &= (\mathbf{X}'\mathbf{X})^{-1}\mathbf{X}'(\mathbf{I}\otimes\mathbf{\Sigma})\mathbf{X}(\mathbf{X}'\mathbf{X})^{-1} \\ &= (\mathbf{X}'\mathbf{X})^{-1}\otimes\mathbf{\Sigma} \\ &= \mathbf{G}\otimes\mathbf{\Sigma} \end{aligned} \tag{4.4.13}$$

The Kronecker product is a $p(q+1)\times p(q+1)$ symmetric covariance matrix of all the $\hat{\beta}_{jk}$. $\mathbf{G}\otimes\mathbf{\Sigma}$ may be drawn as the matrix of scalar products of $\mathbf{\Sigma}$; that is,

$$\left[\begin{array}{c|c|c|c} g_{11}\mathbf{\Sigma} & g_{12}\mathbf{\Sigma} & \cdots & g_{1,q+1}\mathbf{\Sigma} \\ \hline g_{21}\mathbf{\Sigma} & g_{22}\mathbf{\Sigma} & \cdots & g_{2,q+1}\mathbf{\Sigma} \\ \hline \vdots & & \ddots & \vdots \\ \hline g_{q+1,1}\mathbf{\Sigma} & g_{q+1,2}\mathbf{\Sigma} & \cdots & g_{q+1,q+1}\mathbf{\Sigma} \end{array}\right]$$

Each $p\times p$ diagonal block $[g_{jj}]\mathbf{\Sigma}$ is the covariance matrix of one row of the estimated regression coefficients (relating predictor x_j to the criterion measures). We can see that elements of a row of $\hat{\mathbf{B}}$ are interdependent to the extent that y-variables have nonzero covariances in $\mathbf{\Sigma}$. The off-diagonal blocks contain the covariances of the estimated regression coefficients for different predictor variables.

The variance–covariance matrix of a single *column* $\hat{\boldsymbol{\beta}}_k$, is $\sigma_k^2\mathbf{G}$, where σ_k^2 is the conditional variance of y_k. Since $\hat{\mathbf{B}}$ is a linear combination of the y-variates, its elements are normally distributed. Because it is unbiased, the distribution of the column of estimates is

$$\hat{\boldsymbol{\beta}}_k \sim \mathcal{N}_{q+1}(\boldsymbol{\beta}_k, \sigma_k^2\mathbf{G}) \tag{4.4.14}$$

A column of $\hat{\mathbf{B}}$ has exactly the regression weights for predicting the univariate outcome y_k. Thus expression 4.4.14 is the distribution of $\hat{\boldsymbol{\beta}}$ in 4.2.8 and 4.2.9, with the exception of the subscript k to designate the corresponding criterion variate. In general, the partial regression weights for predicting y_k are all interdependent, since the covariance matrix $\sigma_k^2\mathbf{G}$ is nondiagonal.

The most frequently used elements of 4.4.13 are the variances of the coefficients $\hat{\beta}_{jk}$. These are the main diagonal elements of $\mathbf{G}\otimes\mathbf{\Sigma}$, or the diagonal elements of $\sigma_k^2\mathbf{G}$ in expression 4.4.14, for the particular measure y_k. The standard errors of the coefficients are the square roots of these elements. The standard error of $\hat{\beta}_{jk}$ relating predictor x_j and dependent variable y_k is

$$\sigma_{\hat{\beta}_{jk}} = \sqrt{[g_{jj}][\sigma_k^2]} \tag{4.4.15}$$

This is the same as expression 4.2.11 but with the additional subscript on σ^2.

The correlations among the coefficients for any one dependent variable may be obtained by reducing the matrix of variance–covariance factors to correlation form, as in 4.2.12. This does not require the elements of $\mathbf{\Sigma}$. Let $\mathbf{D}_G = \text{diag}\,(\mathbf{G})$. The matrix of correlations is $\mathbf{R}_G = \mathbf{D}_G^{-1/2}\mathbf{G}\mathbf{D}_G^{-1/2}$.

Estimating dispersions

To estimate the precision of $\hat{\mathbf{B}}$ and the interrelationships among variates and coefficients requires a sample value for $\mathbf{\Sigma}$. The estimate is provided by residual variation about the model. The residual sum-of-squares and cross products matrix is

$$\begin{aligned} \mathbf{S}_E &= \hat{\mathbf{E}}'\hat{\mathbf{E}} \\ &= (\mathbf{Y}-\mathbf{X}\hat{\mathbf{B}})'(\mathbf{Y}-\mathbf{X}\hat{\mathbf{B}}) \end{aligned} \tag{4.4.16}$$

Each element has $N-(q+1)$ degrees of freedom. The maximum likelihood estimate of the $p \times p$ covariance matrix is

$$\hat{\mathbf{\Sigma}} = \frac{1}{N-q-1}\mathbf{S}_E$$
$$= \frac{(\mathbf{Y}-\mathbf{X}\hat{\mathbf{B}})'(\mathbf{Y}-\mathbf{X}\hat{\mathbf{B}})}{N-q-1}$$
$$= \frac{\mathbf{Y}'\mathbf{Y}-\hat{\mathbf{B}}'\mathbf{X}'\mathbf{Y}}{N-q-1} \qquad (4.4.17)$$

We note that $\hat{\mathbf{\Sigma}}$ is also identically the covariance matrix of the p outcome measures, given the $q+1$ additional variates, if all $p+q+1$ variates are distributed in multivariate normal form. It is the unbiased estimate of $\mathbf{\Sigma}_{22|1}$ in expression 3.2.10.

The diagonal elements of $\hat{\mathbf{\Sigma}}$ are the variances for each of the p separate measures, $\hat{\sigma}_k^2$, as would be obtained for that variable alone by 4.2.13. The standard deviation of y_k is $\sqrt{\hat{\sigma}_k^2}=\hat{\sigma}_k$. These elements may be used for reducing $\hat{\mathbf{\Sigma}}$ to the matrix of partial correlations and for obtaining interval estimates of the elements in $\mathbf{B}$.

The partial correlations are estimated by substituting $\hat{\mathbf{\Sigma}}$ in Eq. 4.4.11. Let

$$\hat{\mathbf{\Delta}} = \text{diag}\,(\hat{\mathbf{\Sigma}})$$

be the matrix of variances of y at the particular x-values. Then the correlations among the y-variables, holding $\mathbf{X}$ constant, is

$$\hat{\mathcal{R}} = \hat{\mathbf{\Delta}}^{-1/2}\hat{\mathbf{\Sigma}}\,\hat{\mathbf{\Delta}}^{-1/2} \qquad (4.4.18)$$

Each element $\hat{\rho}_{ij}=\hat{\sigma}_{ij}/\hat{\sigma}_i\hat{\sigma}_j$ is the correlation of y_i and y_j, removing any variance in the two measures that is shared by the x-variables.

The standard error of any one regression weight is given by 4.4.15. Substituting $\hat{\sigma}_k^2$ for σ_k^2 will provide the estimate

$$\hat{\sigma}_{\hat{\beta}_{jk}} = \hat{\sigma}_k\sqrt{[g_{jj}]} \qquad (4.4.19)$$

This term is the same as in Eq. 4.2.14, with an additional subscript to denote a particular y-variate from the set.

Assuming that y_k is normally distributed, then

$$t = \frac{\hat{\beta}_{jk}-\beta_{jk}}{\hat{\sigma}_{\hat{\beta}_{jk}}} \qquad (4.4.20)$$

follows a t distribution with $N-q-1$ degrees of freedom. t may be used to test one- or two-tailed hypotheses about β_{jk} or to construct interval estimates. The $1-\alpha$ confidence interval is the same as in expression 4.2.16; that is,

$$\hat{\beta}_{jk}-k\hat{\sigma}_{\hat{\beta}_{jk}} \leqslant \beta_{jk} \leqslant \hat{\beta}_{jk}+k\hat{\sigma}_{\hat{\beta}_{jk}} \qquad (4.2.21)$$

or

$$\beta_{jk}\!: \hat{\beta}_{jk} \pm k\hat{\sigma}_{\hat{\beta}_{jk}} \qquad (4.4.21a)$$

k is the $100\alpha/2$ upper percentage point of the t distribution with $N-q-1$ degrees of freedom.

It is convenient to represent the standard errors of all the elements of $\mathbf{B}$ as a $(q+1)\times p$ matrix $\mathbf{H}$, such that the standard error of $\hat{\beta}_{jk}$ is element $[h_{jk}]$. $\mathbf{H}$ can be constructed element-by-element from Eq. 4.4.19 or as a matrix product. Each standard error has two components. Let $\mathbf{d}'$ be a $1\times p$ row vector of variable standard deviations:

$$\mathbf{d}'=[\hat{\sigma}_1 \quad \hat{\sigma}_2 \quad \cdots \quad \hat{\sigma}_p] \tag{4.4.22}$$

Let $\mathbf{g}$ be the $(q+1)\times 1$ vector of square roots of the diagonal of $\mathbf{G}$:

$$\mathbf{g}=\begin{bmatrix} \sqrt{g_{11}} \\ \sqrt{g_{22}} \\ \vdots \\ \sqrt{g_{q+1,q+1}} \end{bmatrix} \tag{4.4.23}$$

Then the matrix of standard errors is

$$\mathbf{H}=\mathbf{g}\mathbf{d}' = \begin{bmatrix} \mathbf{h}'_1 \\ \mathbf{h}'_2 \\ \vdots \\ \mathbf{h}'_{q+1} \end{bmatrix} \tag{4.4.24}$$

Each row of $\mathbf{H}$ contains the standard errors for the same row of $\hat{\mathbf{B}}$, for predicting all criteria from a single x-variable; that is,

$$\mathbf{h}'_j=[\hat{\sigma}_{\hat{\beta}_{j1}} \quad \hat{\sigma}_{\hat{\beta}_{j2}} \quad \cdots \quad \hat{\sigma}_{\hat{\beta}_{jp}}] \tag{4.4.24a}$$

Intervals may be drawn on an entire row of $\mathbf{B}$, as a set of p simultaneous intervals for one predictor. Let $\boldsymbol{\beta}'_j$ be the jth row vector of $\mathbf{B}$, and $\hat{\boldsymbol{\beta}}'_j$ the same row from the estimate. Then the p intervals are formed by adding and subtracting a multiple of $\mathbf{h}'_j$ from the estimate $\hat{\boldsymbol{\beta}}'_j$.

$$\boldsymbol{\beta}'_j\colon\ \hat{\boldsymbol{\beta}}'_j \pm k\mathbf{h}'_j \tag{4.4.25}$$

where

$$k=\sqrt{\frac{(N-q-1)p}{N-q-p}F_{p,N-q-p,\alpha}} \tag{4.4.26}$$

$F_{p,N-q-p,\alpha}$ is the upper 100α percentage point of the F-distribution with p and $N-q-p$ degrees of freedom. The multiplier k assures that the confidence level for every one of the p separate intervals is *at least* $1-\alpha$. When $p=1$, expression 4.4.25 is identical to 4.4.21 for a single coefficient. As p increases so does k, yielding a wider interval for each separate coefficient in the vector.

We may also draw confidence intervals on a vector that is a linear combination of the rows of $\mathbf{B}$. Let $\mathbf{v}'$ be a $1\times(q+1)$ vector defining a new vector $\mathbf{v}'\mathbf{B}$, which is a weighted sum of the $\boldsymbol{\beta}'_j$. The covariance matrix of the linear combination is

$$\mathscr{V}(\mathbf{v}'\hat{\mathbf{B}}) = \mathbf{v}'\mathscr{V}(\hat{\mathbf{B}})\mathbf{v}$$
$$= \mathbf{v}'(\mathbf{G} \otimes \boldsymbol{\Sigma})\mathbf{v}$$
$$= \mathbf{v}'\mathbf{G}\mathbf{v} \otimes \boldsymbol{\Sigma}$$
$$= w\boldsymbol{\Sigma} \tag{4.4.27}$$

The scalar $w = \mathbf{v}'\mathbf{G}\mathbf{v} = \mathbf{v}'(\mathbf{X}'\mathbf{X})^{-1}\mathbf{v}$.

If we substitute $\hat{\boldsymbol{\Sigma}}$ for $\boldsymbol{\Sigma}$, the variances of the linear combination of coefficients, for p y-variates, are the diagonal elements of $w\hat{\boldsymbol{\Sigma}}$. The estimated standard errors are the square roots, and may be put in vector form:

$$\mathbf{h}' = \sqrt{w}[\hat{\sigma}_1 \;\; \hat{\sigma}_2 \;\; \cdots \;\; \hat{\sigma}_p]$$
$$= \sqrt{w}\,\mathbf{d}' \tag{4.4.28}$$

$\mathbf{d}'$ is the same as in Eq. 4.4.22.

The point estimate of $\mathbf{v}'\mathbf{B}$ is $\mathbf{v}'\hat{\mathbf{B}}$. The $1-\alpha$ interval is

$$\mathbf{v}'\mathbf{B}: \quad \mathbf{v}'\hat{\mathbf{B}} \pm k\mathbf{h}' \tag{4.4.29}$$

where k is defined by Eq. 4.4.26. The confidence level is *at least* $1-\alpha$ for each of the p intervals in the vector. An obvious special case of 4.4.29 is with $\mathbf{v}$ a column of an identity matrix (a unity and all other elements zero). In this instance, $\mathbf{v}'\mathbf{B}$ is simply one row of $\mathbf{B}$, and expression 4.4.29 simplifies to 4.4.25. In other instances, we may wish to draw intervals on differences and weighted differences of the $\boldsymbol{\beta}'_j$ when we are concerned with the comparative impact of multiple predictors upon the criteria.

Some Simple Cases

Let us examine some simple cases algebraically. In the univariate case ($p=1$), expressions 4.4.3 and those following reduce to the forms presented in Section 4.2. Consider the bivariate case with one independent variable ($p=2$; $q=1$). The $N \times 2$ data matrix is

$$\mathbf{Y} = \begin{bmatrix} y_{11} & y_{12} \\ y_{21} & y_{22} \\ \vdots & \vdots \\ y_{N1} & y_{N2} \end{bmatrix}$$

The model matrix is

$$\mathbf{X} = \begin{bmatrix} 1 & x_1 \\ 1 & x_2 \\ \vdots & \vdots \\ 1 & x_N \end{bmatrix}$$

and

$$(\mathbf{X}'\mathbf{X})^{-1} = \frac{1}{N\sum(x_i - x.)^2} \begin{bmatrix} \sum x_i^2 & -\sum x_i \\ -\sum x_i & N \end{bmatrix}$$

as in Section 4.2. The matrix of estimated regression coefficients is

$$\hat{\mathbf{B}} = (\mathbf{X}'\mathbf{X})^{-1}\mathbf{X}'\mathbf{y}$$

$$= \frac{1}{N\sum(x_i - x.)^2} \begin{bmatrix} \sum x_i^2 & -\sum x_i \\ -\sum x_i & N \end{bmatrix} \begin{bmatrix} \sum y_{i1} & \sum y_{i2} \\ \sum x_i y_{i1} & \sum x_i y_{i2} \end{bmatrix}$$

$$= \begin{bmatrix} \hat{\alpha}_1 & \hat{\alpha}_2 \\ \hat{\beta}_1 & \hat{\beta}_2 \end{bmatrix}$$

$$= \begin{bmatrix} y._1 - \hat{\beta}_1 x. & y._2 - \hat{\beta}_2 x. \\ \dfrac{\sum(x_i - x.)(y_{i1} - y._1)}{\sum(x_i - x.)^2} & \dfrac{\sum(x_i - x.)(y_{i2} - y._2)}{\sum(x_i - x.)^2} \end{bmatrix}$$

The first row, or $\boldsymbol{\alpha}'$, preserves the equality of the two sides of the model for both variates simultaneously. $\hat{\beta}_1$ and $\hat{\beta}_2$ are the simple regression coefficients of y_1 on x and y_2 on x, respectively.

Let $\mathbf{e}_i'$ represent the two-element row of $\hat{\mathbf{E}}$, corresponding to observation i, and $\mathbf{x}_i' = [1 \quad x_i]$. Then including the expressions for $\hat{\mathbf{B}}$ in the observational equation,

$$\mathbf{y}_i = \hat{\mathbf{B}}'\mathbf{x}_i + \mathbf{e}_i$$

$$= \begin{bmatrix} y._1 - \hat{\beta}_1 x. & \hat{\beta}_1 \\ y._2 - \hat{\beta}_2 x. & \hat{\beta}_2 \end{bmatrix} \begin{bmatrix} 1 \\ x_i \end{bmatrix} + \begin{bmatrix} e_{i1} \\ e_{i2} \end{bmatrix}$$

$$= \begin{bmatrix} y._1 - \hat{\beta}_1 x. + \hat{\beta}_1 x_i \\ y._2 - \hat{\beta}_2 x. + \hat{\beta}_2 x_i \end{bmatrix} + \begin{bmatrix} e_{i1} \\ e_{i2} \end{bmatrix}$$

$$= \begin{bmatrix} y._1 \\ y._2 \end{bmatrix} - (x_i - x.) \begin{bmatrix} \hat{\beta}_1 \\ \hat{\beta}_2 \end{bmatrix} + \begin{bmatrix} e_{i1} \\ e_{i2} \end{bmatrix}$$

and

$$\mathbf{y}_i - \mathbf{y}. = (x_i - x.) \begin{bmatrix} \hat{\beta}_1 \\ \hat{\beta}_2 \end{bmatrix} + \mathbf{e}_i$$

The elements of $\hat{\mathbf{B}}$ yield two simple prediction equations for y_1 and y_2, respectively. The regression weights relate the x-variable to each of the y-measures, when all three are expressed in mean deviation units.

Example

Using the data of Table 3.3.1, assume that y_1 and y_2 are two dependent variables, to be predicted from a linear combination of three antecedents, x_1, x_2, and x_3. The regression model is

$$[y_{i1} \quad y_{i2}] = [\alpha_1 \quad \alpha_2] + x_{i1}[\beta_{11} \quad \beta_{12}] + x_{i2}[\beta_{21} \quad \beta_{22}] + x_{i3}[\beta_{31} \quad \beta_{32}] + [\epsilon_{i1} \quad \epsilon_{i2}]$$

When models for the $N=15$ subjects are juxtaposed, the matrix of observed outcome variables **Y** has 15 rows and 2 columns, for y_1 and y_2, respectively. The model matrix **X** is 15×4, having the unit vector and $\mathbf{x}_1$, $\mathbf{x}_2$, and $\mathbf{x}_3$, respectively, as columns. **X** is identical to the model matrix for predicting y_1 alone, as in Section 4.2. The complete parameter matrix is

$$\mathbf{B} = \begin{bmatrix} \alpha_1 & \alpha_2 \\ \beta_{11} & \beta_{12} \\ \beta_{21} & \beta_{22} \\ \beta_{31} & \beta_{32} \end{bmatrix} \begin{matrix} \text{Constant} \\ x_1 \\ x_2 \\ x_3 \end{matrix}$$
$$\qquad y_1 \quad y_2$$

E is 15×2, with a column for each y-variate. The univariate equation for y_1 alone is obtained simply by extracting the first column of **Y**, **B**, and **E**.

Following Eq. 4.4.3,

$$\mathbf{G}=(\mathbf{X}'\mathbf{X})^{-1}=10^{-3}\times\begin{bmatrix} 96{,}279.46 & & & (\text{Symmetric}) \\ -32.12 & 2.24 & & \\ -779.26 & -.60 & 7.21 & \\ -204.32 & -5.11 & -.16 & 38.36 \end{bmatrix} \begin{matrix} \text{Constant} \\ x_1 \\ x_2 \\ x_3 \end{matrix}$$
$$\text{Constant} \quad x_1 \quad x_2 \quad x_3$$

$$\mathbf{X}'\mathbf{Y}=\begin{bmatrix} 34.00 & 37.70 \\ 2918.70 & 3225.10 \\ 3934.10 & 4380.20 \\ 585.70 & 651.79 \end{bmatrix} \begin{matrix} \text{Constant} \\ x_1 \\ x_2 \\ x_3 \end{matrix}$$
$$y_1 \quad y_2$$

and

$$\hat{\mathbf{B}}=\begin{bmatrix} -5.613 & -20.353 \\ .086 & .047 \\ .008 & .145 \\ -.017 & .126 \end{bmatrix} \begin{matrix} \text{Constant} \\ x_1 \\ x_2 \\ x_3 \end{matrix}$$
$$y_1 \quad y_2$$

The first column of $\hat{\mathbf{B}}$ is identically $\hat{\boldsymbol{\beta}}$ for predicting y_1 alone in Section 4.2.

The estimated variance–covariance matrix of **Y** given **X** is

$$\hat{\boldsymbol{\Sigma}}=\frac{1}{15-4}(\mathbf{Y}'\mathbf{Y}-\hat{\mathbf{B}}'\mathbf{X}'\mathbf{Y})$$

$$=\frac{1}{11}\begin{bmatrix} 85.38 & 92.21 \\ 92.21 & 105.31 \end{bmatrix}-\begin{bmatrix} 81.79 & 89.83 \\ 89.83 & 101.98 \end{bmatrix}$$

$$=\begin{bmatrix} .33 & .22 \\ .22 & .30 \end{bmatrix} \begin{matrix} y_1 \\ y_2 \end{matrix}$$
$$y_1 \quad y_2$$

The standard deviations of y_1 and y_2 are

$$\hat{\sigma}_1 = \sqrt{.33} = .57$$

$$\hat{\sigma}_2 = \sqrt{.30} = .55$$

The partial correlation of y_1 and y_2 is

$$\hat{\rho}_{12} = .22/\sqrt{.33(.30)} = .69$$

Eliminating the three x-variables, y_1 and y_2 have a high positive correlation. (We may also wish to compare this with the unconditional correlation of y_1 and y_2, without adjusting for the x-values.)

G and $\hat{\mathbf{\Sigma}}$ contain all the information about the dispersion of $\hat{\mathbf{B}}$. The entire variance–covariance matrix of all $p(q+1)$ elements is the Kronecker product $\mathbf{G} \otimes \hat{\mathbf{\Sigma}}$. Extracting the variances and covariances for just the first column, the variance–covariance matrix of $\hat{\boldsymbol{\beta}}_1$ is .33**G**; for just $\hat{\boldsymbol{\beta}}_2$, it is .30**G** (see 4.4.14). The square roots of the diagonal elements are the standard errors. Let

$$\mathbf{d}' = \underset{\displaystyle y_1 \qquad y_2}{[.57 \quad .55]}$$

and

$$\mathbf{g} = \begin{bmatrix} \sqrt{96.28} \\ \sqrt{.0022} \\ \sqrt{.0072} \\ \sqrt{.0384} \end{bmatrix} = \begin{bmatrix} 9.810 \\ .047 \\ .085 \\ .196 \end{bmatrix} \begin{matrix} \text{Constant} \\ x_1 \\ x_2 \\ x_3 \end{matrix}$$

The standard errors are element-by-element products of **g** and **d**′:

$$\mathbf{H} = \begin{bmatrix} 5.608 & 5.395 \\ .027 & .026 \\ .049 & .047 \\ .112 & .108 \end{bmatrix} \begin{matrix} \text{Constant} \\ x_1 \\ x_2 \\ x_3 \end{matrix}$$
$$\qquad y_1 \qquad\quad y_2$$

The first column reproduces the univariate results for y_1 alone in Section 4.2. The standard errors for predicting y_2 alone are $\hat{\sigma}_2$ times the same **G** multipliers.

Confidence intervals may be drawn on single elements according to Eq. 4.2.16 or 4.4.21. A multivariate confidence interval on the vector $[\beta_{11} \quad \beta_{12}]$ may be constructed by 4.4.25 or 4.4.29. Using 4.4.29, let $\mathbf{v}' = [0 \quad 1 \quad 0 \quad 0]$. Then

$$w = \mathbf{v}'\mathbf{G}\mathbf{v} = .0022$$

or simply g_{22}. The vector of standard errors is

$$\sqrt{.0022}[.57 \quad .55] = [.027 \quad .026] = \mathbf{h}'_2$$

the second row of **H**. The .05 F-value is $F_{2,10,.05}=4.10$, and

$$k=\sqrt{\frac{11(2)(4.10)}{10}}=3.00$$

The .95 interval estimate is

$$.086-3(.027) \leqslant \beta_{11} \leqslant .086+3(.027)$$

$$.047-3(.026) \leqslant \beta_{12} \leqslant .047+3(.026)$$

or

$$.005 \leqslant \beta_{11} \leqslant .167$$

$$-.031 \leqslant \beta_{12} \leqslant .125$$

The interval on β_{11} alone is somewhat wider than the univariate interval for β_1 in Section 4.2. Here, the confidence level for *each* coefficient is at least .95. A two-tailed test with $\alpha=.05$ would not allow us to reject H_0: $\beta_{12}=0$.

Prediction

Scores on the p criterion measures as predicted by the model, are the "best" linear combination of x-values

$$\hat{\mathbf{Y}}=\mathbf{X}\hat{\mathbf{B}} \tag{4.4.30}$$

The expectation of $\hat{\mathbf{Y}}$ is

$$\begin{aligned}\mathscr{E}(\hat{\mathbf{Y}}) &= \mathscr{E}(\mathbf{X}\hat{\mathbf{B}})\\ &= \mathbf{X}\mathbf{B}\end{aligned} \tag{4.4.31}$$

The variance–covariance matrix is

$$\begin{aligned}\mathscr{V}(\hat{\mathbf{Y}}) &= \mathscr{V}(\mathbf{X}\hat{\mathbf{B}})\\ &= \mathbf{X}\mathscr{V}(\hat{\mathbf{B}})\mathbf{X}'\\ &= \mathbf{X}\mathbf{G}\mathbf{X}'\otimes\mathbf{\Sigma}\end{aligned} \tag{4.4.32}$$

If $\mathbf{x}_i'$ is a particular $(q+1)$-element vector of values on the independent variables (one row of $\mathbf{X}$), the estimated mean vector at that point is one row of $\hat{\mathbf{Y}}$; that is,

$$\begin{aligned}\hat{\mathbf{y}}_i' &= \mathbf{x}_i'\hat{\mathbf{B}}\\ &= [\mathbf{x}_i'\hat{\boldsymbol{\beta}}_1 \quad \mathbf{x}_i'\hat{\boldsymbol{\beta}}_2 \quad \cdots \quad \mathbf{x}_i'\hat{\boldsymbol{\beta}}_p]\end{aligned} \tag{4.4.33}$$

Each element is the prediction equation for one criterion, as in Eq. 4.2.17a.

The standard errors of the p predicted means are a simple extension of the univariate case (4.2.22). The variance–covariance matrix of the vector is

$$\mathscr{V}(\hat{\mathbf{y}}_i')=(\mathbf{x}_i'\mathbf{G}\mathbf{x}_i)\mathbf{\Sigma} \tag{4.4.34}$$

The square roots of the diagonal elements are the standard errors for the separate variables

$$\sigma_{\hat{y}_{ik}} = \sigma_k (\mathbf{x}_i' \mathbf{G} \mathbf{x}_i)^{1/2} \tag{4.4.35}$$

σ_k is the standard deviation of variable y_k. Substituting the sample value for σ_k yields the estimate $\hat{\sigma}_{\hat{y}_{ik}}$.

Confidence intervals may be constructed on single elements by expression 4.2.23, using the t distribution with $N-q-1$ degrees of freedom. Simultaneous intervals for the elements of $\hat{\mathbf{y}}_i'$ are obtained by juxtaposing the p standard errors:

$$\mathbf{h}' = [\hat{\sigma}_{\hat{y}_{i1}} \quad \hat{\sigma}_{\hat{y}_{i2}} \quad \cdots \quad \hat{\sigma}_{\hat{y}_{ip}}] \tag{4.4.36}$$

The $1-\alpha$ interval estimate of the vector mean is obtained by adding and subtracting a multiple of $\mathbf{h}'$ from the estimate $\hat{\mathbf{y}}_i'$:

$$\mathbf{y}_i': \quad \hat{\mathbf{y}}_i' \pm k\mathbf{h}' \tag{4.4.37}$$

where

$$k = \sqrt{\frac{(N-q-1)p}{N-q-p} F_{p,N-q-p,\alpha}} \tag{4.4.38}$$

$F_{p,N-q-p,\alpha}$ is the upper 100α percentage point of the F distribution, with p and $N-q-p$ degrees of freedom. The confidence level for every individual estimate in the vector is *at least* $1-\alpha$.

The residuals in the multivariate case are the $N \times p$ matrix

$$\begin{aligned} \hat{\mathbf{E}} &= \mathbf{Y} - \hat{\mathbf{Y}} \\ &= \mathbf{Y} - \mathbf{X}\hat{\mathbf{B}} \end{aligned} \tag{4.4.39}$$

The expectation of $\hat{\mathbf{E}}$ is

$$\begin{aligned} \mathscr{E}(\hat{\mathbf{E}}) &= \mathscr{E}(\mathbf{Y} - \mathbf{X}\hat{\mathbf{B}}) \\ &= \mathbf{0} \end{aligned} \tag{4.4.40}$$

$\mathbf{0}$ is of order $N \times p$.

The variance–covariance matrix is

$$\begin{aligned} \mathscr{V}(\hat{\mathbf{E}}) &= \mathscr{V}(\mathbf{Y} - \mathbf{X}\hat{\mathbf{B}}) \\ &= \mathscr{V}(\mathbf{Y} - \mathbf{X}\mathbf{G}\mathbf{X}'\mathbf{Y}) \\ &= \mathscr{V}[(\mathbf{I} - \mathbf{X}\mathbf{G}\mathbf{X}')\mathbf{Y}] \\ &= (\mathbf{I} - \mathbf{X}\mathbf{G}\mathbf{X}')(\mathbf{I} \otimes \mathbf{\Sigma})(\mathbf{I} - \mathbf{X}\mathbf{G}\mathbf{X}')' \\ &= (\mathbf{I} - \mathbf{X}\mathbf{G}\mathbf{X}') \otimes \mathbf{\Sigma} \end{aligned} \tag{4.4.41}$$

The standard errors of the residuals are the square roots of the elements on the main diagonal of 4.4.41. The standard error of the residual for observation i on outcome k is the same as Eq. 4.2.28 for one variable y_k:

$$\sigma_{e_{ik}} = \sigma_k \sqrt{1 - \mathbf{x}_i' \mathbf{G} \mathbf{x}_i} \tag{4.4.42}$$

Substituting $\hat{\sigma}_k$ for σ_k provides the sample value. Assuming normal y, $e_{ik}/\hat{\sigma}_{e_{ik}}$ follows a t distribution with $N-q-1$ degrees of freedom. Expression 4.2.29 may be employed to construct interval estimates.

Summary

In the multivariate case, the original observations $\mathbf{Y}$ are partitioned into orthogonal components $\mathbf{X}\hat{\mathbf{B}}$ and $\hat{\mathbf{E}}$, having additive covariance matrices

$$\mathbf{I} \otimes \boldsymbol{\Sigma} = \mathbf{XGX}' \otimes \boldsymbol{\Sigma} + (\mathbf{I} - \mathbf{XGX}') \otimes \boldsymbol{\Sigma}$$

$\mathbf{X}\hat{\mathbf{B}}$ is determined after the selection of predictors which are hypothesized to be related to a *set* of outcome measures. The predictors may include measures known to be related to $\mathbf{y}$, for which regression weights are required, as well as variables whose contribution to $\mathbf{y}$ is to be tested from the data.

4.5 COMPUTATIONAL FORMS

Inspection of expressions 4.4.3 and 4.4.17 reveals that both $\hat{\mathbf{B}}$ and $\hat{\boldsymbol{\Sigma}}$ may be obtained from sum-of-product matrices $\mathbf{X}'\mathbf{X}$, $\mathbf{X}'\mathbf{Y}$, and $\mathbf{Y}'\mathbf{Y}$. $\mathbf{X}'\mathbf{X}$ and $\mathbf{X}'\mathbf{Y}$ involve the $q+1$ independent variables, and $\mathbf{X}'\mathbf{Y}$ and $\mathbf{Y}'\mathbf{Y}$ the p outcome measures. When N is large, sum-of-products matrices are generally smaller than the data matrices and are easier to utilize in computations.

Let $\mathbf{v}_i$ be the $(p+q)$-element vector containing scores for observation i on all outcome measures *and* all predictor variables; that is,

$$\begin{aligned} \mathbf{v}_i' &= [\mathbf{y}_i', \quad \mathbf{x}_i'] \\ &= [y_{i1} \quad y_{i2} \quad \cdots \quad y_{ip} \mid x_{i1} \quad x_{i2} \quad \cdots \quad x_{iq}] \end{aligned} \tag{4.5.1}$$

$\mathbf{V}$ is the $N \times (p+q)$ matrix having row vectors $\mathbf{v}_i'$ $(i = 1, 2, \ldots, N)$. $\mathbf{V}$ may be written $\mathbf{V} = [\mathbf{Y}, \quad \mathbf{X}]$, or matrix $\mathbf{Y}$ $(N \times p)$ augmented by $\mathbf{X}$ $(N \times q)$.

$$\mathbf{V} = (\mathbf{Y} \mid \mathbf{X}) \tag{4.5.2}$$

The total sum of products for the $p+q$ variables, is

$$\begin{aligned} \mathbf{S}_T &= \sum_{i=1}^{N} \mathbf{v}_i \mathbf{v}_i' \\ &= \mathbf{V}'\mathbf{V} \\ &= [\mathbf{Y}, \mathbf{X}]'[\mathbf{Y}, \mathbf{X}] \end{aligned} \tag{4.5.3}$$

$\mathbf{S}_T$ has $p+q$ rows and columns and can be partitioned into the sums of products for the two parts $\mathbf{Y}$ and $\mathbf{X}$.

$$\mathbf{S}_T = \left[\begin{array}{c|c} \mathbf{Y}'\mathbf{Y} & \mathbf{Y}'\mathbf{X} \\ \hline \mathbf{X}'\mathbf{Y} & \mathbf{X}'\mathbf{X} \end{array}\right] \begin{array}{l} p \text{ rows} \\ q \text{ rows} \end{array}$$

$$p \text{ columns} \quad q \text{ columns}$$

$$= \left[\begin{array}{c|c} \mathbf{S}_T^{(yy)} & \mathbf{S}_T^{(yx)} \\ \hline \mathbf{S}_T^{(xy)} & \mathbf{S}_T^{(xx)} \end{array}\right] \begin{array}{l} p \text{ rows} \\ q \text{ rows} \end{array} \tag{4.5.4}$$

$\mathbf{S}_T^{(yy)}$ is the total sum-of-products matrix for the y-variables alone; $\mathbf{S}_T^{(xx)}$ is the total sum of products of the x-variables; $\mathbf{S}_T^{(yx)}$, the transpose of $\mathbf{S}_T^{(xy)}$, contains the sums of cross products of each y-variable and every x-measure. When p or q is unity, the corresponding element in $\mathbf{S}_T^{(yy)}$ or $\mathbf{S}_T^{(xx)}$ is just the sum of squared scores for the measure.

$\mathbf{X}'\mathbf{X}$ and $\mathbf{Y}'\mathbf{X}$ do not have elements corresponding to the unit vector. The purpose of the unit vector in the $\mathbf{X}$-matrix is only to equate the two sides of the observational equation. Computationally this may be accomplished instead by expressing all observations as mean deviations. The need for the additional column of $\mathbf{X}$ for estimating α is obviated.

Let $\mathbf{v.}$ be the $(p+q)$-element vector mean, containing sample means on all variables:

$$\begin{aligned}\mathbf{v.}' &= [\mathbf{y.}', \quad \mathbf{x.}'] \\ &= \frac{1}{N} \sum_{i=1}^{N} \mathbf{v}_i' \\ &= \frac{1}{\mathbf{1}'\mathbf{1}} \mathbf{1}'\mathbf{V} \end{aligned} \tag{4.5.5}$$

$\mathbf{1}$ is an $N \times 1$ unit vector.

The vector of mean deviation scores for observation i is $\mathbf{v}_i - \mathbf{v.}$ and the sum of products of the deviation vectors is

$$\begin{aligned}\mathbf{S}_w &= \textstyle\sum_i (\mathbf{v}_i - \mathbf{v.})(\mathbf{v}_i - \mathbf{v.})' \\ &= \textstyle\sum_i \mathbf{v}_i \mathbf{v}_i' - N\mathbf{v.}\mathbf{v.}' \\ &= \mathbf{S}_T - N\mathbf{v.}\mathbf{v.}' \end{aligned} \tag{4.5.6}$$

Since both $\mathbf{S}_T$ and $\mathbf{v.}$ may be obtained through accumulation of the vector observations, matrix $\mathbf{V}$ is not necessary to computation.

$\mathbf{S}_w$ is the within-group sum of products, and may be considered partitioned as $\mathbf{S}_T$:

$$\mathbf{S}_w = \left[\begin{array}{c|c} \mathbf{Y}'\mathbf{Y} - N\mathbf{y.}\mathbf{y.}' & \mathbf{Y}'\mathbf{X} - N\mathbf{y.}\mathbf{x.}' \\ \hline \mathbf{X}'\mathbf{Y} - N\mathbf{x.}\mathbf{y.}' & \mathbf{X}'\mathbf{X} - N\mathbf{x.}\mathbf{x.}' \end{array}\right] \begin{array}{l} p \text{ rows} \\ \\ q \text{ rows} \end{array}$$
$$\qquad p \text{ columns} \qquad q \text{ columns}$$

$$= \left[\begin{array}{c|c} \mathbf{S}_w^{(yy)} & \mathbf{S}_w^{(yx)} \\ \hline \mathbf{S}_w^{(xy)} & \mathbf{S}_w^{(xx)} \end{array}\right] \begin{array}{l} p \text{ rows} \\ \\ q \text{ rows} \end{array} \tag{4.5.7}$$

It can be seen that $\mathbf{S}_w$ contains the $\mathbf{X}'\mathbf{X}$, $\mathbf{Y}'\mathbf{Y}$, and $\mathbf{X}'\mathbf{Y}$ components necessary to regression analysis, each adjusted to the overall mean.

$\mathbf{S}_w$ may be reduced to the sample variance–covariance matrix of all the measures. Assuming N independent observations, the degrees of freedom for $\mathbf{S}_w$ is $N-1$. The sample covariance matrix is

$$\mathbf{V}_w = \frac{1}{N-1} \mathbf{S}_w \tag{4.5.8}$$

$\mathbf{V}_w$ contains the marginal or overall variances and covariances, ignoring the other measures in the set. $\mathbf{V}_w$ may be partitioned like $\mathbf{S}_T$ and $\mathbf{S}_w$ into $\mathbf{V}_w^{(yy)}$, $\mathbf{V}_w^{(yx)} = [\mathbf{V}_w^{(xy)}]'$, and $\mathbf{V}_w^{(xx)}$.

$\mathbf{V}_w$ may be reduced to correlational form by dividing each covariance by the product of the respective standard deviations. Let $\mathbf{D}_w$ be the $(p+q)$-element diagonal matrix of variances from $\mathbf{V}_w$. That is,

$$\mathbf{D}_w = \text{diag}\,(\mathbf{V}_w)$$

$$= \left[\begin{array}{cccc|cccc} v_{w_{11}} & & & & & & & \\ & v_{w_{22}} & & & & & (\text{Zero}) & \\ & & \ddots & & & & & \\ & & & v_{w_{pp}} & & & & \\ \hline & & & & v_{w_{p+1,\,p+1}} & & & \\ & (\text{Zero}) & & & & \ddots & & \\ & & & & & & v_{w_{p+q,\,p+q}} & \end{array}\right]$$

$$= \left[\begin{array}{c|c} \mathbf{D}_w^{(yy)} & (\text{Zero}) \\ \hline (\text{Zero}) & \mathbf{D}_w^{(xx)} \end{array}\right] \begin{array}{l} p \text{ rows} \\ q \text{ rows} \end{array} \tag{4.5.9}$$

p columns q columns

$\mathbf{D}_w^{1/2}$ is the diagonal matrix of standard deviations of all variables. $\mathbf{D}_w^{1/2}$, and the matrix of reciprocals, $\mathbf{D}_w^{-1/2}$, may be likewise partitioned.

The complete matrix of intercorrelations is

$$\mathbf{R}_w = \mathbf{D}_w^{-1/2}\mathbf{V}_w\mathbf{D}_w^{-1/2} \tag{4.5.10}$$

$\mathbf{R}_w$ may also be partitioned like $\mathbf{S}_w$, into $\mathbf{R}_w^{(yy)}$, $\mathbf{R}_w^{(yx)} = [\mathbf{R}_w^{(xy)}]'$, and $\mathbf{R}_w^{(xx)}$.

$\mathbf{S}_w$ contains all the information necessary for the estimation of $\mathbf{B}$ and $\mathbf{\Sigma}$. From 4.4.3, $\hat{\mathbf{B}}$ is the $(q+1)\times p$ matrix $\hat{\mathbf{B}} = (\mathbf{X}'\mathbf{X})^{-1}\mathbf{X}'\mathbf{Y}$. Substituting portions of $\mathbf{S}_w$, $\hat{\mathbf{B}}$ becomes the $q \times p$ estimate:

$$\hat{\mathbf{B}} = [\mathbf{S}_w^{(xx)}]^{-1}\,\mathbf{S}_w^{(xy)} \tag{4.5.11a}$$

$$= [\mathbf{V}_w^{(xx)}]^{-1}\,\mathbf{V}_w^{(xy)} \tag{4.5.11b}$$

Equation 4.5.11b follows from 4.5.11a since the scalar $1/(N-1)$ multiplies each element of $\mathbf{S}_w^{(xy)}$ and divides each element of $[\mathbf{S}_w^{(xx)}]^{-1}$, having no effect on the product. $\hat{\mathbf{B}}$ has *no* row for the constant term; $\hat{\alpha}$ has become identically zero by expressing variables as mean deviations, and is not a necessary term.

Comparing the magnitudes of elements of $\hat{\mathbf{B}}$ is hazardous. Not only do the coefficients reflect contribution to regression, but the values are also direct functions of the units of measurement and of the *other* independent variables in the equation. The confounding of scaling effects may be eliminated by standardizing all variables in the equations. Each element of $\mathbf{v}_i - \mathbf{v}.$ is divided by the corresponding sample standard deviation. The vector of standard scores for subject i is

$$\mathbf{z}_i = \mathbf{D}_w^{-1/2}(\mathbf{v}_i - \mathbf{v}.) \tag{4.5.12}$$

The covariance matrix of the standardized variables is

$$\frac{1}{N-1}\sum_i \mathbf{z}_i\mathbf{z}_i' = \frac{1}{N-1}\mathbf{D}_w^{-1/2}\mathbf{S}_w\mathbf{D}_w^{-1/2}$$

$$= \mathbf{R}_w \tag{4.5.13}$$

As in Eq. 4.5.10, $\mathbf{R}_w$ is the sample correlation matrix for all measures. $\mathbf{R}_w$ has unit diagonal elements and off-diagonal elements,

$$r_{ij} = \frac{[v_w]_{ij}}{\sqrt{[d_w]_{ii}[d_w]_{jj}}} \tag{4.5.13a}$$

and $[r_{ij}]$ has limits $-1 \leqslant [r_{ij}] \leqslant 1$.

The *standardized regression coefficients* are the $q \times p$ matrix of weights for standard-score variables. The standard score covariance matrix is $\mathbf{R}_w$, and substitutes for $\mathbf{V}_w$ in 4.5.11b. The standardized weights are

$$\hat{\mathbf{B}} = [\mathbf{R}_w^{(xx)}]^{-1}\,\mathbf{R}_w^{(xy)} \tag{4.5.14}$$

$\hat{\mathbf{B}}$ may also be obtained directly from $\hat{\mathbf{B}}$ by noting the following:

$$\mathbf{R}_w^{(xx)} = [\mathbf{D}_w^{(xx)}]^{-1/2}\mathbf{V}_w^{(xx)}[\mathbf{D}_w^{(xx)}]^{-1/2}$$

and

$$\mathbf{R}_w^{(xy)} = [\mathbf{D}_w^{(xx)}]^{-1/2}\mathbf{V}_w^{(xy)}[\mathbf{D}_w^{(yy)}]^{-1/2}$$

Thus

$$\begin{aligned}\hat{\mathbf{B}} &= [\mathbf{R}_w^{(xx)}]^{-1}\mathbf{R}_w^{(xy)} \\ &= [\mathbf{D}_w^{(xx)}]^{1/2}[\mathbf{V}_w^{(xx)}]^{-1}[\mathbf{D}_w^{(xx)}]^{1/2}[\mathbf{D}_w^{(xx)}]^{-1/2}\mathbf{V}_w^{(xy)}[\mathbf{D}_w^{(yy)}]^{-1/2} \\ &= [\mathbf{D}_w^{(xx)}]^{1/2}\hat{\mathbf{B}}[\mathbf{D}_w^{(yy)}]^{-1/2}\end{aligned} \tag{4.5.15}$$

Each standardized weight $\hat{b}_{jk}$ is the raw coefficient $\hat{\beta}_{jk}$ multiplied by the standard deviation of predictor x_j and divided by the standard deviation of criterion y_k.

The elements of $\hat{\mathbf{B}}$ are more easily interpreted as reflecting the relative contribution of the predictor variables. However, they are still interdependent; removal or addition of x-variables may affect all the weights, dramatically, in either direction. The relative contribution of predictors to the regression equation is best determined by inspecting the simple and multiple correlations of the y- and x-variables, and the partial correlation of y_k with x_j, holding constant the other x-measures.

The information necessary for estimating $\mathbf{\Sigma}$ is also contained in $\mathbf{S}_w$. From Eq. 4.4.16 the residual sum of products is

$$\begin{aligned}\mathbf{S}_E &= \mathbf{Y}'\mathbf{Y} - \hat{\mathbf{B}}'\mathbf{X}'\mathbf{Y} \\ &= \mathbf{Y}'\mathbf{Y} - \mathbf{Y}'\mathbf{X}(\mathbf{X}'\mathbf{X})^{-1}\mathbf{X}'\mathbf{Y}\end{aligned}$$

Using $\mathbf{S}_w$, this is equivalently

$$\mathbf{S}_E = \mathbf{S}_w^{(yy)} - \mathbf{S}_w^{(yx)}[\mathbf{S}_w^{(xx)}]^{-1}\mathbf{S}_w^{(xy)} \tag{4.5.16}$$

The conditional covariance matrix of the y-variables, given $\mathbf{X}$, is

$$\begin{aligned}\hat{\mathbf{\Sigma}} &= \frac{1}{N-q-1}\mathbf{S}_E \\ &= \mathbf{V}_E\end{aligned} \tag{4.5.17}$$

$\mathbf{S}_E$ and $\hat{\mathbf{\Sigma}}$ are $p \times p$ symmetric. The degrees of freedom are $N-q-1 = n_e$.

$\hat{\mathbf{\Sigma}}$ may be standardized to the matrix of partial correlations among the criterion measures. Let

$$\hat{\mathbf{\Delta}} = \text{diag}\,(\hat{\mathbf{\Sigma}}) = \mathbf{D}_E$$

$\mathbf{D}_E$ is the $p \times p$ diagonal matrix of sample variances from $\mathbf{V}_E$. The partial correlations are

$$\hat{\mathscr{R}} = \mathbf{R}_E = \mathbf{D}_E^{-1/2}\mathbf{V}_E\mathbf{D}_E^{-1/2} \tag{4.5.18}$$

The standard errors of the regression weights may be computed as in Eqs. 4.4.22–4.4.24. $[\mathbf{S}_w^{(xx)}]^{-1}$ is identical to the $q \times q$ lower-right-hand submatrix of $\mathbf{G}$, ignoring the row and column for the constant term. The resulting matrix $\mathbf{H}$ is $q \times p$.

Thus, for estimation of regression coefficients and covariance matrices, only the all-variable within-group sum-of-products matrix is necessary. For predicted scores and residuals for each subject, the total data matrix $\mathbf{V}$ is needed. Computation of $\hat{\mathbf{Y}}$ and $\hat{\mathbf{E}}$ is straightforward. We must note that in obtaining $\mathbf{S}_w$ and $\hat{\mathbf{B}}$ we have expressed all variables in mean deviation units. Thus to obtain predicted means in the original $\mathbf{Y}$ metric, we must add the appropriate constants to $\mathbf{X}\hat{\mathbf{B}}$; that is,

$$\hat{\mathbf{Y}} = \mathbf{1}\mathbf{y}_{.}' + \mathbf{X}\hat{\mathbf{B}} - \mathbf{1}\mathbf{x}_{.}'\hat{\mathbf{B}} \tag{4.5.19}$$

If $\hat{\mathbf{B}}$ is $(q+1) \times p$, including the constant term, the additional $\mathbf{y}.$ and $\mathbf{x}.$ terms are unnecessary.

4.6 SAMPLE PROBLEM 1—CREATIVITY AND ACHIEVEMENT

Using the procedures of the preceding sections, let us construct the model matrix and estimate parameters for the achievement-creativity-intelligence problem. Sixty subjects have each been measured on two criterion measures, synthesis (y_1) and evaluation (y_2). The independent variables are intelligence (x_1); three creativity measures—consequences obvious (x_2), consequences remote (x_3), possible jobs (x_4); and three interactive terms—$x_5 = x_1x_2$, $x_6 = x_1x_3$, and $x_7 = x_1x_4$. Terms x_1, x_2, x_3, and x_4 are standardized prior to forming the cross products.

The regression model for observation i on the first outcome measure is

$$y_{i1} = \alpha_1 + \beta_{11}x_{i1} + \beta_{21}x_{i2} + \beta_{31}x_{i3} + \beta_{41}x_{i4} + \beta_{51}x_{i1}x_{i2} + \beta_{61}x_{i1}x_{i3} + \beta_{71}x_{i1}x_{i4} + \epsilon_{i1}$$

For both measures and all observations

$$\mathbf{Y} = \mathbf{X}\mathbf{B} + \mathbf{E}$$

$\mathbf{Y}$ is 60×2 and contains the 60 scores on the two random outcome variables; $\mathbf{X}$ has 60 rows and 8 columns. Each row corresponds to one subject, with a unit element and his scores on the seven predictor variables. $\mathbf{B}$ is 8×2 and contains the regression weights for the two outcomes:

$$\mathbf{B} = \begin{bmatrix} \alpha_1 & \alpha_2 \\ \beta_{11} & \beta_{12} \\ \beta_{21} & \beta_{22} \\ \beta_{31} & \beta_{32} \\ \beta_{41} & \beta_{42} \\ \beta_{51} & \beta_{52} \\ \beta_{61} & \beta_{62} \\ \beta_{71} & \beta_{72} \end{bmatrix} \begin{matrix} \text{Constant} \\ x_1 \\ x_2 \\ x_3 \\ x_4 \\ x_5 \\ x_6 \\ x_7 \end{matrix}$$

$$\qquad y_1 \quad y_2$$

$\mathbf{E}$ is 60×2, with the residual vectors for all 60 subjects. Using the computational forms of Section 4.5, the first column of $\mathbf{X}$ and first row of $\mathbf{B}$ may be eliminated. Remaining two-element rows of $\mathbf{B}$ are $\boldsymbol{\beta}'_j$ $(j = 1, 2, \ldots, 7)$ for the seven predictors.

From Section 3.4, the vector mean after standardizing and forming cross products, for both criteria and predictors, is

$$\mathbf{v}'_{\cdot} = [\mathbf{y}'_{\cdot} \mid \mathbf{x}'_{\cdot}] = \underset{\begin{matrix} y_1 & \quad y_2 & \quad x_1 & \quad x_2 & \quad x_3 & \quad x_4 & \quad x_5 & \quad x_6 & \quad x_7 \end{matrix}}{[2.55 \quad 1.38 \mid 0.0 \quad 0.0 \quad 0.0 \quad 0.0 \quad .09 \quad .40 \quad .46]}$$

The sum of products adjusted to the sample mean is

$$\mathbf{S}_w = \begin{bmatrix} \mathbf{S}_w^{(yy)} & \mathbf{S}_w^{(yx)} \\ \hline \mathbf{S}_w^{(xy)} & \mathbf{S}_w^{(xx)} \end{bmatrix}$$

$$= \left[\begin{array}{rr|rrrrrrr} 178.85 & & & & & & & & \text{(Symmetric)} \\ 110.35 & 186.18 & & & & & & & \\ \hline 65.79 & 56.69 & 59.00 & & & & & & \\ 21.29 & 17.66 & 5.55 & 59.00 & & & & & \\ 35.23 & 40.49 & 24.29 & 3.38 & 59.00 & & & & \\ 40.74 & 33.58 & 27.47 & 31.98 & 25.13 & 59.00 & & & \\ 4.56 & 20.22 & 5.56 & -3.06 & 18.56 & 1.19 & 43.35 & & \\ 45.38 & 40.17 & 28.65 & 18.56 & 38.66 & 24.42 & 22.27 & 104.70 & \\ 31.79 & 29.77 & 17.56 & 1.19 & 24.42 & 14.98 & 19.12 & 57.79 & 64.79 \end{array}\right]$$

$\mathbf{S}_w$ has $60 - 1 = 59$ degrees of freedom.

The variance–covariance matrix is

$$\mathbf{V}_w = \frac{1}{59} \mathbf{S}_w$$

as given in Section 3.4. The variances are

$$\mathbf{D}_w = \operatorname{diag} \underset{\begin{matrix} y_1 & \quad y_2 & \quad x_1 & \quad x_2 & \quad x_3 & \quad x_4 & \quad x_5 & \quad x_6 & \quad x_7 \end{matrix}}{[3.03 \quad 3.16 \mid 1.00 \quad 1.00 \quad 1.00 \quad 1.00 \quad .73 \quad 1.77 \quad 1.10]}$$

The matrix of simple correlations among all nine measures is $\mathbf{R}_w = \mathbf{D}_w^{-1/2} \mathbf{V}_w \mathbf{D}_w^{-1/2}$, which may be partitioned like $\mathbf{S}_w$. In particular, the correlations of the y-variables with the x-variables is

$$\mathbf{R}_w^{(yx)}=\begin{bmatrix} .64 & .21 & .34 & .40 & .05 & .33 & .30 \\ .54 & .17 & .39 & .32 & .23 & .29 & .27 \end{bmatrix}\begin{matrix}\text{Synthesis } (y_1) \\ \text{Evaluation } (y_2)\end{matrix}$$

Intelligence (x_1); Consequences obvious (x_2); Consequences remote (x_3); Possible jobs (x_4); Cons. obvious×intell. (x_5); Cons. remote×intell. (x_6); Possible jobs×intell. (x_7)

Estimation of $\mathbf{B}$ and its precision requires the inverse sum of products for predictors. The 7×7 inverse matrix is

$$\mathbf{G}=[\mathbf{S}_w^{(xx)}]^{-1}=10^{-4}\times\begin{bmatrix} 251 & & & & & & \text{(Symmetric)} \\ 56 & 296 & & & & & \\ -33 & 72 & 302 & & & & \\ -117 & -199 & -122 & 379 & & & \\ 9 & 0+ & -84 & 46 & 296 & & \\ -46 & -92 & -78 & 50 & -14 & 245 & \\ 9 & 81 & 16 & -64 & -56 & -183 & 339 \end{bmatrix}$$

The matrix of raw estimated regression coefficients is

$$\hat{\mathbf{B}}=[\mathbf{S}_w^{(xx)}]^{-1}\mathbf{S}_w^{(xy)}$$

$$=\begin{bmatrix} 1.00 & .86 \\ .28 & .33 \\ .16 & .32 \\ -.04 & -.14 \\ -.16 & .24 \\ -.04 & -.16 \\ .25 & .20 \end{bmatrix}\begin{matrix}\text{Intelligence} \\ \text{Consequences obvious} \\ \text{Consequences remote} \\ \text{Possible jobs} \\ \text{Cons. obvious}\times\text{intelligence} \\ \text{Cons. remote}\times\text{intelligence} \\ \text{Possible jobs}\times\text{intelligence}\end{matrix}$$

Synthesis Evaluation

The prediction equation for synthesis alone is

$$\hat{y}_{i1}-2.55=1.00(x_{i1})+.28(x_{i2})+.16(x_{i3})-.04(x_{i4})$$
$$-.16(x_{i1}x_{i2}-.09)-.04(x_{i1}x_{i3}-.40)+.25(x_{i1}x_{i4}-.46)$$

All variables are expressed as mean deviations. For raw scores, using Eq. 4.5.19, the constant is

$$y_{\cdot 1}-\sum_j x_{\cdot j}\hat{\beta}_{j1} = 2.55+.16(.09)+.04(.40)-.25(.46)=2.47$$

The prediction equation is

$$\hat{y}_{i1}=2.47+1.00(x_{i1})+.28(x_{i2})+.16(x_{i3})-.04(x_{i4})-.16(x_{i1}x_{i2})-.04(x_{i1}x_{i3})+.25(x_{i1}x_{i4})$$

Matrix $\hat{\mathbf{B}}$ may be substituted in the observational equation to provide estimates for both criterion measures. Four of the measures have been standardized in advance of the analysis. Regression coefficients for all nine measures in standardized form may be computed from $\hat{\mathbf{B}}$.

The standard deviations of the nine measures are the square roots of $\mathbf{D}_w$:

$$[\mathbf{D}_w^{(yy)}]^{1/2} = \text{diag}\,(1.74, 1.78)$$

and

$$[\mathbf{D}_w^{(xx)}]^{1/2} = \text{diag}\,(1.00, 1.00, 1.00, 1.00, .86, 1.33, 1.05)$$

The matrix of standardized regression coefficients is

$$\hat{\mathbf{B}} = [\mathbf{D}_w^{(xx)}]^{1/2}\hat{\mathbf{B}}[\mathbf{D}_w^{(yy)}]^{-1/2}$$

$$= \begin{bmatrix} .58 & .48 \\ .16 & .19 \\ .09 & .18 \\ -.02 & -.08 \\ -.08 & .12 \\ -.03 & -.12 \\ .15 & .12 \end{bmatrix} \begin{matrix} \text{Intelligence} \\ \text{Consequences obvious} \\ \text{Consequences remote} \\ \text{Possible jobs} \\ \text{Cons. obvious} \times \text{intelligence} \\ \text{Cons. remote} \times \text{intelligence} \\ \text{Possible jobs} \times \text{intelligence} \end{matrix}$$

Synthesis Evaluation

Prediction of both achievement measures appears to be dominated by intelligence. Although the magnitudes of the coefficients are difficult to interpret, their signs tend to have greater stability. *Both* the synthesis and evaluation measures are predicted by a construct that differentiates intelligence and event consequences from the possible-jobs measure. Although we have no overall strength-of-association measure, $\mathbf{R}_w^{(yx)}$ has the simple correlations for each predictor. All correlations are positive, indicating that the same general construct is being measured. Intelligence has the highest single correlation with both criteria. Although x_2 through x_7 also have moderate correlations with y_1 and y_2, their influence appears diminished in $\hat{\mathbf{B}}$ when the simultaneous prediction includes an intelligence measure.

To estimate standard errors for the $\hat{\beta}_{jk}$, we require an estimate of $\boldsymbol{\Sigma}$, the conditional variance–covariance matrix of the criteria. The conditional sum-of-products matrix is

$$\mathbf{S}_E = \mathbf{S}_w^{(yy)} - \mathbf{S}_w^{(yx)}[\mathbf{S}_w^{(xx)}]^{-1}\mathbf{S}_w^{(xy)}$$

$$= \begin{bmatrix} 178.85 & 110.35 \\ 110.35 & 186.18 \end{bmatrix} - \begin{bmatrix} 81.18 & 69.41 \\ 69.41 & 67.22 \end{bmatrix}$$

$$= \begin{bmatrix} 97.67 & 40.94 \\ 40.94 & 118.97 \end{bmatrix}$$

$\mathbf{S}_E$ has $n_e = 60 - 1 - 7 = 52$ degrees of freedom. The conditional covariance matrix, $\mathbf{V}_E = \hat{\mathbf{\Sigma}}$ is

$$\mathbf{V}_E = \frac{1}{52}\mathbf{S}_E$$

$$= \begin{bmatrix} 1.88 & .79 \\ .79 & 2.29 \end{bmatrix} \begin{matrix} y_1 \\ y_2 \end{matrix}$$

$$\begin{matrix} y_1 & & y_2 \end{matrix}$$

The matrix of adjusted standard deviations is

$$\mathbf{D}_E^{1/2} = \begin{bmatrix} 1.37 & 0 \\ 0 & 1.51 \end{bmatrix}$$

The partial correlations are

$$\mathbf{R}_E = \mathbf{D}_E^{-1/2}\mathbf{V}_E\mathbf{D}_E^{-1/2}$$

$$= \begin{bmatrix} 1.00 & .38 \\ .38 & 1.00 \end{bmatrix} \begin{matrix} y_1 \\ y_2 \end{matrix}$$

$$\begin{matrix} y_1 & & y_2 \end{matrix}$$

The unconditional variances from $\mathbf{V}_w^{(yy)}$ are 3.03 and 3.16, respectively. By comparison to $\mathbf{V}_E$, we can see that roughly 40 percent of the variation in the dependent variables has been lost through removing the effects of the independent variables. However, after "holding constant" the predictor measures, the variances of y_1 and y_2 still appear large enough to be noteworthy, and must be attributed to other factors. One of these is undoubtedly common to the two measures, as the partial correlation is strong positive (.38).

The estimate of $\mathbf{\Sigma}$ is $\mathbf{V}_E$. The matrix of standard errors of the $\hat{\beta}_{jk}$ may be formed by multiplying as vectors, $\mathbf{D}_E^{1/2}$ and $\mathbf{g}$, the square roots of the diagonal elements of $\mathbf{G}$. For the example, these are

$$\mathbf{d}' = [1.37 \quad 1.51]$$

$$\mathbf{g}' = [.16 \quad .17 \quad .17 \quad .19 \quad .17 \quad .16 \quad .18]$$

The standard errors are

$$\mathbf{H} = \mathbf{g}\mathbf{d}' = \begin{bmatrix} .22 & .24 \\ .24 & .26 \\ .24 & .26 \\ .27 & .29 \\ .24 & .26 \\ .21 & .24 \\ .25 & .28 \end{bmatrix} \begin{matrix} \text{Intelligence} \\ \text{Consequences obvious} \\ \text{Consequences remote} \\ \text{Possible jobs} \\ \text{Cons. obvious} \times \text{intelligence} \\ \text{Cons. remote} \times \text{intelligence} \\ \text{Possible jobs} \times \text{intelligence} \end{matrix}$$

$$\begin{matrix} \text{Synthesis} & \text{Evaluation} \end{matrix}$$

$\mathbf{H}$ may be employed in drawing intervals on elements and rows of $\mathbf{B}$.

The matrices of estimated scores and residuals, $\hat{\mathbf{Y}}$ and $\mathbf{Y} - \hat{\mathbf{Y}}$, respectively, provide useful interpretive information. As an example, subject 1 has predictor scores of

$$\mathbf{x}_1' = [1.00 \quad .27 \quad .23 \quad .27 \quad -.28 \quad .06 \quad .07 \quad -.08]$$

The unit element corresponding to the constant is included. The constant for synthesis is 2.47. For evaluation,

$$y_{\cdot 2} - \sum_j x_{\cdot j}\hat{\beta}_{j2} = 1.38 - .05 = 1.33$$

If we include these as the first row of $\hat{\mathbf{B}}$, then predicted scores are

$$\hat{\mathbf{y}}_1' = \mathbf{x}_1'\hat{\mathbf{B}} = [\underset{\text{Synthesis}}{2.83} \quad \underset{\text{Evaluation}}{1.75}]$$

Observed values for the criteria are

$$\mathbf{y}_1' = [\underset{\text{Synthesis}}{5.0} \quad \underset{\text{Evaluation}}{1.0}]$$

The residuals are

$$\mathbf{y}_1' - \hat{\mathbf{y}}_1' = [\underset{\text{Synthesis}}{2.17} \quad \underset{\text{Evaluation}}{-.75}]$$

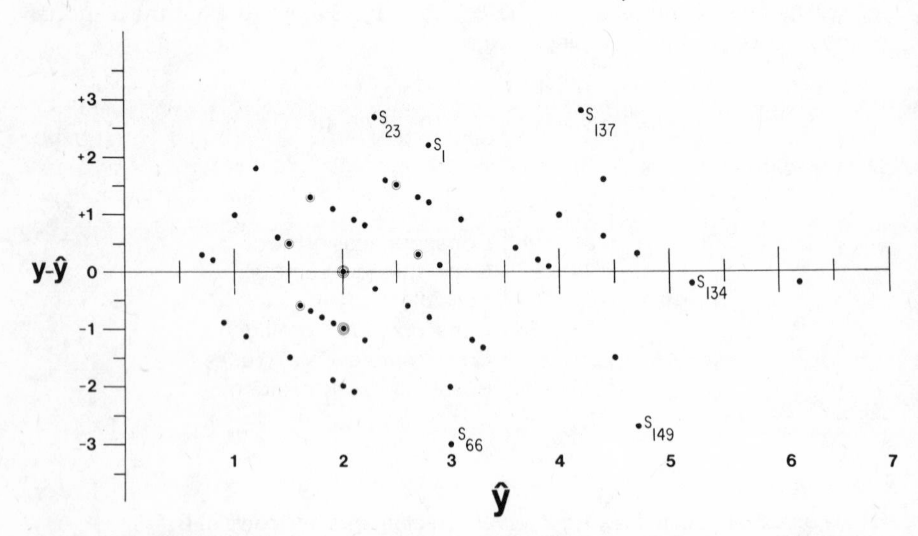

Figure 4.6.1 Predicted scores ($\hat{y}$) and residuals ($y - \hat{y}$) for synthesis outcome variable, for Sample Problem 1.

All sixty residuals have been computed for the *synthesis* criterion variable, and plotted against predicted scores in Figure 4.6.1.

Although the distribution of residuals across ordinate values cannot be clearly seen, the decreasing concentration of points as values move away from zero gives an impression of normality. The frequencies of residuals in unit intervals from -3 to $+3$ are 1, 4, 8, 15, 19, 10, 3, and 0, respectively. With $s = 1.37$, we should expect about 95 percent of the values to be within $1.96s$, or in the range ± 2.69. In fact, four of the residuals, or about 7 percent, have absolute value 2.69 or greater. Thus we may rest comfortably with the assumption of normality.

The scatter of points in Figure 4.6.1 suggests a uniform variability of residuals across the entire range of predicted scores, in accordance with the assumption about ϵ_i. The range of synthesis scores is from zero to seven, with only one individual (subject 137), obtaining the highest score. The individual with the highest predicted score is not that person, however, but instead is s_{134}, with standard scores on intelligence and the three creativity measures of 2.76, .53, 1.80, and 1.56, respectively. His observed synthesis score is 6, and the predicted score is 6.24. The resulting prediction for s_{134} is quite accurate.

By contrast, s_{137} has standard scores on the predictors of 1.21, .97, .27, and 1.56; the lower predicted score of 4.21, and residual of 2.79 can be largely attributed to the lower intelligence score, carrying a high regression weight. The raw intelligence scores for s_{134} and s_{137} are 143 and 120. Both are in a high range. Within this range Smith hypothesized that differences in intelligence alone will not adequately account for divergent achievement. The regression weight derived from a sample representing a broad intelligence range is probably larger than that applicable to individuals in the high-IQ range alone.

Three of the remaining residuals have absolute value above 2.69—those for subjects 23, 66, and 149. Spurious criterion scores may provide a partial explanation. For example, the intelligence and three creativity standard scores for s_{23} are $-.34$, .38, $-.65$, and -1.02, respectively. The predicted synthesis score of 2.26 is far below the observed outcome of 5. The evaluation score for the same individual is zero, further supporting a hypothesis of measurement error for synthesis. For s_{66}, outcomes on both synthesis and evaluation are very low. Scores on the predictors are low, but not sufficiently to predict such extreme divergent achievement results. The finding would suggest an intelligence threshold below which high divergent achievement is not possible. Thus we have a hypothesis for further study.

CHAPTER 

Multiple Regression Analysis: Tests of Significance

The preceding chapter defines the multiple linear regression model and the estimates of unknown parameters. In this chapter we are concerned with testing whether some or all of the parameters are null or are equal to other specified nonzero values. Significance testing proceeds in two stages. The first is partitioning variation (and covariation) in the dependent variables into components for each predictor variable or set of predictors. For example, we may wish to determine the sum of squares (and cross products) in college achievement which can be attributed (a) to high-school grades, (b) to abilities as measured by the Scholastic Aptitude Tests, and (c) to our own measure of motivation. Each effect has a *hypothesis sum of squares* (and cross products), which is a measure of criterion variation attributable to that predictor or set. The hypothesis measures are determined so that they are independent of one another, and can be summed to give the total criterion variation attributable to all predictor variables.

The residual or *error sum of squares* (and cross products) provides a measure of the extent to which criterion variation is not attributable to any of the predictor variables. The second stage of significance testing involves comparing each of the hypothesis measures to the error measure, with one or more test statistics. If the test statistic exceeds the tabled critical value, it is because of the large magnitude of the hypothesis sum of squares relative to the error sum of squares. That is, criterion variation that can be attributed to the predictor(s) is large relative to the variation that cannot. If the test statistic is small, the predictor variables do not contribute to criterion variation, and can be omitted from the model. It may be necessary, then, to reestimate regression weights for predictors that remain in the model after significance testing.

When there is more than a single criterion variable, the hypothesis and error results are matrices of sums of squares and cross products. Multivariate forms of the test statistics are required. Since the multivariate matrices and statistics reduce to the univariate form when $p=1$, the general multivariate case is presented first, and then is specialized for exemplary purposes.

5.1 SEPARATING THE SOURCES OF VARIATION

Model and Error

The multivariate multiple regression model is

$$\mathbf{Y}=\mathbf{XB}+\mathbf{E} \tag{5.1.1}$$

where

$\mathbf{Y}$ is the $N\times p$ matrix of observed outcomes
$\mathbf{X}$ is the $N\times(q+1)$ matrix of predictor values
$\mathbf{B}$ is the $(q+1)\times p$ matrix of regression weights
$\mathbf{E}$ is the $N\times p$ matrix of random errors
N is the number of subjects
p is the number of criterion (dependent) variables
q is the number of predictor (independent) variables

The least-squares estimate of $\mathbf{B}$ is the $(q+1)\times p$ matrix

$$\hat{\mathbf{B}}=(\mathbf{X}'\mathbf{X})^{-1}\mathbf{X}'\mathbf{Y} \tag{5.1.2}$$

We assume that each vector observation $\mathbf{y}_i'$ $(i=1, 2, \ldots, N)$ has the distribution

$$\mathbf{y}_i' \sim \mathcal{N}_p(\mathbf{x}_i'\mathbf{B}, \mathbf{\Sigma}) \tag{5.1.3}$$

$\mathbf{x}_i'$ is the vector of predictor values for observation i. From expression 5.1.3 it follows that the distribution of the kth column of $\hat{\mathbf{B}}$ (the prediction equation for one criterion, y_k) is

$$\hat{\boldsymbol{\beta}}_k \sim \mathcal{N}_{q+1}(\boldsymbol{\beta}_k, \ \sigma_k{}^2\mathbf{G}) \tag{5.1.4}$$

with $\mathbf{G}=(\mathbf{X}'\mathbf{X})^{-1}$. The unbiased maximum likelihood estimate of $\mathbf{\Sigma}$ is

$$\hat{\mathbf{\Sigma}}=\frac{1}{N-q-1}(\mathbf{Y}'\mathbf{Y}-\hat{\mathbf{B}}'\mathbf{X}'\mathbf{X}\hat{\mathbf{B}}) \tag{5.1.5}$$

Computationally, $\hat{\mathbf{B}}$ (without the constant) and $\hat{\mathbf{\Sigma}}$ may be derived from the mean-adjusted sum of squares and cross products for all $p+q$ measures. Let

$$\mathbf{v}_i'=[\mathbf{y}_i', \mathbf{x}_i'] \tag{5.1.6}$$

and

$$\mathbf{V}=[\mathbf{Y}, \mathbf{X}] \tag{5.1.7}$$

as in Eq. 4.5.2. Then

$$\mathbf{v}_.'=\frac{1}{N}\sum_i \mathbf{v}_i' \tag{5.1.8}$$

and

$$\mathbf{S}_w=\mathbf{V}'\mathbf{V}-N\mathbf{v}_.\mathbf{v}_.' \tag{5.1.9}$$

Partitioning $\mathbf{S}_w$ into $\mathbf{S}_w{}^{(yy)}$ $(p\times p)$, $\mathbf{S}_w{}^{(yx)}=[\mathbf{S}_w{}^{(xy)}]'$ $(p\times q)$, and $\mathbf{S}_w{}^{(xx)}$ $(q\times q)$, Eqs. 5.1.2 and 5.1.5 become

$$\hat{\mathbf{B}}=[\mathbf{S}_w{}^{(xx)}]^{-1}\mathbf{S}_w{}^{(xy)} \tag{5.1.10}$$

and

$$\hat{\Sigma} = \frac{1}{N-q-1} [\mathbf{S}_w^{(yy)} - \mathbf{S}_w^{(yx)}(\mathbf{S}_w^{(xx)})^{-1}\mathbf{S}_w^{(xy)}]$$

$$= \frac{1}{n_e}\mathbf{S}_E \qquad (5.1.11)$$

$\hat{\mathbf{B}}$ in expression 5.1.10 is $q \times p$, and does not contain an estimate of the constant α, which is identically zero for mean-deviation scores.

The observational equation is

$$\mathbf{Y} = \mathbf{X}\hat{\mathbf{B}} + \hat{\mathbf{E}} \qquad (5.1.12)$$

The least-squares estimation of $\mathbf{B}$ yields $\hat{\mathbf{E}}$ such that $\Sigma_i \Sigma_k [e_{ik}]^2$ is minimal.

Let us inspect the sum of squares and cross products of the p variates in $\mathbf{Y}$. From Eq. 5.1.12, the matrix is

$$\begin{aligned} \mathbf{Y}'\mathbf{Y} &= (\mathbf{X}\hat{\mathbf{B}} + \hat{\mathbf{E}})'(\mathbf{X}\hat{\mathbf{B}} + \hat{\mathbf{E}}) \\ &= \hat{\mathbf{B}}'\mathbf{X}'\mathbf{X}\hat{\mathbf{B}} + \hat{\mathbf{B}}'\mathbf{X}'\hat{\mathbf{E}} + \hat{\mathbf{E}}'\mathbf{X}\hat{\mathbf{B}} + \hat{\mathbf{E}}'\hat{\mathbf{E}} \\ &= \hat{\mathbf{B}}'\mathbf{X}'\mathbf{X}\hat{\mathbf{B}} + \hat{\mathbf{E}}'\hat{\mathbf{E}} \end{aligned} \qquad (5.1.13)$$

For the final step, note that

$$\begin{aligned} \hat{\mathbf{B}}'\mathbf{X}'\hat{\mathbf{E}} &= \hat{\mathbf{B}}'\mathbf{X}'(\mathbf{Y} - \mathbf{X}\hat{\mathbf{B}}) \\ &= \hat{\mathbf{B}}'\mathbf{X}'\mathbf{Y}' - \hat{\mathbf{B}}'\mathbf{X}'\mathbf{X}(\mathbf{X}'\mathbf{X})^{-1}\mathbf{X}'\mathbf{Y} \\ &= \mathbf{0} = \hat{\mathbf{E}}'\mathbf{X}\hat{\mathbf{B}} \end{aligned}$$

In summary, the $p \times p$ sum of products of the *sample* observations, $\mathbf{Y}'\mathbf{Y}$, can be partitioned into additive components, the sum of products due to the model ($\hat{\mathbf{B}}'\mathbf{X}'\mathbf{X}\hat{\mathbf{B}}$) and the sum of products of the residuals ($\hat{\mathbf{E}}'\hat{\mathbf{E}}$).

Let us continue to denote the total sum of products $\mathbf{Y}'\mathbf{Y}$, as $\mathbf{S}_T^{(yy)}$, and the sum of products for error $\hat{\mathbf{E}}'\hat{\mathbf{E}}$, as $\mathbf{S}_E$. In addition, denote the *sum of products for regression* $\hat{\mathbf{B}}'\mathbf{X}'\mathbf{X}\hat{\mathbf{B}}$, as $\mathbf{S}_R$. Then the partition (Eq. 5.1.13) may be represented as

$$\mathbf{S}_T^{(yy)} = \mathbf{S}_R + \mathbf{S}_E \qquad (5.1.14a)$$

or

$$\mathbf{Y}'\mathbf{Y} = \mathbf{Y}'\mathbf{X}\mathbf{G}\mathbf{X}'\mathbf{Y} + \mathbf{Y}'(\mathbf{I} - \mathbf{X}\mathbf{G}\mathbf{X}')\mathbf{Y} \qquad (5.1.14b)$$

$\mathbf{S}_T^{(yy)}$, $\mathbf{S}_R$, and $\mathbf{S}_E$ are of order $p \times p$; $\mathbf{G}$ is the covariance factor $\mathbf{G} = (\mathbf{X}'\mathbf{X})^{-1}$. $\mathbf{I}$ is an order-N identity matrix.

The diagonal elements of $\mathbf{S}_T^{(yy)}$ are the sums of squared observed scores for each criterion measure. The off-diagonal elements are the sums of cross products. In contrast, the diagonal elements of $\mathbf{S}_R$ are the sums of squares of the *predicted* scores for each outcome, since $\hat{\mathbf{Y}} = \mathbf{X}\hat{\mathbf{B}}$ and $\mathbf{S}_R = \hat{\mathbf{Y}}'\hat{\mathbf{Y}}$. The better the prediction, the closer $[s_r]_{kk}$ will be to $[s_t^{(yy)}]_{kk}$, and the smaller the sum of squared residuals $[s_e]_{kk}$. That is, $\mathbf{S}_E$ provides a measure of the lack of fit of the model, or the extent to which criterion values cannot be known by "best" linear functions of the predictors. Matrices $\mathbf{S}_R$ and $\mathbf{S}_E$ may be compared with each other or with $\mathbf{S}_T^{(yy)}$ to test the fit of the total model to the data. All test criteria of Section 5.2

may be applied. Since the scaling constant is often superfluous, mean-adjusted $\mathbf{S}_w^{(yy)}$ and $\mathbf{S}_w^{(yx)}[\mathbf{S}_w^{(xx)}]^{-1}\mathbf{S}_w^{(xy)}$ (see Eq. 4.5.16) may be substituted for $\mathbf{S}_T^{(yy)}$ and $\mathbf{S}_R$, respectively, for significance tests.

$\mathbf{S}_T^{(yy)}$ is the sum of squares and cross products of N independent vector observations; the total has *N degrees of freedom.* $\mathbf{S}_R$ is the sum of products of $q+1$ linear combinations of the observed values, and has $n_r=q+1$ degrees of freedom (1 for the constant and 1 for each predictor variable). n_r is also termed the *rank of the regression model*, since it is the rank of model matrix $\mathbf{X}$. The remaining terms in $\hat{\mathbf{E}}$ are $N-(q+1)$ independent linear functions of the observations; the degrees of freedom for error are $n_e=N-q-1$.

When the number of criterion measures is one (univariate multiple regression), the $\mathbf{y}$, $\boldsymbol{\beta}$, and $\boldsymbol{\epsilon}$ equivalents of Eq. 5.1.1 are vectors. The variance of y given the x_j variables (5.1.5) is a scalar,

$$\hat{\sigma}^2=\frac{1}{N-q-1}(\mathbf{y}'\mathbf{y}-\hat{\boldsymbol{\beta}}'\mathbf{X}'\mathbf{X}\hat{\boldsymbol{\beta}})$$

The partition of the sum of squares (5.1.14b) is

$$\mathbf{y}'\mathbf{y}=\hat{\mathbf{y}}'\hat{\mathbf{y}}+\hat{\boldsymbol{\epsilon}}'\hat{\boldsymbol{\epsilon}}$$

or

$$\textstyle\sum_i y_i^2=\sum_i \hat{y}_i^2+\sum_i e_i^2$$

These are exactly the values of the diagonal elements of $\mathbf{S}_T^{(yy)}$, $\mathbf{S}_R$, and $\mathbf{S}_E$ in Eq. 5.1.14a, for each criterion measure.

Subsets of Predictor Variables

Tests of significance concerning all predictors simultaneously may be made directly from $\mathbf{S}_R$ and $\mathbf{S}_E$ in Eq. 5.1.14a. In many instances, however, the researcher is concerned with not one but a sequence of hypotheses about the relationship of subsets of predictors to the criteria. Each hypothesis (except the first) involves the contribution of one or more predictors to regression, given that prior sets have already been entered into the regression equations. Independent tests for predictors are not directly obtainable from rows of $\hat{\mathbf{B}}$; in general, the coefficients for pairs of predictors are correlated. This is evidenced by the covariance factor $\mathbf{G}$ in expression 5.1.4, which is rarely diagonal.

A series of independent tests is facilitated by transforming the predictor variables to a new set of uncorrelated measures, in a specified order. We shall substitute for predictor x_j in $\mathbf{X}$ only the linear function or portion of x_j that is uncorrelated with preceding predictors $x_1, x_2, \ldots, x_{j-1}$. That is, we shall find the x_j values that are obtained if we "partial out" or "hold constant" the effects of earlier predictors in the set. Using the transformed variables, we may reestimate the regression coefficients; these will reflect the extent to which each predictor x_j contributes to regression, *above and beyond* the effects of x_1 through x_{j-1}.

The transformation may be accomplished through the Gram-Schmidt orthonormalization of $\mathbf{X}$ in Eq. 5.1.1. The Gram-Schmidt process will create columns of $\mathbf{X}$ that at each stage are orthogonal to (and uncorrelated with) all preceding columns. Formally, the operation is one of factoring $\mathbf{X}$ into the product of a columnwise orthonormal matrix $\mathbf{X}^*$ (with the new set of uncorrelated predictors) and a triangular matrix $\mathbf{T}'$ (relating $\mathbf{X}$ to $\mathbf{X}^*$). That is,

$$\mathbf{X}=\mathbf{X}^*\mathbf{T}' \tag{5.1.15}$$

$\mathbf{X}$ and $\mathbf{X}^*$ are $N\times(q+1)$; $\mathbf{T}'$ is $(q+1)$-square with zeros below the main diagonal. Equation 5.1.15 also satisfies $(\mathbf{X}^*)'\mathbf{X}^*=\mathbf{I}$ and $\mathbf{X}(\mathbf{T}^{-1})'=\mathbf{X}^*$. Substituting in the regression model, $\mathbf{Y}=\mathbf{XB}+\mathbf{E}$ becomes

$$\mathbf{Y}=\mathbf{X}^*\mathbf{T}'\mathbf{B}+\mathbf{E} \tag{5.1.16}$$

$\mathbf{T}'\mathbf{B}$ is the $(q+1)\times p$ matrix of regression weights for $\mathbf{X}$ having orthogonal columns, or for predictors that are uncorrelated in the specified order.

The least-squares estimate of $\mathbf{T}'\mathbf{B}$ is obtained exactly as was $\hat{\mathbf{B}}$, by minimizing tr $(\hat{\mathbf{E}}'\hat{\mathbf{E}})$. The estimate is

$$\begin{aligned}\widehat{\mathbf{T}'\mathbf{B}}&=[(\mathbf{X}^*)'\mathbf{X}^*]^{-1}(\mathbf{X}^*)'\mathbf{Y}\\&=\mathbf{I}(\mathbf{X}^*)'\mathbf{Y}\\&=(\mathbf{X}^*)'\mathbf{Y}\\&=\mathbf{U}\end{aligned} \tag{5.1.17}$$

$\mathbf{U}$ is the $(q+1)\times p$ matrix of *orthogonal estimates* or *semipartial regression coefficients*. Like $\hat{\mathbf{B}}$, each column of $\mathbf{U}$ contains exactly the regression coefficients for one criterion variable; that is, the $q+1$ elements of any one column form one univariate multiple regression equation. Unlike $\hat{\mathbf{B}}$, each row of $\mathbf{U}$ contains the regression weights for the corresponding predictor variable, *eliminating all preceding predictors.* The values of the conditional predictor variables themselves are the columns of $\mathbf{X}^*$.

The conditions for estimating $\mathbf{U}$ are identical to those for $\hat{\mathbf{B}}$; namely, $\mathbf{X}$ must be of rank $q+1$, so $|\mathbf{X}'\mathbf{X}| \neq 0$. This requires that $N\geqslant q+1$ and that no column of $\mathbf{X}$ is exactly a linear combination of other columns. The estimation of the effect of one predictor eliminating those preceding, is termed *stepwise elimination*.

Since $\mathbf{X}$ is a matrix of fixed constants, so are $\mathbf{X}^*$ and $\mathbf{T}'$. Then the estimate $\mathbf{U}=\widehat{\mathbf{T}'\mathbf{B}}$ is a simple transformation of $\hat{\mathbf{B}}$; that is, $\mathbf{U}=\mathbf{T}'\hat{\mathbf{B}}$. The expectation of $\mathbf{U}$ is

$$\begin{aligned}\mathscr{E}(\mathbf{U})&=\mathscr{E}(\mathbf{T}'\hat{\mathbf{B}})\\&=\mathbf{T}'\mathbf{B}\end{aligned} \tag{5.1.18}$$

The variance–covariance matrix of $\mathbf{U}$ is

$$\begin{aligned}\mathscr{V}(\mathbf{U})&=\mathscr{V}(\mathbf{T}'\hat{\mathbf{B}})\\&=\mathbf{T}'\mathscr{V}(\hat{\mathbf{B}})\mathbf{T}\\&=\mathbf{T}'(\mathbf{G}\otimes\boldsymbol{\Sigma})\mathbf{T}\\&=\mathbf{T}'(\mathbf{X}'\mathbf{X})^{-1}\mathbf{T}\otimes\boldsymbol{\Sigma}\\&=\mathbf{I}\otimes\boldsymbol{\Sigma}\end{aligned} \tag{5.1.19}$$

Eq. 5.1.19 follows since $\mathbf{X}'\mathbf{X}=\mathbf{T}(\mathbf{X}^*)'\mathbf{X}^*\mathbf{T}'=\mathbf{T}\mathbf{T}'$ and $(\mathbf{X}'\mathbf{X})^{-1}=(\mathbf{T}^{-1})'\mathbf{T}^{-1}$.

$\mathbf{U}$ is an unbiased estimate of the population orthogonal coefficients $\mathbf{T}'\mathbf{B}$. More important, rows of $\mathbf{U}$ (the coefficients for multiple predictor variables) are uncorrelated. From Eq. 5.1.19, the variance–covariance matrix of column k of $\mathbf{U}$, for predicting y_k from the orthogonal predictors, is

$$\mathscr{V}(\mathbf{u}_k) = \sigma_k^2\mathbf{I} \tag{5.1.20}$$

Each coefficient has variance σ_k^2; each pair of coefficients has zero covariance. The regression weights for orthogonal predictor vectors, unlike those for the original x_j measures, are independent.

Let us obtain regression sums of products for the first predictor only, for the second predictor eliminating (holding constant) the first, for the third eliminating the first two, and so on. Let $\mathbf{u}'_j$ be the jth row of the orthogonal regression coefficients $\mathbf{U}$. $\mathbf{u}'_j$ relates the p criteria to one predictor, eliminating those preceding. That is,

$$\mathbf{U} = \begin{bmatrix} \mathbf{u}'_1 \\ \hline \mathbf{u}'_2 \\ \hline \mathbf{u}'_3 \\ \hline \vdots \\ \hline \mathbf{u}'_{q+1} \end{bmatrix} \begin{matrix} \text{Constant} \\ x_1\text{, eliminating constant} \\ x_2\text{, eliminating constant and } x_1 \\ \vdots \\ x_q\text{, eliminating constant, } x_1, x_2, \ldots, x_{q-1} \end{matrix} \tag{5.1.21}$$

p columns

The squares and products for regression for the first predictor alone, is the $p \times p$ matrix

$$\mathbf{u}_1\mathbf{u}'_1$$

The squares and products for just the second predictor, eliminating the first, is

$$\mathbf{u}_2\mathbf{u}'_2$$

The last predictor variable has squares and products

$$\mathbf{u}_{q+1}\mathbf{u}'_{q+1}$$

This term measures the contribution to regression of just the final predictor variable, removing the effects of the constant and x_1 through x_{q-1}. Each matrix $\mathbf{u}_j\mathbf{u}'_j$ has a single degree of freedom.

The sum of the independent matrices $\mathbf{u}_j\mathbf{u}'_j$ is exactly the overall regression sum of squares and cross products, as in Eq. 5.1.14; that is,

$$\begin{aligned} \textstyle\sum_j \mathbf{u}_j\mathbf{u}'_j &= \mathbf{U}'\mathbf{U} \\ &= \hat{\mathbf{B}}'\mathbf{T}\mathbf{T}'\hat{\mathbf{B}} \\ &= \hat{\mathbf{B}}'\mathbf{X}'\mathbf{X}\hat{\mathbf{B}} \\ &= \mathbf{S}_R \end{aligned} \tag{5.1.22}$$

$\mathbf{S}_R$ has one degree of freedom for each $\mathbf{u}_j\mathbf{u}'_j$; that is, $q+1$. Predictable variation has not been increased or decreased by transforming to orthogonal predictors, but has been redistributed among the x_j's in a particular order. The order of predictors is fixed by the researcher, prior to the stepwise elimination and the computing of squares and products. The error sum of cross products is

$$\mathbf{S}_E = \mathbf{Y}'\mathbf{Y} - \mathbf{U}'\mathbf{U} \tag{5.1.23}$$

with $n_e = N - q - 1$ degrees of freedom.

The complete partition of sums of squares and cross products is given in Table 5.1.1. Assessing the expected squares and cross products is facilitated by considering the triangular factor in $\mathbf{U} = \mathbf{T}'\hat{\mathbf{B}}$ to be partitioned by rows. Let $\mathbf{t}'_j$ be the jth row of $\mathbf{T}'$. That is,

$$\mathbf{T}' = \begin{bmatrix} t_{11} & t_{12} & t_{13} & \cdots & t_{1,q+1} \\ 0 & t_{22} & t_{23} & \cdots & t_{2,q+1} \\ 0 & 0 & t_{33} & \cdots & t_{3,q+1} \\ \vdots & & & & \vdots \\ 0 & 0 & 0 & \cdots & t_{q+1,q+1} \end{bmatrix} = \begin{bmatrix} \mathbf{t}'_1 \\ \mathbf{t}'_2 \\ \mathbf{t}'_3 \\ \vdots \\ \mathbf{t}'_{q+1} \end{bmatrix} \tag{5.1.24}$$

Then rows of $\mathbf{U}$ are linear functions of rows of $\hat{\mathbf{B}}$, and may be diagrammed as:

$$\mathbf{U} = \mathbf{T}'\hat{\mathbf{B}}$$

$$= \begin{bmatrix} \mathbf{t}'_1\hat{\mathbf{B}} \\ \mathbf{t}'_2\hat{\mathbf{B}} \\ \vdots \\ \mathbf{t}'_{q+1}\hat{\mathbf{B}} \end{bmatrix} = \begin{bmatrix} \mathbf{u}'_1 \\ \mathbf{u}'_2 \\ \vdots \\ \mathbf{u}'_{q+1} \end{bmatrix} \tag{5.1.25}$$

Each simple matrix $\mathbf{u}_j\mathbf{u}'_j$ is equivalently $\hat{\mathbf{B}}'\mathbf{t}_j\mathbf{t}'_j\hat{\mathbf{B}}$, with expectation $\mathbf{B}'\mathbf{t}_j\mathbf{t}'_j\mathbf{B} + \mathbf{\Sigma}$, over repeated samplings.

The orthogonal regression weights yield squares and product matrices that are additive; they can be summed to provide tests of the joint contribution of two or more predictors. In general, we shall let q_h ($1 \leqslant q_h \leqslant q+1$) represent the num-

Table 5.1.1 Partition of Sums of Products for Multivariate Regression Analysis

Source of Variation	*Degrees of Freedom*	*Sum of Squares and Cross Products*	*Expected Sum of Products*
Constant	1	$\mathbf{u}_1\mathbf{u}'_1$	$\mathbf{B}'\mathbf{t}_1\mathbf{t}'_1\mathbf{B} + \mathbf{\Sigma}$
x_1 eliminating constant	1	$\mathbf{u}_2\mathbf{u}'_2$	$\mathbf{B}'\mathbf{t}_2\mathbf{t}'_2\mathbf{B} + \mathbf{\Sigma}$
x_2 eliminating constant and x_1	1	$\mathbf{u}_3\mathbf{u}'_3$	$\mathbf{B}'\mathbf{t}_3\mathbf{t}'_3\mathbf{B} + \mathbf{\Sigma}$
$\vdots$	$\vdots$	$\vdots$	$\vdots$
x_q eliminating constant and $x_1, x_2, \ldots, x_{q-1}$	1	$\mathbf{u}_{q+1}\mathbf{u}'_{q+1}$	$\mathbf{B}'\mathbf{t}_{q+1}\mathbf{t}'_{q+1}\mathbf{B} + \mathbf{\Sigma}$
All regression	$q+1$	$\mathbf{S}_R = \mathbf{U}'\mathbf{U}$	$\mathbf{B}'\mathbf{X}'\mathbf{X}\mathbf{B} + (q+1)\mathbf{\Sigma}$
Residual	$n_e = N - q - 1$	$\mathbf{S}_E = \mathbf{Y}'\mathbf{Y} - \mathbf{U}'\mathbf{U}$ $= \mathbf{S}_w^{(yy)} - \mathbf{S}_w^{(yx)}[\mathbf{S}_w^{(xx)}]^{-1}\mathbf{S}_w^{(xy)}$	$(N-q-1)\mathbf{\Sigma}$
Total	N	$\mathbf{S}_T^{(yy)} = \mathbf{Y}'\mathbf{Y}$	

ber of rows of **U** (number of predictor variables) being combined for one statistical test. The sum of the squares and cross products is the *sum of products for hypothesis*, $\mathbf{S}_H$. q_h represents the *degrees of freedom for the hypothesis matrix*. In Table 5.1.1, each $\mathbf{S}_H$ is simply one $\mathbf{u}_j\mathbf{u}'_j$; all corresponding q_h values are unity.

At times the predictors form logical groupings, such as items or subtests of the predictor variables, or several measures of the same construct. To test for the joint contribution of x_1, x_2, and x_3 in Table 5.1.1, we can obtain hypothesis matrix $\mathbf{S}_H = \mathbf{u}_2\mathbf{u}'_2 + \mathbf{u}_3\mathbf{u}'_3 + \mathbf{u}_4\mathbf{u}'_4$, with $q_h = 3$ degrees of freedom. The expected value is

$$\mathscr{E}(\mathbf{S}_H) = \sum_{j=2}^{4} \mathbf{B}'\mathbf{t}_j\mathbf{t}'_j\mathbf{B} + 3\mathbf{\Sigma}$$

Only adjacent $\mathbf{u}_j\mathbf{u}'_j$ may be combined in this manner. Sample Problem 1 (creativity and intelligence) utilizes such groupings to test for the joint effects of three creativity measures, and then for three interaction terms. The p diagonal elements of each $\mathbf{S}_H$ are the squares or sums of squares for individual criterion variables, attributable to the q_h predictors. That is, they are exactly the univariate regression sums of squares for each y-measure.

Computationally, some steps may be bypassed. The orthonormalization of a large **X**-matrix to estimate **U** is a formidable task. Instead we may utilize the fact that **T** is also the triangular Cholesky factor of $\mathbf{X}'\mathbf{X}$. Further, let $\mathbf{S}_w$ be the $(p+q)$-square sum of products of mean deviations as in Eq. 5.1.9. Then $\mathbf{S}_w^{(xx)}$ is the $q \times q$ sum of products of mean deviations for the predictors. The $q \times q$ Cholesky factor without the constant term may be obtained from $\mathbf{S}_w^{(xx)}$. That is,

$$\mathbf{S}_w^{(xx)} = \mathbf{T}\mathbf{T}' \tag{5.1.26}$$

and

$$[\mathbf{S}_w^{(xx)}]^{-1} = (\mathbf{T}^{-1})'\mathbf{T}^{-1} \tag{5.1.27}$$

The $q \times p$ matrix of orthogonal regression coefficients, with no constant term, is

$$\begin{aligned} \mathbf{U} &= \mathbf{T}'\hat{\mathbf{B}} \\ &= \mathbf{T}'[\mathbf{S}_w^{(xx)}]^{-1}\mathbf{S}_w^{(xy)} \\ &= \mathbf{T}^{-1}\mathbf{S}_w^{(xy)} \end{aligned} \tag{5.1.28}$$

Even for orthogonal estimation, $\mathbf{S}_w$ contains all the necessary summary data.

The regression sum of products, excluding the constant, is

$$\begin{aligned} \mathbf{S}_R &= \mathbf{U}'\mathbf{U} \\ &= \mathbf{S}_w^{(yx)}[\mathbf{S}_w^{(xx)}]^{-1}\mathbf{S}_w^{(xy)} \end{aligned} \tag{5.1.29}$$

and

$$\mathbf{S}_E = \mathbf{S}_w^{(yy)} - \mathbf{S}_w^{(yx)}[\mathbf{S}_w^{(xx)}]^{-1}\mathbf{S}_w^{(xy)} \tag{5.1.30}$$

as in Eq. 5.1.11. The "total" sum of products without the constant is $\mathbf{S}_w^{(yy)}$ with $N-1$ degrees of freedom.

The diagonal elements of $\mathbf{S}_R$ and $\mathbf{S}_E$ are the univariate sums of squares for regression and error, respectively, for each of the p criterion variables. Off-diagonal elements are the sums of cross products, which are useful in multivariate tests and confidence limits.

When $p = 1$, **u** is a vector, and each $\mathbf{u}_j\mathbf{u}'_j$ is the scalar u_j^2. The sum of squares for a set of predictors is simply the sum of two or more scalars $\Sigma_j u_j^2$. These terms are exactly the diagonal elements of $\mathbf{S}_H$ when there are multiple criterion measures; their sum is a scalar $\mathbf{S}_R$ in Eq. 5.1.22.

Order of Predictors

The orthogonal regression weights **U** are a patterned function of the intercorrelated weights **B**. For simplicity, let us assume a univariate model, with $\boldsymbol{\beta}' = [\alpha \quad \beta_1 \quad \beta_2 \quad \cdots \quad \beta_q]$. Then **u** in Eq. 5.1.25 estimates $\mathbf{T}'\boldsymbol{\beta}$, with

$$\mathbf{T}'\boldsymbol{\beta} = \begin{bmatrix} t_{11}\alpha + t_{12}\beta_1 + \cdots + t_{1q}\beta_{q-1} + t_{1,q+1}\beta_q \\ 0 + t_{22}\beta_1 + \cdots + t_{2q}\beta_{q-1} + t_{2,q+1}\beta_q \\ \vdots \\ 0 + 0 + \cdots + t_{qq}\beta_{q-1} + t_{q,q+1}\beta_q \\ 0 + 0 + \cdots + 0 \qquad + t_{q+1,q+1}\beta_q \end{bmatrix} \begin{matrix} \text{Constant } (u_1) \\ x_1 \text{ eliminating constant } (u_2) \\ \vdots \\ x_{q-1} \text{ eliminating all above } (u_q) \\ x_q \text{ eliminating all above } (u_{q+1}) \end{matrix} \tag{5.1.31}$$

With $p > 1$, each column of **U** is the same function of the corresponding column of $\hat{\mathbf{B}}$.

Inspection of $\mathbf{T}'\boldsymbol{\beta}$ reveals that the first element is a weighted combination of all elements of $\boldsymbol{\beta}$. The second element involves all of $\boldsymbol{\beta}$ except α. The third element involves all of $\boldsymbol{\beta}$ except α and β_1, and so on. The last element of the product is a scalar multiple of only the last element of $\boldsymbol{\beta}$. It is the triangular nature of $\mathbf{T}'$ that produces this pattern and has also produced the orthogonal $\mathbf{X}^*$ from **X**. Interchanging the order of predictor variables will alter both the corresponding **U** vectors and the hypothesis sums of products.

The last row of **U** contains the only terms that are not composites of two or more regression weights. That is, u_{q+1} reflects the effect of x_q, eliminating (and unbiased by) any other predictors. Only if we decide (through significance tests) that β_q is zero will all other rows of **U** be unconfounded with x_q effects. Thus variables that make doubtful contribution to regression or those reflecting complex antecedents (for example, interactions) should be placed last in the order of elimination. If they do not add to predicting the criterion measures above and beyond simpler or better-known predictors, they may be quickly deleted from the model. The earlier terms may then be tested without confounding from these predictors.

Example

In the previous chapter we estimated regression weights for the data of Table 3.3.1. y_1 and y_2 are criterion measures; x_1, x_2, and x_3 are predictors. The raw coefficients are

$$\hat{\mathbf{B}} = \begin{bmatrix} -5.613 & -20.353 \\ .086 & .047 \\ .008 & .145 \\ -.017 & .126 \end{bmatrix} \begin{matrix} \text{Constant} \\ x_1 \\ x_2 \\ x_3 \end{matrix}$$
$$\qquad y_1 \qquad\quad y_2$$

The total sums of products for predictors, criteria, and the cross products of the two are

$$\mathbf{X}'\mathbf{X} = \begin{bmatrix} 15.00 & & & \text{(Symmetric)} \\ 1263.00 & 107{,}009.00 & & \\ 1733.00 & 145{,}976.00 & 200{,}363.00 & \\ 255.30 & 21{,}585.00 & 29{,}503.90 & 4383.13 \end{bmatrix} \begin{matrix} \text{Constant} \\ x_1 \\ x_2 \\ x_2 \end{matrix}$$
$$\qquad \text{Constant} \quad x_1 \quad x_2 \quad x_3$$

$$\mathbf{Y}'\mathbf{Y} = \begin{bmatrix} 85.38 & 92.21 \\ 92.21 & 105.31 \end{bmatrix} \begin{matrix} y_1 \\ y_2 \end{matrix}$$
$$y_1 \quad y_2$$

$$\mathbf{Y}'\mathbf{X} = \begin{bmatrix} 34.00 & 2918.70 & 3934.10 & 585.70 \\ 37.70 & 3225.10 & 4380.20 & 651.79 \end{bmatrix} \begin{matrix} y_1 \\ y_2 \end{matrix}$$
$$\text{Constant} \quad x_1 \quad x_2 \quad x_3$$

$\mathbf{Y}'\mathbf{Y}$ is $\mathbf{S}_T^{(yy)}$, the total sum of squares and cross products for the dependent variables. The sum of products for regression is

$$\mathbf{S}_R = \hat{\mathbf{B}}'\mathbf{X}'\mathbf{X}\hat{\mathbf{B}} = \begin{bmatrix} 81.79 & 89.83 \\ 89.83 & 101.98 \end{bmatrix} \begin{matrix} y_1 \\ y_2 \end{matrix}$$
$$y_1 \quad y_2$$

The error sum of products is

$$\mathbf{S}_E = \mathbf{S}_T^{(yy)} - \mathbf{S}_R = \begin{bmatrix} 3.59 & 2.38 \\ 2.38 & 3.33 \end{bmatrix} \begin{matrix} y_1 \\ y_2 \end{matrix}$$
$$y_1 \quad y_2$$

$\mathbf{S}_T^{(yy)}$ has 15 degrees of freedom, $\mathbf{S}_R$ has 4 degrees of freedom, $\mathbf{S}_E$ has $n_e =$ 11 degrees of freedom. As in Chapter 4, $\mathbf{\Sigma}$ may be estimated by $\mathbf{S}_E/n_e$, with error variances 3.59/11 and 3.33/11, respectively.

To obtain sums of products for the constant and for each predictor alone, we transform to orthogonal predictors. Let us maintain the order of predictors x_1 through x_3 to test whether x_3 contributes to criterion variation above and beyond x_1 and x_2. The full orthonormalization is $\mathbf{X} = \mathbf{X}^*\mathbf{T}'$ where $\mathbf{T}'$ is the Cholesky factor of $\mathbf{X}'\mathbf{X}$. Rather than obtain the orthogonal predictors themselves ($\mathbf{X}^*$) let us obtain the regression weights for them ($\mathbf{U}$). For this we only require the triangular factor $\mathbf{T}'$. Factoring $\mathbf{X}'\mathbf{X}$, we obtain

$$\mathbf{T}' = \begin{bmatrix} 3.87 & 326.07 & 447.27 & 65.89 \\ & 25.77 & 2.22 & 3.44 \\ & & 11.78 & .05 \\ \text{(Zero)} & & & 5.10 \end{bmatrix}$$

and

$$\mathbf{U} = \mathbf{T}'\hat{\mathbf{B}} = \begin{bmatrix} 8.779 & 9.734 \\ 2.169 & 1.969 \\ .097 & 1.715 \\ -.088 & .641 \end{bmatrix} \begin{matrix} \text{Constant} \\ x_1 \text{ eliminating constant} \\ x_2 \text{ eliminating constant and } x_1 \\ x_3 \text{ eliminating constant, } x_1 \text{ and } x_2 \end{matrix}$$
$$\qquad\qquad y_1 \qquad y_2$$

It is easily verified that $\mathbf{U}'\mathbf{U} = \mathbf{S}_R$. The squares and cross products for the constant are formed from the first row alone. We probably do not wish to test hypotheses about α.

$$\mathbf{u}_1\mathbf{u}'_1 = \begin{bmatrix} 8.779 \\ 9.734 \end{bmatrix} [8.779 \quad 9.734]$$
$$= \begin{bmatrix} 77.07 & 85.45 \\ 85.45 & 94.75 \end{bmatrix} \begin{matrix} y_1 \\ y_2 \end{matrix}$$
$$y_1 \qquad y_2$$

To test for the joint contribution of x_1 and x_2 to criterion variation, we use the second and third rows:

$$\mathbf{S}_{H_1} = \mathbf{u}_2\mathbf{u}'_2 + \mathbf{u}_3\mathbf{u}'_3$$
$$= \begin{bmatrix} 4.71 & 4.44 \\ 4.44 & 6.82 \end{bmatrix} \begin{matrix} y_1 \\ y_2 \end{matrix}$$
$$y_1 \qquad y_2$$

For x_3, removing the effects of the constant, x_1, and x_2,

$$\mathbf{S}_{H_2} = \mathbf{u}_4\mathbf{u}'_4$$
$$= \begin{bmatrix} .01 & -.06 \\ -.06 & .41 \end{bmatrix} \begin{matrix} y_1 \\ y_2 \end{matrix}$$
$$y_1 \qquad y_2$$

The subscript 1 or 2 is added to $\mathbf{S}_H$ so that matrices for separate hypotheses may be distinguished. $\mathbf{S}_{H_1}$ has 2 degrees of freedom, and $\mathbf{S}_{H_2}$ has 1 degree of freedom. The sum of the $\mathbf{S}_{H_j}$ matrices plus $\mathbf{u}_1\mathbf{u}'_1$ is $\mathbf{S}_R$. We now have all necessary results to describe the partition of variation in a table like 5.1.1.

In testing the significance of the predictor variables, each of the $\mathbf{S}_{H_j}$ is compared with $\mathbf{S}_E$. The diagonal elements of $\mathbf{S}_{H_j}$ are the sums of squares of the separate criteria that can be attributed to the particular predictor variables. These are the results that would be obtained for the individual dependent measures. Univariate test criteria apply only to the diagonal elements of $\mathbf{S}_{H_j}$ and $\mathbf{S}_E$; multivariate criteria apply to the entire matrices.

Had $\mathbf{S}_w^{(yy)}$ been used in place of $\mathbf{S}_T^{(yy)}$, the constant term would not appear in $\hat{\mathbf{B}}$ or $\mathbf{U}$. $\mathbf{u}_1\mathbf{u}'_1$ would not be computed. $\mathbf{S}_R$ is then $\mathbf{S}_{H_1} + \mathbf{S}_{H_2}$, with 3 degrees of freedom.

5.2 TEST CRITERIA

Statistical test criteria may be applied to hypothesis and error matrices to determine whether the corresponding predictor variables account for significant variation in the criterion measures. It is through test criteria and their associated distributions that we judge whether the elements of the hypothesis matrix represent only random effects in the data or also represent fixed population effects that are nonzero. Multivariate test statistics provide a single hypothesis test for more than one criterion measure. (For example, does this predictor variable contribute to variation in the *set* of outcomes?) In particular, we shall employ a general *likelihood ratio statistic* through which a variety of multivariate hypotheses may be tested. A special case of the likelihood ratio is Hotelling's T^2 statistic, appropriate when the number of predictors for the hypothesis is unity.

When the number of criteria is one, the general forms reduce to the usual univariate F tests for multiple regression. Also multiple univariate results may be obtained by considering only the diagonal elements of the sum-of-products matrices. The univariate results are primarily of use in identifying the criteria least and most affected by the independent variable(s). Step-down analysis provides tests of the hypothesis of no effect when there is a particular specified order of criteria (for example, by time or complexity). When no logical ordering can be supported, step-down results are of dubitable value. Other tests of significance, associated with the simple, multiple, and canonical correlations of the predictors and criteria, are presented in the next chapter. In most cases these are shown to be identical to the corresponding test statistics presented here.

Hypotheses

The general hypothesis we shall consider is that the last q_h row(s) of $\mathbf{B}$ are null. This is the hypothesis that the final q_h x-variables do not contribute to criterion variation, above and beyond earlier measures. q_h may be 1 or greater, up to all q predictors.

If we have q predictor variables and $q+1$ rows in $\mathbf{B}$, then $\mathbf{B}$ may be considered partitioned into two parts. The first ($\mathbf{B}_0$) contains weights for the predictors not being tested. The second ($\mathbf{B}_h$) contains the weights for the q_h predictors whose contribution to regression is being tested. That is,

$$\mathbf{B} = \begin{bmatrix} \mathbf{B}_0 \\ \hline \mathbf{B}_h \end{bmatrix} \begin{matrix} q+1-q_h \text{ rows [Constant and predictors not tested]} \\ \\ q_h \text{ rows [Predictors being tested]} \end{matrix} \tag{5.2.1}$$

p columns

The null hypothesis is

$$H_0\colon \mathbf{B}_h = \mathbf{0} \tag{5.2.2}$$

where $\mathbf{B}_h$ and $\mathbf{0}$ are both $q_h \times p$ matrices. The alternate hypothesis is that at least one element of $\mathbf{B}_h$ is not zero.

Hypothesis 5.2.2 asserts that the regression coefficients for the final q_h

predictors are null; that eliminating or holding constant the preceding independent variables, x_{q+1-q_h} through x_q do not contribute to variation in the set of criteria; and that there is no significant relationship of these predictors to the p dependent variables, above and beyond earlier predictors.

Corresponding to $\mathbf{B}_h$ there are q_h rows of the orthogonal coefficients $\mathbf{u}'_j$. If we are testing the contribution of a single variable to regression, q_h is unity and there is one associated row of $\mathbf{U}$ (the final row). If we wish to test for the joint contribution of multiple predictors, then $q_h > 1$ and there are multiple rows of $\mathbf{B}$ and $\mathbf{U}$. The sum of squares and cross products of the one or more rows of $\mathbf{U}$ form the matrix of hypothesis sums of squares and cross products ($\mathbf{S}_H$), as in Section 5.1. We may also obtain $\mathbf{S}_H$ by partitioning $\mathbf{U}$ exactly as we did $\mathbf{B}$,

$$\mathbf{U} = \begin{bmatrix} \mathbf{U}_0 \\ \hline \mathbf{U}_h \end{bmatrix} \begin{matrix} q+1-q_h \text{ rows} \\ q_h \text{ rows} \end{matrix} \tag{5.2.3}$$

p columns

Then $\mathbf{S}_H = \mathbf{U}'_h \mathbf{U}_h$, with q_h degrees of freedom.

The test criteria we shall consider are the likelihood ratio criterion for a single decision regarding 5.2.2 and the univariate F ratios for testing H_0 one column at a time. Also, step-down test statistics provide multiple tests of H_0 for the first dependent variable, for the second dependent variable eliminating the first, and so on until the final dependent variable y_p, eliminating all others. All of these criteria yield the usual univariate F ratio for regression when $p=1$, regardless of whether we are testing the effect of one or more predictors.

In most research employing regression methods, we are concerned with multiple hypotheses of the form of Eq. 5.2.2. For example we may wish to test whether the motivation variable adds to our knowledge of college achievement, above and beyond ability and past achievement. Upon completing the test of this hypothesis we may wish to test whether the other two predictor variables are also significantly related to achievement. The conditions for conducting this test are determined by whether or not the first hypothesis is supported. In general the testing procedures of this section may be applied more than once, for different subsets of predictor variables. Each may be tested eliminating all other significant predictors. We shall discuss testing a single hypothesis first, and then consider the effects of variable order and multiple significance tests.

Likelihood Ratio Criterion

The likelihood ratio criterion (Wilks, 1932) is a general statistic that may be used to test Eq. 5.2.2 with any values of q_h and p. The null and alternate hypotheses are regarded as representing two models. Let $\mathbf{x}'_i$ be the predictor values for observation i. The vector may be partitioned like $\mathbf{B}$ in Eq. 5.2.1. That is,

$$\begin{aligned} \mathbf{x}'_i &= [1 \quad x_{i1} \quad \cdots \quad x_{i,q-q_h} \mid x_{i,q+1-q_h} \quad \cdots \quad x_{iq}] \\ &= [\qquad \mathbf{x}'_{i0} \qquad \mid \qquad \mathbf{x}'_{ih} \qquad] \end{aligned} \tag{5.2.4}$$

First $q+1-q_h$ predictors   Final q_h predictors

If the null hypothesis is true, then the correct model for the data is

$$\mathbf{y}_i' = \mathbf{x}_{i0}' \mathbf{B}_0 + \boldsymbol{\epsilon}_{i0}' \tag{5.2.5}$$

The terms of $\mathbf{B}_h$ are null; $\mathbf{x}_{ih}' \mathbf{B}_h$ reflects only random variation and may be subsumed in $\boldsymbol{\epsilon}_{i0}$.

If the alternate hypothesis is true, a better prediction model is Eq. 5.1.1, or

$$\mathbf{y}_i' = \mathbf{x}_i' \mathbf{B} + \boldsymbol{\epsilon}_i' \tag{5.2.6}$$

The outcome is expressed as a weighted sum of all $q+1$ terms. The model given in Eq. 5.2.6 will yield better predictions of $\mathbf{y}_i$ than 5.2.5, and the variance of the ϵ_i's will be notably smaller than the variance of the ϵ_{i0}'s. To the extent that the variances of ϵ_i are smaller than those of ϵ_{i0} in a given sample, we may say that Eq. 5.2.6 is a more *likely* representation of the population relationship of **y** and **x**. If, after fitting both models to sample data, the alternate model does not appear to be a more likely representation, the principle of scientific parsimony dictates that the simpler model (Eq. 5.2.5) is maintained, and H_0 is supported.

The likelihood ratio criterion is the ratio of a measure of the likelihood of Eq. 5.2.5, compared with the likelihood for Eq. 5.2.6. The smaller the ratio in the sample, the more inclined we shall be to reject H_0 and to conclude that the additional predictor(s) are necessary to the model. The likelihood measure for each model is obtained by evaluating the joint density function (Eq. 3.2.1) of the p variates, for the sample outcomes $\mathbf{y}_i$ $(i = 1, 2, \ldots, N)$. The resulting index is proportional to the probability that these sample values would be observed, if the population model is correct. Thus we may evaluate Eq. 3.2.1 assuming 5.2.5 and again assuming 5.2.6, and compare the results.

Anderson (1958) has derived the likelihood ratio in detail for this and other hypotheses. The results are both mathematically and intuitively meaningful. Let L_0 represent the likelihood of the data under the null hypothesis, or model 5.2.5, in which $\mathbf{B}_h = \mathbf{0}$ and the additional predictors are excluded. If this model is correct then the maximum likelihood estimate of the variance–covariance matrix of errors $(\boldsymbol{\epsilon}_{i0})$ is

$$\begin{aligned}\hat{\boldsymbol{\Sigma}}_0 &= \frac{1}{N}(\mathbf{Y} - \mathbf{X}_0\hat{\mathbf{B}}_0)'(\mathbf{Y} - \mathbf{X}_0\hat{\mathbf{B}}_0) \\ &= \frac{1}{N}(\mathbf{Y}'\mathbf{Y} - \hat{\mathbf{B}}_0'\mathbf{X}_0'\mathbf{X}_0\hat{\mathbf{B}}_0)\end{aligned} \tag{5.2.7}$$

$\mathbf{X}_0$ contains the leading $q+1-q_h$ columns of $\mathbf{X}$, with row vectors $\mathbf{x}_{i0}'$.

Similarly, let L represent the value of the likelihood of the data under the alternate hypothesis, or model 5.2.6 with the additional predictors included. If this model is correct then the estimate of the variance–covariance matrix of errors $(\boldsymbol{\epsilon}_i)$ is

$$\begin{aligned}\hat{\boldsymbol{\Sigma}} &= \frac{1}{N}(\mathbf{Y} - \mathbf{X}\hat{\mathbf{B}})'(\mathbf{Y} - \mathbf{X}\hat{\mathbf{B}}) \\ &= \frac{1}{N}(\mathbf{Y}'\mathbf{Y} - \hat{\mathbf{B}}'\mathbf{X}'\mathbf{X}\hat{\mathbf{B}})\end{aligned} \tag{5.2.8}$$

The likelihood ratio criterion Λ is a function of the ratio L_0/L. After evaluation and simplification, Λ is

$$\Lambda = \frac{|\hat{\boldsymbol{\Sigma}}|}{|\hat{\boldsymbol{\Sigma}}_0|} \tag{5.2.9}$$

The range of Λ is from 0 to 1. If Λ is sufficiently small in the sample, we reject H_0 and conclude that the final predictor(s) contribute to criterion variation. If Λ is close to unity, the alternate model is not noticeably more likely. We maintain H_0 and delete the final predictors from the model.

If we think of the determinant of the covariance matrix as a p-dimensional or generalized variance of the residuals, we can see how Eq. 5.2.9 corresponds to comparing the fit of the two models. If the alternate model holds, then the additional predictors do account for some criterion variation. We would expect $|\hat{\boldsymbol{\Sigma}}|$ to be noticeably smaller than $|\hat{\boldsymbol{\Sigma}}_0|$, as additional sources of variation have been eliminated from $\hat{\mathbf{E}}$. If the null hypothesis is true, the residual variances $|\hat{\boldsymbol{\Sigma}}|$ and $|\hat{\boldsymbol{\Sigma}}_0|$ estimate the same random variation and will be similar in value; Λ will be close to unity.

With appropriate distributional assumptions, we may choose critical values of Λ at which to reject H_0. Because of the complexity of the likelihood ratio, complete tables of the distribution of Λ have not been constructed or widely disseminated. Several functions of Λ have been developed, however, that have probability distributions very close to the well-known χ^2 (chi-square) and F distributions. We may test H_0 employing one of the transformations of Λ as a test statistic.

Bartlett (1938) has shown that the statistic

$$\chi^2 = -m \log_e \Lambda \tag{5.2.10}$$

has approximately a χ^2 distribution with $q_h p$ degrees of freedom. The multiplier is

$$m = n_e - (p+1-q_h)/2 \tag{5.2.11}$$

where q_h is the number of predictor variables being tested and n_e is the degrees of freedom for $\hat{\boldsymbol{\Sigma}}$; that is, $n_e = N-q-1$. H_0 is rejected with confidence $1-\alpha$ if χ^2 exceeds the 100α upper percentage point of the χ^2 distribution with $q_h p$ degrees of freedom. Schatzoff (1966) has shown that the χ^2 approximation is reasonably accurate as long as the number of observations exceeds the total number of variables by 30 or more, even in large models (say, $pq_h = 70$).

Rao (1952) has given a more accurate approximation for the distribution of Λ. The test statistic is

$$F = \frac{1-\Lambda^{1/s}}{\Lambda^{1/s}} \cdot \frac{ms+1-q_h p/2}{q_h p} \tag{5.2.12}$$

where

$$s = \left(\frac{p^2 q_h^2 - 4}{p^2 + q_h^2 - 5}\right)^{1/2} \tag{5.2.13}$$

and m is defined by Eq. 5.2.11. In Eqs. 5.2.10 and 5.2.12 small values of Λ result in large test statistics. The F statistic has approximately an F distribution with

$q_h p$ and $ms+1-q_h p/2$ degrees of freedom. H_0 is rejected with confidence $1-\alpha$ if F exceeds the 100α percent critical value of the corresponding F distribution.

Note that F is undefined when $pq_h = 2$, since s vanishes. However, setting s to unity provides an appropriate test statistic in either the univariate ($p=1$, $q_h = 2$) or bivariate ($p = 2$, $q_h = 1$) case.

The F approximation is generally more accurate than the χ^2 approximation, although with large N they will yield the same results. When either p or q_h has values of 1 or 2, the F statistic has *exactly* the corresponding F distribution. With other values the inaccuracy of the F statistic is of the order of m^{-4}, which is less than .01 for m-values as low as 4. It is possible for the denominator degrees of freedom to be fractional. Rounding to the next lower integer provides a conservative test if computing routines for fractional values are not available.

If H_0 is rejected, inspection of the univariate F ratios (see the following section) may identify the particular variates affected by the predictors.

Computationally, Λ can be obtained from the error sum of products $\mathbf{S}_E$ and the hypotheses matrix $\mathbf{S}_H = \mathbf{U}_h'\mathbf{U}_h$. Note that

$$\begin{aligned}\Lambda &= \frac{|\hat{\mathbf{\Sigma}}|}{|\hat{\mathbf{\Sigma}}_0|} \\ &= \frac{|N\hat{\mathbf{\Sigma}}|}{|N\hat{\mathbf{\Sigma}}_0|}\end{aligned} \tag{5.2.14}$$

From Eq. 5.2.8,

$$\begin{aligned}N\hat{\mathbf{\Sigma}} &= \mathbf{Y}'\mathbf{Y}-\hat{\mathbf{B}}'\mathbf{X}'\mathbf{X}\hat{\mathbf{B}} \\ &= \mathbf{S}_E\end{aligned} \tag{5.2.15}$$

From Eq. 5.2.7,

$$\begin{aligned}N\hat{\mathbf{\Sigma}}_0 &= \mathbf{Y}'\mathbf{Y}-\hat{\mathbf{B}}_0'\mathbf{X}_0'\mathbf{X}_0\hat{\mathbf{B}}_0 \\ &= (\mathbf{Y}'\mathbf{Y}-\hat{\mathbf{B}}'\mathbf{X}'\mathbf{X}\hat{\mathbf{B}}) + (\hat{\mathbf{B}}'\mathbf{X}'\mathbf{X}\hat{\mathbf{B}} - \hat{\mathbf{B}}_0'\mathbf{X}_0'\mathbf{X}_0\hat{\mathbf{B}}_0) \\ &= \mathbf{S}_E+(\mathbf{U}'\mathbf{U}-\mathbf{U}_0'\mathbf{U}_0) \\ &= \mathbf{S}_E+\mathbf{S}_H\end{aligned} \tag{5.2.16}$$

Then

$$\Lambda = \frac{|\mathbf{S}_E|}{|\mathbf{S}_E+\mathbf{S}_H|} \tag{5.2.17}$$

This form may be applied directly to any of the matrices obtained in partitioning criterion variation. When testing the hypothesis that the entire matrix $\mathbf{B}$ is null, $\mathbf{S}_H = \mathbf{U}'\mathbf{U} = \mathbf{S}_R$ is the entire sum of products for regression.

The condition for conducting the test of significance on Λ is that $|\mathbf{S}_E|$ be greater than zero; that is, $\mathbf{S}_E$ must be of full rank. This requires that $N-q-1$ be at least p or that there be more subjects than the total number of variables, $p+q$. Also, no criterion variable can be exactly a linear combination of other measures (for example, subtests and total test score, or percentages that sum to 100 for every subject will violate this requisite). When the condition is not met, one or more criteria must be deleted or tested separately; all of the information for the test is contained in the linearly independent subset of criterion variates.

Example

Using the data of Table 3.3.1, let us test for the contribution of x_3 to the prediction of both y_1 and y_2. The hypothesis is H_0: $\boldsymbol{\beta}'_4 = \mathbf{0}'$, where $\boldsymbol{\beta}'_4$ is the final row of $\mathbf{B}$. The hypothesis and error matrices from Section 5.1 are

$$\mathbf{S}_{H_2} = \begin{bmatrix} .01 & -.06 \\ -.06 & .41 \end{bmatrix}$$

and

$$\mathbf{S}_E = \begin{bmatrix} 3.59 & 2.38 \\ 2.38 & 3.33 \end{bmatrix}$$

respectively. The degrees of freedom for the two matrices are $q_h = 1$ and $n_e = 11$. The likelihood ratio is

$$\Lambda = \frac{|\mathbf{S}_E|}{|\mathbf{S}_E + \mathbf{S}_{H_2}|}$$

$$= \frac{6.30}{8.07} = .78$$

The multipliers are

$$m = 11 - (2 + 1 - 1)/2 = 10$$

and

$$s = 1 \text{ (by substitution)}$$

The F transformation is

$$F = \frac{1 - .78}{.78} \cdot \frac{10(1) + 1 - (1)(2)/2}{(1)(2)}$$

$$= .28 \cdot \frac{10}{2} = 1.41$$

with 2 and 10 degrees of freedom. The critical F value is not exceeded and H_0 is accepted. x_3 does not contribute to criterion variation, above and beyond x_1 and x_2.

Hotelling's T^2

The T^2 statistic (Hotelling, 1931) is a special instance of the likelihood ratio criterion when the degrees of freedom for hypothesis are unity. When there is a single predictor variable (and multiple criteria) being tested, the general likelihood ratio of the preceding section may be employed; the results will be identical to those from T^2. Several other hypotheses having one degree of freedom are more conveniently tested through the T^2 statistic.

Hypothesis 1: As a special case of the likelihood ratio criterion, we may use T^2 to test that a row of regression weights for predicting multiple criteria from one predictor is equal to a vector of constants. The hypothesis is

$$H_0\colon\ \boldsymbol{\beta}' = \boldsymbol{\beta}_0' \tag{5.2.18}$$

$\boldsymbol{\beta}_0'$ is any $1\times p$ vector of constants, including the null vector as it is in Eq. 5.2.2. The regression weights may comprise one row of $\mathbf{B}$ in Eq. 5.1.2 or may be weights for the only predictor, when $q=1$. If the constants are other than zero, the T^2 statistic is usually more convenient. The alternate hypothesis is that the two vectors are not the same, for all elements.

To construct the T^2 statistic, let the corresponding row estimate be $\hat{\boldsymbol{\beta}}'$. The expectation of $\hat{\boldsymbol{\beta}}'$ is $\boldsymbol{\beta}'$ and the variance–covariance matrix is

$$\mathscr{V}(\hat{\boldsymbol{\beta}}') = (\mathbf{x}'\mathbf{x})^{-1}\boldsymbol{\Sigma} \tag{5.2.19}$$

$\mathbf{x}$ is the vector of all N scores on the corresponding x predictor variable. The estimate of $\boldsymbol{\Sigma}$ is given by Eq. 5.1.5. If observations $\mathbf{y}_i'$ are distributed in p-variate normal fashion, then so is $\hat{\boldsymbol{\beta}}'$.

Consider a transformation of the elements of $\hat{\boldsymbol{\beta}}'$. Let us factor $\boldsymbol{\Sigma}$ into the product of the Cholesky triangular factor $\mathbf{T}$ and its transpose; that is,

$$\boldsymbol{\Sigma} = \mathbf{T}\mathbf{T}' \tag{5.2.20}$$

and

$$\boldsymbol{\Sigma}^{-1} = (\mathbf{T}^{-1})'\mathbf{T}^{-1} \tag{5.2.21}$$

Let us transform $\hat{\boldsymbol{\beta}}'$ to $\boldsymbol{\gamma}$ by

$$\boldsymbol{\gamma} = \sqrt{\mathbf{x}'\mathbf{x}}\,\mathbf{T}^{-1}(\hat{\boldsymbol{\beta}} - \boldsymbol{\beta}_0) \tag{5.2.22}$$

The distribution of $\boldsymbol{\gamma}$ is p-variate normal, being a linear function of the normally distributed elements $[\hat{\beta}_k]$. The expectation of $\boldsymbol{\gamma}$ is

$$\mathscr{E}(\boldsymbol{\gamma}) = \sqrt{\mathbf{x}'\mathbf{x}}\,\mathbf{T}^{-1}(\boldsymbol{\beta} - \boldsymbol{\beta}_0) \tag{5.2.23}$$

The variance–covariance matrix is

$$\begin{aligned}\mathscr{V}(\boldsymbol{\gamma}) &= \mathbf{x}'\mathbf{x}\,\mathscr{V}[\mathbf{T}^{-1}(\hat{\boldsymbol{\beta}} - \boldsymbol{\beta}_0)] \\ &= \mathbf{x}'\mathbf{x}[\mathbf{T}^{-1}\mathscr{V}(\hat{\boldsymbol{\beta}})(\mathbf{T}^{-1})'] \\ &= \mathbf{x}'\mathbf{x}[\mathbf{T}^{-1}(\mathbf{x}'\mathbf{x})^{-1}\boldsymbol{\Sigma}(\mathbf{T}^{-1})'] \\ &= \mathbf{I}\end{aligned} \tag{5.2.24}$$

$\mathbf{I}$ is a $p\times p$ identity matrix. The elements of $\boldsymbol{\gamma}$ are independent and normal, each with unit variance.

Under the null hypothesis that $\boldsymbol{\beta} = \boldsymbol{\beta}_0$ the expectation of $\boldsymbol{\gamma}$ is zero. Each $[\gamma_k]$ is an independent standard normal random variable. The product $\boldsymbol{\gamma}'\boldsymbol{\gamma}$ is the sum of squares of p such variates, and follows a χ^2 distribution with p degrees of freedom. That is,

$$\begin{aligned}\boldsymbol{\gamma}'\boldsymbol{\gamma} &= (\mathbf{x}'\mathbf{x})[\hat{\boldsymbol{\beta}} - \boldsymbol{\beta}_0]'(\mathbf{T}^{-1})'\mathbf{T}^{-1}[\hat{\boldsymbol{\beta}} - \boldsymbol{\beta}_0] \\ &= (\mathbf{x}'\mathbf{x})[\hat{\boldsymbol{\beta}} - \boldsymbol{\beta}_0]'\boldsymbol{\Sigma}^{-1}[\hat{\boldsymbol{\beta}} - \boldsymbol{\beta}_0] \\ &\sim \chi_p^2\end{aligned} \tag{5.2.25}$$

As $\hat{\boldsymbol{\beta}}$ departs from $\boldsymbol{\beta}_0$, the χ^2 value will increase, and we shall be more inclined to reject H_0. If H_0 is true, $\hat{\boldsymbol{\beta}}$ will generally be closer to $\boldsymbol{\beta}_0$ and the χ^2 value will be small.

When $\boldsymbol{\Sigma}$ is estimated from a sample, the test statistic is Hotelling's T^2,

$$T^2 = (\mathbf{x}'\mathbf{x})[\hat{\boldsymbol{\beta}} - \boldsymbol{\beta}_0]'\hat{\boldsymbol{\Sigma}}^{-1}[\hat{\boldsymbol{\beta}} - \boldsymbol{\beta}_0] \tag{5.2.26}$$

Tables of T^2 are not widely distributed, although a partial set has been published by Jensen and Howe (1968). However a simple transformation of T^2 can be compared directly to tables of the F distribution. The transformation is

$$F = \frac{(n_e - p + 1)T^2}{pn_e} \tag{5.2.27}$$

Expression 5.2.27 exactly follows an F distribution with p and $n_e - p + 1$ degrees of freedom, where n_e is the degrees of freedom for the error matrix $\boldsymbol{\Sigma}$. In the regression model $n_e = N - q - 1$. Thus we reject H_0 with confidence $1-\alpha$, if F exceeds the critical F value, or if

$$T^2 \geqslant \frac{p(N-q-1)}{N-p-q} F_{p,N-p-q,\alpha}$$

$F_{p,N-p-q,\alpha}$ is the 100α percentage point of the F distribution with p and $N-p-q$ degrees of freedom.

Let us consider several special cases:

1. If T^2 is being used to test the nullity of regression weights for one predictor *out of several*, a row of orthogonal estimates $\mathbf{U}$ replaces $\hat{\boldsymbol{\beta}}'$ in Eq. 5.2.26. The vector of regression weights is the jth row of $\mathbf{U}$ ($\mathbf{u}'_j$), and the x-values are the corresponding vector ($\mathbf{x}_j^*$) of orthonormal predictors from $\mathbf{X}^*$ in Eq. 5.1.15. Then

$$\begin{aligned} T^2 &= (\mathbf{x}_j^*)'\mathbf{x}_j^*[\mathbf{u}_j - \mathbf{0}]'\hat{\boldsymbol{\Sigma}}^{-1}[\mathbf{u}_j - \mathbf{0}] \\ &= \mathbf{u}'_j\hat{\boldsymbol{\Sigma}}^{-1}\mathbf{u}_j \end{aligned} \tag{5.2.28}$$

since $(\mathbf{X}^*)'\mathbf{X}^* = \mathbf{I}$.

For the same hypothesis, the likelihood ratio criterion is

$$\Lambda = \frac{|\mathbf{S}_E|}{|\mathbf{S}_E + \mathbf{S}_H|}$$

with $\mathbf{S}_H = \mathbf{u}_j\mathbf{u}'_j$. Simplifying,

$$\begin{aligned} \Lambda &= \frac{|\mathbf{S}_E^{-1}|}{|\mathbf{S}_E^{-1}|}\frac{|\mathbf{S}_E|}{|\mathbf{S}_E + \mathbf{u}_j\mathbf{u}'_j|} \\ &= \frac{1}{|\mathbf{I} + \mathbf{S}_E^{-1}\mathbf{u}_j\mathbf{u}'_j|} \end{aligned}$$

Let $\mathbf{S}_E^{-1}\mathbf{u}_j = \mathbf{a}$ and $\mathbf{u}'_j = \mathbf{b}'$. Applying the rule of determinants from Section 2.3,

$$\Lambda = \frac{1}{1 + \mathbf{u}'_j\mathbf{S}_E^{-1}\mathbf{u}_j}$$

Since $\hat{\boldsymbol{\Sigma}} = (1/n_e)\mathbf{S}_E$, it follows that

$$\mathbf{S}_E^{-1} = \frac{1}{n_e}\hat{\boldsymbol{\Sigma}}^{-1}$$

and

$$\Lambda = \frac{1}{1+\dfrac{\mathbf{u}'_j\hat{\boldsymbol{\Sigma}}^{-1}\mathbf{u}_j}{n_e}}$$

$$= \frac{1}{1+\dfrac{T^2}{n_e}} \qquad (5.2.29)$$

Then

$$T^2 = n_e \cdot \frac{1-\Lambda}{\Lambda} \qquad (5.2.29a)$$

That is, when $q_h = 1$, the likelihood ratio criterion and T^2 statistic for $\boldsymbol{\beta}_0 = \mathbf{0}$ are monotonically related. The F transformation of Λ is the same as the exact F statistic for T^2 by Eq. 5.2.27. If H_0 is rejected, we conclude that predictor x_j is significantly related to the p criterion scores.

2. When the regression model is a trivial one of the form

$$\mathbf{y}_i = \boldsymbol{\alpha} + \boldsymbol{\epsilon}_i \qquad (5.2.30)$$

T^2 provides a test that the population mean vector (for p variates) is equal to a vector of constants; that is,

$$H_0\colon \boldsymbol{\alpha} = \boldsymbol{\alpha}_0 \qquad (5.2.31a)$$

or

$$H_0\colon \boldsymbol{\mu} = \boldsymbol{\alpha}_0 \qquad (5.2.31b)$$

Under Eq. 5.2.30, $\hat{\boldsymbol{\alpha}}$ is the sample mean vector for the y-measures. That is,

$$\hat{\boldsymbol{\alpha}}' = (\mathbf{1}'\mathbf{1})^{-1}\mathbf{1}'\mathbf{Y}$$

$$= \mathbf{y}'_{\cdot} \qquad (5.2.32)$$

$\mathbf{1}$ is an N-element unit vector. $\hat{\boldsymbol{\Sigma}}$ is the simple variance–covariance matrix

$$\hat{\boldsymbol{\Sigma}} = \frac{1}{N-1}\sum_i (\mathbf{y}_i - \mathbf{y}_{\cdot})(\mathbf{y}_i - \mathbf{y}_{\cdot})'$$

$$= \mathbf{V}_w \qquad (5.2.33)$$

Substituting in Eq. 5.2.26,

$$T^2 = N[\mathbf{y}_{\cdot} - \boldsymbol{\alpha}_0]'\mathbf{V}_w^{-1}[\mathbf{y}_{\cdot} - \boldsymbol{\alpha}_0] \qquad (5.2.34)$$

T^2 may be converted to F by Eq. 5.2.27, with $n_e = N-1$. H_0 is rejected if F exceeds the critical value of the F distribution with p and $N-p$ degrees of freedom. T^2 is the multivariate form of the ordinary t test that a population mean μ is equal to a specified constant.

Example

The sample means of y_1 and y_2 of Table 3.3.1 are

$$\mathbf{y.}=\begin{bmatrix}2.27\\2.51\end{bmatrix}$$

for required and elective courses, respectively. The variance–covariance matrix is

$$\hat{\boldsymbol{\Sigma}}=\begin{bmatrix}.59 & .48\\.48 & .75\end{bmatrix}$$

The sample size is 15.

The university mean freshman grade point average for all courses is 2.40. To test whether this vector score deviates from the overall mean, we test

$$H_0\colon \begin{bmatrix}\mu_1\\\mu_2\end{bmatrix}=\begin{bmatrix}2.40\\2.40\end{bmatrix}$$

against the alternate that the two are not equal.

Hotelling's T^2 is

$$T^2=15[(2.27 \quad 2.51)-(2.40 \quad 2.40)]\begin{bmatrix}.59 & .48\\.48 & .75\end{bmatrix}^{-1}\begin{bmatrix}(2.27-2.40)\\(2.51-2.40)\end{bmatrix}$$

$$=15[-.13 \quad .11]\begin{bmatrix}3.51 & -2.25\\-2.25 & 2.76\end{bmatrix}\begin{bmatrix}-.13\\.11\end{bmatrix}$$

$$=2.49$$

The F transformation is

$$F=\frac{(14-2+1)(2.49)}{2.14}$$
$$=1.15$$

The .05 critical F value with 2 and 13 degrees of freedom is 3.81. H_0 is maintained; students do not score significantly above or below average in courses classified by requirement.

3. When there is only a single criterion measure, T^2 is the square of the simple t test on one regression coefficient. When $p=1$, $\hat{\boldsymbol{\Sigma}}$ in Eq. 5.2.26 is the variance of the single measure $\hat{\sigma}^2$; $\hat{\beta}$ is a single estimate and β_0 is a scalar. Then

$$T^2=\frac{(\hat{\beta}-\beta_0)^2}{\hat{\sigma}^2/\sum_i x_i^2} \tag{5.2.35}$$

The variance of a single weight $\hat{\beta}$ in Chapter 4 is identically the denominator of 5.2.35 ($\hat{\sigma}_{\hat{\beta}}^2$). Further when p is unity in 5.2.27, T^2 is also the F value. The univariate t statistic is

$$t=\sqrt{T^2}=\frac{\hat{\beta}-\beta_0}{\hat{\sigma}_{\hat{\beta}}} \tag{5.2.36}$$

t follows a t distribution with n_e degrees of freedom; T^2 is distributed as F with 1 and n_e degrees of freedom. H_0 is rejected if either statistic exceeds the respective critical value.

Hypothesis 2: The T^2 statistic can be employed to test for values of any linear combination of regression coefficients. Let $\mathbf{B}$ be the $(q+1)\times p$ matrix of regression coefficients, and $\mathbf{v}$ a $(q+1)$-element vector of weights. The null hypothesis is

$$H_0\text{: } \mathbf{v}'\mathbf{B} = (\mathbf{v}'\mathbf{B})_0 \tag{5.2.37}$$

The alternate hypothesis is that the two products are not the same. $\mathbf{v}'\mathbf{B}$ is a $1\times p$ vector, and $\mathbf{v}'\hat{\mathbf{B}}$ the corresponding vector estimate.

The expectation of the vector of linear combinations is

$$\mathscr{E}(\mathbf{v}'\hat{\mathbf{B}}) = \mathbf{v}'\mathbf{B} \tag{5.2.38}$$

The $p\times p$ variance–covariance matrix is

$$\begin{aligned}\mathscr{V}(\mathbf{v}'\hat{\mathbf{B}}) &= \mathbf{v}'\mathscr{V}(\hat{\mathbf{B}})\mathbf{v} \\ &= [\mathbf{v}'(\mathbf{X}'\mathbf{X})^{-1}\mathbf{v}]\mathbf{\Sigma}\end{aligned} \tag{5.2.39}$$

Substituting in Eq. 5.2.26,

$$T^2 = \frac{1}{\mathbf{v}'(\mathbf{X}'\mathbf{X})^{-1}\mathbf{v}}[\mathbf{v}'\hat{\mathbf{B}}-(\mathbf{v}'\mathbf{B})_0]\hat{\mathbf{\Sigma}}^{-1}[\mathbf{v}'\hat{\mathbf{B}}-(\mathbf{v}'\mathbf{B})_0]' \tag{5.2.40}$$

T^2 may be transformed to F by 5.2.27. H_0 is rejected in favor of H_A if F exceeds the critical F value, with p and n_e-p+1 degrees of freedom.

Univariate Statistics

Summary matrices for multivariate analysis are efficient devices for obtaining p separate univariate results simultaneously. In the case of regression analysis, elements of $\mathbf{S}_H$ and $\mathbf{S}_E$ may be employed to provide tests of the contribution of q_h (≥ 1) predictor variables to *each* of the criteria.

Let $\mathbf{S}_E$ and $\mathbf{S}_H$ represent $p\times p$ sums of products for error and for hypothesis, having n_e and q_h degrees of freedom, respectively. $\mathbf{S}_H$ is the matrix product of q_h row vectors of $\mathbf{U}$. The univariate F ratio for one criterion variable y_k is the ratio of two *mean squares*, one for hypothesis and one for error. Each mean square is a sum of squares divided by its degrees of freedom.

The mean square for regression for y_k is the kk diagonal element of $\mathbf{S}_H$ divided by its degrees of freedom. Dividing the entire matrix $\mathbf{S}_H$ by q_h produces the $p\times p$ matrix of mean squares and cross products

$$\mathbf{M}_H = \frac{\mathbf{S}_H}{q_h} \tag{5.2.41}$$

The diagonal element is

$$[m_h]_{kk} = \frac{[s_h]_{kk}}{q_h} \tag{5.2.41a}$$

Similarly the error mean squares and cross products are

$$\hat{\boldsymbol{\Sigma}} = \mathbf{M}_E = \frac{\mathbf{S}_E}{n_e} \tag{5.2.42}$$

The error mean square for y_k is

$$[m_e]_{kk} = \frac{[s_e]_{kk}}{n_e} \tag{5.2.42a}$$

Expression 5.2.42a is identically the *kk* diagonal element of $\hat{\boldsymbol{\Sigma}}$, that is, $\hat{\sigma}_k^2$.

A univariate test statistic for the effect of the predictor(s) on y_k is

$$F_k = \frac{[m_h]_{kk}}{[m_e]_{kk}} \tag{5.2.43}$$

F may be referred to critical values of the *F* distribution, with q_h and n_e degrees of freedom.

Example

Using the data of Table 3.3.1, let us obtain test statistics for the contribution of x_3 to variation in y_1 and y_2 separately. The hypothesis matrix is

$$\mathbf{S}_{H_2} = \begin{bmatrix} .01 & -.06 \\ -.06 & .41 \end{bmatrix}$$

with 1 degree of freedom. Thus $\mathbf{M}_{H_2} = \mathbf{S}_{H_2}$. The error matrix is

$$\mathbf{S}_E = \begin{bmatrix} 3.59 & 2.38 \\ 2.38 & 3.33 \end{bmatrix}$$

with 11 degrees of freedom. The mean-squares-and-products matrix is

$$\mathbf{M}_E = \frac{1}{11}\mathbf{S}_E = \begin{bmatrix} .33 & .22 \\ .22 & .30 \end{bmatrix}$$

The *F* ratios for y_1 and y_2 alone are

$$F_1 = \frac{.01}{.33} = .03 \quad (y_1)$$

$$F_2 = \frac{.41}{.30} = 1.36 \quad (y_2)$$

Neither exceeds the .05 critical value of *F* with 1 and 11 degrees of freedom.

Multiple univariate *F* ratios for any one hypothesis (one or more predictors) are not statistically independent. When the criterion variables form a meaningful set, a multivariate test statistic should be used for a single decision about H_0 (Eq. 5.2.2). Both clarity and statistical validity are thus maintained. Hummel and Sligo (1971) have recommended a two-stage significance-testing procedure. At the first stage, a decision is made about H_0 from a multivariate result (such as Wilk's Λ). If H_0 is rejected, the separate univariate ratios may be inspected to determine where the significant effects are located.

The largest univariate F ratio is obtained for the variable the most affected by the q_h predictors, the smallest for the variable least affected, and so on. However, there is no necessary relationship of the significance of univariate and multivariate tests for one hypothesis. For example, one or more univariate F's may be significant and not the multivariate statistic, or vice versa. In the regression model, inspection of simple and multiple correlations is likely to be more useful for interpretation.

Matrices $\mathbf{S}_H$ and $\mathbf{S}_w^{(yy)}$ can provide a univariate measure of the percentage of variation in y_k attributable to the predictors. The regression sum of squares is $[s_h]_{kk}$; the sum of squares for y_k before eliminating the effects of the predictors is $[s_w^{(yy)}]_{kk}$. The percent of variation in y_k due to the predictors, above and beyond preceding independent variables, is

$$\frac{100[s_h]_{kk}}{[s_w^{(yy)}]_{kk}} \tag{5.2.44}$$

When there is only a single criterion measure, the F transformation from Wilk's Λ is identically the univariate F ratio for y. From Eq. 5.2.17,

$$\Lambda = \frac{|\mathbf{S}_E|}{|\mathbf{S}_E + \mathbf{S}_H|}$$

When $p=1$, both matrices are scalars and $\Lambda = \mathbf{S}_E/(\mathbf{S}_E + \mathbf{S}_H)$. The multipliers for F (Eq. 5.2.12) are

$$s = \left(\frac{q_h^2 - 4}{q_h^2 - 4}\right)^{1/2} = 1$$

and

$$m = n_e - (2 - q_h)/2 = n_e - 1 + q_h/2$$

Then

$$\begin{aligned} F &= \frac{1-\Lambda}{\Lambda} \cdot \frac{n_e - 1 + q_h/2 + 1 - q_h/2}{q_h} \\ &= \frac{\mathbf{S}_E}{\mathbf{S}_H} \cdot \frac{q_h}{n_e} \end{aligned}$$

F is identically the univariate ratio as in Eqs. 5.2.41–5.2.43.

Step-down Analysis

Step-down analysis, described by Roy (1958) and by Roy and Bargmann (1958), provides p univariate test statistics to test H_0 (Eq. 5.2.2), which are statistically independent but depend upon an *a priori* ordering of criterion measures. Logical orderings of criterion measures arise when subjects have been tested repeatedly over time, when measures involve progressively more complex behaviors, or whenever there exists a systematic progression from one outcome measure to another. If no logical or theoretical ordering can be justified, step-down tests will be of little scientific value, and a general test like Wilk's Λ may be employed.

Step-down analysis is a stepwise procedure in that variables are considered in a predetermined order; at each stage only the unique contribution of the additional variable is estimated and tested. The term "step-down" is used to indicate that it is the criterion variables, as opposed to the predictors, that are being considered in an elimination process. The distinction is somewhat arbitrary, however; the step-down statistic for the criterion variable y_k is identical to the univariate test that would have been obtained if preceding criteria were listed in **X** as predictors, ahead of those actually under consideration.

Step-down test statistics are computed from hypothesis and error matrices $\mathbf{S}_H$ and $\mathbf{S}_E$, with q_h and n_e degrees of freedom, respectively. Step-down analysis enables the researcher to test the relationship between the q_h predictors and y_1, with y_2 eliminating y_1, y_3 eliminating y_1 and y_2, and so on. The test statistics depend upon the conditional variance of each measure, given preceding criteria.

Let us factor $\mathbf{S}_E$ into the product of the triangular Cholesky factor and its transpose,

$$\mathbf{S}_E = \mathbf{T}_E \mathbf{T}_E' \tag{5.2.45}$$

The p diagonal elements of $\mathbf{T}_E$ are the square roots of the error sums of squares for variable y_k, given y_1 through y_{k-1}. The square $[t_e]_{kk}^2$ is the sum of squares for the conditional y_k, and has degrees of freedom $n_e - k + 1$; one degree of freedom has been attributed to each preceding variable eliminated. The conditional error variance, or mean square for y_k given preceding measures, is

$$\frac{[t_e]_{kk}^2}{n_e - k + 1} \tag{5.2.46}$$

Let us now compute a "total" matrix for this hypothesis:

$$\mathbf{S} = \mathbf{S}_E + \mathbf{S}_H \tag{5.2.47}$$

S may be factored like $\mathbf{S}_E$ to obtain conditional "total" sums of squares for each variate, eliminating preceding measures. By the Cholesky method,†

$$\mathbf{S} = \mathbf{T}^* [\mathbf{T}^*]' \tag{5.2.48}$$

The "total" sum of squares for y_k given y_1 through y_{k-1} is $[t^*]_{kk}^2$. Thus the hypothesis sum of squares for y_k given y_1 through y_{k-1} is $[t^*]_{kk}^2 - [t_e]_{kk}^2$, with q_h degrees of freedom. The hypothesis mean square for y_k, eliminating preceding criteria is

$$\frac{[t^*]_{kk}^2 - [t_e]_{kk}^2}{q_h} \tag{5.2.49}$$

The step-down F statistic is a ratio of the conditional mean squares as given in Eqs. 5.2.49 and 5.2.46. It is the univariate F ratio for y_k, eliminating y_1 through y_{k-1}. The kth F statistic is

$$F_k^* = \frac{[t^*]_{kk}^2 - [t_e]_{kk}^2}{[t_e]_{kk}^2} \cdot \frac{n_e - k + 1}{q_h} \tag{5.2.50}$$

†Note that the Λ criterion and step-down statistics are easily computed at the same time. Λ requires $|\mathbf{S}_E|$ and $|\mathbf{S}|$, which is efficiently computed through Cholesky factors, as described in Chapter 2.

Any matrix $\mathbf{S}_H$ will yield p F^* statistics. F_k^* is referred to critical values of the F distribution, with q_h and n_e-k+1 degrees of freedom. H_0 is accepted if and only if none of the F statistics exceeds its critical value.

Since the first F^* statistic has no prior variates eliminated, it is equal to the simple univariate F ratio for y_1.

$$F_1^* = \frac{[t^*]_{11}{}^2 - [t_e]_{11}{}^2}{[t_e]_{11}{}^2} \cdot \frac{n_e}{q_h}$$

$$= \frac{\{[s_e]_{11} + [s_h]_{11}\} - [s_e]_{11}}{[s_e]_{11}} \cdot \frac{n_e}{q_h}$$

$$= \frac{[s_h]_{11}}{[s_e]_{11}} \cdot \frac{n_e}{q_h}$$

$$= F_1$$

F_2^* through F_p^*, however, are tests of the effect of the q_h predictors upon response variable y_k, eliminating any portion of the effect that can be attributed to preceding dependent variables. Under the null hypothesis for variable y_k, F_k^* is statistically independent of F_1^* through F_{k-1}^*. Under the alternative hypothesis that the effect on y_k is not zero, F_1^* through F_{k-1}^* are not independent of F_k^*.

The appropriate technique for interpreting the step-down statistics is to begin with F_p^* and proceed backward toward F_1^*. At each stage a hypothesis is tested concerning prediction of a specific criterion, eliminating earlier measures in $\mathbf{S}_E$ and $\mathbf{S}_H$. If F_k^* is not significant, the corresponding variable is not significantly related to the predictors above and beyond y_1 through y_{k-1}. We proceed with inspection of F_{k-1}^*. Testing stops if a significant F^* statistic is encountered, and H_0 is rejected. Variables earlier in the order of elimination cannot be validly tested; F_1^* through F_{k-1}^* are all confounded with significant variation due to y_k. If no F^* statistic is significant, H_0 is accepted.

It has been suggested by Bock (1966, p. 828) that criterion variables known to be important be ordered first, and the "more dubious" or more complex variables later. In this manner the value of the latter variables in contributing to the regression upon the predictors may be tested first. In the search for parsimonious explanations of behavior these complex or doubtful contributors may be eliminated, whereas the earlier and simpler explanatory variables are retained. The logical ordering of measures is critical, since the step-down results will change with a permutation of the criterion variables. Step-down statistics are the only tests that are influenced by the order of the criteria.

It is possible to assign differing type-*I* error rates to the step-down tests, maintaining a constant overall probability of falsely rejecting at least one of the p null hypotheses. If we assign probability α_k to statistic F_k^*, then the overall probability is

$$\alpha = 1 - \prod_{k=1}^{p} (1 - \alpha_k) \tag{5.2.51}$$

Further consideration of step-down decision rules has been given by Das Gupta (1970).

Example

Using the data of Table 3.3.1, let us test H_0: $\boldsymbol{\beta}'_4 = \mathbf{0}'$ employing $\mathbf{S}_{H_2}$ and $\mathbf{S}_E$:

$$\mathbf{S}_{H_2} = \begin{bmatrix} .01 & -.06 \\ -.06 & .41 \end{bmatrix} \quad (q_h = 1)$$

$$\mathbf{S}_E = \begin{bmatrix} 3.59 & 2.38 \\ 2.38 & 3.33 \end{bmatrix} \quad (n_e = 11)$$

To use the step-down method, we must assume a natural order to y_1 and y_2. There is *no* inherent order in the measures as they appear in this example. Therefore the following results, though mathematically correct, are less informative than the likelihood ratio test.

Factoring $\mathbf{S}_E$, the Cholesky factor is

$$\mathbf{T}_E = \begin{bmatrix} 1.89 & 0.00 \\ 1.25 & 1.32 \end{bmatrix}$$

The "total" matrix is

$$\mathbf{S} = \begin{bmatrix} 3.60 & 2.32 \\ 2.32 & 3.74 \end{bmatrix}$$

The Cholesky factor of $\mathbf{S}$ is

$$\mathbf{T}^* = \begin{bmatrix} 1.90 & 0.00 \\ 1.22 & 1.50 \end{bmatrix}$$

The F^* ratios are

$$F_1^* = \frac{1.90^2 - 1.89^2}{1.89^2} \cdot \frac{11-1+1}{1} = .03 \quad (1, 11 \text{ d.f.})$$

$$F_2^* = \frac{1.50^2 - 1.32^2}{1.32^2} \cdot \frac{11-2+1}{1} = 2.78 \quad (1, 10 \text{ d.f.})$$

Finding F_2^* not significant at $\alpha = .05$, we inspect F_1^*. F_1^* is also not significant and H_0 is accepted. Had F_2^* been significant, we would have no separate test for y_1, but H_0 would be rejected. If F_1^* were significant but not F_2^*, we should conclude that H_0 is rejected but that y_2 does not relate to x_3 above and beyond y_1. If both tests are conducted with $\alpha_1 = \alpha_2 = .05$, the α for H_0 is $1 - .95^2 = .10$.

5.3 MULTIPLE HYPOTHESES

Frequently we wish to test multiple hypotheses about rows or sections of the matrix $\mathbf{B}$. For example, in Table 5.1.1 we have partitioned predictable variation into components for each of the predictor variables eliminating preceding measures. Regression variation in the accompanying example, based on the data of Table 3.3.1, is partitioned into sums of products for the constant, the first two predictors jointly, and the final predictor eliminating the constant and the first two predictors. In each case we may wish to test several hypotheses about subsets of predictor variables.

We assume a fixed order of predictor variables. "Stepwise" procedures which attempt all possible orderings, or search for the best single prediction equation do not generally yield valid test statistics, and must be interpreted with caution. With a predetermined order of predictor variables, valid sequential test statistics are obtained. Using a fixed order, it is also possible to test important combinations or *sets* of variables.

Notationally, we may designate the multiple hypotheses by adding a subscript to the terms of the preceding section. Hypothesis *j* is

$$H_{0_j}\colon\ \mathbf{B}_{h_j} = \mathbf{0} \tag{5.3.1}$$

$\mathbf{B}_{h_j}$ is section *j* of the entire matrix $\mathbf{B}$, having q_{h_j} rows and p columns. The regression sum of products for H_{0_j} is

$$\mathbf{S}_{H_j} = \mathbf{U}'_{h_j}\mathbf{U}_{h_j} \tag{5.3.2}$$

$\mathbf{S}_{H_j}$ is the sum of products of the corresponding q_{h_j} rows of the orthogonal estimates $\mathbf{U}$. The total number of hypotheses is $j = 1, 2, \ldots, J$.

For example, in testing q hypotheses about the contribution of each predictor to criterion variation eliminating preceding predictors, $\mathbf{B}_{h_1}$ through $\mathbf{B}_{h_q}$ are each a single row of $\mathbf{B}$, with all $q_{h_j} = 1$. Each matrix $\mathbf{S}_{H_j}$ is a squares-and-cross-products matrix of one row of $\mathbf{U}$, as in Table 5.1.1.

For the example based on Table 3.3.1.,

$$\mathbf{B} = \begin{bmatrix} \mathbf{B}_0 \\ \hline \mathbf{B}_{h_1} \\ \hline \mathbf{B}_{h_2} \end{bmatrix} \begin{matrix} \text{Constant} \\ x_1 \\ x_2 \\ x_3 \end{matrix} \qquad \mathbf{U} = \begin{bmatrix} \mathbf{U}_0 \\ \hline \mathbf{U}_{h_1} \\ \hline \mathbf{U}_{h_2} \end{bmatrix} \begin{matrix} \text{Constant} \\ x_1 \\ x_2 \\ x_3 \end{matrix} \tag{5.3.3}$$

H_{0_1} is $\mathbf{B}_{h_1} = \mathbf{0}$; the sum of products for regression is $\mathbf{S}_{H_1} = \mathbf{U}'_{h_1}\mathbf{U}_{h_1} = \mathbf{u}_2\mathbf{u}'_2 + \mathbf{u}_3\mathbf{u}'_3$, with $q_{h_1} = 2$ degrees of freedom. H_{0_2} is $\mathbf{B}_{h_2} = \mathbf{0}$; the sum of products for x_3, eliminating the constant, x_1, and x_2, is $\mathbf{S}_{H_2} = \mathbf{U}'_{h_2}\mathbf{U}_{h_2}$, with $q_{h_2} = 1$ degree of freedom (see p. 144).

For purposes of significance testing we proceed in an order opposite to the order in which we have eliminated predictors. The effect of the last predictor or set, eliminating all others, is tested for significance first, using $\mathbf{S}_{H_J}$. If the null hypothesis is accepted that $\mathbf{B}_{h_J}$ is zero, then we proceed to test $H_{0_{J-1}}$ using $\mathbf{S}_{H_{J-1}}$. If $H_{0_{J-1}}$ is accepted, we proceed to test $H_{0_{J-2}}$, and so on. If any H_{0_j} is rejected, then predictors earlier in the elimination *cannot* be validly tested in this order.

The rationale for the order of testing can be seen algebraically by examining $\mathbf{U}$ in Eq. 5.1.31. Let us assume that we are testing the effect of each predictor separately. The last element u_{q+1} is a function of only β_q. If the null hypothesis is accepted, then β_q is zero and disappears from all preceding u-terms. In this situation we may test the contribution of x_{q-1} using u_q, and the results will not be confounded with x_q variation. Similarly if β_{q-1} is judged to be null, no preceding terms are confounded with x_{q-1} variation; they may be validly tested. The same logic applies to sets of predictors. For example, if the last two regression weights are simultaneously judged to be null, then both coefficients disappear from all preceding u-terms.

If however, H_0 is rejected from u_{q+1}, and β_q is not zero, then all preceding u-terms contain nonzero functions of x_q, in addition to the other β-weights they reflect. A test employing u_q, for example, would not reveal whether β_{q-1} alone was null (note also that the elements t_{ij} can be either positive or negative). In order to obtain valid test statistics for any predictors preceding x_q, it is necessary to order predictor x_q *ahead* of the other predictors (earlier in the order of elimination), and to reorthogonalize. The resulting orthogonal coefficients will reflect the corresponding predictors eliminating nonzero x_q effects. The same procedure is used with x_{q-1} or for any predictors found to contribute to criterion variation.

Tests made in various orders of predictors are not independent of one another. The number of orders of predictors should be kept to a minimum to avoid multiplying statistical error rates. The error rates associated with regression procedures attempting all possible orderings (or finding the best predictor at each stage) are generally so high as to render the tests invalid. Also, a variable may appear insignificant because it is entered into regression following other predictors. If entered first, however, its contribution may be larger. This does not imply that the variable is unimportant, but only that it is correlated with other measures.

In general it is best to determine an initial ordering of predictors, with the most crucial or complex variables last. Their contributions to regression are tested first, and with the least confounding. Control variables or measures *known* to be associated with the criteria are ordered first. In this manner, variables preliminary or central to our hypotheses are validly tested for their contribution to regression, above and beyond those about which there is little doubt or concern.

For each hypothesis, a decision about H_0 is made from an appropriate test statistic. When $p > 1$, a multivariate testing procedure should be employed (Wilk's Λ, step-down analysis, or the canonical correlation tests of the next chapter). The multiple univariate F statistics, as well as simple and multiple correlations, provide information about the criteria least and most affected by the antecedent(s). These should not be used for a decision regarding H_0 so long as the criteria form a conceptually meaningful set (see Hummel and Sligo, 1971).

If the last hypothesis H_{0_J} is accepted, then $\mathbf{S}_{H_J}$ contains only random variation and may be pooled with $\mathbf{S}_E$ to provide a better estimate of error dispersion; q_{h_J} is pooled with n_e. Testing and pooling continues in backward order with $\mathbf{S}_{H_{J-1}}$, $\mathbf{S}_{H_{J-2}}$, and so on. At each stage, we test the next hypothesis with the maximum statistical power (Anderson, 1962). If any H_{0_j} is rejected, hypothesis testing must stop, in this order. If earlier variables require significance tests, they must be reordered to follow the significant predictors. $\mathbf{U}$ is recomputed and repartitioned in the alternate order. Under this pooling procedure, we may derive an exactly-determined type-*I* error rate for one order of predictors. Differing α-levels may be assigned to each of the *J* hypotheses (α_j). The overall probability of falsely rejecting at least one null hypothesis out of *J* is

$$\alpha = 1 - \prod_{j=1}^{J} (1-\alpha_j) \tag{5.3.4}$$

α_j may be chosen so as to fix the overall α at a particular value, say .05 or .01.

Example

In Section 5.1 we partitioned criterion variation in y_1 and y_2 of Table 3.3.1 into sums of products for error, plus regression effects for the constant, x_1 and x_2 simultaneously, and x_3 eliminating the constant, x_1, and x_2. The error and hypothesis matrices are

$$\mathbf{S}_E = \begin{bmatrix} 3.59 & 2.38 \\ 2.38 & 3.33 \end{bmatrix} \qquad n_e = 11$$

$$\mathbf{S}_{H_1} = \begin{bmatrix} 4.71 & 4.44 \\ 4.44 & 6.82 \end{bmatrix} \qquad q_{h_1} = 2 \ (x_1 \text{ and } x_2, \text{ eliminating constant})$$

$$\mathbf{S}_{H_2} = \begin{bmatrix} .01 & -.06 \\ -.06 & .41 \end{bmatrix} \qquad q_{h_2} = 1 \ (x_3 \text{ eliminating all else})$$

$\mathbf{S}_{H_1}$ and $\mathbf{S}_{H_2}$ correspond to the partitions of $\mathbf{B}$ and $\mathbf{U}$ in Eq. 5.3.3.

In Section 5.2 we tested H_{0_2}: $\mathbf{B}_{h_2} = \mathbf{0}$ using univariate and multivariate test criteria. H_0 was accepted in all cases. Thus we may pool $\mathbf{S}_{H_2}$ with $\mathbf{S}_E$. The revised error matrix is

$$\mathbf{S}'_E = \begin{bmatrix} 3.60 & 2.32 \\ 2.32 & 3.74 \end{bmatrix}$$

with $n'_e = 12$ degrees of freedom. Using $\mathbf{S}'_E$ and $\mathbf{S}_{H_1}$ we may test H_{0_1}: $\mathbf{B}_{h_1} = \mathbf{0}$ for predictors x_1 and x_2 jointly. The likelihood ratio is

$$\Lambda = \frac{|\mathbf{S}'_E|}{|\mathbf{S}'_E + \mathbf{S}_{H_1}|} = \frac{8.07}{42.11} = .192$$

The multipliers are

$$m = 12 - (2+1-2)/2 = 11.5$$

$$s = \left(\frac{2^2(2^2)-4}{2^2+2^2-5} \right)^{1/2} = 2$$

The *F* transformation is

$$F = \frac{1-\sqrt{.192}}{\sqrt{.192}} \cdot \frac{11.5(2)+1-(2)(2)/2}{2(2)}$$

$$= 1.28 \cdot \frac{22}{4}$$

$$= 7.06$$

F does exceed the .05 critical value of 2.82, with 4 and 22 degrees of freedom. H_{0_1} is rejected; x_1 and x_2 do contribute significantly to criterion variation. (Had H_{0_2} been rejected, it would have been necessary to order x_3 ahead of x_1 and x_2, and to recalculate $\mathbf{U}$ to test H_{0_1} for x_1 and x_2, eliminating x_3.)

To inspect the effects of x_1 and x_2, let us compute univariate statistics for y_1 and y_2 separately:

$$F_1 = \frac{4.71/2}{3.60/12} = 7.85 \quad (y_1)$$

$$F_2 = \frac{6.82/2}{3.74/12} = 10.95 \quad (y_2)$$

Each F ratio has 2 and 12 degrees of freedom. Both are significantly related to the two predictors, although y_2 is more affected by x_1 and x_2 than is y_1.

Reestimation

The final predictors that do not contribute to criterion variation are ultimately discarded from the model. Remaining are early predictors that were not tested but were assumed necessary to the model (for example, the constant, known predictors, control variables), plus other tested variables that make significant additional contributions to regression. Altogether c ($\leq q$) predictors remain; c is the *rank of the model for estimation*.

The original estimate $\hat{\mathbf{B}}$ was a "best fit" for the q simultaneous predictor variables. The rows of $\hat{\mathbf{B}}$ are interdependent and change with the deletion of variables. Thus we shall reestimate $\mathbf{B}$ to obtain best estimates for only the leading c predictors. This may be accomplished from $\mathbf{X}_c$, the leading c columns of $\mathbf{X}$, by

$$\hat{\mathbf{B}}_c = (\mathbf{X}_c'\mathbf{X}_c)^{-1}\mathbf{X}_c'\mathbf{Y} \tag{5.3.5}$$

Or, let $\mathbf{T}_c$ be the leading c rows and columns of the Cholesky factor of $\mathbf{X}'\mathbf{X}$. $\mathbf{T}$ is also the triangular factor from the orthonormalization of $\mathbf{X}$ in Eq. 5.1.15. Then

$$\hat{\mathbf{B}}_c = (\mathbf{T}_c^{-1})'\mathbf{U}_c \tag{5.3.6}$$

$\mathbf{U}_c$ represents the leading c rows of $\mathbf{U}$.

Corresponding variances and standard errors for $\hat{\mathbf{B}}_c$ are obtained by pooling the nonsignificant effects with error variation. The variance–covariance matrix of column k of $\hat{\mathbf{B}}_c$ is $(\mathbf{X}_c'\mathbf{X}_c)^{-1}\sigma_k^2$. The "final" estimate of $\mathbf{\Sigma}$ is

$$\begin{aligned}\hat{\hat{\mathbf{\Sigma}}} &= \frac{1}{N-c}[\mathbf{Y}'\mathbf{Y} - \hat{\mathbf{B}}_c'\mathbf{X}_c'\mathbf{X}_c\hat{\mathbf{B}}_c] \\ &= \frac{1}{N-c}[\mathbf{S}_T^{(yy)} - \mathbf{U}_c'\mathbf{U}_c]\end{aligned} \tag{5.3.7}$$

Under ideal circumstances, these final estimates should be obtained from a sample other than the one used for significance tests.

5.4 SAMPLE PROBLEM 1—CREATIVITY AND ACHIEVEMENT

Three hypotheses are of concern in the creativity-intelligence-achievement example. It is asserted by the researcher that both intelligence and creativity play significant roles in determining an individual's level of divergent achievement. In addition, individuals high in both intelligence and creativity are expected to perform particularly well, whereas a low degree of intelligence or creativity, or both, will result in low levels of divergent achievement. Thus the third hypothesis asserts that an interaction of the two predictors is a determinant of an individual's achievement level.

The two criterion variables are measures of the divergent achievements synthesis (y_1) and evaluation (y_2). The seven predictors are intelligence (x_1), three creativity measures (x_2, x_3, x_4), and three interaction or cross-product variables (x_5, x_6, x_7). The sum-of-products matrix of mean deviations for all nine measures ($\mathbf{S}_w$) is given in Section 3.4, along with means, standard deviations, and correlations. The partitions of $\mathbf{S}_w$ for y, x, and their cross products, are

$$\mathbf{S}_w^{(yy)} = \begin{bmatrix} 178.85 & 110.35 \\ 110.35 & 186.18 \end{bmatrix} \begin{matrix} y_1 \\ y_2 \end{matrix}$$
$$\qquad\qquad y_1 \qquad\quad y_2$$

$$\mathbf{S}_w^{(xx)} = \begin{bmatrix} 59.00 & & & & & & (\text{Symmetric}) \\ 5.55 & 59.00 & & & & & \\ 24.29 & 3.38 & 59.00 & & & & \\ 27.47 & 31.98 & 25.13 & 59.00 & & & \\ 5.56 & -3.06 & 18.56 & 1.19 & 43.35 & & \\ 28.65 & 18.56 & 38.66 & 24.42 & 22.27 & 104.70 & \\ 17.56 & 1.19 & 24.42 & 14.98 & 19.12 & 57.79 & 64.79 \end{bmatrix} \begin{matrix} x_1 \\ x_2 \\ x_3 \\ x_4 \\ x_5 \\ x_6 \\ x_7 \end{matrix}$$
$$x_1 \qquad x_2 \qquad x_3 \qquad x_4 \qquad x_5 \qquad x_6 \qquad x_7$$

$$\mathbf{S}_w^{(yx)} = [\mathbf{S}_w^{(xy)}]' = \begin{bmatrix} 65.79 & 21.29 & 35.23 & 40.74 & 4.56 & 45.38 & 31.79 \\ 56.69 & 17.66 & 40.49 & 33.58 & 20.22 & 40.17 & 29.77 \end{bmatrix} \begin{matrix} y_1 \\ y_2 \end{matrix}$$
$$x_1 \qquad x_2 \qquad x_3 \qquad x_4 \qquad x_5 \qquad x_6 \qquad x_7$$

The estimated regression coefficients are given in Chapter 4. The matrix (without the constant) is

$$\hat{\mathbf{B}} = [\mathbf{S}_w^{(xx)}]^{-1}\mathbf{S}_w^{(xy)} = \begin{bmatrix} 1.00 & .86 \\ .28 & .33 \\ .16 & .32 \\ -.04 & -.14 \\ -.16 & .24 \\ -.04 & -.16 \\ .25 & .20 \end{bmatrix} \begin{matrix} x_1 \\ x_2 \\ x_3 \\ x_4 \\ x_5 \\ x_6 \\ x_7 \end{matrix}$$
$$y_1 \qquad y_2$$

The three hypotheses may be represented as tests on portions of $\mathbf{B}$.

$$\mathbf{B}=\left[\begin{array}{c} \mathbf{B}_{h_1} \\ \hline \\ \mathbf{B}_{h_2} \\ \\ \hline \\ \mathbf{B}_{h_3} \\ \\ \end{array}\right]\begin{array}{ll} x_1 & \text{Intelligence} \\ x_2 & \\ x_3 & \text{Creativity} \\ x_4 & \\ x_5 & \\ x_6 & \text{Interactions} \\ x_7 & \end{array}$$

$$\quad y_1 \quad y_2$$

The three null hypotheses are H_{0_j}: $\mathbf{B}_{h_j}=\mathbf{0}$ ($j=1, 2, 3$). To test the hypotheses, the orthogonal estimates are computed and partitioned like $\mathbf{B}$. The lower triangular Cholesky factor of $\mathbf{S}_w^{(xx)}$ is

$$\mathbf{T}=\begin{bmatrix} 7.68 & & & & & & \text{(Zero)} \\ .72 & 7.65 & & & & & \\ 3.16 & .14 & 7.00 & & & & \\ 3.58 & 3.84 & 1.90 & 5.28 & & & \\ .72 & -.47 & 2.33 & -.76 & 6.05 & & \\ 3.73 & 2.07 & 3.80 & -.78 & 1.83 & 8.25 & \\ 2.29 & -.06 & 2.46 & .45 & 1.99 & 4.45 & 5.43 \end{bmatrix}$$

The orthogonal estimates are given by

$$\mathbf{U}=\mathbf{T}'\hat{\mathbf{B}}$$

$$=\left[\begin{array}{cc} 8.56 & 7.38 \\ \hline 1.97 & 1.61 \\ 1.12 & 2.42 \\ .07 & -.68 \\ \hline -.54 & 1.57 \\ .74 & -.40 \\ 1.35 & 1.11 \end{array}\right]=\left[\begin{array}{c} \mathbf{u}'_1 \\ \hline \mathbf{u}'_2 \\ \mathbf{u}'_3 \\ \mathbf{u}'_4 \\ \hline \mathbf{u}'_5 \\ \mathbf{u}'_6 \\ \mathbf{u}'_7 \end{array}\right]\begin{array}{l} \text{Intelligence} \\ \\ \text{Creativity, eliminating intelligence} \\ \\ \text{Interactions, eliminating} \\ \text{intelligence and creativity} \\ \\ \end{array}$$

The squares and products of the rows of $\mathbf{U}$ are combined for tests of hypotheses. The first in the order of elimination relates to intelligence, and has $q_{h_1}=1$ degree of freedom. That is,

$$\mathbf{S}_{H_1}=\mathbf{u}_1\mathbf{u}'_1=\mathbf{U}'_{h_1}\mathbf{U}_{h_1}$$

$$=\begin{bmatrix} 73.36 & 63.22 \\ 63.22 & 54.48 \end{bmatrix}\begin{array}{l} y_1 \\ y_2 \end{array}$$

$$\quad y_1 \qquad y_2$$

The second hypothesis matrix is for the three creativity measures, with $q_{h_2}=3$. That is,

$$\mathbf{S}_{H_2} = \sum_{i=2}^{4} \mathbf{u}_i\mathbf{u}'_i = \mathbf{U}'_{h_2}\mathbf{U}_{h_2} = \begin{bmatrix} 5.17 & 5.85 \\ 5.85 & 8.91 \end{bmatrix} \begin{matrix} y_1 \\ y_2 \end{matrix}$$
$$\qquad\qquad\qquad\qquad y_1 \quad y_2$$

The third hypothesis matrix, involving the interaction terms, has $q_{h_3}=3$ degrees of freedom. That is,

$$\mathbf{S}_{H_3} = \sum_{i=5}^{7} \mathbf{u}_i\mathbf{u}'_i = \mathbf{U}'_{h_3}\mathbf{U}_{h_3}$$
$$= \begin{bmatrix} 2.65 & .34 \\ .34 & 3.83 \end{bmatrix} \begin{matrix} y_1 \\ y_2 \end{matrix}$$
$$\quad y_1 \quad y_2$$

The error sum of products is

$$\mathbf{S}_E = \mathbf{S}_w^{(yy)} - \mathbf{U}'\mathbf{U}$$
$$= \begin{bmatrix} 178.85 & 110.35 \\ 110.35 & 186.18 \end{bmatrix} - \begin{bmatrix} 81.18 & 69.41 \\ 69.41 & 67.22 \end{bmatrix}$$
$$= \begin{bmatrix} 97.67 & 40.94 \\ 40.94 & 118.97 \end{bmatrix} \begin{matrix} y_1 \\ y_2 \end{matrix}$$
$$\quad y_1 \quad y_2$$

Error degrees of freedom are $n_e = 60-7-1 = 52$.

The hypothesis tested first is last in the order of elimination—that is, the interaction terms or H_{0_3}: $\mathbf{B}_{h_3} = \mathbf{0}$. The univariate F ratios for synthesis and evaluation are ratios of hypothesis and error mean squares. The interaction sum of products is $\mathbf{S}_{H_3}$. Then

$$F_1 = \frac{2.65/3}{97.67/52} = .47 \qquad F_2 = \frac{3.83/3}{118.97/52} = .56$$

Each has 3 and 52 degrees of freedom; neither exceeds the .05 critical value. The proportions of variation in y_1 and y_2 attributable to interaction, above and beyond intelligence and creativity, are $2.65/178.85 = .015$ and $3.83/186.18 = .021$, respectively.

For the multivariate and step-down tests of the same hypothesis, we form

$$\mathbf{S} = \mathbf{S}_E + \mathbf{S}_{H_3} = \begin{bmatrix} 100.32 & 41.28 \\ 41.28 & 122.80 \end{bmatrix}$$

The Cholesky factors of $\mathbf{S}_E$ and $\mathbf{S}$ may be used to find $|\mathbf{S}_E|$ and $|\mathbf{S}_E + \mathbf{S}_{H_3}|$, as well as to provide the conditional variances for step-down analysis. The factors are

$$\mathbf{T}_E = \begin{bmatrix} 9.88 & 0.00 \\ 4.14 & 10.09 \end{bmatrix} \qquad \mathbf{T}^* = \begin{bmatrix} 10.02 & 0.00 \\ 4.12 & 10.29 \end{bmatrix}$$

The determinant of a symmetric matrix is the squared product of the diagonal elements of the Cholesky factor (see Chapter 2). Thus

$$\begin{aligned}\Lambda &= \frac{|\mathbf{S}_E|}{|\mathbf{S}|} \\ &= \frac{(9.88\times 10.09)^2}{(10.02\times 10.29)^2} \\ &= .94\end{aligned}$$

within rounding error. For computing the multivariate F statistic, $p=2$, $s=2$ and $m=52$. The resulting value is $F=.5649$, with 6 and 102 degrees of freedom The critical F value is not exceeded.

The diagonal elements of $\mathbf{T}_E$ and $\mathbf{T}^*$ are employed in the step-down analysis The step-down statistic for synthesis is

$$\begin{aligned}F_1^* &= \frac{(10.02^2-9.88^2)}{9.88^2}\cdot\frac{52-1+1}{3} \\ &= .47\end{aligned}$$

F_1^* has 3 and 52 degrees of freedom. For evaluation, eliminating synthesis,

$$\begin{aligned}F_2^* &= \frac{(10.29^2-10.09^2)}{10.09^2}\cdot\frac{52-2+1}{3} \\ &= .67\end{aligned}$$

F_2^* has 3 and 51 degrees of freedom. Neither step-down F exceeds the corresponding critical value. From all results, H_{0_3} is accepted; $\mathbf{B}_{h_3}$ is null. *Interactions* of creativity and intelligence, above and beyond their individual effects, do not account for divergent achievement levels.

Finding no significant interaction, we may pool $\mathbf{S}_{H_3}$ with the error sum of products. The new estimate is

$$\begin{aligned}\mathbf{S}_E' &= \mathbf{S}_E + \mathbf{S}_{H_3} \\ &= \begin{bmatrix} 100.32 & 41.28 \\ 41.28 & 122.80 \end{bmatrix}\end{aligned}$$

$\mathbf{S}_E'$ has $52+3=55$ degrees of freedom. (The procedure is also computationally efficient, since the Cholesky factor of $[\mathbf{S}_E+\mathbf{S}_{H_3}]$ was computed for testing the interaction hypothesis. $\mathbf{T}^*$ may now be employed as the factor of $\mathbf{S}_E$ for the test of the next-to-last, or creativity, hypothesis.)

Should the interaction terms have been significant, tests of the creativity effects would not be valid (a) because the sums of products for creativity are confounded with nonzero interaction components and (b) because interaction in particular indicates that any main effect of intelligence does not apply equally across creativity levels, and vice versa.

Having accepted H_{0_3}, we repeat the testing procedure for creativity, eliminating intelligence (H_{0_2}). The hypothesis matrix is $\mathbf{S}_{H_2}$; the error matrix is $\mathbf{S}_E'$. The univariate tests for the two criterion measures are

$$F_1 = \frac{5.17/3}{100.32/55} = .94 \qquad F_2 = \frac{8.91/3}{122.80/55} = 1.33$$

Each ratio has 3 and 55 degrees of freedom. Neither exceeds the .05 critical F value of 2.8. The percentages of variation accounted for by creativity, beyond that accounted for by intelligence, are $100\times(5.17/178.85)=2.89$ for synthesis, and $100\times(8.91/186.18)=4.78$ for evaluation. Neither is appreciably larger than the variation attributable to the interaction terms.

For the multivariate tests, the matrix to be factored is

$$\mathbf{S}=\mathbf{S}_E'+\mathbf{S}_{H_2}=\begin{bmatrix}105.49 & 47.13\\ 47.13 & 131.71\end{bmatrix}$$

The Cholesky factor is

$$\mathbf{T}^*=\begin{bmatrix}10.27 & 0.00\\ 4.59 & 10.52\end{bmatrix}$$

Using the diagonal elements of $\mathbf{T}^*$ and the factor of $\mathbf{S}_E'$,

$$\begin{aligned}\Lambda &= \frac{|\mathbf{S}_E'|}{|\mathbf{S}|}\\ &= \frac{(10.02\times 10.29)^2}{(10.27\times 10.52)^2}\\ &= .91\end{aligned}$$

The multivariate F statistic is computed with $m=55$ (assuming $n_e=55$). The value is $F=.8749$, with 6 and 108 degrees of freedom. We have insufficient data to reject H_{0_2}.

The step-down statistic for synthesis is

$$\begin{aligned}F_1^* &= \frac{(10.27^2-10.02^2)}{10.02^2}\cdot\frac{55-1+1}{3}\\ &= .94\end{aligned}$$

F_1^* has 3 and 55 degrees of freedom. For evaluation, eliminating synthesis,

$$\begin{aligned}F_2^* &= \frac{(10.52^2-10.29^2)}{10.29^2}\cdot\frac{55-2+1}{3}\\ &= .82\end{aligned}$$

F_2^* has 3 and 54 degrees of freedom. No test statistic is significant. Creativity does not play a role in divergent achievement outcomes, above and beyond intelligence. H_{0_2} is accepted.

Finding creativity nonsignificant, we proceed with the test of the intelligence effect. (Had the creativity effect been significant, intelligence could not be tested with this order of predictors.) $\mathbf{S}_{H_2}$ may be pooled with the sum of products for error to obtain $\mathbf{S}_E''=[\mathbf{S}_E'+\mathbf{S}_{H_2}]$ with $55+3=58$ degrees of freedom. The hypothesis matrix is $\mathbf{S}_{H_1}=\mathbf{u}_1\mathbf{u}_1'$. The univariate F statistics are

$$F_1=\frac{73.36/1}{105.49/58}=40.33 \qquad F_2=\frac{54.48/1}{131.71/58}=23.99$$

Each has 1 and 58 degrees of freedom. Both exceed the .05 critical F value.

For multivariate tests, the "total" matrix is $\mathbf{S} = \mathbf{S}_E'' + \mathbf{S}_{H_1}$. The Cholesky factor of $\mathbf{S}$ is

$$\mathbf{T}^* = \begin{bmatrix} 13.37 & 0.00 \\ 8.25 & 10.87 \end{bmatrix}$$

From the diagonal elements,

$$\begin{aligned} \Lambda &= \frac{|\mathbf{S}_E''|}{|\mathbf{S}|} \\ &= \frac{(10.27 \times 10.52)^2}{(13.37 \times 10.87)^2} \\ &= .55 \end{aligned}$$

The corresponding F statistic has the multiplier $m=57$. The F value is 23.0717 with 2 and 57 degrees of freedom. H_{0_1} is rejected at $\alpha = .05$.

The step-down test statistic for synthesis is

$$\begin{aligned} F_1^* &= \frac{(13.37^2 - 10.27^2)}{10.27^2} \cdot \frac{58-1+1}{1} \\ &= 40.33 \end{aligned}$$

F_1^* has 1 and 58 degrees of freedom. The step-down statistic for evaluation, eliminating synthesis, is

$$\begin{aligned} F_2^* &= \frac{(10.87^2 - 10.52^2)}{10.52^2} \cdot \frac{58-2+1}{1} \\ &= 3.84 \end{aligned}$$

F_2^* has 1 and 57 degrees of freedom. F_2^* does not exceed the .05 critical value, while F_1^* is significant. We conclude that the relationship between the criterion and predictor variables is concentrated in the synthesis measure. If we assume that evaluation is the more complex process, it appears that the simpler process of synthesis is sufficient to account for the significant relationship with intelligence.

The percentages of variation in synthesis and evaluation accounted for by intelligence are $100 \times (73.36/178.85) = 41.02$, and $100 \times (54.48/186.18) = 29.26$, respectively. Since the hypothesis involves only the first predictor variable in the order of elimination, these values are simply the squared correlations between achievement and intelligence, as contained in $\mathbf{R}_w$.

The findings are summarized in Table 5.4.1. Mean squares and cross products $[\mathbf{M}_{H_j} = \mathbf{S}_{H_j}/q_{h_j}]$ are presented in place of sums of squares for ease of interpretation (especially for the error matrix). The table is read from the bottom upward. Hypotheses are maintained or rejected by the multivariate test statistic. In Table 5.4.1, no significant Λ is encountered until intelligence. Finding this, we inspect the univariate results to isolate the source of the effect. When criterion measures have a natural order (as they may have here, by complexity), the step-down results may be used in place of Λ for the decision about H_0. In the

Table 5.4.1 Summary of Results for Creativity and Achievement Significance Tests

Source of Variation	Mean Squares and Products: Synthesis	Mean Squares and Products: Evaluation	Degrees of freedom	Multivariate Λ	Multivariate F	Univariate F (percent of variation): Synthesis	Univariate F (percent of variation): Evaluation
lligence	73.36	63.22	$q_{h_1}=1$	.55	23.07*	40.33*	23.99*
	63.22	54.48				(41.02)	(29.26)
ativity, liminating ntelligence	1.72	1.95	$q_{h_2}=3$	.91	.87	.94	1.33
	1.95	2.97				(2.89)	(4.78)
raction, liminating reativity and ntelligence	.88	.11	$q_{h_3}=3$	.94	.56	.47	.56
	.11	1.28				(1.48)	(2.06)
idual	$\hat{\Sigma}=$ 1.88	.79	$n_e=52$				
	.79	2.29					
al Sum of roducts)	$\mathbf{S}_w^{(yy)}=$ 178.85	110.35	$N-1=59$				
	110.35	186.18					

*Significant at $p<.05$.

data under consideration, only general intelligence plays a role in divergent achievement. There does not appear to be a differential creativity effect, either across all intelligence levels (there is a wide range of intelligence scores) or at particular levels of intelligence. The univariate results indicate that synthesis is more affected by intelligence than is evaluation. The step-down statistics indicate that in fact the more complex trait, evaluation, does not contribute to the association with the predictors. The relationship between the two sets of measures is parsimoniously summarized in the correlation of the two simplest constructs, intelligence and synthesis.

Bargmann (1967) has recommended that prior to testing individual components of a linear model the researcher should consider the overall relationship of the independent and dependent variables. At times we are concerned only with such a relationship, such as in deciding whether to employ covariates in analysis-of-variance designs. The test is obtained by repeating the test procedure with the overall regression sum of products,

$$\mathbf{S}_R = \textstyle\sum_j \mathbf{S}_{H_j} = \mathbf{U}'\mathbf{U}$$

The test criterion is

$$\Lambda = \frac{|\mathbf{S}_E|}{|\mathbf{S}_E+\mathbf{S}_R|} = \frac{|\mathbf{S}_E|}{|\mathbf{S}_w^{(yy)}|}$$

For the example, the Cholesky factor of $\mathbf{S}_w^{(yy)}$ is

$$\mathbf{T}^* = \begin{bmatrix} 13.37 & 0.00 \\ 8.25 & 10.87 \end{bmatrix}$$

and

$$\Lambda = \frac{(9.88 \times 10.09)^2}{(13.37 \times 10.87)^2} = .47$$

Applying the F approximation,

$$m = 52 - \frac{2+1-7}{2} = 54$$

and $F = 3.3329$. F has 14 and 102 degrees of freedom. With $\alpha = .05$, we rejec the null hypothesis that the entire $q \times p$ matrix $\mathbf{B}$ is null.

Having decided that only intelligence is related to the criterion measures we will reestimate $\mathbf{B}$ and $\mathbf{\Sigma}$ with only the single predictor. The final estimates ar

$$\hat{\mathbf{B}}_1 = (\mathbf{T}_1^{-1})'\mathbf{U}_1 = (\sqrt{59})^{-1}[8.56 \quad 7.38] = [1.11 \quad .96]$$

Synthesis Evaluation

and

$$\hat{\mathbf{\Sigma}} = \frac{1}{N-1-1}(\mathbf{S}_w^{(yy)} - \mathbf{U}_1'\mathbf{U}_1) = \begin{bmatrix} 1.82 & .81 \\ .81 & 2.27 \end{bmatrix} \begin{matrix} \text{Synthesis} \\ \text{Evaluation} \end{matrix}$$

Synthesis Evaluation

With the other independent variables eliminated from the model, the re gression coefficients for intelligence have gone from 1.00 to 1.11, and from .8 to .96, for the two criterion variables. $\mathbf{\Sigma}$ is now more efficiently estimated wit 58 degrees of freedom. Thus the "best" prediction model is

$$\begin{bmatrix} y_{i1} - y_{\cdot 1} \\ y_{i2} - y_{\cdot 2} \end{bmatrix} = \begin{bmatrix} 1.11 \\ .96 \end{bmatrix} (x_i - x_\cdot) + \begin{bmatrix} e_{i1} \\ e_{i2} \end{bmatrix}$$

y_1 is the synthesis random variable, y_2 evaluation, and x intelligence.

CHAPTER 6

Correlation

The social scientist often requires a measure of the strength of association of one or more criterion measures, with one or more antecedents. For this purpose we have the *correlation coefficient*, a measure of the degree of interrelation of two random variables.

We shall denote the correlation of random variables x and y, as ρ_{xy}. The squared value, ${\rho_{xy}}^2$, is the *proportion of variation in y that can be attributed to x.* Equivalently, ${\rho_{xy}}^2$ is the proportion of decrease in y-variation if the effects of x are removed. Let us represent the variance of y by $\mathscr{V}(y)$, and the conditional variance of y *given* x or of y for all subjects having the same x-value, as $\mathscr{V}(y|x)$. The squared correlation coefficient is

$$ {\rho_{xy}}^2 = \frac{\mathscr{V}(y) - \mathscr{V}(y|x)}{\mathscr{V}(y)} \tag{6.0.1} $$

Since $\mathscr{V}(y) \geqslant \mathscr{V}(y|x)$, it follows that $0 \leqslant {\rho_{xy}}^2 \leqslant 1$; for the coefficient itself, $-1 \leqslant \rho_{xy} \leqslant 1$.

If much of the variation in y can be attributed to the x-measure, $\mathscr{V}(y|x)$ will be small and ρ_{xy} large. If $\mathscr{V}(y|x)$ is close to $\mathscr{V}(y)$, x does not account for the y-variance, and ρ_{xy} is close to zero. When $\rho_{xy} = 0$, x and y are said to be *uncorrelated.* The correlation coefficient is symmetric ($\rho_{xy} = \rho_{yx}$) by interchanging y and x in Eq. 6.0.1. Thus when we use measures of correlation, the designation of independent and dependent variables is arbitrary.

For tests of significance on correlations, we shall assume that x and y have a bivariate normal distribution. In earlier chapters we assumed instead that the values of x (the predictor variables) are fixed constants and known without error. However, it was shown that the conditional distribution of y given x has the same variance in either case. If the x values are regarded as fixed constants, ρ_{xy} can still be defined as in 6.0.1, and the appropriate estimator remains unchanged, although the derivation is different. Under the normality assumption, uncorrelated variables are also statistically independent.

In this section we discuss only linear measures of correlation. Thus, positive ρ_{xy} will indicate the extent to which high values of x are associated with proportionally high values of y, across the entire range of both measures. Negative ρ_{xy} is indicative of the extent to which low y is associated with high x and high y with low x, across the entire range of both.

Correlational measures may be categorized according to the number of variates being related. In the case of *simple correlation*, ρ_{xy} is an indicator of the association of the two individual measured variables. The *partial correlation* is an index of association of two variables holding constant or eliminating q (≥ 1) additional variables, or *covariables*. The *multiple correlation* is a measure of association of a single variate, with a weighted linear function of q (≥ 1) additional measures. The *canonical correlation* reflects the association of two variates, of which each is itself a linear function of two or more original measures.

The simple correlation may be considered the association of one y measure with one x measure. (The partial correlation is a special case of simple correlation.) In contrast, the multiple correlation is the association of one y-measure with two or more x-measures. The canonical correlation is the correlation of two or more y-measures with two or more x-measures. Unlike the simpler coefficients, more than a single canonical correlation may be necessary to describe the relationship between two sets of variables. In each case the more general measure subsumes the simpler. A canonical correlation involving one y- or one x-measure is identically the multiple correlation of that measure with the other set. The multiple correlation of one y-measure and one x-variable is identically the simple correlation of the two.

Let $\mathbf{y}$ be a $p \times 1$ vector variable, with component measures y_j ($j = 1, 2, \ldots, p$); let $\mathbf{x}$ be a $q \times 1$ vector variable with component measures x_k ($k = 1, 2, \ldots, q$). $\mathbf{v}$ is the $(p+q) \times 1$ vector of measures for all y- and x-variables. That is,

$$\mathbf{v}' = [\mathbf{y}', \mathbf{x}']$$

The expectation of $\mathbf{v}$ is

$$\mathscr{E}(\mathbf{v}) = \boldsymbol{\mu} = \begin{bmatrix} \boldsymbol{\mu}_y \\ \boldsymbol{\mu}_x \end{bmatrix} \tag{6.0.2}$$

The variance–covariance matrix of all measures is $(p+q)$-symmetric.

$$\mathscr{V}(\mathbf{v}) = \mathscr{E}\left[\begin{pmatrix} \mathbf{y} \\ \mathbf{x} \end{pmatrix} - \begin{pmatrix} \boldsymbol{\mu}_y \\ \boldsymbol{\mu}_x \end{pmatrix}\right]\left[\begin{pmatrix} \mathbf{y} \\ \mathbf{x} \end{pmatrix} - \begin{pmatrix} \boldsymbol{\mu}_y \\ \boldsymbol{\mu}_x \end{pmatrix}\right]'$$

$$= \left[\begin{array}{c|c} \boldsymbol{\Sigma}^{(yy)} & \boldsymbol{\Sigma}^{(yx)} \\ \hline \boldsymbol{\Sigma}^{(xy)} & \boldsymbol{\Sigma}^{(xx)} \end{array}\right] \begin{array}{l} p \text{ rows} \\ \\ q \text{ rows} \end{array}$$

$$\begin{array}{cc} p & q \\ \text{columns} & \text{columns} \end{array}$$

$$= \boldsymbol{\Sigma} \tag{6.0.3}$$

The simple correlation is the correlation of y and x when there is only one variable in each set ($p = q = 1$). Partial correlation is the association of y_1 and y_2 ($p = 2$) on the conditional distribution of q (≥ 1) x-variables. Multiple correlation is the correlation of y and $\mathbf{x}$ with $p = 1$ and $q \geq 1$. Canonical correlation is the association measure for $\mathbf{y}$ and $\mathbf{x}$ when $p \geq 1$ and $q \geq 1$.

To estimate $\boldsymbol{\Sigma}$, let $\mathbf{y}_i$ be the vector of y-scores for observation i, and $\mathbf{x}_i$ be the vector of x-scores for the same subject. The augmented vector is

$$\mathbf{v}_i' = [\mathbf{y}_i' \ \mathbf{x}_i'] \tag{6.0.4}$$

The estimate of $\boldsymbol{\mu}$ is

$$\begin{aligned}\mathbf{v}_.' &= \frac{1}{N}\sum_{i=1}^{N} \mathbf{v}_i' \\ &= [\mathbf{y}_.', \mathbf{x}_.']\end{aligned} \tag{6.0.5}$$

where N is the total number of observations.

The sum of products of mean deviations is given by Eq. 3.3.7:

$$\mathbf{S}_w = \sum_{i=1}^{N} (\mathbf{v}_i - \mathbf{v}_.)(\mathbf{v}_i - \mathbf{v}_.)' \tag{6.0.6}$$

$\mathbf{S}_w$ may be partitioned for $\mathbf{y}$ and $\mathbf{x}$ in the same way as $\boldsymbol{\Sigma}$ in Eq. 6.0.3. That is,

$$\mathbf{S}_w = \left[\begin{array}{c|c} \mathbf{S}_w^{(yy)} & \mathbf{S}_w^{(yx)} \\ \hline \mathbf{S}_w^{(xy)} & \mathbf{S}_w^{(xx)} \end{array}\right] \begin{array}{l} p \text{ rows} \\ q \text{ rows} \end{array} \tag{6.0.6a}$$

p columns q columns

The unbiased sample covariance matrix is

$$\begin{aligned}\hat{\boldsymbol{\Sigma}} &= \mathbf{V}_w \\ &= \frac{1}{N-1}\mathbf{S}_w \\ &= \left[\begin{array}{c|c} \mathbf{V}_w^{(yy)} & \mathbf{V}_w^{(yx)} \\ \hline \mathbf{V}_w^{(xy)} & \mathbf{V}_w^{(xx)} \end{array}\right] \begin{array}{l} p \text{ rows} \\ q \text{ rows} \end{array}\end{aligned} \tag{6.0.7}$$

p columns q columns

$\mathbf{V}_w$ may be partitioned for $\mathbf{y}$ and $\mathbf{x}$ in the same way as $\boldsymbol{\Sigma}$ and $\mathbf{S}_w$. Sample correlation results may be derived from these matrices. When there is more than a single subgroup of observations, the pooled $\mathbf{S}_W$ from Eq. 3.3.21 must replace Eq. 6.0.6 to avoid biasing variances and correlations by mean differences.

6.1 SIMPLE CORRELATION

The simple correlation of y and x is obtained by substituting in Eq. 6.0.1, with $p=q=1$. Terms $\boldsymbol{\Sigma}^{(yy)}=\sigma_y^2$, $\boldsymbol{\Sigma}^{(xx)}=\sigma_x^2$ and $\boldsymbol{\Sigma}^{(yx)}=\sigma_{yx}$ of 6.0.3 are scalars. The variance of y is $\mathscr{V}(y)=\sigma_y^2$. The conditional variance of y eliminating x is given by Eq. 3.2.7; that is,

$$\mathscr{V}(y|x) = \sigma_y^2 - \frac{\sigma_{yx}^2}{\sigma_x^2} \tag{6.1.1}$$

The squared correlation is

$$\rho_{yx}{}^2 = \frac{\sigma_y{}^2 - [\sigma_y{}^2 - (\sigma_{yx}{}^2/\sigma_x{}^2)]}{\sigma_y{}^2}$$

$$= \frac{\sigma_{yx}{}^2}{\sigma_y{}^2\,\sigma_x{}^2} \tag{6.1.2}$$

The correlation is

$$\rho_{yx} = \frac{\sigma_{yx}}{\sigma_y\,\sigma_x} \tag{6.1.3}$$

ρ_{yx} is positive or negative depending upon the sign of the covariance σ_{yx}. By the Cauchy-Schwarz inequality, $-1 \leq \rho_{yx} \leq 1$. Since $\sigma_{yx} = \sigma_{xy}$ then $\rho_{yx} = \rho_{xy}$.

It is demonstrated in Chapter 3 that Eq. 6.1.3 is the covariance of variables y and x after both have been standardized. We may simultaneously obtain the matrix of simple correlations between *every pair* of $p+q$ measures in $\mathbf{y}$ and $\mathbf{x}$ by standardizing the entire vector $\mathbf{v}$. Let

$$\boldsymbol{\Delta} = \text{diag}\,(\boldsymbol{\Sigma}) \tag{6.1.4}$$

where $\boldsymbol{\Delta}$ is the diagonal matrix of variances. Then the vector of standard scores is

$$\mathbf{z} = \boldsymbol{\Delta}^{-1/2}(\mathbf{v} - \boldsymbol{\mu}) \tag{6.1.5}$$

The variance–covariance matrix of $\mathbf{z}$ is the $(p+q)$–square correlation matrix

$$\mathcal{R} = \boldsymbol{\Delta}^{-1/2}\boldsymbol{\Sigma}\boldsymbol{\Delta}^{-1/2} \tag{6.1.6}$$

The diagonal elements of $\mathcal{R}$ are unity; the jk off-diagonal element is ρ_{jk}, the correlation of variates v_j and v_k.

The estimate of $\mathcal{R}$ is obtained by performing the same operations on $\hat{\boldsymbol{\Sigma}}$ in Eq. 6.0.7. The estimated matrix is

$$\hat{\mathcal{R}} = \mathbf{R}_w = \mathbf{D}_w{}^{-1/2}\mathbf{V}_w\mathbf{D}_w{}^{-1/2} \tag{6.1.7}$$

with

$$\mathbf{D}_w = \text{diag}\,(\mathbf{V}_w) \tag{6.1.8}$$

$\mathbf{D}_w$ is the diagonal matrix of sample variances; $\mathbf{D}_w{}^{-1/2}$ contains the inverse standard deviations. The jk element of $\mathbf{R}_w$ is the sample correlation of v_j and v_k. Let us represent the element as $[r_w]_{jk}$ or r_{jk}. Then

$$r_{jk} = \frac{[v_w]_{jk}}{\sqrt{[v_w]_{jj}[v_w]_{kk}}}$$

$$= \frac{\hat{\sigma}_{jk}}{\hat{\sigma}_j\hat{\sigma}_k} \tag{6.1.9}$$

$[v_w]_{jk}$ is the sample covariance, and $[v_w]_{jj}$ and $[v_w]_{kk}$ are the variances from $\mathbf{V}_w$.

Eq. 6.1.9 may also be expressed in raw-score form. Let v_{ij} be the score for observation i on variable v_j; let v_{ik} be the score on variable v_k. Then Eq. 6.1.9 is equivalently

$$r_{jk}=\frac{\sum_{i=1}^{N}(v_{ij}-v_{\cdot j})(v_{ik}-v_{\cdot k})}{\sqrt{\sum_{i=1}^{N}(v_{ij}-v_{\cdot j})^2\sum_{i=1}^{N}(v_{ik}-v_{\cdot k})^2}} \tag{6.1.9a}$$

$v_{\cdot j}$ and $v_{\cdot k}$ are the means on v_j and v_k respectively, from $\mathbf{v}_{\cdot}$ (see Eq. 6.0.5). Expressions 6.1.9 and 6.1.9a are the simple Pearsonian correlation of v_j and v_k, and agree with common elementary statistical presentations.

The estimate of $\mathcal{R}$ or ρ_{jk} is not unbiased. Olkin and Pratt (1958) have provided a minimum-variance unbiased estimator for each coefficient, as a function of the sample value. The actual estimation is quite complex. However, for N of 9 or greater, a less-biased estimate is obtained by multiplying r_{jk} by a simple correction factor (see Olkin, 1966). The adjusted estimate is

$$r_{jk}^{*}=r_{jk}\left\{1+\frac{1-r_{jk}^{2}}{2(N-4)}\right\} \tag{6.1.10}$$

All of the correlations in $\mathbf{R}_w$ may be of interest. When data are analyzed through a regression model, it is likely that the intercorrelations between the criterion variables and the predictors are of primary concern. $\mathbf{R}_w$ may be partitioned like $\mathbf{\Sigma}$ and $\mathbf{S}_w$. That is,

$$\mathbf{R}_w=\left[\begin{array}{c|c}\mathbf{R}_w^{(yy)} & \mathbf{R}_w^{(yx)}\\ \hline \mathbf{R}_w^{(xy)} & \mathbf{R}_w^{(xx)}\end{array}\right]\begin{array}{l}p \text{ rows}\\ q \text{ rows}\end{array} \tag{6.1.11}$$

$$\quad p \text{ columns} \qquad q \text{ columns}$$

The intercorrelations of predictors and criteria comprise the $p\times q$ submatrix $\mathbf{R}_w^{(yx)}$.

The square of any element $[r_{jk}]^2$ of $\mathbf{R}_w^{(yx)}$, is the proportion of variance of y_j attributable to the particular predictor x_k. No other variable is considered in evaluating r_{jk}. Thus r_{jk} is perhaps the simplest and most useful measure of association for interpreting the regression results. The x-variable having the highest simple correlation with y_j is the *single best predictor*; the x-variable having lowest correlation with y_j is the poorest predictor. Further, the sign on r_{jk} indicates the direction in which y_j and x_k covary, positively or negatively.

In addition to the sign and magnitude of the correlations, we may wish to test hypotheses about the population value ρ_{jk}. In particular, we shall consider three hypotheses:

1. We may wish to test whether there is any nonzero correlation of y_j and x_k in the population. The null hypothesis is

$$H_0\colon\ \rho_{jk}=0 \tag{6.1.12}$$

To test H_0 against the alternative that $\rho_{jk}\neq 0$, the test statistic is

$$t=\frac{r_{jk}\sqrt{N-2}}{\sqrt{1-r_{jk}^{2}}} \tag{6.1.13}$$

where t follows a t distribution with $N-2$ degrees of freedom. H_0 is rejected against the two-tailed alternative if $|t|$ exceeds the upper $100\alpha/2$ percentage point of t with $N-2$ degrees of freedom. One-tailed alternatives are considered in the usual manner. Also, tables of the critical values of $|r_{jk}|$, above which H_0 is rejected, are provided in numerous books (e.g., Fisher and Yates, 1942; Edwards, 1960; Glass and Stanley, 1970). The test that $\rho_{jk}=0$ is equivalent to a simultaneous test that $\beta_{jk}=\beta_{kj}=0$, where β_{jk} and β_{kj} are the simple regression weights for y_j and x_k.

2. It is possible to test whether ρ_{jk} is equal to a value other than zero. The null hypothesis is

$$H_0\colon\ \rho_{jk}=\rho^* \tag{6.1.14}$$

where ρ^* is any constant between -1 and 1.

When population ρ_{jk} is nonzero, the distribution of r_{jk} is significantly more complex. For small samples, and ρ_{jk} to tenths of units, David (1938) has provided tables of the distribution of r_{jk} in intervals of .05. To test H_0, r_{jk} is computed and compared to David's tables, with parameters N and ρ^*. From the table we read the probability of observing r_{jk}, assuming ρ^* to be the population value. If the probability is less than α, H_0 is rejected with confidence $1-\alpha$; otherwise H_0 is maintained.

As N increases, r_{jk} assumes a normal-like form regardless of ρ_{jk}. However, the closer $|\rho_{jk}|$ is to unity, the higher N must be to attain normality. Fisher (1921) has provided a transformation of r_{jk} that takes a normal form with smaller N than is required for r_{jk} itself. Fisher's transformation is

$$z'=1/2\log_e\left[\frac{1+r_{jk}}{1-r_{jk}}\right] \tag{6.1.15}$$

z' tends toward a normal distribution with large N. The expectation and variance of z' are approximately

$$\mathscr{E}(z')\approx 1/2\log_e\left[\frac{1+\rho_{jk}}{1-\rho_{jk}}\right]+\frac{\rho_{jk}}{2(N-1)} \tag{6.1.16}$$

and

$$\mathscr{V}(z')\approx\frac{1}{N-1}+\frac{4-\rho_{jk}^2}{2(N-1)^2} \tag{6.1.17}$$

For even moderate N, the second term in Eq. 6.1.16 is small, and $\mathscr{V}(z')$ is close to $1/(N-3)$. These simpler forms are generally those seen in textbook presentations.

To use z' to test $H_0\colon\ \rho_{jk}=\rho^*$, let

$$\zeta=1/2\log_e\left[\frac{1+\rho^*}{1-\rho^*}\right] \tag{6.1.18}$$

The test statistic is

$$Z=(z'-\zeta)\sqrt{N-3} \tag{6.1.19}$$

Z has approximately a standard normal distribution. H_0 is rejected with confidence $1-\alpha$ if $|Z|$ exceeds the $100\alpha/2$ upper percentage point of the standard normal distribution. Tables of the transformation from r_{jk} to z' are provided in most elementary textbooks.

Fisher's transformation may also be used to obtain an interval estimate of ρ_{jk}. The interval is first computed for the transformed coefficient, ζ. The $1-\alpha$ interval is

$$\left(z' - \frac{Z_{\alpha/2}}{\sqrt{N-3}}\right) \leqslant \zeta \leqslant \left(z' + \frac{Z_{\alpha/2}}{\sqrt{N-3}}\right) \tag{6.1.20}$$

Both limits are referred to the z' tables. The corresponding r_{jk} values are the limits for the $1-\alpha$ interval on the population coefficient ρ_{jk}.

To compare the correlations between variates y_j and x_k across two or more independent groups, the z' transforms may be treated as the dependent variable in analysis-of-variance designs. Each z' is assumed to be distributed normally with variance $1/(N-3)$. Nonorthogonal analysis models are required if the correlations are based upon different numbers of observations. In using z' transforms with programs designed for tests on means, $N-3$ is substituted for the number of observations in subclasses. That is, the z' score is treated as a mean score for a particular group, having $N-3$ independent observations. In this manner, the homogeneity of correlations may be tested across one or more sampling factors, just as we conduct tests on means.

3. We may test whether two variables have the same correlation with a third. This test is of particular value in comparing the simple predictive power of two x-variables, or in comparing the effects of the same x_k on two criterion measures.

The null hypothesis is

$$H_0\colon\ \rho_{jk} = \rho_{jl} \tag{6.1.21}$$

H_0 asserts that the correlation of y_j and x_k is the same as that of y_j and x_l. Since the two correlations are from a common population, they are not independent. The standard error of the difference, $d = r_{jk} - r_{jl}$, must take into account the correlation of x_k and x_l—that is, r_{kl}. It is shown in Olkin and Siotani (1964) that an appropriate test statistic is

$$Z = \frac{r_{jk} - r_{jl}}{\hat{\sigma}_d} \tag{6.1 22}$$

where

$$\hat{\sigma}_d^2 = \frac{1}{N-1}[(1-r_{jk}^2)^2 + (1-r_{jl}^2)^2 - 2r_{kl}^3 - (2r_{kl} - r_{jk}r_{jl})(1 - r_{jk}^2 - r_{jl}^2 - r_{kl}^2)] \tag{6.1.23}$$

Z is distributed in standard normal form. H_0 is rejected in favor of the two-sided alternative if $|Z|$ exceeds the $100\alpha/2$ upper percentage point of the unit normal distribution.

Example

The intercorrelations of the five measures of Table 3.3.1 are given in Chapter 3.

$$\mathbf{R}_w = \left[\begin{array}{cc|ccc} 1.00 & & & & \text{(Symmetric)} \\ .72 & 1.00 & & & \\ \hline .75 & .61 & 1.00 & & \\ .17 & .63 & .19 & 1.00 & \\ .40 & .51 & .56 & .11 & 1.00 \end{array}\right] \begin{array}{c} y_1 \\ y_2 \\ x_1 \\ x_2 \\ x_3 \end{array}$$

$$\quad y_1 \quad y_2 \quad x_1 \quad x_2 \quad x_3$$

The total sample size is $N=15$. All of the correlations are positive. Let us test to see whether there is any significant correlation of y_1 and x_2. The correlation is $r_{12}=.17$. The test statistic is

$$t=\frac{.17\sqrt{15-2}}{\sqrt{1-.17^2}}=.63$$

t does not exceed the .05 critical t value with 13 degrees of freedom. The correlation is not significant.

To determine whether y_1 is predicted better than y_2 from x_1 alone, we may test

$$H_0\colon \rho_{11} \leqslant \rho_{21}$$

against the alternative that $\rho_{11} > \rho_{21}$. The difference is $d=.75-.61=.14$. The variance is

$$\hat{\sigma}_d^2=\frac{1}{14}\{(1-.75^2)^2+(1-.61^2)^2-2(.72^3)$$
$$-[2(.72)-.75(.61)]\cdot(1-.75^2-.61^2-.72^2)\}=.0204$$

and

$$\hat{\sigma}_d=.143$$

The test statistic is

$$Z=\frac{.14}{.14}=1.00$$

Z does not exceed the .05 critical value of the standard normal distribution. Although the correlations are in the direction of H_A, they are not significantly different.

Tests on one or a few correlations are useful in providing information about particular hypothesized relationships. Correlations among many variables for the same sample of observations are not independent, however. Care should be taken to minimize the number of individual tests that are conducted. When many tests are made from the same data and are not independent, statistical error rates may be inflated sufficiently to invalidate all of them.

6.2 PARTIAL CORRELATION

The partial correlation of variates y_i and y_j is their simple correlation evaluated on the conditional distribution of q (≥ 1) additional variates, x_k. Restricting the correlation to specific values of the x-variables is termed "holding the x_k's constant," or "removing the effects of the x_k." The partial correlation is the estimate of ρ_{ij} that would be obtained if all observations had identical scores on the x_k measures. If all variables are normal, the conditional distributions of y_i and y_j have the same covariance matrix, regardless of the values of the x_k assumed. Thus the partial correlation does not depend on which values of x_k are observed.

Let $\mathbf{v}' = [\mathbf{y}', \mathbf{x}']$ be the $(p+q)$-element normal vector random variable, with expectation and covariance matrices given by Eqs. 6.0.2 and 6.0.3, respectively. The conditional distribution of $\mathbf{y}$, given $\mathbf{x}$, is p-variate normal, with expectation given by Eq. 3.2.9. That is,

$$\mathscr{E}(\mathbf{y}|\mathbf{x}) = \boldsymbol{\Sigma}^{(yx)}[\boldsymbol{\Sigma}^{(xx)}]^{-1}(\mathbf{x}-\boldsymbol{\mu}_x)+\boldsymbol{\mu}_y \tag{6.2.1}$$

The covariance matrix of $\mathbf{y}$ given $\mathbf{x}$, regardless of the $\mathbf{x}$-value, is given by Eq. 3.2.10. That is,

$$\begin{aligned}\mathscr{V}(\mathbf{y}|\mathbf{x}) &= \boldsymbol{\Sigma}^{(yy)} - \boldsymbol{\Sigma}^{(yx)}[\boldsymbol{\Sigma}^{(xx)}]^{-1}\boldsymbol{\Sigma}^{(xy)} \\ &= \boldsymbol{\Sigma}_{yy|x}\end{aligned} \tag{6.2.2}$$

The estimate of $\boldsymbol{\Sigma}$ is obtained from the partition of $\mathbf{S}_w$ in expression 6.0.6a. The sum of products for $\mathbf{y}$ given $\mathbf{x}$ is

$$\mathbf{S}_E = \mathbf{S}_w^{(yy)} - \mathbf{S}_w^{(yx)}[\mathbf{S}_w^{(xx)}]^{-1}\mathbf{S}_w^{(xy)} \tag{6.2.3}$$

Note that Eq. 6.2.3 is the error sum of products, or sum of products of $\mathbf{y}$ given $\mathbf{x}$ under the linear regression model, as in expression 5.1.11. $\mathbf{S}_w^{(yy)}$ has $N-1$ degrees of freedom. The sum of products of q linear functions of $\mathbf{y}$ are subtracted, leaving $N-q-1$ degrees of freedom for $\mathbf{S}_E$. The estimate of $\boldsymbol{\Sigma}_{yy|x}$ is

$$\begin{aligned}\hat{\boldsymbol{\Sigma}}_{yy|x} &= \frac{1}{N-q-1}\mathbf{S}_E \\ &= \mathbf{V}_E\end{aligned} \tag{6.2.4}$$

$\mathbf{V}_E$ is $p \times p$ symmetric.

The diagonal elements of $\mathbf{V}_E$ are the variances of the p y-variates, eliminating the x-measures. The off-diagonal elements are the "adjusted" covariances. The diagonal elements of $\mathbf{S}_E$ are always smaller than the corresponding elements of $\mathbf{S}_w^{(yy)}$. That is, subtracting the effects due to the x-variables in general reduces the y-variances. The cross products (off-diagonal terms), however, may be either increased or decreased from $\mathbf{S}_w^{(yy)}$ to $\mathbf{S}_E$.

To obtain the partial correlations, the conditional covariance matrix may be converted to correlational form. Let $\mathbf{D}_E = \text{diag}\,(\mathbf{V}_E)$ be the diagonal matrix of partial variances. Then the sample partial correlations are

$$\mathbf{R}_E = \mathbf{D}_E^{-1/2}\mathbf{V}_E\mathbf{D}_E^{-1/2} \tag{6.2.5}$$

Note that these are also the correlations of the errors obtained under the linear regression model in Chapter 4.

The distribution of the partial correlation coefficient is the same as the simple correlation, but with q fewer degrees of freedom. Thus to test the hypothesis that a partial correlation $\rho_{\epsilon_{ij}}$ is equal to a specified value ρ^*, we may apply Fisher's z' transformation (Eq. 6.1.15). Element $[r_e]_{ij}$ and ρ^* are transformed to z' and ζ, respectively. The test statistic is

$$Z=(z'-\zeta)\sqrt{N-q-3} \tag{6.2.6}$$

H_0 is rejected if $|Z|$ exceeds the critical Z-value from the standard normal distribution. Partial correlations for the data of Table 3.3.1 are given in Section 4.4.

6.3 MULTIPLE CORRELATION

The multiple correlation coefficient, like the simple or partial correlation, is a measure of association of two random variables. Unlike the former, the multiple correlation is the correlation of one random variable y, with a linear combination of q ($\geqslant 1$) variates x_k. Weights are chosen for the x_k so as to maximize the relationship of the linear function with y. In the special case with $q=1$, the multiple correlation is the ordinary simple correlation of y and x. Individual x-variables may have both positive and negative correlations with y. The multiple correlation is defined to be only positive, with limits 0 and 1.

The weights that maximize the correlation are the vector of regression coefficients of y on $\mathbf{x}$. Let $\boldsymbol{\beta}$ be the $q\times 1$ vector, assuming that all variables are expressed as mean deviations. The multiple correlation is the simple correlation of the vector of y-values, and the linear combinations $\mathbf{X}'\boldsymbol{\beta}$. Under the univariate multiple regression model $\mathbf{y}=\mathbf{X}\boldsymbol{\beta}+\boldsymbol{\epsilon}$, the vector $\mathbf{X}\boldsymbol{\beta}$ is the set of scores predicted from the x-variables; $\hat{\mathbf{y}}=\mathbf{X}\hat{\boldsymbol{\beta}}$ is the sample value (Eq. 4.2.17). Thus, the multiple correlation is an index of association of observed and predicted values; the better the prediction, the higher the correlational measure.

The multiple correlation may be found by computing the predicted scores and their correlation with the observed values. Or we may apply Eq. 6.0.1 directly. Let the squared correlation be R^2. Then

$$R^2=\frac{\mathscr{V}(y)-\mathscr{V}(y|\mathbf{x})}{\mathscr{V}(y)} \tag{6.3.1}$$

The terms of Eq. 6.3.1 may be obtained from $\boldsymbol{\Sigma}$ (Eq. 6.0.3) with $p=1$. The variance of y is $\boldsymbol{\Sigma}^{(yy)}=\sigma^2$. The variance of y given $\mathbf{x}$ (from Eq. 3.2.10) is the scalar

$$\mathscr{V}(y|\mathbf{x})=\sigma^2-\boldsymbol{\Sigma}^{(yx)}[\boldsymbol{\Sigma}^{(xx)}]^{-1}\boldsymbol{\Sigma}^{(xy)} \tag{6.3.2}$$

Substituting in Eq. 6.3.1, we have

$$R^2=\frac{\boldsymbol{\Sigma}^{(yx)}[\boldsymbol{\Sigma}^{(xx)}]^{-1}\boldsymbol{\Sigma}^{(xy)}}{\sigma^2} \tag{6.3.3}$$

An estimate of R^2 is obtained by substituting sections of $\mathbf{V}_w$ for $\boldsymbol{\Sigma}$ in Eq. 6.3.3. The sample value is

$$\hat{R}^2 = \frac{\mathbf{V}_w^{(yx)}[\mathbf{V}_w^{(xx)}]^{-1}\mathbf{V}_w^{(xy)}}{\mathbf{V}_w^{(yy)}} \tag{6.3.4}$$

Since $\mathbf{S}_w = (N-1)\mathbf{V}_w$, Eq. 6.3.4 may also be expressed in terms of the sum-of-products matrix, as follows:

$$\hat{R}^2 = \frac{\mathbf{S}_w^{(yx)}[\mathbf{S}_w^{(xx)}]^{-1}\mathbf{S}_w^{(xy)}}{\mathbf{S}_w^{(yy)}} \tag{6.3.4a}$$

Eq. 6.3.4a can be analyzed to inspect the properties of $\hat{R}^2$. In addition to being the squared correlation of predicted and observed y-scores, $\hat{R}^2$ is a ratio of their respective sums of squares. The sum of squared mean deviations for y is $\mathbf{S}_w^{(yy)}$. Under the regression model,

$$\hat{\boldsymbol{\beta}} = [\mathbf{S}_w^{(xx)}]^{-1}\mathbf{S}_w^{(xy)}$$

and with all variables as mean deviations,

$$\hat{\mathbf{y}} = \mathbf{X}\hat{\boldsymbol{\beta}}$$

The regression sum of squares is the sum of squared predicted scores. That is,

$$\mathbf{S}_R = \hat{\mathbf{y}}'\hat{\mathbf{y}} = \hat{\boldsymbol{\beta}}'\mathbf{X}'\mathbf{X}\hat{\boldsymbol{\beta}} = \mathbf{S}_w^{(yx)}[\mathbf{S}_w^{(xx)}]^{-1}\mathbf{S}_w^{(xy)}$$

Eq. 6.3.4a is the ratio of $\mathbf{S}_R$ to $\mathbf{S}_w^{(yy)}$. That is, the squared multiple correlation is the ratio of predictable variation to total variation in y. The closer the observed and predicted y-values, the closer $\mathbf{S}_R$ is to $\mathbf{S}_w^{(yy)}$. If the prediction is poor, $\mathbf{S}_R$ will be small compared to $\mathbf{S}_w^{(yy)}$, and instead the difference $\mathbf{S}_E = \mathbf{S}_w^{(yy)} - \mathbf{S}_R$ will be large. In this case, $\hat{R}^2$ is close to zero.

The conditions for estimability of R are the same as those for the regression weights $\boldsymbol{\beta}$; namely, $|\mathbf{S}_w^{(xx)}|$ must exceed zero. This requires that no variable x_k can be expressible as a linear combination of other antecedents. Also, N must be at least $q+1$.

The multiple correlation $\hat{R}$ is the positive square root of $\hat{R}^2$. The sign of R does not denote the direction of relationship, as for simple and partial correlation. However, the signs of the elements of $\hat{\boldsymbol{\beta}}$ reveal the direction for the separate variates x_k. The simple correlations between y and each of the x_k may also be used to identify the direction of relationship, as well as the antecedents least and most highly correlated with y.

In addition to estimating R^2 for an entire set of q variates x_k, it is possible to estimate the contribution to R^2 made by *each* of the x_k. In order to do so, it is useful to establish a prior order of variables x_k. Then we may transform the x-variables to an orthogonal set, and reestimate the regression coefficients. The orthogonal estimates are given by Eq. 5.1.17. Factoring $\mathbf{S}_w^{(xx)}$ by the Cholesky method,

$$\mathbf{S}_w^{(xx)} = \mathbf{T}\mathbf{T}' \tag{6.3.5}$$

The orthogonal regression weights are

$$\mathbf{u} = \mathbf{T}'\hat{\boldsymbol{\beta}} \tag{6.3.6}$$

The sum of squares for **u** is the regression sum of squares,

$$\mathbf{u}'\mathbf{u}=\mathbf{S}_R \tag{6.3.7}$$

Each u_k^2 reflects the contribution to y variation for just variable x_k, eliminating all preceding variables $x_1, x_2, \ldots, x_{k-1}$. The total of these terms is the numerator of Eq. 6.3.4a. Thus

$$P_k=\frac{u_k^2}{\mathbf{S}_w^{(yy)}} \tag{6.3.8}$$

is the proportion of criterion variation attributable to just x_k, eliminating $x_1, x_2, \ldots, x_{k-1}$. P_k may be multiplied by 100 to convert to a percentage measure. The sum of the P_k terms is the squared multiple correlation of y with all q predictors

$$\sum_{k=1}^{q} P_k=\frac{\mathbf{S}_R}{\mathbf{S}_w^{(yy)}}=\hat{R}^2 \tag{6.3.9}$$

Each component P_k is termed the *increment* in $\hat{R}^2$ for predictor x_k.

R may be tested for departure from zero by means of a likelihood ratio test. The null hypothesis asserts that there is no correlation of y and all q x-variates;

$$H_0\colon\ R=0 \tag{6.3.10}$$

The alternative is that the population correlation is greater than zero. The test statistic is

$$F=\frac{\hat{R}^2}{1-\hat{R}^2}\cdot\frac{N-q-1}{q} \tag{6.3.11}$$

H_0 is rejected with confidence $1-\alpha$ if F exceeds the 100α upper percentage point of the F distribution with q and $N-q-1$ degrees of freedom. Otherwise H_0 is maintained. Testing Eq. 6.3.10 is equivalent to testing that the entire vector $\boldsymbol{\beta}$ is null, under the linear regression model in Chapter 5.

Although we accept H_0 that R is zero, the sample value may still be nonzero. The expected value, or average over many samples, is

$$\mathscr{E}(\hat{R}^2|R=0)=\frac{q}{N-1} \tag{6.3.12}$$

Even if R is zero, sample values $\hat{R}$ tend to approach unity as q approaches N. To avoid obtaining a false image of strong predictive power, N must be large relative to q.

If $N-1$ is equal to the number of predictors, the sample correlation is always unity. This can be seen since **X** is square and can itself be inverted. Then the predicted scores are

$$\begin{aligned}\hat{\mathbf{y}}&=\mathbf{X}\hat{\boldsymbol{\beta}}\\&=\mathbf{X}(\mathbf{X}'\mathbf{X})^{-1}\mathbf{X}'\mathbf{y}\\&=\mathbf{X}\mathbf{X}^{-1}(\mathbf{X}')^{-1}\mathbf{X}'\mathbf{y}\\&=\mathbf{y}\end{aligned} \tag{6.3.13}$$

The sum of the squared predicted scores is equal to the sum of squared observed outcomes. There is little point to the prediction of N outcomes from an equal number of antecedents. No parsimony is gained but the complexities in interpreting linear functions $\mathbf{X}\hat{\boldsymbol{\beta}}$ are added.

Multiple Criteria

When there is more than a single dependent variable, the multiple correlation of *each* criterion measure with all of the predictors may be obtained simultaneously, from summary matrices. If $p>1$, then $\boldsymbol{\Sigma}^{(yy)}$ (see Eq. 6.0.3) and $\mathbf{S}_w^{(yy)}$ (see Eq. 6.0.6a) are $p \times p$ matrices. The p diagonal elements are the variances and observed sums of squares, respectively, for each outcome measure.

$\boldsymbol{\Sigma}^{(yx)}$ and $\mathbf{S}_w^{(yx)}$ are not vectors but $p \times q$ matrices. The regression weights form a $q \times p$ matrix

$$\hat{\mathbf{B}} = [\mathbf{S}_w^{(xx)}]^{-1}\mathbf{S}_w^{(xy)}$$

$\mathbf{S}_R$ is the $p \times p$ sum of squares and cross products for regression:

$$\mathbf{S}_R = \mathbf{S}_w^{(yx)}[\mathbf{S}_w^{(xx)}]^{-1}\mathbf{S}_w^{(xy)}$$

Like $\mathbf{S}_w^{(yy)}$, $\mathbf{S}_R$ has the sum of squares for each outcome measure in the diagonal positions. In both matrices these elements are determined without reference to the other variables in the set. That is, the results are the same as those that would have been obtained in univariate analyses of the particular measures alone.

The squared multiple correlation of variate y_j with all q x-measures may be obtained from the jj diagonal elements of $\mathbf{S}_R$ and $\mathbf{S}_w^{(yy)}$.

$$\hat{R}_j^2 = \frac{[s_r]_{jj}}{[s_w^{(yy)}]_{jj}} \tag{6.3.14}$$

The subscript j is necessary to distinguish the criterion variable; j has values from 1 to p.

The contribution of individual predictors to $\hat{R}_j^2$, eliminating earlier predictors, is obtained as in Eq. 6.3.8. The matrix of orthogonal weights is

$$\mathbf{U} = \mathbf{T}'\hat{\mathbf{B}}$$

If $\mathbf{u}'_k$ is the kth *row* of $\mathbf{U}$, then the squares and products for x_k, eliminating x_1 through x_{k-1} is the $p \times p$ matrix

$$\mathbf{S}_H = \mathbf{u}_k\mathbf{u}'_k$$

The diagonal elements of $\mathbf{S}_H$ are the u_k^2 of Eq. 6.3.8 for separate measures. Any diagonal element may be divided by the corresponding element of $\mathbf{S}_w^{(yy)}$ to estimate the increment in R_j^2. That is,

$$P_{jk} = \frac{[s_h]_{jj}}{[s_w^{(yy)}]_{jj}} \tag{6.3.15}$$

The total of the P_{jk} across predictors (rows of $\mathbf{U}$) is $\hat{R}_j^2$, the squared correlation of criterion y_j with all x's (see Eq. 6.3.9).

A univariate test of the multiple correlation between one y_j and all x's may be conducted using Eq. 6.3.11. Multiple univariate tests are not independent, however, since the criterion variables are themselves intercorrelated. We may turn instead to one of several multivariate procedures. A simultaneous test of *all* the multiple correlations (all relationships between **y** and **x**) is equivalent to testing that the entire matrix $\mathbf{B}$ or $\boldsymbol{\Sigma}^{(yx)}$ is null. Since the likelihood ratio test of this hypothesis is described in Section 5.2, it will not be repeated here. $\mathbf{S}_R = \mathbf{U}'\mathbf{U}$ and $\mathbf{S}_E$ are the hypothesis and error matrices, with q and $N-q-1$ degrees of freedom, respectively. If the criterion variables have a natural ordering (by complexity, time, and so on) step-down F tests may be conducted. The step-down analysis will enable the researcher to determine whether there is any relationship between all the predictors and y_1; between all predictors and y_2, eliminating y_1; between all predictors and y_3, eliminating y_1 and y_2; and so on. Through the step-down analysis, it may be possible to isolate predictable variation as residing primarily in the simpler, or earlier criterion measures. $\mathbf{S}_R$ and $\mathbf{S}_E$ are the hypothesis and error matrices for the step-down analysis. The step-down tests are described in Section 5.2 also.

Example

The within matrix $\mathbf{S}_w$ for the data of Table 3.3.1 is given in Chapter 3. The sum of products for criteria is

$$\mathbf{S}_w^{(yy)} = \begin{bmatrix} 8.31 & 6.76 \\ 6.76 & 10.56 \end{bmatrix} \begin{matrix} y_1 \\ y_2 \end{matrix}$$
$$\qquad \begin{matrix} y_1 & \quad y_2 \end{matrix}$$

$\mathbf{S}_w^{(yy)}$ has $N-1=14$ degrees of freedom. The regression sum of products of y_1 and y_2 on $q=3$ predictors is found from the computational forms of Section 4.5.

$$\mathbf{S}_R = \begin{bmatrix} 4.72 & 4.38 \\ 4.38 & 7.23 \end{bmatrix} \begin{matrix} y_1 \\ y_2 \end{matrix}$$
$$\qquad \begin{matrix} y_1 & \quad y_2 \end{matrix}$$

The squared correlations of y_1 with the three x-variables, and y_2 with the three x-variables are

$$\hat{R}_1^2 = \frac{4.72}{8.31} = .568 \quad (y_1)$$

$$\hat{R}_2^2 = \frac{7.23}{10.56} = .685 \quad (y_2)$$

The correlations are $\hat{R}_1 = .75$ and $\hat{R}_2 = .83$, respectively.

We may test $H_0: R_j = 0$ for the two correlations separately. For y_1,

$$F_1 = \frac{.568}{1-.568} \cdot \frac{15-3-1}{3} = 4.82$$

F_1 has 3 and 11 degrees of freedom. H_0 is rejected at $\alpha = .05$ (but not at .01).

For y_2,

$$F_2 = \frac{.685}{1-.685} \cdot \frac{15-3-1}{3} = 7.97$$

H_0 is rejected at $\alpha = .01$. The two F tests are not independent. Either the likelihood ratio criterion or step-down techniques should be employed for a single decision about the relationship of the y- and x-variables.

The orthogonal regression coefficients for these data are obtained in Section 5.1. Without the constant term,

$$\mathbf{U} = \begin{bmatrix} 2.17 & 1.97 \\ .10 & 1.72 \\ -.09 & .64 \end{bmatrix} \begin{matrix} x_1 \\ x_2\text{, eliminating } x_1 \\ x_3\text{, eliminating } x_1 \text{ and } x_2 \end{matrix}$$
$$\quad y_1 \qquad y_2$$

The proportion of variation in y_1 attributable to x_1 is

$$P_{11} = \frac{2.17^2}{8.31} = .566$$

For x_2, eliminating x_1,

$$P_{12} = \frac{.10^2}{8.31} = .001$$

For x_3, eliminating x_1 and x_2,

$$P_{13} = \frac{(-.09)^2}{8.31} = .001$$

After attributing all possible variation to x_1, little remains to be attributed additionally to x_2 or x_3. The sum of the P_{1k} is .568, identically $\hat{R}_1^2$. The same procedure may be followed for y_2 using the second column of **U**.

6.4 CANONICAL CORRELATION

The canonical correlation coefficient is the simple correlation of two random variables, each of which is a linear function of two or more original variates. Canonical correlation analysis can provide proportion-of-shared-variation measures to describe the relationships of two *sets* of random variables, each set consisting of multiple measures. The technique is useful for understanding the overlap of information content in two batteries of tests.

To describe completely the relationships between p measures y_j and q measures x_k, $s = \min(p, q)$ correlations are necessary. Each is a product-moment correlation of one linear combination of the y_j and a separate compound of the x_k. The weights defining the linear functions are chosen so as to maximize the association measure. Tests of significance may be employed to determine whether the relationship between the two sets of variables can be described by a subset of the s compounds.

When either p or q is unity, the specific form is the multiple correlation of the one measure with the other set. The weights are the partial regression coefficients. When both p and q are unity, the measure is the simple correlation of y and x.

Let us define the desirable properties of a measure of association between two linear composites. Represent the ith canonical correlation between $\mathbf{y}$ and $\mathbf{x}$ as R_i ($i = 1, 2, \ldots, s$). R_i is the simple correlation of linear compounds

$$v_i = [\boldsymbol{\alpha}_i^{(y)}]'\mathbf{y}^* \tag{6.4.1a}$$

and

$$w_i = [\boldsymbol{\alpha}_i^{(x)}]'\mathbf{x}^* \tag{6.4.1b}$$

$\boldsymbol{\alpha}_i^{(y)}$ and $\boldsymbol{\alpha}_i^{(x)}$ are weight vectors having p and q elements, respectively. $\mathbf{y}^*$ and $\mathbf{x}^*$ are p- and q-element mean deviation vectors, $\mathbf{y}^* = \mathbf{y} - \boldsymbol{\mu}_y$ and $\mathbf{x}^* = \mathbf{x} - \boldsymbol{\mu}_x$. The vectors $\boldsymbol{\alpha}_i$ are determined so as to maximize R_i. v_i and w_i are termed the *canonical variates* for $\mathbf{y}$ and $\mathbf{x}$.

$\boldsymbol{\alpha}_i^{(y)}$ and $\boldsymbol{\alpha}_i^{(x)}$ may be multiplied by any arbitrary constants without affecting R_i. The usual convention of restricting the weight vectors to unit variance is employed. The variances of the composites are

$$\begin{aligned}\mathscr{V}(v_i) &= [\boldsymbol{\alpha}_i^{(y)}]'\mathscr{V}(\mathbf{y}^*)\boldsymbol{\alpha}_i^{(y)}\\ &= [\boldsymbol{\alpha}_i^{(y)}]'\boldsymbol{\Sigma}^{(yy)}\boldsymbol{\alpha}_i^{(y)}\end{aligned} \tag{6.4.2a}$$

and

$$\begin{aligned}\mathscr{V}(w_i) &= [\boldsymbol{\alpha}_i^{(x)}]'\mathscr{V}(\mathbf{x}^*)\boldsymbol{\alpha}_i^{(x)}\\ &= [\boldsymbol{\alpha}_i^{(x)}]'\boldsymbol{\Sigma}^{(xx)}\boldsymbol{\alpha}_i^{(x)}\end{aligned} \tag{6.4.2b}$$

When Eqs. 6.4.2a and b are restricted to unit value, both composites have unit variance.

The expectation of both composites is zero. That is,

$$\begin{aligned}\mathscr{E}(v_i) &= \mathscr{E}([\boldsymbol{\alpha}_i^{(y)}]'\mathbf{y}^*)\\ &= [\boldsymbol{\alpha}_i^{(y)}]'\mathscr{E}(\mathbf{y}^*)\\ &= 0\\ &= \mathscr{E}(w_i)\end{aligned} \tag{6.4.3}$$

The correlation between v_i and w_i across all observations is

$$\begin{aligned}R_i &= \mathscr{E}[v_i - \mathscr{E}(v_i)][w_i - \mathscr{E}(w_i)]\\ &= \mathscr{E}[(\{\boldsymbol{\alpha}_i^{(y)}\}'\mathbf{y}^*)(\{\boldsymbol{\alpha}_i^{(x)}\}'\mathbf{x}^*)']\\ &= [\boldsymbol{\alpha}_i^{(y)}]'\mathscr{E}(\mathbf{y}^*[\mathbf{x}^*]')\boldsymbol{\alpha}_i^{(x)}\\ &= [\boldsymbol{\alpha}_i^{(y)}]'\boldsymbol{\Sigma}^{(yx)}\boldsymbol{\alpha}_i^{(x)}\end{aligned} \tag{6.4.4}$$

$\mathscr{E}(\mathbf{y}^*[\mathbf{x}^*]') = \boldsymbol{\Sigma}^{(yx)}$ is the matrix of covariances of each element of $\mathbf{y}^*$ and every element of $\mathbf{x}^*$.

The first canonical correlation (R_1) is the simple correlation of v_1 and w_1. R_1 and the weight vectors $\boldsymbol{\alpha}_1^{(x)}$ and $\boldsymbol{\alpha}_1^{(y)}$ are obtained by maximizing Eq. 6.4.4 with respect to the $\boldsymbol{\alpha}_i$. R_1 is the maximum correlation of any linear composites of the two sets of variables.

The second canonical correlation (R_2) is the maximum correlation between composites

$$v_2 = [\boldsymbol{\alpha}_2^{(y)}]'\mathbf{y}^* \quad \text{and} \quad w_2 = [\boldsymbol{\alpha}_2^{(x)}]'\mathbf{x}^* \tag{6.4.5}$$

R_2 is subject to the additional constraint that v_2 and w_2 are uncorrelated with v_1 and w_1, respectively. That is,

$$\begin{aligned} \mathscr{E}(v_1v_2) &= [\boldsymbol{\alpha}_1^{(y)}]'\boldsymbol{\Sigma}^{(yy)}\boldsymbol{\alpha}_2^{(y)} \\ &= 0 \\ &= \mathscr{E}(w_1w_2) \end{aligned} \tag{6.4.6}$$

The third correlation (R_3) is the maximum correlation of composites defined by $\boldsymbol{\alpha}_3^{(y)}$ and $\boldsymbol{\alpha}_3^{(x)}$. The intercorrelations of v_3 and w_3 with *both* of the first two composites are null, and so on. Together, s correlations and their respective weight vectors are estimated, each defining composites that are uncorrelated with those preceding.

These properties can be described in matrix notation. Let $\mathbf{A}^{(y)}$ be the $p \times s$ matrix having column vectors $\boldsymbol{\alpha}_i^{(y)}$; let $\mathbf{A}^{(x)}$ be the $q \times s$ matrix of column vectors, $\boldsymbol{\alpha}_i^{(x)}$. If, in addition, $\mathbf{R}$ is an $s \times s$ diagonal matrix of canonical correlations, Eqs. 6.4.2 and 6.4.4 can be expressed as

$$[\mathbf{A}^{(y)}]'\boldsymbol{\Sigma}^{(yy)}\mathbf{A}^{(y)} = \mathbf{I} \tag{6.4.7a}$$

$$[\mathbf{A}^{(x)}]'\boldsymbol{\Sigma}^{(xx)}\mathbf{A}^{(x)} = \mathbf{I} \tag{6.4.7b}$$

and

$$[\mathbf{A}^{(y)}]'\boldsymbol{\Sigma}^{(yx)}\mathbf{A}^{(x)} = \mathbf{R} \tag{6.4.8}$$

It is shown in Anderson (1958, pp. 289ff.), that maximum values for R_i and associated vectors $\boldsymbol{\alpha}_i^{(y)}$ and $\boldsymbol{\alpha}_i^{(x)}$ may be obtained as the solutions of the homogeneous equations

$$(\boldsymbol{\Sigma}^{(yx)}[\boldsymbol{\Sigma}^{(xx)}]^{-1}\boldsymbol{\Sigma}^{(xy)} - R_i^2\boldsymbol{\Sigma}^{(yy)})\boldsymbol{\alpha}_i^{(y)} = \mathbf{0} \tag{6.4.9}$$

where R_i satisfies

$$|\boldsymbol{\Sigma}^{(yx)}[\boldsymbol{\Sigma}^{(xx)}]^{-1}\boldsymbol{\Sigma}^{(xy)} - R_i^2\boldsymbol{\Sigma}^{(yy)}| = 0 \tag{6.4.10}$$

Estimates of R_i, $\boldsymbol{\alpha}_i^{(y)}$, and $\boldsymbol{\alpha}_i^{(x)}$ are obtained by substituting sample values for $\boldsymbol{\Sigma}$, and solving the eigenequations. That is, let the estimate of $\boldsymbol{\Sigma}$ be $\mathbf{V}_w$ as in Eq. 6.0.7, partitioned for y- and x-measures. In the sample, Eq. 6.4.9 is

$$(\mathbf{V}_w^{(yx)}[\mathbf{V}_w^{(xx)}]^{-1}\mathbf{V}_w^{(xy)} - \hat{R}_i^2\mathbf{V}_w^{(yy)})\mathbf{a}_i^{(y)} = \mathbf{0} \tag{6.4.11}$$

where $\hat{R}_i^2$ satisfies

$$|\mathbf{V}_w^{(yx)}[\mathbf{V}_w^{(xx)}]^{-1}\mathbf{V}_w^{(xy)} - \hat{R}_i^2\mathbf{V}_w^{(yy)}| = 0 \tag{6.4.12}$$

The sum of products $\mathbf{S}_w$ may be used in place of $\mathbf{V}_w$ in Eqs. 6.4.11 and 6.4.12. The eigenvalues are identical; the vectors from $\mathbf{S}_w$ must be multiplied by $\sqrt{N-1}$ to maintain identities 6.4.7 and 6.4.8. The sample value $\hat{\boldsymbol{\alpha}}_i$ is represented as $\mathbf{a}_i$.

Solutions to Eq. 6.4.11 may be found through the expansion of 6.4.12 in the sample. Computer routines discussed in Chapter 2 are essential for most real-data problems. The two-matrix problem of Eq. 6.4.11 may be transformed to a single-matrix equation (see Chapter 2) by factoring $\mathbf{V}_w^{(yy)}$ by the Cholesky method. That is, let

$$\mathbf{V}_w^{(yy)} = \mathbf{T}_w\mathbf{T}'_w \tag{6.4.13}$$

and

$$\mathbf{a}_i^{(y)} = (\mathbf{T}_w^{-1})'\mathbf{g}_i \tag{6.4.14}$$

Then Eq. 6.4.11 becomes

$$\{\mathbf{V}_w^{(yx)}[\mathbf{V}_w^{(xx)}]^{-1}\mathbf{V}_w^{(xy)} - \hat{R}_i^2\mathbf{T}_w\mathbf{T}'_w\}(\mathbf{T}_w^{-1})'\mathbf{g}_i = \mathbf{0} \tag{6.4.15}$$

and

$$\{\mathbf{T}_w^{-1}\mathbf{V}_w^{(yx)}[\mathbf{V}_w^{(xx)}]^{-1}\mathbf{V}_w^{(xy)}(\mathbf{T}_w^{-1})' - \hat{R}_i^2\mathbf{I}\}\mathbf{g}_i = \mathbf{0}$$

or

$$(\mathbf{C} - \hat{R}_i^2\mathbf{I})\mathbf{g}_i = \mathbf{0} \tag{6.4.15a}$$

$\hat{R}_i^2$ and $\mathbf{g}_i$ are the eigenvalues and eigenvectors of the symmetric matrix $\mathbf{C}$. $\mathbf{a}_i^{(y)}$ is obtained from $\mathbf{g}_i$ by Eq. 6.4.14.

Let $\hat{\mathbf{A}}^{(y)}$ be the $p \times s$ matrix of sample coefficients for the y-variables; $\hat{\mathbf{A}}^{(y)}$ has columns $\mathbf{a}_i^{(y)}$. The sample coefficients for the x-variables comprise $\hat{\mathbf{A}}^{(x)}$ with columns $\mathbf{a}_i^{(x)}$. $\hat{\mathbf{A}}^{(x)}$ may be obtained directly by solving the reverse eigen-equations:

$$(\mathbf{V}_w^{(xy)}[\mathbf{V}_w^{(yy)}]^{-1}\mathbf{V}_w^{(yx)} - \hat{R}_i^2\mathbf{V}_w^{(xx)})\mathbf{a}_i^{(x)} = \mathbf{0} \tag{6.4.16}$$

Without recomputing, however, $\hat{\mathbf{A}}^{(x)}$ may be obtained by

$$\begin{aligned}\hat{\mathbf{A}}^{(x)} &= [\mathbf{V}_w^{(xx)}]^{-1}\mathbf{V}_w^{(xy)}\hat{\mathbf{A}}^{(y)}\hat{\mathbf{R}}^{-1} \\ &= \hat{\mathbf{B}}\hat{\mathbf{A}}^{(y)}\hat{\mathbf{R}}^{-1}\end{aligned} \tag{6.4.17}$$

$\hat{\mathbf{B}}$ is the $q \times p$ matrix of regression coefficients of the y-variates on the x_k measures. $\hat{\mathbf{R}}$ is the diagonal matrix of sample canonical correlations $\sqrt{\hat{R}_i^2}$. Note, however, that the canonical correlations are symmetric; the solution of Eq. 6.4.16 yields identical roots to those of 6.4.11.

$\mathbf{A}^{(y)}$ and $\mathbf{A}^{(x)}$ may be estimated in a form for standardized measures y_j and x_k. This is accomplished by substitution of the correlation matrix $\mathbf{R}_w$ for the covariance matrix $\mathbf{V}_w$ in Eq. 6.4.11. Or the raw weights may be multiplied by appropriate vectors of variable standard deviations. Let

$$\mathbf{D}_w^{(yy)} = \text{diag}\,\{\mathbf{V}_w^{(yy)}\} \tag{6.4.18a}$$

and

$$\mathbf{D}_w^{(xx)} = \text{diag}\,\{\mathbf{V}_w^{(xx)}\} \tag{6.4.18b}$$

$\mathbf{D}_w^{(yy)}$ and $\mathbf{D}_w^{(xx)}$ are the $p \times p$ and $q \times q$ diagonal matrices of variances for the y- and x-variates, respectively. The matrices of standardized coefficients are

$$\hat{\mathbf{A}}^{(y)} = [\mathbf{D}_w^{(yy)}]^{1/2}\hat{\mathbf{A}}^{(y)} \tag{6.4.19a}$$

and

$$\hat{\mathbf{A}}^{(x)} = [\mathbf{D}_w^{(xx)}]^{1/2}\hat{\mathbf{A}}^{(x)} \tag{6.4.19b}$$

Each weight is multiplied by the respective variable standard deviation.

Like regression coefficients, the canonical weights are dependent upon the selection of variables as well as their scales. The relative or absolute magnitudes of the weights should be interpreted with extreme caution. Addition or deletion of variables in either set may produce major alterations in the remaining coefficients. Although standardization to $\hat{\mathbf{A}}^{(y)}$ and $\hat{\mathbf{A}}^{(x)}$ removes scaling effects the interdependencies still remain.

Bargmann (1962) has recommended computing the intercorrelations of the original scales with the composite measures. The correlations are obtained in matrix form.

$$[\mathbf{D}_w^{(yy)}]^{-1/2}\mathbf{V}_w^{(yy)}\hat{\mathbf{A}}^{(y)} = \mathbf{R}_w^{(yy)}\hat{\mathbf{A}}^{(y)} \tag{6.4.20a}$$

$$[\mathbf{D}_w^{(xx)}]^{-1/2}\mathbf{V}_w^{(xx)}\hat{\mathbf{A}}^{(x)} = \mathbf{R}_w^{(xx)}\hat{\mathbf{A}}^{(x)} \tag{6.4.20b}$$

Equations 6.4.20a and b are $p \times s$ and $q \times s$ matrices of correlations between each of the original variates and each of the canonical or composite variates. The correlations are more stable than either the raw or standardized weights under the addition and deletion of variables. They more accurately reflect the contribution of each measure to canonical variates v_i and w_i.

Meredith (1964) has provided an important addition to the theory of canonical correlation, for the case when there is a correction for unreliability in some or all of the measures. Assume that $\boldsymbol{\delta}$ is a $p \times p$ diagonal matrix of variances of the errors of measurement in $\mathbf{y}$. The reliability-adjusted covariance matrix is $\hat{\boldsymbol{\Sigma}} - \boldsymbol{\delta}$, which may be substituted in Eq. 6.4.11 in place of $\hat{\boldsymbol{\Sigma}} = \mathbf{V}_w$. Meredith indicates that the following likelihood ratio tests may be employed even when $\boldsymbol{\delta}$ is estimated from the sample, if N is sufficiently large.

The canonical correlations may be used to estimate the percentage of variation in the y- or x-measures attributable to each linear combination of the other set. The squared canonical correlation is divided by the total of the standardized variances of the variables in the opposing set. Since standardized variables have unit variance, the denominators are simply p and q, respectively. $\hat{R}_i^2/p$ is the proportion of variation in the set of y-measures accounted for by $w_i = [\mathbf{a}_i^{(x)}]'\mathbf{x}^*$; $\hat{R}_i^2/q$ is the proportion of variation in the set of x-mesures accounted for by $v_i = [\mathbf{a}_i^{(y)}]'\mathbf{y}^*$. The overall percentage of variance accounted for in the p y-variates by the q x-measures is

$$P_y = \frac{100 \sum_{i=1}^{s} \hat{R}_i^2}{p} \tag{6.4.21}$$

Each of the $\hat{R}_i^2$ represents an orthogonal component. Simply, the percentage of variance of the x-variates attributable to the y set, is

$$P_x = \frac{100 \sum_{i=1}^{s} \hat{R}_i^2}{q} \tag{6.4.22}$$

Other measures of shared variance of two sets of variables are given by Stewart and Love (1968) and by Miller and Farr (1971).

As with the other correlation measures, the canonical correlations may be tested for departure from zero. A simultaneous test of all s correlations will reveal whether or not there is any correlation between the sets of variables in the population. We may then test whether all correlations minus the largest, all minus the largest two, and so on, are jointly significant. In this manner we may be able to isolate one or a small number of linear composites of the measures that describe all significant relationships between the two sets. For each significant dimension, the correlation of the linear composite with the original variables may be inspected to determine which measures contribute to the correlation, and in which direction.

The joint test of nullity of all s canonical correlations is made using Wilk's Λ criterion. The test of H_0: $R_i=0$, for all i, is equivalent to the test of the nullity of $\mathbf{\Sigma}^{(yx)}$ or the entire $q\times p$ matrix $\mathbf{B}$. The test statistic in terms of correlations is

$$\Lambda_1=\prod_{i=1}^{s}(1-\hat{R}_i^2) \tag{6.4.23}$$

Bartlett's transformation is

$$\chi^2=-m\log_e\Lambda_1 \tag{6.4.24}$$

where

$$m=[N-1-(p+q+1)/2] \tag{6.4.25}$$

The test statistic follows a chi-square distribution, with pq degrees of freedom. H_0 is rejected with confidence $1-\alpha$, if χ^2 exceeds the 100α upper percentage point of χ_{pq}^2. If H_0 is rejected, we conclude that at least one (and perhaps more) of the correlations is nonzero.

It can be seen that this test is equivalent to the test of the contribution of all q predictor variables to regression (Eq. 5.2.17), since

$$\begin{aligned}\Lambda_1&=\prod_{i=1}^{s}(1-\hat{R}_i^2)\\&=|\mathbf{I}-\hat{\mathbf{R}}\hat{\mathbf{R}}|\\&=\frac{|\mathbf{S}_w^{(yy)}-\mathbf{S}_w^{(yx)}[\mathbf{S}_w^{(xx)}]^{-1}\mathbf{S}_w^{(xy)}|}{|\mathbf{S}_w^{(yy)}|}\\&=\frac{|\mathbf{S}_E|}{|\mathbf{S}_E+\mathbf{S}_w^{(yx)}[\mathbf{S}_w^{(xx)}]^{-1}\mathbf{S}_w^{(xy)}|}\end{aligned}$$

Thus predictable criterion variation is neither increased nor decreased in transforming the data to the canonical variables. Instead, it is reallocated so that the best prediction can be made in terms of the fewest measures.

Sequential tests of all canonical correlations, all except the first (largest), all but the first two, and so on, are also possible. The test of the joint nullity of correlations j through s is made with

$$\Lambda_j=\prod_{i=j}^{s}(1-\hat{R}_i^2) \tag{6.4.26}$$

The test statistic is

$$\chi^2 = -m \log_e \Lambda_j \tag{6.4.26a}$$

where m is defined by Eq. 6.4.25. χ^2 has $(p-j+1)(q-j+1)$ degrees of freedom. The null hypothesis is rejected if χ^2 exceeds the 100α upper percentage point of $\chi^2_{(p-j+1)(q-j+1)}$. Accepting H_0 is commensurate with the conclusion that any relationship between the two sets is "concentrated" in the first or preceding $j-1$ canonical variates. The more precise F transformation of Wilk's criterion (expression 5.2.12) may be employed in place of the χ^2 transformation.

Once it has been determined that the largest $j-1$ canonical correlations summarize all significant association between the y- and x-variables, it is necessary to interpret the linear functions that define these relationships. This may be accomplished by inspection of the correlations of the canonical variates (v_i and w_i) and the original measures. Although these correlations have some stability, they do depend upon the particular variables included in either set. Perhaps the most useful explanations of association are the simplest—those derived from simple and multiple correlations, and from simple percentages of explained variation. Canonical correlation analysis introduces complexities into the data that are not usually offset by the gain in parsimony. Since explained criterion variation is not increased, the use of canonical correlation may be of little value to social scientists.

The following section provides further examples of the simpler correlation techniques, plus an illustration of canonical correlation methodology.

6.5 SAMPLE PROBLEM 1—CREATIVITY AND ACHIEVEMENT

The sum of products for the creativity-intelligence-achievement example, with $N=60$, is given in Section 3.4, and partitioned in Section 4.6 for predictors and criteria. The matrix is

$$\mathbf{S}_w = \left[\begin{array}{c|c} \mathbf{S}_w^{(yy)} & \mathbf{S}_w^{(yx)} \\ \hline \mathbf{S}_w^{(xy)} & \mathbf{S}_w^{(xx)} \end{array}\right]$$

$$= \left[\begin{array}{cc|ccccccc}
178.85 & & & & & & & & \text{(Symmetric)} \\
110.35 & 186.18 & & & & & & & \\
\hline
65.79 & 56.69 & 59.00 & & & & & & \\
21.29 & 17.66 & 5.55 & 59.00 & & & & & \\
35.23 & 40.49 & 24.29 & 3.38 & 59.00 & & & & \\
40.74 & 33.58 & 27.47 & 31.98 & 25.13 & 59.00 & & & \\
4.56 & 20.22 & 5.56 & -3.06 & 18.56 & 1.19 & 43.35 & & \\
45.38 & 40.17 & 28.65 & 18.56 & 38.66 & 24.42 & 22.27 & 104.70 & \\
31.79 & 29.77 & 17.56 & 1.19 & 24.42 & 14.98 & 19.12 & 57.79 & 64.79
\end{array}\right]$$

Reducing $\mathbf{S}_w$ to correlation form, and extracting $\mathbf{R}_w^{(yx)}$, yields

$$\mathbf{R}_w^{(yx)}=\begin{bmatrix} .64 & .21 & .34 & .40 & .05 & .33 & .30 \\ .54 & .17 & .39 & .32 & .23 & .29 & .27 \end{bmatrix}\begin{matrix}\text{Synthesis}\\ \text{Evaluation}\end{matrix}$$

Columns: Intelligence; Consequences obvious; Consequences remote; Possible jobs; Cons. obvious × intelligence; Cons. remote × intelligence; Poss. jobs × intelligence

All of the correlations are positive. Intelligence has the highest relationship with both outcomes. The *t*-value required to reject H_0: $\rho_{jk} \leqslant 0$, with $60-2=58$ degrees of freedom and $\alpha=.05$, is 1.67. Substituting in Eq. 6.1.13, we find that the corresponding value of r_{jk} must be .214 or greater. Thus intelligence, consequences remote, and possible jobs have significant relationships with the criterion measures, while consequences obvious is not significantly related to either outcome. This does not imply, however, that the multivariate tests will be significant. Most of the interaction terms are individually related to the criteria, although they may not explain criterion variance that is not attributable to the simpler measures.

The error sum of products, or conditional sum of products of **y** given **x**, is

$$\begin{aligned}\mathbf{S}_E&=\mathbf{S}_w^{(yy)}-\mathbf{S}_w^{(yx)}[\mathbf{S}_w^{(xx)}]^{-1}\mathbf{S}_w^{(xy)}\\ &=\begin{bmatrix}178.85 & 110.35\\ 110.35 & 186.18\end{bmatrix}-\begin{bmatrix}81.18 & 69.41\\ 69.41 & 67.22\end{bmatrix}\\ &=\begin{bmatrix}97.67 & 40.94\\ 40.94 & 118.97\end{bmatrix}\begin{matrix}\text{Synthesis}\\ \text{Evaluation}\end{matrix}\\ &\quad\ \ \text{Synthesis}\quad\ \text{Evaluation}\end{aligned}$$

Extracting the diagonal elements of $\mathbf{S}_E$ and $\mathbf{S}_w^{(yy)}$, the squared multiple correlations of the criteria with all seven predictors are

$$\hat{R}_1^2=\frac{178.85-97.67}{178.85}=.45 \quad \text{Synthesis}$$

and

$$\hat{R}_2^2=\frac{186.18-118.97}{186.18}=.36 \quad \text{Evaluation}$$

The univariate tests of the two correlations yield *F* statistics of $F_1=6.17$ and $F_2=4.20$. Both exceed the .05 critical *F* value, with 7 and 52 degrees of freedom; R_1 and R_2 are greater than zero.

Taken individually, both criteria are significantly explained by scores on the seven predictor variables. To determine which measures are the best predictors, we may inspect $\mathbf{R}_w^{(yx)}$, or examine orthogonal variance components in a particular order of antecedents. The regression coefficients are

$$\hat{\mathbf{B}} = \begin{bmatrix} 1.00 & .86 \\ .28 & .33 \\ .16 & .32 \\ -.04 & -.14 \\ -.16 & .24 \\ -.04 & -.16 \\ .25 & .20 \end{bmatrix} \begin{matrix} \text{Intelligence } (x_1) \\ \text{Consequences obvious } (x_2) \\ \text{Consequences remote } (x_3) \\ \text{Possible jobs } (x_4) \\ \text{Cons. obvious} \times \text{intelligence } (x_5) \\ \text{Cons. remote} \times \text{intelligence } (x_6) \\ \text{Possible jobs} \times \text{intelligence } (x_7) \end{matrix}$$

Synthesis Evaluation

The triangular Cholesky factor of $\mathbf{S}_w^{(xx)}$ is $\mathbf{T}$ (from Section 5.4). The orthogonal estimates are

$$\mathbf{U} = \mathbf{T}'\hat{\mathbf{B}} = \begin{bmatrix} 8.56 & 7.38 \\ 1.97 & 1.61 \\ 1.12 & 2.42 \\ .07 & -.68 \\ -.54 & 1.57 \\ .74 & -.40 \\ 1.35 & 1.11 \end{bmatrix} \begin{matrix} x_1 \\ x_2\text{, eliminating } x_1 \\ x_3\text{, eliminating } x_1 \text{ and } x_2 \\ x_4\text{, eliminating } x_1, x_2\text{, and } x_3 \\ x_5\text{, eliminating } x_1, x_2, x_3\text{, and } x_4 \\ x_6\text{, eliminating } x_1, x_2, x_3, x_4\text{, and } x_5 \\ x_7\text{, eliminating all others} \end{matrix}$$

Synthesis Evaluation

The proportions of variation attributable to intelligence are

$$P_{11} = \frac{8.56^2}{178.85} = .41 \quad \text{Synthesis}$$

$$P_{21} = \frac{7.38^2}{186.18} = .29 \quad \text{Evaluation}$$

The *additional* proportion of variation due to creativity (three measures) is

$$\frac{1.97^2 + 1.12^2 + .07^2}{178.85} = .03 \quad \text{Synthesis}$$

$$\frac{1.61^2 + 2.42^2 + .68^2}{186.18} = .05 \quad \text{Evaluation}$$

The proportions of additional variation attributable to interactions, above and beyond all other measures, are

$$\frac{.54^2 + .74^2 + 1.35^2}{178.85} = .01 \quad \text{Synthesis}$$

$$\frac{1.57^2 + .40^2 + 1.11^2}{186.18} = .02 \quad \text{Evaluation}$$

The numerators of the measures are the diagonal elements of matrices $\mathbf{S}_{H_j}$, used for testing regression hypotheses in Chapter 5. The sum of the proportion measures for either criterion is the respective squared multiple correlation (for example, $.41 + .03 + .01 = .45$).

Step-down tests of R_1 and R_2 are obtained from Cholesky factors of $\mathbf{S}_E$ and $\mathbf{S}_w^{(yy)}$. The respective triangular factors are

$$\mathbf{T}_E = \begin{bmatrix} 9.88 & 0.00 \\ 4.14 & 10.09 \end{bmatrix} \qquad \mathbf{T}^* = \begin{bmatrix} 13.37 & 0.00 \\ 8.25 & 10.87 \end{bmatrix}$$

The step-down statistic for syntheses (R_1) is equivalent to the first univariate test.

$$F_1^* = \frac{13.37^2 - 9.88^2}{9.88^2} \cdot \frac{52-1+1}{7} = 6.17$$

F_1^* exceeds the .05 critical F-value with 7 and 52 degrees of freedom. The step-down statistic for evaluation, eliminating synthesis (R_2) is

$$F_2^* = \frac{10.87^2 - 10.09^2}{10.09^2} \cdot \frac{52-2+1}{7} = 1.17$$

F_2^* has 7 and 51 degrees of freedom. F_2^* does not exceed the critical F-value. Thus we may conclude that the correlation of divergent achievement with intelligence, creativity, and their interactions is concentrated in the variable synthesis. Synthesis in turn is presumably basic to the more complex behaviors of evaluation. When scores on synthesis are accounted for, evaluation does not add any further predictable variation, at least with these seven antecedent measures.

The canonical correlations between the two sets of variates are the ($s=2$) unique solutions of

$$|\mathbf{S}_w^{(yx)}[\mathbf{S}_w^{(xx)}]^{-1}\mathbf{S}_w^{(xy)} - \hat{R}_i^2\mathbf{S}_w^{(yy)}| = 0$$

or

$$\begin{vmatrix} -97.67\hat{R}_i^2 & -40.94 \\ -40.94 & -118.97\hat{R}_i^2 \end{vmatrix} = 0$$

Expanding the determinant and solving for the roots, $\hat{R}_1^2 = .50$ and $\hat{R}_2^2 = .06$. These values are substituted in

$$\{\mathbf{S}_w^{(yx)}[\mathbf{S}_w^{(xx)}]^{-1}\mathbf{S}_w^{(xy)} - \hat{R}_i^2\mathbf{S}_w^{(yy)}\}\mathbf{a}_i = \mathbf{0}$$

The nontrivial solutions for $\mathbf{a}_i$ are $\mathbf{a}_1' = [.40 \quad .23]$ and $\mathbf{a}_2' = [.60 \quad -.67]$, respectively (after multiplying by the constant $\sqrt{59}$). These vectors are juxtaposed as the columns of $\hat{\mathbf{A}}^{(y)}$.

The corresponding coefficients for the predictor variables are

$$\hat{\mathbf{A}}^{(x)} = \hat{\mathbf{B}}\hat{\mathbf{A}}^{(y)}\hat{\mathbf{R}}^{-1}$$

$$= \begin{bmatrix} 1.00 & .86 \\ .28 & .33 \\ .16 & .32 \\ -.04 & -.14 \\ -.16 & .24 \\ -.04 & -.16 \\ .25 & .20 \end{bmatrix} \begin{bmatrix} .40 & .60 \\ .23 & -.67 \end{bmatrix} \begin{bmatrix} 1/\sqrt{.50} & 0 \\ 0 & 1/\sqrt{.06} \end{bmatrix}$$

$$
= \begin{bmatrix} .85 & .10 \\ .27 & -.23 \\ .19 & -.47 \\ -.06 & .28 \\ -.01 & -1.04 \\ -.08 & .32 \\ .21 & .05 \end{bmatrix}
$$

The weights for the canonical variates may be standardized to assist in interpretation or may be transformed to correlations with the original variates. The matrices of intercorrelations are found from Eqs. 6.4.20a and b. The diagonal matrices of variances are $\mathbf{D}_w^{(yy)} = \text{diag}\,(\mathbf{S}_w^{(yy)}/59)$ and $\mathbf{D}_w^{(xx)} = \text{diag}\,(\mathbf{S}_w^{(xx)}/59)$. Then

$$
[\mathbf{D}_w^{(yy)}]^{-1/2}\mathbf{V}_w^{(yy)}\hat{\mathbf{A}}^{(y)} = \begin{bmatrix} .95 & .32 \\ .83 & -.56 \end{bmatrix} \begin{matrix} \text{Synthesis} \\ \text{Evaluation} \end{matrix}
$$

	Variate 1	Variate 2	

$$
[\mathbf{D}_w^{(xx)}]^{-1/2}\mathbf{V}_w^{(xx)}\hat{\mathbf{A}}^{(x)} = \begin{bmatrix} .95 & .09 \\ .30 & .06 \\ .56 & -.42 \\ .58 & .13 \\ .18 & -.87 \\ .49 & .01 \\ .45 & -.06 \end{bmatrix} \begin{matrix} \text{Intelligence} \\ \text{Cons. obvious} \\ \text{Cons. remote} \\ \text{Possible jobs} \\ \text{Cons. obv.} \times \text{intell.} \\ \text{Cons. remote} \times \text{intell.} \\ \text{Poss. jobs} \times \text{intell.} \end{matrix}
$$

Although the raw weights are useful for scoring subjects on the canonical variates, the intercorrelations are more stable and should be used for interpretation. The differences between the weights and the correlations are often large.

The first canonical correlation is the correlation of a linear combination of predictors, heavily loaded with intelligence, with a composite of the two criteria. Both criterion measures have similar positive weights. This suggests that the two outcome measures share common behaviors, which in turn resemble those of intelligence. The first canonical correlation explains $.50/2 = .25$ of all variation in the criterion measures and $.50/7 = .07$ of variation in the predictors.

In contrast, the second correlation accounts for only $.06/2 = .03$ of the variation in the criterion measures. Thus the total percentage of variation in the criteria attributable to the seven independent variables is $100 \times (.25 + .03) = 28$ percent. The variation in independent variables attributable to criteria is $100 \times (.07 + .01) = 8$ percent. As with the other correlation measures, the designation of independent and dependent variables is arbitrary, and does not affect the index of association.

The test of the nullity of both canonical correlations is equivalent to the overall test of the relationship between the two sets of measures under the regression model. From the correlations, the χ^2 approximation is

$$
\begin{aligned}
\chi^2 &= -54(\log_e .50 + \log_e .94) \\
&= 40.68
\end{aligned}
$$

χ^2 has 14 degrees of freedom. The null hypothesis of no relationship between the sets of variates is rejected at $\alpha = .05$.

Test of all correlations excluding the largest (which in this case is the test of only the smaller) is made with $\Lambda_2 = (1-.06) = .94$. The χ^2 statistic is

$$\chi^2 = -54 \log_e .94$$
$$= 3.38$$

This χ^2 has $(2-1)(7-1) = 6$ degrees of freedom. H_0 is not rejected; R_2^2 is zero in the population. All linear relationship between the two sets is concentrated in the correlation of the first pair of composites of the variables.

6.6 CONDENSING THE VARIATES: PRINCIPAL COMPONENTS

When confronted with a large number of variables measuring a single construct, it may be desirable to represent the set by some smaller number of variables that convey all or most of the information in the original set. *Principal components* are linear transformations of a set of random variables that summarize the information contained in the variates. The transformations are chosen so that the first component accounts for the maximal amount of variation of the measures of any possible linear transform; the second component accounts for the maximal amount of residual variation; and so on. The principal components are constructed so that they represent transformed scores on dimensions which are mutually orthogonal. A set of p measures is transformed into p composites or principal components. A subset of the components may account for a large portion of variation of the original measures.

Let $\mathbf{y}$ represent the p-element vector random variable consisting of p outcome measures, with expectation

$$\mathscr{E}(\mathbf{y}) = \boldsymbol{\mu} \tag{6.6.1}$$

and covariance matrix

$$\mathscr{V}(\mathbf{y}) = \boldsymbol{\Sigma} \tag{6.6.2}$$

Let $\boldsymbol{\alpha}_1$ be the p-element vector defining the first component or first composite of the outcome measures. The principal component transformation is

$$v_1 = \boldsymbol{\alpha}_1'\mathbf{y} \tag{6.6.3}$$

v_1 has expectation

$$\mathscr{E}(v_1) = \boldsymbol{\alpha}_1'\boldsymbol{\mu} \tag{6.6.4}$$

The variance of v_1 is

$$\mathscr{V}(v_1) = \boldsymbol{\alpha}_1'\boldsymbol{\Sigma}\boldsymbol{\alpha}_1 \tag{6.6.5}$$

To provide a single maximum value for $\mathscr{V}(v_1)$, it is necessary to restrict the values that $\boldsymbol{\alpha}_1$ can have. The convenient and usual restriction is to set the length of $\boldsymbol{\alpha}_1$ to unity; that is, $\boldsymbol{\alpha}_1'\boldsymbol{\alpha}_1=1$. With this limitation, we may rewrite the expression for $\mathcal{V}(v_1)$ and differentiate with respect to $\boldsymbol{\alpha}_1$. Thus

$$\begin{aligned}\mathcal{V}(v_1) &= \boldsymbol{\alpha}_1'\boldsymbol{\Sigma}\boldsymbol{\alpha}_1 \\ &= \boldsymbol{\alpha}_1'\boldsymbol{\Sigma}\boldsymbol{\alpha}_1 - \lambda_1(\boldsymbol{\alpha}_1'\boldsymbol{\alpha}_1 - 1)\end{aligned}$$

Setting the first derivatives with respect to $\boldsymbol{\alpha}_1$ to zero, we have

$$2\boldsymbol{\Sigma}\boldsymbol{\alpha}_1 - 2\lambda_1\boldsymbol{\alpha}_1 = \mathbf{0}$$

and

$$(\boldsymbol{\Sigma}-\lambda_1\mathbf{I})\boldsymbol{\alpha}_1 = \mathbf{0} \tag{6.6.6}$$

Equation 6.6.6 has nontrivial solutions if and only if

$$|\boldsymbol{\Sigma}-\lambda_1\mathbf{I}| = 0 \tag{6.6.7}$$

λ_1 and $\boldsymbol{\alpha}_1$ are the largest characteristic root and vector of $\boldsymbol{\Sigma}$, with λ_1 also being the variance of the composite $\boldsymbol{\alpha}_1'\mathbf{y}$.

The second principal component is the maximal solution

$$(\boldsymbol{\Sigma}-\lambda_2\mathbf{I})\boldsymbol{\alpha}_2 = \mathbf{0} \tag{6.6.8}$$

$\boldsymbol{\alpha}_2$ is restricted additionally to be orthogonal to $\boldsymbol{\alpha}_1$. Since eigenvectors of symmetric matrices are orthogonal, $\boldsymbol{\alpha}_2$ is the second eigenvector of $\boldsymbol{\Sigma}$. The associated root is λ_2. $\boldsymbol{\alpha}_2$ summarizes the maximal amount of criterion variation under the additional restriction, and is also confined to unit length.

The process of defining components continues in the manner of Eqs. 6.6.6 and 6.6.7 until all p roots and vectors are extracted from $\boldsymbol{\Sigma}$. The relationships among the components may be summarized as follows. Let $\boldsymbol{\Lambda}$ be the $p \times p$ diagonal matrix of characteristic roots; let $\mathbf{A}$ be the $p \times p$ matrix having $\boldsymbol{\alpha}_i$ as the ith column. Then

$$\mathbf{A}'\mathbf{A} = \mathbf{I} \tag{6.6.9}$$

$$\mathbf{A}'\boldsymbol{\Sigma}\mathbf{A} = \boldsymbol{\Lambda} \tag{6.6.10}$$

$$|\boldsymbol{\Sigma}| = |\boldsymbol{\Lambda}| = \prod_{i=1}^{p} \lambda_i \tag{6.6.11}$$

$$\text{tr}\,(\boldsymbol{\Sigma}) = \text{tr}\,(\boldsymbol{\Lambda}) = \sum_{i=1}^{p} \lambda_i \tag{6.6.12}$$

We may use property 6.6.12 to obtain a measure of the degree to which criterion variation is summarized by any one of the components. The proportion of variation of the original measures attributable to the ith principal component is

$$P_i = \frac{\lambda_i}{\sum_{i=1}^{p} \lambda_i} \tag{6.6.13}$$

The sum of all the P_i is, of course, 1.00.

The component weights may provide insight into the basic structure of the measures. For example, we may wish to know what single linear function summarizes the maximum share of variation of the p measures. For this we might inspect the first principal component and the associated weights.

The principal component solution is only meaningful when (1) the original measures are all in the same units and (2) components are extracted from the covariance matrix. Standardizing dissimilar measures to provide an arbitrarily similar unit does not yield components that account for the structure of the original measures. There is no simple relationship between the components of a covariance matrix and the respective correlation matrix, except when all the variances are equal.

There are times, however, when the components of a correlation matrix yield useful interpretive information. The coefficients in **A** may be examined in an attempt to understand the structure of the set of variates. Care should be exercised in their interpretation. The magnitudes are dependent upon the particular set of variables and may change considerably under the addition or deletion of measures. The signs of the coefficients tend to be more stable. Thus the components are best interpreted in terms of similarities and differences of the original variables that explain "total" variation.

To aid in the interpretation of component weights, subsets of the weights may be used to estimate the original covariance or correlation matrix. The difference between the original matrix and the estimated matrix can be used for information about the omitted components. First it is necessary to scale the vectors $\boldsymbol{\alpha}_i$ to length equal to the variance of the component λ_i. This is accomplished by multiplying each element of $\boldsymbol{\alpha}_i$ by $\sqrt{\lambda_i}$. The set of p rescaled weight vectors is contained in the $p \times p$ matrix $\mathbf{A}^*$. That is,

$$\mathbf{A}^* = \mathbf{A}\boldsymbol{\Lambda}^{1/2} \tag{6.6.14}$$

where $\boldsymbol{\Lambda}^{1/2}$ is the diagonal matrix of square roots of the p eigenvalues. The length of each column of $\mathbf{A}^*$ (that is, $\boldsymbol{\alpha}_i^*$) is λ_i, since

$$\begin{aligned} [\mathbf{A}^*]'\mathbf{A}^* &= \boldsymbol{\Lambda}^{1/2}\mathbf{A}'\mathbf{A}\boldsymbol{\Lambda}^{1/2} \\ &= \boldsymbol{\Lambda} \end{aligned} \tag{6.6.15}$$

The original covariance matrix can be reproduced directly from $\mathbf{A}^*$:

$$\begin{aligned} \mathbf{A}^*[\mathbf{A}^*]' &= \mathbf{A}\boldsymbol{\Lambda}^{1/2}(\mathbf{A}\boldsymbol{\Lambda}^{1/2})' \\ &= \mathbf{A}\boldsymbol{\Lambda}\mathbf{A}' \\ &= \boldsymbol{\Sigma} \end{aligned} \tag{6.6.16}$$

Equation 6.6.16 follows from 6.6.10, since a square matrix orthonormal by columns is of necessity also orthonormal by rows.

The product $\mathbf{A}^*[\mathbf{A}^*]'$ is the sum of matrix products of the p vectors of adjusted weights $(\boldsymbol{\alpha}_i^*)'$. That is,

$$\mathbf{A}^*[\mathbf{A}^*]' = \sum_{i=1}^{p} \boldsymbol{\alpha}_i^*(\boldsymbol{\alpha}_i^*)' \tag{6.6.17}$$

To understand the variation and covariation attributable to the first component, $\boldsymbol{\Sigma}$ may be reproduced omitting $\boldsymbol{\alpha}_1^*$. That is,

$$\boldsymbol{\Sigma}^* = \sum_{i=2}^{p} \boldsymbol{\alpha}_i^*(\boldsymbol{\alpha}_i^*)' \tag{6.6.18}$$

Either $\boldsymbol{\Sigma}^*$, or $\boldsymbol{\Sigma}-\boldsymbol{\Sigma}^*=\boldsymbol{\alpha}_1^*(\boldsymbol{\alpha}_1^*)'$, can be used for interpretation. In similar fashion, $\boldsymbol{\Sigma}^*$ may be obtained by omitting any of the other components or by omitting particular subsets, such as those with smallest variance. If components have originally been extracted from a correlation matrix $\mathcal{R}$, the product $\mathbf{A}^*[\mathbf{A}^*]'$ will also be the correlation matrix.

To further facilitate understanding the principal component variates, the weights may be converted to standardized form. Each element of the resulting matrix is the product-moment correlation of an original variate y_j and a component variable v_i. Let $\boldsymbol{\Delta}=\text{diag}\,(\boldsymbol{\Sigma})$ be a diagonal matrix of variances from $\boldsymbol{\Sigma}$. Then the variables $\times$ components matrix of correlations (termed "factor loadings" in factor analysis models) is

$$\boldsymbol{\Delta}^{-1/2}\mathbf{A}\boldsymbol{\Lambda}^{1/2}=\boldsymbol{\Delta}^{-1/2}\mathbf{A}^* \tag{6.6.19}$$

The intercorrelations are somewhat more stable than the raw weights under addition or deletion of variables, and have limits ± 1. When components are extracted from the correlation matrix, the adjustment (Eq. 6.6.19) is unnecessary, since $\boldsymbol{\Delta}=\mathbf{I}$. The correlations of components and variates is always the scaled matrix necessary to reproduce $\mathcal{R}$ by Eq. 6.6.16, since

$$\begin{aligned}\boldsymbol{\Delta}^{-1/2}\mathbf{A}\boldsymbol{\Lambda}^{1/2}(\boldsymbol{\Delta}^{-1/2}\mathbf{A}\boldsymbol{\Lambda}^{1/2})' &= \boldsymbol{\Delta}^{-1/2}\boldsymbol{\Sigma}\boldsymbol{\Delta}^{-1/2}\\ &= \mathcal{R}\end{aligned} \tag{6.6.20}$$

Estimates of the principal components are obtained by substituting the estimate of $\hat{\boldsymbol{\Sigma}}$ for $\boldsymbol{\Sigma}$ in eigenequations 6.6.6 and 6.6.8, and solving for $\hat{\lambda}_i$ and $\hat{\boldsymbol{\alpha}}_i$. The estimate of $\boldsymbol{\Sigma}$ may be either the variance–covariance matrix of mean deviations (3.3.8), the pooled within-groups matrix (3.3.22), or the residual matrix in a regression model (4.4.17).

Test of the hypothesis that a principal component does not account for any of the variation in the outcome measures is not particularly meaningful. Even the smallest root may be increased in importance by the addition of measures of the specific behaviors represented by the component. If it is judged that sufficient variation is accounted for by a subset of components, however, scores for individuals on just these variables may be obtained. The jth component score for observation i is

$$v_{ij}=\mathbf{y}_i'\hat{\boldsymbol{\alpha}}_j \tag{6.6.21}$$

If the number of components required is much less than p, an economy of representation is achieved. Otherwise, the simpler original measures provide more information for quantitative analysis.

Sample Problem 1 – Creativity and Achievement

In the creativity-intelligence-achievement example, principal components may be extracted from the correlation matrix for the conceptually similar creativity and divergent achievement measures (synthesis, evaluation,

Table 6.6.1 Principal Components of Divergent Achievement and Creativity Intercorrelations

Component	Variance (eigen-value)	Percentage of Variation Accounted for	*Component Weights* Syn-thesis	Evalu-ation	Cons. Obv.	Cons. Rem.	Poss. Jobs
1	2.42	48.3	−.76	−.74	−.52	−.64	−.77
2	1.10	22.0	.29	.39	−.77	.33	−.41
3	.76	15.1	−.37	−.33	−.16	.65	.25
4	.41	8.2	.40	−.40	−.20	−.09	.20
5	.32	6.4	−.18	.18	−.26	−.22	.37

consequences remote the obvious, and possible jobs). The adjusted sample coefficients $\hat{\mathbf{A}}^*$, and the corresponding component variances are given in Table 6.6.1. The largest component accounts for $100(2.42/5) = 48.3$ percent of between-individual variation. The compound is an effect common to all measures. This is indicated by the similar negative weights for the five variables in constituting v_1.

All of the remaining components also account for large portions of variation and cannot be ignored. The second, accounting for an additional 22 percent of test variation, appears to be a contrast between the "consequence obvious" and "possible jobs" measures and the remaining measures. These two tests in particular do not require the degree of abstraction required by the three other measures. The operations in listing obvious event consequences and jobs are noticeably more concrete.

Numerous interpretations of the remaining weights may be forwarded. However, in view of the finding that a much smaller number of components does not summarize a large portion of the variation of the original five measures, such interpretation is unnecessary. A return to the original measures rather than linear combinations of them is both simpler and more lucid.

Sample Problem 3 – Dental Calculus Reduction

From the toothpaste-additive study, the covariance matrix of the calculus measures for the six anterior mandibular teeth is

$$\hat{\boldsymbol{\Sigma}} = \begin{bmatrix} 1.38 & & & & & \text{(Symmetric)} \\ 1.02 & 2.62 & & & & \\ .81 & 2.18 & 4.24 & & & \\ 1.07 & 2.60 & 4.31 & 6.19 & & \\ .74 & 1.67 & 2.43 & 3.49 & 3.09 & \\ .91 & 1.01 & 1.12 & 1.30 & 1.21 & 1.58 \end{bmatrix} \begin{matrix} \text{Right canine} \\ \text{Right lateral incisor} \\ \text{Right central incisor} \\ \text{Left central incisor} \\ \text{Left lateral incisor} \\ \text{Left canine} \end{matrix}$$

Right canine, Right lateral incisor, Right central incisor, Left central incisor, Left lateral incisor, Left canine

Solving for the roots of $|\hat{\boldsymbol{\Sigma}}-\hat{\lambda}_i\mathbf{I}|=0$, the six eigenvalues in descending order are the diagonal elements of $\hat{\boldsymbol{\Lambda}}$. That is,

$$\hat{\boldsymbol{\Lambda}} = \text{diag}\,(13.82, 2.02, 1.28, .88, .71, .38)$$

Their sum is 19.09, equal to the sum of the diagonal elements of $\hat{\boldsymbol{\Sigma}}$.

The matrix of coefficients, with vectors normalized to the corresponding eigenvalues, is

Component

$$\hat{\mathbf{A}}^* = \hat{\mathbf{A}}\hat{\boldsymbol{\Lambda}}^{1/2} = \begin{array}{c} \\ \end{array}\begin{bmatrix} -.57 & .83 & -.08 & -.14 & .49 & .32 \\ -1.26 & .58 & -.55 & .59 & -.22 & -.09 \\ -1.87 & -.35 & -.52 & -.51 & -.28 & .17 \\ -2.38 & -.50 & .13 & .12 & .46 & -.23 \\ -1.51 & .04 & .77 & .21 & -.31 & .26 \\ -.72 & .79 & .30 & -.44 & -.16 & -.35 \end{bmatrix} \begin{array}{l} \text{Right canine} \\ \text{Right lateral incisor} \\ \text{Right central incisor} \\ \text{Left central incisor} \\ \text{Left lateral incisor} \\ \text{Left canine} \end{array}$$

(columns: components 1, 2, 3, 4, 5, 6)

The inverse matrix of variable standard deviations is

$$\hat{\boldsymbol{\Delta}}^{-1/2} = \text{diag}\,(1/\sqrt{1.38},\ 1/\sqrt{2.62},\ 1/\sqrt{4.24},\ 1/\sqrt{6.19},\ 1/\sqrt{3.09},\ 1/\sqrt{1.58})$$

Multiplying $\hat{\boldsymbol{\Delta}}^{-1/2}\hat{\mathbf{A}}^*$ yields the matrix of intercorrelations between the components and the original measures. These are presented in Table 6.6.2.

The first component accounts for about 72 percent of between-individual variation in the calculus measures. The effect appears to be common to all teeth, with the contribution to the component increasing as the teeth approach the front of the mouth. Probably this component is simply reflecting the greater mean and variance of calculus accumulation of the anterior teeth.

The second component, accounting for an additional 10.6 percent of the variation, is largely a comparison of the frontmost teeth with the canines. The component probably reflects both differential usage in eating and brushing, as well as proximity to the salivary glands.

Table 6.6.2 Correlations of Principal Components with Calculus Measures for Six Anterior Teeth

Component	*Variance (eigenvalue)*	*Percentage of Variation Accounted for*	*Right Canine*	*Right Lateral Incisor*	*Right Central Incisor*	*Left Central Incisor*	*Left Lateral Incisor*	*Left Canine*
1	13.82	72.4	−.49	−.78	−.91	−.95	−.86	−.57
2	2.02	10.6	.70	.36	−.17	−.20	.02	.63
3	1.28	6.7	−.07	−.34	−.25	.05	.44	.24
4	.88	4.6	−.12	.36	−.25	.05	.12	−.35
5	.71	3.7	.42	−.14	−.13	.19	−.18	−.13
6	.38	2.0	.27	−.05	.08	−.09	.15	−.28
Sum	19.09	100.0	1.00	1.00	1.00	1.00	1.00	1.00
					(Sum of squares)			

The third component accounts for an additional 6.7 percent of score variation. This component reflects differential calculus formation on the two sides of the mouth. It appears that there exists a tendency of individuals to have a greater calculus formation on one or the other side of the mouth. This may reflect lateral favoritism in biting and/or brushing. The remaining three components account for a total of about 10 percent of between-individual variation. As such, they depict only minor trends in the teeth data.

CHAPTER 7

Analysis of Variance: Models

7.1 CONSTRUCTING THE MODEL

Univariate Case

Through the analysis-of-variance model, attention is centered on subpopulation means. The model may be formulated in a fashion similar to that for linear regression. Consider that observations have been sampled from, or assigned to, J distinct populations. The groups are distinguishable by a single sampling characteristic or *factor*. The sample of observations from one population comprises a *group* or *subclass* of observations. These are sometimes referred to as the observations of a single *cell* in the sampling design.

The additive linear model for an observation in one subclass is

$$y_{ij}=\mu+\alpha_j+\epsilon_{ij} \tag{7.1.1}$$

where y_{ij} is the random outcome for observation i in the jth subclass ($j=1, 2, \ldots, J$). μ is a fixed parameter representing the mean of all observations. α_j is the (fixed) mean deviation from μ, of the observations in subclass j. ϵ_{ij} is the random deviation of observation i in subclass j from the subclass mean; that is, the unique deviation from $\mu+\alpha_j$.

The analysis-of-variance model may be appropriate whenever the observations are subdivided into identifiable groups, whether these are naturally *or* experimentally formed. The purposes of fitting the model to sample data are three: testing the fit of the model, estimating the fixed parameters, and providing interpretations of the random outcomes in terms of the fixed group-membership variable(s).

Testing the fit of the model usually involves deciding whether or not the entire model "explains" the observations. Is a large or significant portion of variation in y_{ij} nonrandom *and* attributable to an overall population constant μ, plus systematic group deviations from μ? Is variation attributable to $\mu+\alpha_j$, as compared with that attributable to ϵ, a large proportion of the variation of the y_{ij}? Also we test the model to decide whether variation in the outcome may be more economically attributed to a subset of terms. That is, do the data indicate that the α_j's are not zero? Are there nonzero differences among the α_j (or among subpopulation means) that make the term worthy of inclusion in the model?

After deciding that a subset of terms in the model is nonzero, we may wish to obtain "best" estimates from the sample data, of only those parameters and their dispersions. Ultimately we face the question of how the results y_{ij} can best be explained in terms of the constructs underlying the measures and subgroup definitions. Here we must combine forces with the theory of the discipline from which the data are drawn.

Suppose that $J=4$ and that there is a single observation per group. The models for all subjects may be written as

$$\begin{aligned} y_{11} &= \mu + \alpha_1 \qquad\qquad\qquad\qquad + \epsilon_{11} \\ y_{12} &= \mu \qquad + \alpha_2 \qquad\qquad\qquad + \epsilon_{12} \\ y_{13} &= \mu \qquad\qquad + \alpha_3 \qquad\quad + \epsilon_{13} \\ y_{14} &= \mu \qquad\qquad\qquad\quad + \alpha_4 + \epsilon_{14} \end{aligned} \tag{7.1.2}$$

The set of models may be formulated in vector notation. First, let us fill in zero-one coefficients. Eq. 7.1.2 is, equivalently,

$$\begin{aligned} y_{11} &= 1\mu + 1\alpha_1 + 0\alpha_2 + 0\alpha_3 + 0\alpha_4 + \epsilon_{11} \\ y_{12} &= 1\mu + 0\alpha_1 + 1\alpha_2 + 0\alpha_3 + 0\alpha_4 + \epsilon_{12} \\ y_{13} &= 1\mu + 0\alpha_1 + 0\alpha_2 + 1\alpha_3 + 0\alpha_4 + \epsilon_{13} \\ y_{14} &= 1\mu + 0\alpha_1 + 0\alpha_2 + 0\alpha_3 + 1\alpha_4 + \epsilon_{14} \end{aligned} \tag{7.1.2a}$$

Any observation can be expressed as the product of a vector of ones and zeros and a vector of fixed effects. For example,

$$y_{11} = [1 \quad 1 \quad 0 \quad 0 \quad 0] \begin{bmatrix} \mu \\ \alpha_1 \\ \alpha_2 \\ \alpha_3 \\ \alpha_4 \end{bmatrix} + \epsilon_{11} \tag{7.1.3}$$

or

$$y_{11} = [1 \quad 1 \quad 0 \quad 0 \quad 0]\boldsymbol{\theta}^* + \epsilon_{11} \tag{7.1.3a}$$

$\boldsymbol{\theta}^*$ is an $m \times 1$ vector of analysis-of-variance *effects* or parameters. In Eq. 7.1.3, $m=5$. Testing the fit of the model involves deciding whether some or all of the terms of $\boldsymbol{\theta}^*$ are null or are equal to each other. For example, testing that $\alpha_1 = \alpha_2 = \alpha_3 = \alpha_4$ is equivalent to testing that linear combinations of the rows of $\boldsymbol{\theta}^*$ are null. Estimation in analysis of variance involves obtaining best estimates of $\boldsymbol{\theta}^*$ or linear combinations of the elements. These objectives are identical to those encountered relative to the vector of regression weights $\boldsymbol{\beta}$ in the linear regression model (Chapter 4).

Models for all N observations (Eq. 7.1.2a) may also be displayed in matrix form. That is,

$$\begin{bmatrix} y_{11} \\ y_{12} \\ y_{13} \\ y_{14} \end{bmatrix} = \begin{bmatrix} 1 & 1 & 0 & 0 & 0 \\ 1 & 0 & 1 & 0 & 0 \\ 1 & 0 & 0 & 1 & 0 \\ 1 & 0 & 0 & 0 & 1 \end{bmatrix} \begin{bmatrix} \mu \\ \alpha_1 \\ \alpha_2 \\ \alpha_3 \\ \alpha_4 \end{bmatrix} + \begin{bmatrix} \epsilon_{11} \\ \epsilon_{12} \\ \epsilon_{13} \\ \epsilon_{14} \end{bmatrix} \tag{7.1.4}$$

or

$$\mathbf{y}=\mathbf{A}\boldsymbol{\theta}^{*}+\boldsymbol{\epsilon} \tag{7.1.4a}$$

where **y** and $\boldsymbol{\epsilon}$ are $N\times 1$ random vectors, and **A** is the $N\times m$ analysis-of-variance *model matrix.* **A** has a row for each observation and a column corresponding to each of the m parameters. The entry is 1 if the subclass has the corresponding parameter in its model and 0 if it does not. The unknown coefficients or effects to be estimated are contained in vector $\boldsymbol{\theta}^{*}$. The same vector multiples each row of **A** to produce the set of models given in Eq. 7.1.2.

The terms in Eq. 7.1.4a parallel those of the linear regression model $\mathbf{y}=\mathbf{X}\boldsymbol{\beta}+\boldsymbol{\epsilon}$. However, **A** contains only ones and zeros, designating whether the observation has the corresponding effect or not. The regression matrix **X** contains measured scores indicating the *extent* to which the parameter is contained in each equation. That is, the measured variables reflect varying degrees of presence of the independent variables; in Eq. 7.1.4 the observation either belongs to a group having a particular parameter or to a qualitatively distinct group lacking the parameter.

The analysis-of-variance distributional assumptions are two in number. First, each ϵ_{ij} is assumed to be normally distributed with expectation zero, and common variance σ^2; that is,

$$\epsilon_{ij}\sim\mathcal{N}(0,\ \sigma^2) \tag{7.1.5}$$

Further, pairs ϵ_{ij} and $\epsilon_{i'j'}$ ($ij\neq i'j'$) are assumed independent of each other. Under normality, this implies zero covariance of pairs of errors. The entire distributional assumption may be written as

$$\begin{bmatrix}\epsilon_{11}\\ \epsilon_{12}\\ \epsilon_{13}\\ \epsilon_{14}\end{bmatrix}\sim\mathcal{N}\left[\begin{pmatrix}0\\0\\0\\0\end{pmatrix},\begin{pmatrix}\sigma^2&0&0&0\\0&\sigma^2&0&0\\0&0&\sigma^2&0\\0&0&0&\sigma^2\end{pmatrix}\right] \tag{7.1.6}$$

or

$$\boldsymbol{\epsilon}\sim\mathcal{N}(\mathbf{0},\ \sigma^2\mathbf{I}) \tag{7.1.6a}$$

If a cell in the design contains responses for more than a single observation, all observations in the group will have the same model—that is, the same row of **A**. It is convenient to represent the models only in terms of subclass means. Thus, for the one-way design, we may write

$$\begin{aligned}y_{\cdot 1}&=\mu+\alpha_1 &&&&+\epsilon_{\cdot 1}\\ y_{\cdot 2}&=\mu &&+\alpha_2 &&+\epsilon_{\cdot 2}\\ y_{\cdot 3}&=\mu &&&+\alpha_3 &+\epsilon_{\cdot 3}\\ y_{\cdot 4}&=\mu &&&&+\alpha_4+\epsilon_{\cdot 4}\end{aligned} \tag{7.1.7}$$

or

$$\mathbf{y}_{\cdot}=\mathbf{A}\boldsymbol{\theta}^{*}+\boldsymbol{\epsilon}_{\cdot} \tag{7.1.7a}$$

Let N_j be the number of observations in subgroup j. Then $y_{\cdot j}=\Sigma_i y_{ij}/N_j$ and $\epsilon_{\cdot j}=\Sigma_i\epsilon_{ij}/N_j$. The distributional assumptions are that each $\epsilon_{\cdot j}$ follows a normal distribution, with expectation zero and variance σ^2/N_j. That is,

$$\epsilon_{\cdot j}\sim\mathcal{N}(0,\ \sigma^2/N_j)$$

Further, every pair $\epsilon_{\cdot j}$ and $\epsilon_{\cdot k}$ ($j \neq k$) is independently distributed. This assumption may be represented in matrix terms by letting the N_j be the nonzero elements of a diagonal matrix **D**:

$$\mathbf{D} = \text{diag}\,(N_1, N_2, N_3, N_4) \tag{7.1.8}$$

The complete distributional assumption is

$$\begin{bmatrix} \epsilon_{\cdot 1} \\ \epsilon_{\cdot 2} \\ \epsilon_{\cdot 3} \\ \epsilon_{\cdot 4} \end{bmatrix} \sim \mathcal{N}\left[\begin{pmatrix} 0 \\ 0 \\ 0 \\ 0 \end{pmatrix}, \begin{pmatrix} \sigma^2/N_1 & 0 & 0 & 0 \\ 0 & \sigma^2/N_2 & 0 & 0 \\ 0 & 0 & \sigma^2/N_3 & 0 \\ 0 & 0 & 0 & \sigma^2/N_4 \end{pmatrix}\right] \tag{7.1.9}$$

or

$$\boldsymbol{\epsilon}_{\cdot} \sim \mathcal{N}(\mathbf{0},\ \sigma^2\mathbf{D}^{-1}) \tag{7.1.9a}$$

There is no restriction on the frequencies N_j. However the variance σ^2 is the same for all groups.

The matrix model for higher-order designs may be constructed in the same fashion. Consider a situation in which subjects have been sampled from six populations, representing the crossing of two experimental factors. Let factors A and B have two and three levels, respectively. The linear model for the mean in subclass jk is

$$y_{\cdot jk} = \mu + \alpha_j + \beta_k + (\alpha\beta)_{jk} + \epsilon_{\cdot jk} \tag{7.1.10}$$

where μ is a population effect common to all groups; α_j and β_k are the deviations from μ due to the mean having been drawn from level j of the first sampling factor and level k of the second; $(\alpha\beta)_{jk}$ is the nonadditive, or *interaction*, effect specific to the mean of subclass jk. $(\alpha\beta)_{jk}$ represents the extent to which treatment effects α_j are not equally effective across all levels of the other factor(s) in the design; $\epsilon_{\cdot jk}$ is the random deviation of the observed mean from the model, $\mu+\alpha_j+\beta_k+(\alpha\beta)_{jk}$; $\epsilon_{\cdot jk}$ is assumed to have expectation zero, and variance σ^2/N_{jk}.

In terms of the larger model, Eq. 7.1.10, the purposes of the analysis include deciding whether there are nonzero differences among population means—that is, whether the model $\mu+\alpha_j+\beta_k+(\alpha\beta)_{jk}$ fits the data. In particular, we must decide whether variation among means is confined to a subset of terms in the model. For example, are some treatment effects significant, but not others, or are perhaps, the interactions null? Ultimately, we will want to obtain "best" estimates of those terms deemed nonzero, to aid in interpreting the observed outcomes.

Models for all six subclass means may be written as

$$\begin{aligned}
y_{\cdot 11} &= \mu+\alpha_1 \quad +\beta_1 \quad +(\alpha\beta)_{11} + \epsilon_{\cdot 11} \\
y_{\cdot 12} &= \mu+\alpha_1 \quad +\beta_2 \quad +(\alpha\beta)_{12} + \epsilon_{\cdot 12} \\
y_{\cdot 13} &= \mu+\alpha_1 \quad +\beta_3 \quad +(\alpha\beta)_{13} + \epsilon_{\cdot 13} \\
y_{\cdot 21} &= \mu \quad +\alpha_2+\beta_1 \quad +(\alpha\beta)_{21} + \epsilon_{\cdot 21} \\
y_{\cdot 22} &= \mu \quad +\alpha_2 \quad +\beta_2 \quad +(\alpha\beta)_{22} + \epsilon_{\cdot 22} \\
y_{\cdot 23} &= \mu \quad +\alpha_2 \quad +\beta_3 \quad +(\alpha\beta)_{23} + \epsilon_{\cdot 23}
\end{aligned} \tag{7.1.11}$$

Equivalently, we may write

$$\begin{bmatrix} y_{\cdot 11} \\ y_{\cdot 12} \\ y_{\cdot 13} \\ y_{\cdot 21} \\ y_{\cdot 22} \\ y_{\cdot 23} \end{bmatrix} = \begin{bmatrix} 1 & 1 & 0 & 1 & 0 & 0 & 1 & 0 & 0 & 0 & 0 & 0 \\ 1 & 1 & 0 & 0 & 1 & 0 & 0 & 1 & 0 & 0 & 0 & 0 \\ 1 & 1 & 0 & 0 & 0 & 1 & 0 & 0 & 1 & 0 & 0 & 0 \\ 1 & 0 & 1 & 1 & 0 & 0 & 0 & 0 & 0 & 1 & 0 & 0 \\ 1 & 0 & 1 & 0 & 1 & 0 & 0 & 0 & 0 & 0 & 1 & 0 \\ 1 & 0 & 1 & 0 & 0 & 1 & 0 & 0 & 0 & 0 & 0 & 1 \end{bmatrix} \begin{bmatrix} \mu \\ \alpha_1 \\ \alpha_2 \\ \beta_1 \\ \beta_2 \\ \beta_3 \\ (\alpha\beta)_{11} \\ (\alpha\beta)_{12} \\ (\alpha\beta)_{13} \\ (\alpha\beta)_{21} \\ (\alpha\beta)_{22} \\ (\alpha\beta)_{23} \end{bmatrix} + \begin{bmatrix} \epsilon_{\cdot 11} \\ \epsilon_{\cdot 12} \\ \epsilon_{\cdot 13} \\ \epsilon_{\cdot 21} \\ \epsilon_{\cdot 22} \\ \epsilon_{\cdot 23} \end{bmatrix} \tag{7.1.12}$$

or

$$\mathbf{y}_{\cdot} = \mathbf{A}\boldsymbol{\theta}^* + \boldsymbol{\epsilon}_{\cdot} \tag{7.1.12a}$$

As in the one-way example, $\mathbf{y}.$ is the J-element mean vector. J is the total number of subclasses of observations, formed by the crossing of the two design factors ($J=6$ in the example). $\mathbf{A}$ is the $J \times m$ analysis-of-variance model matrix. Thus $\boldsymbol{\theta}^*$ is the $m \times 1$ vector of unknown coefficients or effects. $\boldsymbol{\epsilon}.$ is the $J \times 1$ vector of mean errors. Should any of the J subclasses contain no observations, corresponding rows of $\mathbf{y}.$, $\mathbf{A}$, and $\boldsymbol{\epsilon}.$ may be deleted, leaving J_0 rows for that number of subclasses with subjects. The vector of parameters $\boldsymbol{\theta}^*$ is unaffected by missing cells.

Constructing mean and error vectors for designs of any dimensionality follows the same pattern. So, for example, for a $2 \times 2 \times 2$ factorial arrangement, the model matrix for main effects α, β, and γ alone is

$$\mathbf{A} = \begin{bmatrix} 1 & 1 & 0 & 1 & 0 & 1 & 0 \\ 1 & 1 & 0 & 1 & 0 & 0 & 1 \\ 1 & 1 & 0 & 0 & 1 & 1 & 0 \\ 1 & 1 & 0 & 0 & 1 & 0 & 1 \\ 1 & 0 & 1 & 1 & 0 & 1 & 0 \\ 1 & 0 & 1 & 1 & 0 & 0 & 1 \\ 1 & 0 & 1 & 0 & 1 & 1 & 0 \\ 1 & 0 & 1 & 0 & 1 & 0 & 1 \end{bmatrix} \tag{7.1.13a}$$

with

$$[\boldsymbol{\theta}^*]' = [\mu \quad \alpha_1 \quad \alpha_2 \quad \beta_1 \quad \beta_2 \quad \gamma_1 \quad \gamma_2] \tag{7.1.13b}$$

Model matrices for nested designs may also be constructed in this manner. For example, in a situation where school classes have been randomly assigned to treatment conditions, and pupils randomly assigned to classes, we may have the following setup:

Treatment 1		*Treatment 2*		
Class 1	*Class 2*	*Class 3*	*Class 4*	*Class 5*

Here classes 1 and 2 are subjected to the first experimental condition and classes 3, 4, and 5 are subjected to the second. In addition, there may be further effects crossed with treatments and classes (such as ability or sex groups) that have the same definition for all treatment conditions.

The mean model for class i under condition j, assuming no other factors, is

$$y_{\cdot ij} = \mu + \alpha_j + b_{i(j)} + \epsilon_{\cdot ij} \tag{7.1.14}$$

where α_j is the (fixed) treatment effect and $b_{i(j)}$ is the random class effect under treatment condition j. For all groups, the models are

$$\begin{aligned}
y_{\cdot 11} &= \mu + \alpha_1 + b_{1(1)} + \epsilon_{\cdot 11} \\
y_{\cdot 21} &= \mu + \alpha_1 + b_{2(1)} + \epsilon_{\cdot 21} \\
y_{\cdot 12} &= \mu + \alpha_2 + b_{1(2)} + \epsilon_{\cdot 12} \\
y_{\cdot 22} &= \mu + \alpha_2 + b_{2(2)} + \epsilon_{\cdot 22} \\
y_{\cdot 32} &= \mu + \alpha_2 + b_{3(2)} + \epsilon_{\cdot 32}
\end{aligned} \tag{7.1.14a}$$

In Eq. 7.1.14 the b-effects are not the same for α_1 as they are for α_2 since experimental groups are not crossed with conditions. Specifically, class i for treatment 1 is not the same as class i for treatment 2. We say that classes are *nested* within experimental conditions and represent the effect of the ith class within the jth experimental condition only as $b_{i(j)}$. Since the subjects (pupils) are also different from class to class, subjects are said to be nested within classes. If the entire design were crossed with pupil sex, subjects would be nested within sex×class combinations or interactions. In this sense, all crossed designs with replications have subjects nested within the smallest cell formed by the crossing of the design factors.

Multivariate Case

When each subject has been measured on more than a single outcome measure (dependent variable), a multivariate form of the analysis-of-variance model is appropriate. The correlations among the measures may form any arbitrary pattern. For joint confidence intervals or tests of significance to be interpretable, the measures must form a conceptually meaningful set.

Assume that each subject in the one-way design with $J=4$, has been measured on p ($\geqslant 1$) outcome variables. Each outcome variable is a random variable that comprises a portion of the total response. For the p measures, the one-way model for observation i in subclass j is

$$\begin{aligned}
&[y_{ij}^{(1)} \quad y_{ij}^{(2)} \quad \cdots \quad y_{ij}^{(p)}] \\
&= [\mu^{(1)} \quad \mu^{(2)} \quad \cdots \quad \mu^{(p)}] + [\alpha_j^{(1)} \quad \alpha_j^{(2)} \quad \cdots \quad \alpha_j^{(p)}] + [\epsilon_{ij}^{(1)} \quad \epsilon_{ij}^{(2)} \quad \cdots \quad \epsilon_{ij}^{(p)}]
\end{aligned} \tag{7.1.15}$$

The model is formed by juxtaposing the p separate univariate models. A superscript is added to designate the outcome variable; $y_{ij}^{(k)}$ is the score for subject ij on dependent variable y_k; $\mu^{(k)}$ and $\alpha_j^{(k)}$ are the parameter values for y_k alone. It is necessary to estimate parameters μ and α_j for *each* variate. Confidence intervals and tests of hypotheses are made for the total set of measures. In this we must take into account the nonzero intercorrelations among the variates.

Equation 7.1.15 is the sum of p-element row vectors

$$\mathbf{y}'_{ij} = \boldsymbol{\mu}' + \boldsymbol{\alpha}'_j + \boldsymbol{\epsilon}'_{ij} \tag{7.1.15a}$$

where $\mathbf{y}'_{ij}$ is a single vector observation, or one row of the entire data matrix. With $J=4$ and one observation per cell, the complete set of models is

$$\begin{aligned}
\mathbf{y}'_{11} &= \boldsymbol{\mu}' + \boldsymbol{\alpha}'_1 \qquad\qquad\qquad\quad + \boldsymbol{\epsilon}'_{11} \\
\mathbf{y}'_{12} &= \boldsymbol{\mu}' \qquad + \boldsymbol{\alpha}'_2 \qquad\qquad + \boldsymbol{\epsilon}'_{12} \\
\mathbf{y}'_{13} &= \boldsymbol{\mu}' \qquad\qquad + \boldsymbol{\alpha}'_3 \qquad + \boldsymbol{\epsilon}'_{13} \\
\mathbf{y}'_{14} &= \boldsymbol{\mu}' \qquad\qquad\qquad + \boldsymbol{\alpha}'_4 + \boldsymbol{\epsilon}'_{14}
\end{aligned} \tag{7.1.16}$$

or

$$\begin{bmatrix} y_{11}{}^{(1)} & y_{11}{}^{(2)} & \cdots & y_{11}{}^{(p)} \\ y_{12}{}^{(1)} & y_{12}{}^{(2)} & \cdots & y_{12}{}^{(p)} \\ y_{13}{}^{(1)} & y_{13}{}^{(2)} & \cdots & y_{13}{}^{(p)} \\ y_{14}{}^{(1)} & y_{14}{}^{(2)} & \cdots & y_{14}{}^{(p)} \end{bmatrix} = \begin{bmatrix} 1 & 1 & 0 & 0 & 0 \\ 1 & 0 & 1 & 0 & 0 \\ 1 & 0 & 0 & 1 & 0 \\ 1 & 0 & 0 & 0 & 1 \end{bmatrix} \begin{bmatrix} \mu^{(1)} & \mu^{(2)} & \cdots & \mu^{(p)} \\ \alpha_1{}^{(1)} & \alpha_1{}^{(2)} & \cdots & \alpha_1{}^{(p)} \\ \vdots & & & \vdots \\ \alpha_4{}^{(1)} & \alpha_4{}^{(2)} & \cdots & \alpha_4{}^{(p)} \end{bmatrix}$$

$$+ \begin{bmatrix} \epsilon_{11}{}^{(1)} & \epsilon_{11}{}^{(2)} & \cdots & \epsilon_{11}{}^{(p)} \\ \epsilon_{12}{}^{(1)} & \epsilon_{12}{}^{(2)} & \cdots & \epsilon_{12}{}^{(p)} \\ \epsilon_{13}{}^{(1)} & \epsilon_{13}{}^{(2)} & \cdots & \epsilon_{13}{}^{(p)} \\ \epsilon_{14}{}^{(1)} & \epsilon_{14}{}^{(2)} & \cdots & \epsilon_{14}{}^{(p)} \end{bmatrix} \tag{7.1.16a}$$

Expression 7.1.16a may be represented as

$$\mathbf{Y} = \mathbf{A}\boldsymbol{\Theta}^* + \mathbf{E} \tag{7.1.17}$$

where $\mathbf{Y}$ is the $N \times p$ data matrix having row vectors $\mathbf{y}'_{ij}$. $\mathbf{E}$ is the $N \times p$ matrix of residuals for all observations with rows $\boldsymbol{\epsilon}'_{ij}$. $\mathbf{A}$ is the analysis-of-variance model matrix, and is identical to $\mathbf{A}$ for the univariate case (7.1.4); the structure underlying group membership is the same for each variate. $\boldsymbol{\Theta}^*$ is the $m \times p$ matrix of effects having a column for each of the p variates,

$$\boldsymbol{\Theta}^* = \begin{bmatrix} \boldsymbol{\mu}' \\ \boldsymbol{\alpha}'_1 \\ \boldsymbol{\alpha}'_2 \\ \boldsymbol{\alpha}'_3 \\ \boldsymbol{\alpha}'_4 \end{bmatrix} \tag{7.1.18}$$

$\boldsymbol{\Theta}^*$, like the regression matrix $\mathbf{B}$, contains the parameters to be estimated from sample data and upon which we conduct tests of significance.

The distributional assumptions concerning $\mathbf{E}$ are: (1) The errors for the p measures for one subject follow a multivariate normal distribution with expectation $\mathbf{0}$, and common $p \times p$ covariance matrix $\boldsymbol{\Sigma}$. That is,

$$\boldsymbol{\epsilon}'_{ij} \sim \mathcal{N}(\mathbf{0}', \boldsymbol{\Sigma}) \tag{7.1.19}$$

The elements of $\boldsymbol{\epsilon}'_{ij}$ represent multiple errors for the same observation (1 row of $\mathbf{E}$), which are generally intercorrelated. (2) The errors for any pair of subjects are independent. That is,

$$\mathscr{E}(\boldsymbol{\epsilon}_{ij}\boldsymbol{\epsilon}'_{i'j'})=\mathscr{E}(\boldsymbol{\epsilon}_{ij})\mathscr{E}(\boldsymbol{\epsilon}'_{i'j'})=\mathbf{0} \qquad (ij \neq i'j') \tag{7.1.20}$$

where $\mathbf{0}$ is the $p\times p$ null matrix.

If $\mathbf{E}$ has N rows, we may represent the covariance matrix of all Np elements in Kronecker product form (see Chapter 4). The covariance matrix of elements of $\mathbf{E}$ is

$$\mathscr{V}(\mathbf{E})=\mathbf{I}\otimes\boldsymbol{\Sigma}=\text{diag}\,(\boldsymbol{\Sigma},\boldsymbol{\Sigma},\ldots,\boldsymbol{\Sigma})$$
$$=\begin{bmatrix}\boldsymbol{\Sigma} & \mathbf{0} & \mathbf{0} & \mathbf{0}\\ \mathbf{0} & \boldsymbol{\Sigma} & \mathbf{0} & \mathbf{0}\\ \mathbf{0} & \mathbf{0} & \boldsymbol{\Sigma} & \mathbf{0}\\ \mathbf{0} & \mathbf{0} & \mathbf{0} & \boldsymbol{\Sigma}\end{bmatrix} \tag{7.1.21}$$

All submatrices $\boldsymbol{\Sigma}$ and $\mathbf{0}$ are $p\times p$ symmetric. The matrices on the diagonal are $\boldsymbol{\Sigma}$, the covariance matrix of any one row of $\mathbf{E}$; the rs off-diagonal matrix $\mathbf{0}$ is the matrix of covariances of elements in the rth and sth row of $\mathbf{E}$ ($r\neq s$). Thus the distribution of the entire matrix $\mathbf{E}$ is

$$\mathbf{E}\sim\mathscr{N}_{Np}(\mathbf{0},\mathbf{I}\otimes\boldsymbol{\Sigma}) \tag{7.1.22}$$

where $\mathbf{0}$ is an $N\times p$ null matrix.

If there are multiple observations in each subclass, it is convenient to represent the model and distributional assumptions in terms of vector means. For the one-way case, the mean model is

$$\mathbf{y}'_{\bullet j}=\boldsymbol{\mu}'+\boldsymbol{\alpha}'_j+\boldsymbol{\epsilon}'_{\bullet j} \tag{7.1.23}$$

where $\mathbf{y}'_{\bullet j}$, $\boldsymbol{\mu}'$, $\boldsymbol{\alpha}'_j$, and $\boldsymbol{\epsilon}'_{\bullet j}$ are $1\times p$ vectors. The means are $\mathbf{y}_{\bullet j}=\Sigma_i\mathbf{y}_{ij}/N_j$ and $\boldsymbol{\epsilon}_{\bullet j}=\Sigma_i\boldsymbol{\epsilon}_{ij}/N_j$. Juxtaposing the models for $J=4$ groups,

$$\begin{bmatrix} y_{\bullet 1}^{(1)} & y_{\bullet 1}^{(2)} & \cdots & y_{\bullet 1}^{(p)}\\ y_{\bullet 2}^{(1)} & y_{\bullet 2}^{(2)} & \cdots & y_{\bullet 2}^{(p)}\\ y_{\bullet 3}^{(1)} & y_{\bullet 3}^{(2)} & \cdots & y_{\bullet 3}^{(p)}\\ y_{\bullet 4}^{(1)} & y_{\bullet 4}^{(2)} & \cdots & y_{\bullet 4}^{(p)}\end{bmatrix}=\begin{bmatrix}1&1&0&0&0\\1&0&1&0&0\\1&0&0&1&0\\1&0&0&0&1\end{bmatrix}\begin{bmatrix}\mu^{(1)} & \mu^{(2)} & \cdots & \mu^{(p)}\\ \alpha_1^{(1)} & \alpha_1^{(2)} & \cdots & \alpha_1^{(p)}\\ \vdots & & & \vdots\\ \alpha_4^{(1)} & \alpha_4^{(2)} & \cdots & \alpha_4^{(p)}\end{bmatrix}$$
$$+\begin{bmatrix}\epsilon_{\bullet 1}^{(1)} & \epsilon_{\bullet 1}^{(2)} & \cdots & \epsilon_{\bullet 1}^{(p)}\\ \epsilon_{\bullet 2}^{(1)} & \epsilon_{\bullet 2}^{(2)} & \cdots & \epsilon_{\bullet 2}^{(p)}\\ \epsilon_{\bullet 3}^{(1)} & \epsilon_{\bullet 2}^{(2)} & \cdots & \epsilon_{\bullet 3}^{(p)}\\ \epsilon_{\bullet 4}^{(1)} & \epsilon_{\bullet 4}^{(2)} & \cdots & \epsilon_{\bullet 4}^{(p)}\end{bmatrix} \tag{7.1.24}$$

or

$$\mathbf{Y}_{\bullet}=\mathbf{A}\boldsymbol{\Theta}^*+\mathbf{E}_{\bullet} \tag{7.1.24a}$$

where $\mathbf{A}$ and $\boldsymbol{\Theta}^*$ are the same as given in Eq. 7.1.16. $\mathbf{Y}_{\bullet}$ and $\mathbf{E}_{\bullet}$ are both $J\times p$.

Rows of $\mathbf{E}_{\bullet}$ are distributed independently and with expectation zero. The covariance matrix of a row of means is inversely proportional to the number of observations in the group. N_j is the number of subjects in subclass j. The covariance matrix of row vector $\boldsymbol{\epsilon}'_{\cdot j}$ is

$$\mathscr{V}(\boldsymbol{\epsilon}'_{\cdot j}) = \frac{1}{N_j}\boldsymbol{\Sigma} \tag{7.1.25}$$

The square roots of the diagonal elements of Eq. 7.1.25 are the standard errors of the means for variates y_k (that is, $\sigma_k/\sqrt{N_j}$).

Let $\mathbf{D}$ be the diagonal matrix of subclass frequences as in Eq. 7.1.8. Then the covariance matrix of $\mathbf{E}.$ is

$$\mathscr{V}(\mathbf{E}.) = \mathbf{D}^{-1} \otimes \boldsymbol{\Sigma} = \text{diag}\left(\frac{1}{N_1}\boldsymbol{\Sigma},\ \frac{1}{N_2}\boldsymbol{\Sigma},\ \frac{1}{N_3}\boldsymbol{\Sigma},\ \frac{1}{N_4}\boldsymbol{\Sigma}\right) \tag{7.1.26}$$

The complete distribution of $\mathbf{E}.$ is

$$\mathbf{E}. \sim \mathscr{N}_{Jp}(\mathbf{0},\ \mathbf{D}^{-1} \otimes \boldsymbol{\Sigma}) \tag{7.1.27}$$

Again, under the general-model analysis, the N_j elements are not restricted to being equal or proportional to one another. The variance–covariance matrix of observations, $\boldsymbol{\Sigma}$, is the same for all groups.

In parallel fashion, we may write the model for the multivariate two-way or many-way situation. For example, in the toothpaste evaluation (Sample Problem 3) there are two years of experimentation, five experimental conditions, and six outcome measures taken from the anterior mandibular teeth. The six-variate model for means is

$$\mathbf{y}'_{\cdot jk} = \boldsymbol{\mu}' + \boldsymbol{\alpha}'_j + \boldsymbol{\beta}'_k + (\boldsymbol{\alpha\beta})'_{jk} + \boldsymbol{\epsilon}'_{\cdot jk} \tag{7.1.28}$$

with $j=1, 2$, and $k=1, 2, \ldots, 5$. Juxtaposing the vector means for the ten groups, we have Eq. 7.1.24a with $\mathbf{Y}.$ and $\mathbf{E}.$ as 10×6 matrices. The model matrix is

$$\mathbf{A} = \left[\begin{array}{cccccccc|cccccccccc}
1 & 1 & 0 & 1 & 0 & 0 & 0 & 0 & 1 & 0 & 0 & 0 & 0 & 0 & 0 & 0 & 0 & 0 \\
1 & 1 & 0 & 0 & 1 & 0 & 0 & 0 & 0 & 1 & 0 & 0 & 0 & 0 & 0 & 0 & 0 & 0 \\
1 & 1 & 0 & 0 & 0 & 1 & 0 & 0 & 0 & 0 & 1 & 0 & 0 & 0 & 0 & 0 & 0 & 0 \\
1 & 1 & 0 & 0 & 0 & 0 & 1 & 0 & 0 & 0 & 0 & 1 & 0 & 0 & 0 & 0 & 0 & 0 \\
1 & 1 & 0 & 0 & 0 & 0 & 0 & 1 & 0 & 0 & 0 & 0 & 1 & 0 & 0 & 0 & 0 & 0 \\
1 & 0 & 1 & 1 & 0 & 0 & 0 & 0 & 0 & 0 & 0 & 0 & 0 & 1 & 0 & 0 & 0 & 0 \\
1 & 0 & 1 & 0 & 1 & 0 & 0 & 0 & 0 & 0 & 0 & 0 & 0 & 0 & 1 & 0 & 0 & 0 \\
1 & 0 & 1 & 0 & 0 & 1 & 0 & 0 & 0 & 0 & 0 & 0 & 0 & 0 & 0 & 1 & 0 & 0 \\
1 & 0 & 1 & 0 & 0 & 0 & 1 & 0 & 0 & 0 & 0 & 0 & 0 & 0 & 0 & 0 & 1 & 0 \\
1 & 0 & 1 & 0 & 0 & 0 & 0 & 1 & 0 & 0 & 0 & 0 & 0 & 0 & 0 & 0 & 0 & 1
\end{array}\right] \tag{7.1.29}$$

The final 10 columns comprise an order-ten identity matrix that multiplies the interaction effects. $\boldsymbol{\Theta}^*$ is an 18×6 matrix:

$$[\boldsymbol{\Theta}^*]' = [\boldsymbol{\mu}\quad \boldsymbol{\alpha}_1\quad \boldsymbol{\alpha}_2\quad \boldsymbol{\beta}_1\quad \boldsymbol{\beta}_2\quad \boldsymbol{\beta}_3\quad \boldsymbol{\beta}_4\quad \boldsymbol{\beta}_5\quad (\boldsymbol{\alpha\beta})_{11}\quad (\boldsymbol{\alpha\beta})_{12}\quad \cdots\quad (\boldsymbol{\alpha\beta})_{25}]. \tag{7.1.30}$$

Each vector has the corresponding effect for all criterion variables, for example $\boldsymbol{\beta}'_1 = [\beta_1^{(1)}\beta_1^{(2)} \quad \cdots \quad \beta_1^{(6)}]$.

In the example, three treatment-year combinations have no observations. The diagonal matrix of subclass frequencies is

$$\mathbf{D} = \text{diag}\,(8, 9, 7, 5, 0, 28, 0, 24, 0, 26). \tag{7.1.31}$$

The J=10 rows of $\mathbf{Y}.$, $\mathbf{A}$, and $\mathbf{E}.$ may be reduced to J_0=7 by eliminating rows corresponding to the null subclasses. The resulting model matrix is

$$\mathbf{A} = \left[\begin{array}{cccccccc|cccccccccc} 1 & 1 & 0 & 1 & 0 & 0 & 0 & 0 & 1 & 0 & 0 & 0 & 0 & 0 & 0 & 0 & 0 & 0 \\ 1 & 1 & 0 & 0 & 1 & 0 & 0 & 0 & 0 & 1 & 0 & 0 & 0 & 0 & 0 & 0 & 0 & 0 \\ 1 & 1 & 0 & 0 & 0 & 1 & 0 & 0 & 0 & 0 & 1 & 0 & 0 & 0 & 0 & 0 & 0 & 0 \\ 1 & 1 & 0 & 0 & 0 & 0 & 1 & 0 & 0 & 0 & 0 & 1 & 0 & 0 & 0 & 0 & 0 & 0 \\ 1 & 0 & 1 & 1 & 0 & 0 & 0 & 0 & 0 & 0 & 0 & 0 & 0 & 1 & 0 & 0 & 0 & 0 \\ 1 & 0 & 1 & 0 & 0 & 1 & 0 & 0 & 0 & 0 & 0 & 0 & 0 & 0 & 0 & 1 & 0 & 0 \\ 1 & 0 & 1 & 0 & 0 & 0 & 0 & 1 & 0 & 0 & 0 & 0 & 0 & 0 & 0 & 0 & 0 & 1 \end{array}\right] \tag{7.1.32}$$

It can be seen that three interactions cannot be estimated, since three columns of the reduced **A** have no nonzero elements. This is an effect of the null subclasses. Parameters which are unique to the empty groups cannot be estimated or tested. In this example, there are three fewer degrees of freedom for interaction.

The covariance matrix of the 7×6 matrix $\mathbf{E}.$ is given by Eq. 7.1.26.

$$\mathscr{V}(\mathbf{E}.) = \mathbf{D}^{-1} \otimes \boldsymbol{\Sigma} = \text{diag}\left(\frac{1}{8}\boldsymbol{\Sigma},\ \frac{1}{9}\boldsymbol{\Sigma},\ \frac{1}{7}\boldsymbol{\Sigma},\ \frac{1}{5}\boldsymbol{\Sigma},\ \frac{1}{28}\boldsymbol{\Sigma},\ \frac{1}{24}\boldsymbol{\Sigma},\ \frac{1}{26}\boldsymbol{\Sigma}\right) \tag{7.1.33}$$

$\boldsymbol{\Sigma}$ is the 6×6 matrix of variances and covariances of the six tooth measures. Zero elements have been eliminated from **D**, resulting in a 7×7 diagonal matrix. Error variances and standard errors may be drawn from the diagonal of $\mathbf{D}^{-1} \otimes \boldsymbol{\Sigma}$. For example, the standard error of the mean for the first tooth, in group (1, 2), is $\sqrt{\sigma_1^2/9}$.

For further illustration, consider the remedial instruction experiment (Sample Problem 5). Three cognitive achievement measures are hypothesized to increase with a televised remedial program. With class means as the unit of analysis, 18 randomly selected classes conducted the "usual" instructional program, without special consideration for absenteeism, and 19 experimental classes utilized machine-programmed curriculum materials. These materials were assigned to students who had been absent, upon their return. Sex of the student is considered as an additional design factor, crossed with classes and experimental conditions.

The model for the mean vector in class k, within treatment group j, for sex l, is

$$\mathbf{y}'_{\cdot jkl} = \boldsymbol{\mu}' + \boldsymbol{\alpha}'_j + \boldsymbol{\beta}'_l + (\boldsymbol{\alpha\beta})'_{jl} + \mathbf{c}'_{k(j)} + \boldsymbol{\epsilon}'_{\cdot jkl} \tag{7.1.34}$$

with j=1, 2; l=1, 2; and k=1, 2, . . . , 19 for j=1, and k=1, 2, . . . , 18 for j=2. All terms are three-element vectors; $\boldsymbol{\mu}$, $\boldsymbol{\alpha}_j$, and $\boldsymbol{\beta}_l$ are fixed effects; and $\mathbf{c}_{k(j)}$ is a random class effect.

The model matrix for all 74 class-sex combinations is extensive, and so is represented here for only the first two classes within each treatment condition.

$$
\mathbf{A} = \left[\begin{array}{c|cc|cc|cccc|cccc}
1 & 1 & 0 & 1 & 0 & 1 & 0 & 0 & 0 & 1 & 0 & 0 & 0 \\
1 & 1 & 0 & 0 & 1 & 0 & 1 & 0 & 0 & 1 & 0 & 0 & 0 \\
1 & 1 & 0 & 1 & 0 & 1 & 0 & 0 & 0 & 0 & 1 & 0 & 0 \\
1 & 1 & 0 & 0 & 1 & 0 & 1 & 0 & 0 & 0 & 1 & 0 & 0 \\
 & & & & & \cdot & \cdot & \cdot & & & & & \\
1 & 0 & 1 & 1 & 0 & 0 & 0 & 1 & 0 & 0 & 0 & 1 & 0 \\
1 & 0 & 1 & 0 & 1 & 0 & 0 & 0 & 1 & 0 & 0 & 1 & 0 \\
1 & 0 & 1 & 1 & 0 & 0 & 0 & 1 & 0 & 0 & 0 & 0 & 1 \\
1 & 0 & 1 & 0 & 1 & 0 & 0 & 0 & 1 & 0 & 0 & 0 & 1 \\
 & & & & & \cdot & \cdot & \cdot & & & & &
\end{array}\right] \qquad (7.1.35)
$$

The parameters are

$$
[\boldsymbol{\Theta}^*]' = [\boldsymbol{\mu} \quad \boldsymbol{\alpha}_1 \quad \boldsymbol{\alpha}_2 \quad \boldsymbol{\beta}_1 \quad \boldsymbol{\beta}_2 \quad (\boldsymbol{\alpha\beta})_{11} \quad (\boldsymbol{\alpha\beta})_{12} \quad (\boldsymbol{\alpha\beta})_{21} \quad (\boldsymbol{\alpha\beta})_{22} \quad \mathbf{c}_{1(1)} \quad \mathbf{c}_{2(1)} \quad \mathbf{c}_{1(2)} \quad \mathbf{c}_{2(2)}] \qquad (7.1.36)
$$

The mean matrix and residuals $\mathbf{Y}.$ and $\mathbf{E}.$, are 74×3. The covariance matrix of any row of $\mathbf{E}.$ is the 3×3 matrix $\boldsymbol{\Sigma}$. The design will require further consideration for tests of significance, since both class and residual effects are random. A model of this sort, with one or more fixed effects and at least two sources of random variation, is termed the analysis-of-variance *mixed model*. Univariate model 7.1.14 is another example.

7.2 LEAST-SQUARES ESTIMATION FOR ANALYSIS-OF-VARIANCE MODELS

Let us assume a general analysis-of-variance model for means, as in the preceding section (Eq. 7.1.24a). That is,

$$
\mathbf{Y}. = \mathbf{A}\boldsymbol{\Theta}^* + \mathbf{E}. \qquad (7.2.1)
$$

where $\mathbf{Y}.$ is the $J \times p$ matrix mean; $\mathbf{A}$ is the $J \times m$ model matrix; $\boldsymbol{\Theta}^*$ is the $m \times p$ matrix of fixed parameters; and $\mathbf{E}.$ is the $J \times p$ matrix of mean errors. J is the number of subclasses of observations (or J_0, should some subclasses be empty); m is the total number of parameters in the analysis-of-variance model; and p is the number of criterion measures. In addition, let $\mathbf{D}$ be the $J \times J$ diagonal matrix of subclass frequencies, N_j, and the total number of observations $N = \Sigma_j N_j$.

Multivariate point estimates of the effects in $\boldsymbol{\Theta}^*$ consist of p separate sets of univariate estimates. Thus we shall consider estimation only for the more general multivariate case. It is in the construction of joint confidence intervals and test statistics for the p outcomes that the multivariate results depart from the univariate.

The distributional assumption for $\mathbf{E}.$ is given by Eq. 7.1.27. Rows of $\mathbf{E}.$ are independently distributed in p-variate normal fashion, with expectation $\mathbf{0}'$ and $p \times p$ covariance matrix $(1/N_j)\boldsymbol{\Sigma}$. For the entire matrix,

$$
\mathbf{E}. \sim \mathcal{N}(\mathbf{0}, \ \mathbf{D}^{-1} \otimes \boldsymbol{\Sigma}) \qquad (7.2.2)
$$

We shall seek the estimate of $\mathbf{\Theta}^*$ that yields the minimal sum of squared residuals in the sample. Minimizing the sum of squared errors for each variable separately will satisfy this condition. However, each row of the sample $\hat{\mathbf{E}}.$ must be weighted by the number of subjects in the corresponding group of observations. Let $[e.]_{jk}$ be the jk element of sample matrix $\hat{\mathbf{E}}.$ and let $\mathbf{e}._k$ be the kth column. The quantity to be minimized to obtain the estimate $\hat{\mathbf{\Theta}}^*$ is

$$\begin{aligned} q &= \textstyle\sum_k \sum_j N_j [e.]_{jk}^2 \\ &= \textstyle\sum_k \mathbf{e}'._k \mathbf{D}\, \mathbf{e}._k \\ &= \operatorname{tr}(\hat{\mathbf{E}}'. \mathbf{D} \hat{\mathbf{E}}.) \\ &= \operatorname{tr}(\mathbf{Y}. - \mathbf{A}\hat{\mathbf{\Theta}}^*)'\mathbf{D}(\mathbf{Y}. - \mathbf{A}\hat{\mathbf{\Theta}}^*) \end{aligned} \tag{7.2.3}$$

In the univariate case, Eq. 7.2.3 reduces to the scalar $q = \mathbf{e}'.\mathbf{D}\mathbf{e}.$; in the multivariate case, q is the sum of p sums of squares, one for each criterion measure. Minimization of q yields the estimates which give minimal sum of squared residuals for every outcome variable.

We may examine the distribution of errors for any one variate to see the role of matrix $\mathbf{D}$ in Eq. 7.2.3 (which does not appear in the regression model). The distribution of one column of $\mathbf{E}.$ (mean errors for J groups on one variable) is given by univariate expression 7.1.9. That is,

$$\boldsymbol{\epsilon}._k \sim \mathcal{N}(\mathbf{0}, \sigma_k^2 \mathbf{D}^{-1}) \tag{7.2.4}$$

We append the subscript k to indicate that y_k is one of several criterion measures. $\mathbf{e}._k$ is the sample value for $\boldsymbol{\epsilon}._k$.

The elements of $\boldsymbol{\epsilon}._k$ do not generally have equal variance, since the subclass frequencies may be unequal. To minimize $\mathbf{e}'._k \mathbf{e}._k$ would yield an estimate of $\mathbf{\Theta}^*$ that relies more heavily upon smaller groups of subjects than upon larger groups. If the subclass frequencies are arbitrary and unrelated to finite population sizes, then q should be the sum of squared *equal-variance* components of $\boldsymbol{\epsilon}._k$. We may obtain these components as follows.

First, factor $\mathbf{D}^{-1}$ by the Cholesky method. The Cholesky factor $\mathbf{T}$ is a diagonal matrix with elements $1/\sqrt{N_j}$. Second, we may define a new vector

$$\boldsymbol{\gamma} = \mathbf{T}^{-1} \boldsymbol{\epsilon}._k \tag{7.2.5}$$

The variance–covariance matrix of $\boldsymbol{\gamma}$ is

$$\begin{aligned} \mathcal{V}(\boldsymbol{\gamma}) &= \mathcal{V}(\mathbf{T}^{-1}\boldsymbol{\epsilon}._k) \\ &= \mathbf{T}^{-1}\sigma_k^2 \mathbf{D}^{-1}(\mathbf{T}^{-1})' \\ &= \sigma_k^2 \mathbf{T}^{-1}\mathbf{T}\mathbf{T}'(\mathbf{T}^{-1})' \\ &= \sigma_k^2 \mathbf{I} \end{aligned} \tag{7.2.6}$$

The elements of $\boldsymbol{\gamma}$ are uncorrelated; under normality, they are also independent. Each γ_j has variance σ_k^2. Thus $\boldsymbol{\gamma}$, as defined by Eq. 7.2.5, is a transformation of $\boldsymbol{\epsilon}._k$ to an equal number of independent, equal-variance random variables.

The sum of squares of the elements of $\boldsymbol{\gamma}$ is

$$\begin{aligned}\sum_{j=1}^{J} \gamma_j^{\,2} &= \boldsymbol{\gamma}'\boldsymbol{\gamma} \\ &= \boldsymbol{\epsilon}'_{\cdot k}(\mathbf{T}^{-1})'\mathbf{T}^{-1}\boldsymbol{\epsilon}_{\cdot k} \\ &= \boldsymbol{\epsilon}'_{\cdot k}\mathbf{D}\boldsymbol{\epsilon}_{\cdot k} \end{aligned} \tag{7.2.7}$$

Expression 7.2.7 pertains only to variate y_k. In the multivariate case, the sum of squares is computed for each variate and their total is minimized in the sample (Eq. 7.2.3) to provide the least-squares estimate of $\boldsymbol{\Theta}^*$.

Let us minimize Eq. 7.2.3, first assuming that $p=1$, with $\mathbf{y}.$ and $\boldsymbol{\theta}^*$ as vectors. The sum to be minimized is

$$\begin{aligned} q &= (\mathbf{y}.-\mathbf{A}\hat{\boldsymbol{\theta}}^*)'\mathbf{D}(\mathbf{y}.-\mathbf{A}\hat{\boldsymbol{\theta}}^*) \\ &= \mathbf{y}.'\mathbf{D}\mathbf{y}. - 2[\hat{\boldsymbol{\theta}}^*]'\mathbf{A}'\mathbf{D}\mathbf{y}. + [\hat{\boldsymbol{\theta}}^*]'\mathbf{A}'\mathbf{D}\mathbf{A}\hat{\boldsymbol{\theta}}^* \end{aligned} \tag{7.2.8}$$

Setting the first derivative of q with respect to $\hat{\boldsymbol{\theta}}^*$ to zero can yield a minimum value. The derivative is

$$\frac{\partial q}{\partial[\hat{\boldsymbol{\theta}}^*]'} = -2\mathbf{A}'\mathbf{D}\mathbf{y}. + 2\mathbf{A}'\mathbf{D}\mathbf{A}\hat{\boldsymbol{\theta}}^* \tag{7.2.9}$$

Setting the derivative to zero, the normal equations are

$$(\mathbf{A}'\mathbf{D}\mathbf{A})\hat{\boldsymbol{\theta}}^* = \mathbf{A}'\mathbf{D}\mathbf{y}. \tag{7.2.10}$$

In the general p-variate case, the expression to be minimized is the sum of terms like Eq. 7.2.8, summed across all measures (see Eq. 7.2.3). This value has a minimum when the least-squares criterion is individually met for every y_k-variable. The multivariate normal equations are similar to Eq. 7.2.10, but with a column of $\boldsymbol{\Theta}^*$ and $\mathbf{Y}.$ for each criterion variable:

$$(\mathbf{A}'\mathbf{D}\mathbf{A})\hat{\boldsymbol{\Theta}}^* = \mathbf{A}'\mathbf{D}\mathbf{Y}. \tag{7.2.11}$$

Normal equations 7.2.10 or 7.2.11 are easily solved for $\hat{\boldsymbol{\Theta}}^*$ if we premultiply both sides by $(\mathbf{A}'\mathbf{D}\mathbf{A})^{-1}$. We note, however, that $\mathbf{A}'\mathbf{D}\mathbf{A}$ is of deficient rank, and cannot be inverted. Since there may be more columns (parameters) in $\mathbf{A}$ than subclasses, $\mathbf{A}'\mathbf{D}\mathbf{A}$ is of order m, but of rank no greater than the smaller dimension J. Further, columns of $\mathbf{A}$ are simple linear combinations of one another. For example, in the one-way matrix

$$\mathbf{A} = \begin{bmatrix} 1 & 1 & 0 & 0 & 0 \\ 1 & 0 & 1 & 0 & 0 \\ 1 & 0 & 0 & 1 & 0 \\ 1 & 0 & 0 & 0 & 1 \end{bmatrix}$$

the first column is equal to the simple sum of all the others.

In the model matrix for the 2×3 crossed design (Eq. 7.1.12) the difference of the two dimensions is still greater. Column 1 is equal to the sum of columns 2 and 3; to the sum of columns 4, 5, and 6; and to the sum of columns 7 through 12.

In common terminology, we should like to estimate five parameters in the one-way model, but have only four *degrees of freedom among means* (1 for μ plus 3 for the α_j). In the two-way model, we would like to estimate 12 parameters, but have only six degrees of freedom among means (1 for μ, 1 for the α_j, 2 for the β_k, and 2 for the $[\alpha\beta]_{jk}$). Thus the analysis-of-variance model is termed the *model of deficient rank*.

The maximum degrees of freedom available among means is J, the number of groups with observations, also the number of rows of **A**. This is the maximal number of effects that may be estimated, or the maximum rank of (**A**′**DA**). If $J-J_0$ subclasses have no observations, then the corresponding diagonal element of **D** is zero, and the rank is restricted still further to J_0. That is, we may only estimate as many effects as the total number of subclasses with at least one observation.

Three classes of solutions have been proposed for the situation. The first of these is the definition of a *generalized inverse* for **A**′**DA**, which does not restrict the rank of the matrix. This solution basically involves rearranging columns of **A**, or ignoring columns, such that only a $J \times J$ submatrix of **A**′**DA**, of rank J, is inverted.

The second and most common solution involves bringing **A** up to rank m by adding $m-J$ rows, which destroy the linear dependencies among columns. These rows form additional equations, which are usually interpreted as restrictions upon the parameters. For example, the one-way univariate model is

$$\begin{bmatrix} y_{\cdot 1} \\ y_{\cdot 2} \\ y_{\cdot 3} \\ y_{\cdot 4} \end{bmatrix} = \begin{bmatrix} 1 & 1 & 0 & 0 & 0 \\ 1 & 0 & 1 & 0 & 0 \\ 1 & 0 & 0 & 1 & 0 \\ 1 & 0 & 0 & 0 & 1 \end{bmatrix} \begin{bmatrix} \mu \\ \alpha_1 \\ \alpha_2 \\ \alpha_3 \\ \alpha_4 \end{bmatrix} + \begin{bmatrix} \epsilon_{\cdot 1} \\ \epsilon_{\cdot 2} \\ \epsilon_{\cdot 3} \\ \epsilon_{\cdot 4} \end{bmatrix}$$

The dependency among the columns may be broken by adding an equation restricting

$$\sum_{j=1}^{4} \alpha_j = 0$$

The model with the restriction is

$$\begin{bmatrix} y_{\cdot 1} \\ y_{\cdot 2} \\ y_{\cdot 3} \\ y_{\cdot 4} \\ 0 \end{bmatrix} = \begin{bmatrix} 1 & 1 & 0 & 0 & 0 \\ 1 & 0 & 1 & 0 & 0 \\ 1 & 0 & 0 & 1 & 0 \\ 1 & 0 & 0 & 0 & 1 \\ 0 & 1 & 1 & 1 & 1 \end{bmatrix} \begin{bmatrix} \mu \\ \alpha_1 \\ \alpha_2 \\ \alpha_3 \\ \alpha_4 \end{bmatrix} + \begin{bmatrix} \epsilon_{\cdot 1} \\ \epsilon_{\cdot 2} \\ \epsilon_{\cdot 3} \\ \epsilon_{\cdot 4} \\ 0 \end{bmatrix}$$

or

$$\mathbf{y}^*_{\cdot} = \mathbf{A}^*\boldsymbol{\theta}^* + \boldsymbol{\epsilon}^*_{\cdot}$$

$(\mathbf{A}^*)'\mathbf{D}\mathbf{A}^*$ is of full rank and columns of $\mathbf{A}^*$ are not multiples of one another.

The normal equations may be solved through usual inversion procedures, using $\mathbf{A}^*$ in place of **A**. In parallel fashion in the two-way design, we may restrict the sum of the α_j's, the sum of the β_k's, and the sums of interactions across each main effect to zero. These restrictions are equations added to the model for the purpose of bringing **A** to the rank m, and making the parameters estimable. The restrictions in the multivariate case are the same but apply to the vector effects; for example, $\Sigma_j \boldsymbol{\alpha}_j = \mathbf{0}$.

A third solution for the model of deficient rank is to select and estimate l ($\leq J$) *linear combinations* of the parameters that are of scientific interest. These combinations are expressed as *contrasts* among subpopulation means and can be explicitly chosen in accordance with the experimental design and procedures. This solution has the advantage of providing direct results concerning the experimental outcomes. It is usually differences among group means that are of concern in analysis-of-variance models. If we do not restrict the sum of the parameters, the connotation is avoided that experimental effects somehow nullify one another. (Are the summative effects of three and six hours of sensory deprivation null?)

The linear combinations of m parameters are l alternate parameters, which are selected so that all may be estimated. The alternate parameters replace the original set in the matrix $\boldsymbol{\Theta}^*$. To maintain the equality of the two sides of the model equation, a modified model matrix is also required. The substitution of alternate parameters and performing the necessary model alterations is termed *reparameterization*.

7.3 REPARAMETERIZATION

In the analysis-of-variance model (Eq. 7.2.1), the matrix **A** has rank less than its column order m. Thus all parameters are not estimable. We may choose instead l linear combinations of the parameters, which are all uniquely estimable. l is the *rank of the model for significance testing*, and must satisfy $l \leq J$.

The weights defining l linear combinations of rows of $\boldsymbol{\Theta}^*$ are constructed as the rows of an $l \times m$ *contrast matrix* **L**, such that its rank is also l. That is, l parameters in $\mathbf{L}\boldsymbol{\Theta}^* = \boldsymbol{\Theta}$ are to be estimated, as an alternative to the estimation of the m parameters in $\boldsymbol{\Theta}^*$. The "new" parameters for all variates are contained in the $l \times p$ matrix $\boldsymbol{\Theta}$.

Since the multivariate formulation reduces to the univariate when $p=1$ ($\boldsymbol{\Theta}^*$ and $\boldsymbol{\Theta}$ are vectors), the more inclusive multivariate model is emphasized here. Reparameterizing the independent variables is not affected by the number of criteria. The alternate parameters in $\boldsymbol{\Theta}$, like those of $\boldsymbol{\Theta}^*$, have the same form for every outcome measure, although their numerical values will differ.

For the alternate set of parameters, $\boldsymbol{\Theta}$, an alternate model matrix is also necessary. Represent the model matrix for the l alternate parameters as a $J \times l$ matrix **K**. **K** is termed the *basis* for the design. The model as originally formulated is

$$\mathbf{Y}_{\cdot} = \mathbf{A}\boldsymbol{\Theta}^* + \mathbf{E}. \tag{7.3.1}$$

Eq. 7.3.1 is reparameterized to the alternate model,

$$\begin{aligned} \mathbf{Y.} &= \mathbf{K}(\mathbf{L}\boldsymbol{\Theta}^*) + \mathbf{E.} \\ &= \mathbf{K}\boldsymbol{\Theta} + \mathbf{E.} \end{aligned} \tag{7.3.2}$$

Through the careful selection of contrasts in **L**, **K** has full rank l. Eq. 7.3.2 is then identical in form to the regression model (Eq. 4.3.3), with **K** in place of **X** and $\boldsymbol{\Theta}$ in place of **B**.

To estimate $\boldsymbol{\Theta}$, we utilize the multivariate least-squares criterion and minimize tr $(\hat{\mathbf{E}}.'\mathbf{D}\hat{\mathbf{E}}.)$. The normal equations for the reparameterized model are the same as Eq. 7.2.11 but with **K** and $\boldsymbol{\Theta}$ in place of **A** and $\boldsymbol{\Theta}^*$. That is,

$$(\mathbf{K}'\mathbf{D}\mathbf{K})\hat{\boldsymbol{\Theta}} = \mathbf{K}'\mathbf{D}\mathbf{Y.} \tag{7.3.3}$$

$\mathbf{K}'\mathbf{D}\mathbf{K}$ has full rank and can be inverted. The least-squares solution for the estimate of $\boldsymbol{\Theta}$ is obtained by premultiplying both sides of the equations by $(\mathbf{K}'\mathbf{D}\mathbf{K})^{-1}$. Then

$$(\mathbf{K}'\mathbf{D}\mathbf{K})^{-1}(\mathbf{K}'\mathbf{D}\mathbf{K})\hat{\boldsymbol{\Theta}} = (\mathbf{K}'\mathbf{D}\mathbf{K})^{-1}\mathbf{K}'\mathbf{D}\mathbf{Y.}$$

and

$$\hat{\boldsymbol{\Theta}} = (\mathbf{K}'\mathbf{D}\mathbf{K})^{-1}\mathbf{K}'\mathbf{D}\mathbf{Y.} \tag{7.3.4}$$

The usual research procedure involves (1) constructing **A** and $\boldsymbol{\Theta}^*$, (2) selecting **L** and evaluating the basis **K**, and (3) the estimation of $\hat{\boldsymbol{\Theta}}$ according to Eq. 7.3.4.

Comparison of Eqs. 7.3.1 and 7.3.2 reveals that **A** is replaced by the product **KL** in the reparameterized model. This sets the conditions for evaluating **K** once **L** is selected. That is,

$$\mathbf{A} = \mathbf{K}\mathbf{L} \tag{7.3.5}$$

and

$$\mathbf{A}\mathbf{L}' = \mathbf{K}\mathbf{L}\mathbf{L}'$$

Then

$$\mathbf{A}\mathbf{L}'(\mathbf{L}\mathbf{L}')^{-1} = \mathbf{K}\mathbf{L}\mathbf{L}'(\mathbf{L}\mathbf{L}')^{-1}$$

and

$$\mathbf{K} = \mathbf{A}\mathbf{L}'(\mathbf{L}\mathbf{L}')^{-1} \tag{7.3.6}$$

K is the $J \times l$ model matrix for the alternate parameters; **L** is the $l \times m$ contrast matrix, so that $\mathbf{L}\mathbf{L}'$ is $l \times l$.

Consider the one-way model with four subclasses of observations. The mean models are

$$\mathbf{Y.} = \begin{bmatrix} 1 & 1 & 0 & 0 & 0 \\ 1 & 0 & 1 & 0 & 0 \\ 1 & 0 & 0 & 1 & 0 \\ 1 & 0 & 0 & 0 & 1 \end{bmatrix} \begin{bmatrix} \boldsymbol{\mu}' \\ \boldsymbol{\alpha}_1' \\ \boldsymbol{\alpha}_2' \\ \boldsymbol{\alpha}_3' \\ \boldsymbol{\alpha}_4' \end{bmatrix} + \mathbf{E.} \tag{7.3.7}$$

or

$$\mathbf{Y.} = \quad \mathbf{A} \quad \boldsymbol{\Theta}^* + \mathbf{E.} \tag{7.3.7a}$$

The model matrix **A** has only four rows but $m=5$ columns. The final column is exactly the first column minus the sum of the remaining three. Thus the rank of **A** is $J=4$. Given the limitation, we can select at most four linear combinations of the elements in $\boldsymbol{\Theta}^*$ that are uniquely estimable.

For exemplary purposes, let us assume that the fourth experimental group is a control group and that the other three groups represent three experimental conditions. A useful set of parameters might be an overall population constant, plus the contrasts of $\boldsymbol{\alpha}_1$, $\boldsymbol{\alpha}_2$, and $\boldsymbol{\alpha}_3$ respectively, with $\boldsymbol{\alpha}_4$. For this situation, the contrast matrix is

$$\mathbf{L}=\begin{bmatrix} 1 & 1/4 & 1/4 & 1/4 & 1/4 \\ 0 & 1 & 0 & 0 & -1 \\ 0 & 0 & 1 & 0 & -1 \\ 0 & 0 & 0 & 1 & -1 \end{bmatrix} \tag{7.3.8}$$

The alternate set of parameters is

$$\mathbf{L}\boldsymbol{\Theta}^*=\boldsymbol{\Theta}$$
$$=\begin{bmatrix} \boldsymbol{\mu}'+1/4\sum_j \boldsymbol{\alpha}'_j \\ \boldsymbol{\alpha}'_1-\boldsymbol{\alpha}'_4 \\ \boldsymbol{\alpha}'_2-\boldsymbol{\alpha}'_4 \\ \boldsymbol{\alpha}'_3-\boldsymbol{\alpha}'_4 \end{bmatrix} \tag{7.3.9}$$

$\boldsymbol{\Theta}$, like $\boldsymbol{\Theta}^*$, has a column for each criterion measure. Rows of $\boldsymbol{\Theta}$ are contrasts among the parameters in $\boldsymbol{\Theta}^*$.

Once **L** is selected, **K** may be computed by Eq. 7.3.6.

$$\mathbf{K}=\mathbf{AL}'(\mathbf{LL}')^{-1}$$
$$=\begin{bmatrix} 1.25 & 1 & 0 & 0 \\ 1.25 & 0 & 1 & 0 \\ 1.25 & 0 & 0 & 1 \\ 1.25 & -1 & -1 & -1 \end{bmatrix}\begin{bmatrix} 1.25 & 0 & 0 & 0 \\ 0 & 2 & 1 & 1 \\ 0 & 1 & 2 & 1 \\ 0 & 1 & 1 & 2 \end{bmatrix}^{-1}$$
$$=\begin{bmatrix} 1.25 & 1 & 0 & 0 \\ 1.25 & 0 & 1 & 0 \\ 1.25 & 0 & 0 & 0 \\ 1.25 & -1 & -1 & -1 \end{bmatrix}\begin{bmatrix} .80 & 0 & 0 & 0 \\ 0 & .75 & -.25 & -.25 \\ 0 & -.25 & .75 & -.25 \\ 0 & -.25 & -.25 & .75 \end{bmatrix}$$
$$=\begin{bmatrix} 1.00 & .75 & -.25 & -.25 \\ 1.00 & -.25 & .75 & -.25 \\ 1.00 & -.25 & -.25 & .75 \\ 1.00 & -.25 & -.25 & -.25 \end{bmatrix} \tag{7.3.10}$$

K may be employed in the estimation of $\boldsymbol{\Theta}$ by Eq. 7.3.4.

Let us examine how this reparameterization has altered the original models.

For simplicity, let $p=1$. The four mean models are

$$
\begin{aligned}
y_{\cdot 1} &= \mu + \alpha_1 \qquad\qquad\qquad\quad + \epsilon_{\cdot 1} \\
y_{\cdot 2} &= \mu \qquad + \alpha_2 \qquad\qquad + \epsilon_{\cdot 2} \\
y_{\cdot 3} &= \mu \qquad\qquad + \alpha_3 \qquad + \epsilon_{\cdot 3} \\
y_{\cdot 4} &= \mu \qquad\qquad\qquad + \alpha_4 + \epsilon_{\cdot 4}
\end{aligned}
$$

In reparameterizing, we have substituted parameters $\alpha_j - \alpha_4$ for the α_j. In order to maintain the equalities, terms have been added to or subtracted from μ. The reformulated models are $\mathbf{y}_{\cdot} = \mathbf{K}\boldsymbol{\theta} + \boldsymbol{\epsilon}_{\cdot}$ or, in extended form,

$$
\begin{aligned}
y_{\cdot 1} &= 1\left(\mu + 1/4 \textstyle\sum_j \alpha_j\right) + .75(\alpha_1 - \alpha_4) - .25(\alpha_2 - \alpha_4) - .25(\alpha_3 - \alpha_4) + \epsilon_{\cdot 1} \\
y_{\cdot 2} &= 1\left(\mu + 1/4 \textstyle\sum_j \alpha_j\right) - .25(\alpha_1 - \alpha_4) + .75(\alpha_2 - \alpha_4) - .25(\alpha_3 - \alpha_4) + \epsilon_{\cdot 2} \\
y_{\cdot 3} &= 1\left(\mu + 1/4 \textstyle\sum_j \alpha_j\right) - .25(\alpha_1 - \alpha_4) - .25(\alpha_2 - \alpha_4) + .75(\alpha_3 - \alpha_4) + \epsilon_{\cdot 3} \\
y_{\cdot 4} &= 1\left(\mu + 1/4 \textstyle\sum_j \alpha_j\right) - .25(\alpha_1 - \alpha_4) - .25(\alpha_2 - \alpha_4) - .25(\alpha_3 - \alpha_4) + \epsilon_{\cdot 4}
\end{aligned}
$$

The reader may wish to verify that these models constitute a simple regrouping of terms in the original models. The total value is not changed. For example, the first model is

$$
\mu + 1/4 \textstyle\sum_j \alpha_j + .75\alpha_1 - .75\alpha_4 - .25\alpha_2 + .25\alpha_4 - .25\alpha_3 + .25\alpha_4 = \mu + \alpha_1
$$

The first term in the alternate models absorbs the scaling effects of the reparameterization. As a result, it estimates a somewhat complex constant term. The contrasts among parameters replace the original parameters themselves. Some manipulation of coefficients is required in order to assure that the same parameters are estimated in all four equations.

The effects in $\boldsymbol{\theta}$ are estimated from the constants in **K**, rather than from the zero-one coefficients of the original model matrix. The vectors of **K** appear similar to contrast vectors, but should not be mistaken for them. Other than as an intermediate step in the computations, the basis assumes no further importance in the analysis.

Conditions for the Selection of Contrasts

There are two conditions which the contrast matrix **L** must satisfy. First, since **A**=**KL** (Eq. 7.3.5), rows of **L** must be linear combinations of the rows of **A**. Only if this is the case can the relationship between the two matrices be accounted for by matrix multiplication with **K**. That is, each row of **K** defines a linear combination of the rows of **L** to yield a row of **A**. If rows of **L** are not linear functions of the rows of **A**, then matrix multiplication cannot transform one into the other.

The rows of **L** in the one-way example (Eq. 7.3.8) are linear combinations of the rows of **A**, as required. The first row of **L** is the average of the rows of **A**, $1/4\, \Sigma_j \mathbf{a}'_j$; the remaining three rows of **L** are the differences of rows one through three of **A**, respectively, and row four, $\mathbf{a}'_j - \mathbf{a}'_4$. Note that an estimate of $\boldsymbol{\mu}$ alone is not possible in the presence of main effects $\boldsymbol{\alpha}_j$, since the vector $[1 \quad 0 \quad 0 \quad 0 \quad 0]$ cannot be expressed as a function of the rows of **A**. Should tests of significance indicate that all $\boldsymbol{\alpha}_j$ are *equal*, however, the first term in $\hat{\boldsymbol{\Theta}}$ will estimate the population mean, $\boldsymbol{\mu}+\boldsymbol{\alpha}.$ common to all groups.

Condition one is not difficult to meet. Almost all contrasts among parameters α_j (or the other parameters in higher-order designs) can obviously and simply be expressed as functions of the rows of the model matrix. Thus it is easiest to construct the weight vectors first by considering the parameter matrix and then to check that the contrasts selected satisfy the dependency criterion.

The second condition is that the $l \times m$ matrix **L** must be of rank l. This is necessary to assure the inversion of **LL**′ in Eq. 7.3.6. It requires (1) that we do not choose more contrasts than the rank of **A**. Rows of **L** are functions of rows of **A**, and the rank of **A** is maximally J. Any more than J linear functions will necessarily be dependent upon the first J functions. That is, we have no more than J degrees of freedom among means and can estimate no more than J alternate parameters (although we may estimate fewer).

It is also required that (2) the rows of **L**, or contrasts, cannot be exact linear functions of one another. For example, in the one-way model, the contrast vector for comparing $\boldsymbol{\alpha}_1-\boldsymbol{\alpha}_2$, or $[0 \quad 1 \quad -1 \quad 0 \quad 0]$, could not be included in **L** as the fourth vector in place of $\boldsymbol{\alpha}_3-\boldsymbol{\alpha}_4$. This vector is exactly the difference of the weights for $\boldsymbol{\alpha}_1-\boldsymbol{\alpha}_4$ and $\boldsymbol{\alpha}_2-\boldsymbol{\alpha}_4$, the second and third rows of **L**. On the other hand, the rows of **L** *need not* be orthogonal.

Some Simple Cases

Let us consider the reparameterization of a two-way model (univariate). Consider a main-effects model for a crossed design having two and three levels of the design factors, respectively. The mean models are

$$
\begin{aligned}
y_{\cdot 11} &= \mu+\alpha_1 \qquad +\beta_1 \qquad\qquad +\epsilon_{\cdot 11}\\
y_{\cdot 12} &= \mu+\alpha_1 \qquad\qquad +\beta_2 \qquad +\epsilon_{\cdot 12}\\
y_{\cdot 13} &= \mu+\alpha_1 \qquad\qquad\qquad +\beta_3+\epsilon_{\cdot 13}\\
y_{\cdot 21} &= \mu \qquad +\alpha_2+\beta_1 \qquad\qquad +\epsilon_{\cdot 21}\\
y_{\cdot 22} &= \mu \qquad +\alpha_2 \qquad +\beta_2 \qquad +\epsilon_{\cdot 22}\\
y_{\cdot 23} &= \mu \qquad +\alpha_2 \qquad\qquad\qquad +\beta_3+\epsilon_{\cdot 23}
\end{aligned}
\tag{7.3.11}
$$

or

$$
\begin{aligned}
\mathbf{y}. &= \begin{bmatrix} 1 & 1 & 0 & 1 & 0 & 0 \\ 1 & 1 & 0 & 0 & 1 & 0 \\ 1 & 1 & 0 & 0 & 0 & 1 \\ 1 & 0 & 1 & 1 & 0 & 0 \\ 1 & 0 & 1 & 0 & 1 & 0 \\ 1 & 0 & 1 & 0 & 0 & 1 \end{bmatrix} \begin{bmatrix} \mu \\ \alpha_1 \\ \alpha_2 \\ \beta_1 \\ \beta_2 \\ \beta_3 \end{bmatrix} + \boldsymbol{\epsilon}. \\
&= \qquad\qquad \mathbf{A} \qquad\qquad \boldsymbol{\theta}^* \; + \boldsymbol{\epsilon}.
\end{aligned}
\tag{7.3.11a}
$$

Again we note the dependencies among the columns of **A**. Specifically, columns two and three sum to column one, as do four, five, and six. The rank of **A** is four. We shall reparameterize to four linear combinations of the effects which are of interest in the research. In addition to a constant term, we will have one alternate effect in the α factor and two in β. These quantities are the usual "between groups degrees of freedom" for the model.

Four useful alternative parameters for the model might be the constant term, the difference $\alpha_1-\alpha.$, and the differences $\beta_1-\beta.$ and $\beta_2-\beta.$, where $\alpha.=(\alpha_1+\alpha_2)/2$ and $\beta.=(\beta_1+\beta_2+\beta_3)/3$. This reparameterization is equivalent to altering the original models, by appropriately adding and subtracting identical terms. That is,

$$\begin{aligned}
y._{11} &= 1(\mu+\alpha.+\beta.)+1(\alpha_1-\alpha.)+1(\beta_1-\beta.)+0(\beta_2-\beta.)+\epsilon._{11}\\
y._{12} &= 1(\mu+\alpha.+\beta.)+1(\alpha_1-\alpha.)+0(\beta_1-\beta.)+1(\beta_2-\beta.)+\epsilon._{12}\\
y._{13} &= 1(\mu+\alpha.+\beta.)+1(\alpha_1-\alpha.)-1(\beta_1-\beta.)-1(\beta_2-\beta.)+\epsilon._{13}\\
y._{21} &= 1(\mu+\alpha.+\beta.)-1(\alpha_1-\alpha.)+1(\beta_1-\beta.)+0(\beta_2-\beta.)+\epsilon._{21}\\
y._{22} &= 1(\mu+\alpha.+\beta.)-1(\alpha_1-\alpha.)+0(\beta_1-\beta.)+1(\beta_2-\beta.)+\epsilon._{22}\\
y._{23} &= 1(\mu+\alpha.+\beta.)-1(\alpha_1-\alpha.)-1(\beta_1-\beta.)-1(\beta_2-\beta.)+\epsilon._{23}
\end{aligned} \qquad (7.3.12)$$

In matrix form, these are

$$\mathbf{y}.= \quad \mathbf{K} \quad \boldsymbol{\theta} \quad +\boldsymbol{\epsilon}. \qquad (7.3.13)$$

$$= \begin{bmatrix} 1 & 1 & 1 & 0 \\ 1 & 1 & 0 & 1 \\ 1 & 1 & -1 & -1 \\ 1 & -1 & 1 & 0 \\ 1 & -1 & 0 & 1 \\ 1 & -1 & -1 & -1 \end{bmatrix} \begin{bmatrix} \mu+\alpha.+\beta. \\ \alpha_1-\alpha. \\ \beta_1-\beta. \\ \beta_2-\beta. \end{bmatrix} +\boldsymbol{\epsilon}. \qquad (7.3.13a)$$

$\boldsymbol{\theta}$ in Eq. 7.3.13a is the product of the contrast matrix $\mathbf{L}$ and the original vector of effects $\boldsymbol{\theta}^*$.

$$\begin{bmatrix} \mu+\alpha.+\beta. \\ \alpha_1+\alpha. \\ \beta_1-\beta. \\ \beta_2-\beta. \end{bmatrix} = \begin{bmatrix} \mu+\dfrac{\alpha_1+\alpha_2}{2}+\dfrac{\beta_1+\beta_2+\beta_3}{3} \\ \alpha_1-\dfrac{\alpha_1+\alpha_2}{2} \\ \beta_1-\dfrac{\beta_1+\beta_2+\beta_3}{3} \\ \beta_2-\dfrac{\beta_1+\beta_2+\beta_3}{3} \end{bmatrix}$$

$$= \begin{bmatrix} 1 & 1/2 & 1/2 & 1/3 & 1/3 & 1/3 \\ 0 & 1/2 & -1/2 & 0 & 0 & 0 \\ 0 & 0 & 0 & 2/3 & -1/3 & -1/3 \\ 0 & 0 & 0 & -1/3 & 2/3 & -1/3 \end{bmatrix} \begin{bmatrix} \mu \\ \alpha_1 \\ \alpha_2 \\ \beta_1 \\ \beta_2 \\ \beta_3 \end{bmatrix} \qquad (7.3.14)$$

$$= \quad \mathbf{L} \quad \boldsymbol{\theta}^* \qquad (7.3.14a)$$

If there is more than one criterion variable, matrix $\boldsymbol{\Theta}$ has a similar column for each outcome measure.

The contrast matrix **L** is of rank 4. It meets the condition that its rows can be constructed as linear functions of the rows of **A**. For example, the constant term is the simple average of the rows of **A**,

$$\frac{1}{6}\sum_{j=1}^{6}\mathbf{a}'_j$$

The second row of **L** is the contrast in α. It is constructed by subtracting the average of all rows of **A** from the average of the three first rows having α_1; that is,

$$\frac{1}{3}\sum_{j=1}^{3}\mathbf{a}'_j-\frac{1}{6}\sum_{j=1}^{6}\mathbf{a}'_j$$

The contrasts in β are also estimable, since their weights are obtainable from the rows of **A**. For example, the vector $[0 \quad 0 \quad 0 \quad 2/3 \quad -1/3 \quad -1/3]$ in **L** can be obtained by subtracting the average of all rows of **A** from the average of those containing a nonzero β_1 coefficient. That is,

$$\frac{1}{2}(\mathbf{a}'_1+\mathbf{a}'_4)-\frac{1}{6}\sum_{j=1}^{6}\mathbf{a}'_j$$

In altering the models, a more complex constant becomes the first parameter to be estimated. Only in the absence of main effects does the term estimate μ alone. If interactions are included in the model, then main effects are similarly confounded with interactions. Only if the interactions are null do the main-effect contrasts estimate simple differences of the α_j's and β_k's.

The coefficients in **K** can be seen clearly in the reparameterized models of Eq. 7.3.12. They can also be found algebraically once **L** is defined. For the two-way example, the basis matrix in Eq. 7.3.13a is identically the product $\mathbf{K}=\mathbf{AL}'(\mathbf{LL}')^{-1}$, where

$$\mathbf{AL}'=\begin{bmatrix}11/6 & 1/2 & 2/3 & -1/3\\ 11/6 & 1/2 & -1/3 & 2/3\\ 11/6 & 1/2 & -1/3 & -1/3\\ 11/6 & -1/2 & 2/3 & -1/3\\ 11/6 & -1/2 & -1/3 & 2/3\\ 11/6 & -1/2 & -1/3 & -1/3\end{bmatrix}$$

$$\mathbf{LL}'=\begin{bmatrix}11/6 & 0 & 0 & 0\\ 0 & 1/2 & 0 & 0\\ 0 & 0 & 2/3 & -1/3\\ 0 & 0 & -1/3 & 2/3\end{bmatrix}$$

and

$$(\mathbf{LL}')^{-1}=\begin{bmatrix}6/11 & 0 & 0 & 0\\ 0 & 2 & 0 & 0\\ 0 & 0 & 2 & 1\\ 0 & 0 & 1 & 2\end{bmatrix}$$

The reader may wish to complete the demonstration. **K** may be used in Eq. 7.3.4 for the estimation of $\mathbf{\Theta}$.

Example

The data of Table 3.3.2 comprise four groups of the design formed by crossing two levels of sampling factor *A* with two levels of *B*. The matrix mean for the $p=2$ variates is

$$\mathbf{Y.}=\begin{bmatrix} .50 & .75 \\ 3.17 & 3.67 \\ 2.20 & 2.40 \\ 3.43 & 3.57 \end{bmatrix}\begin{matrix}\text{Group 11}\\ \text{Group 12}\\ \text{Group 21}\\ \text{Group 22}\end{matrix}$$
$$\quad y_1 \quad\quad y_2$$

The subclass frequencies, in diagonal matrix form, are

$$\mathbf{D}=\text{diag}\,(4, 6, 5, 7)$$

The fixed-effects analysis-of-variance model with interaction is

$$\mathbf{y}'_{\cdot jk}=\boldsymbol{\mu}'+\boldsymbol{\alpha}'_j+\boldsymbol{\beta}'_k+\boldsymbol{\gamma}'_{jk}+\boldsymbol{\epsilon}'_{\cdot jk}$$

All terms are two-element vectors. The matrix model is

$$\mathbf{Y.}=\mathbf{A}\mathbf{\Theta}^*+\mathbf{E.}$$

with

$$\mathbf{A}=\begin{bmatrix} 1 & 1 & 0 & 1 & 0 & 1 & 0 & 0 & 0 \\ 1 & 1 & 0 & 0 & 1 & 0 & 1 & 0 & 0 \\ 1 & 0 & 1 & 1 & 0 & 0 & 0 & 1 & 0 \\ 1 & 0 & 1 & 0 & 1 & 0 & 0 & 0 & 1 \end{bmatrix}\begin{matrix}\text{Group 11}\\ \text{Group 12}\\ \text{Group 21}\\ \text{Group 22}\end{matrix}$$

and

$$[\mathbf{\Theta}^*]'=[\boldsymbol{\mu} \quad \boldsymbol{\alpha}_1 \quad \boldsymbol{\alpha}_2 \quad \boldsymbol{\beta}_1 \quad \boldsymbol{\beta}_2 \quad \boldsymbol{\gamma}_{11} \quad \boldsymbol{\gamma}_{12} \quad \boldsymbol{\gamma}_{21} \quad \boldsymbol{\gamma}_{22}]$$

The columns of $[\mathbf{\Theta}^*]'$ have two elements for variables y_1 and y_2.

The model matrix **A** is of rank four. The linear dependencies can be easily seen. Thus we shall choose four linear combinations of the parameters that are of interest in the research.

The first alternate parameter is a population constant, necessary to equate the two sides of the model. The constant is the average of all four groups' observations. To obtain the row of **L** for the constant then, we average the four rows of **A**:

$$\boldsymbol{l}'_1=[1 \quad .5 \quad .5 \quad .5 \quad .5 \quad .25 \quad .25 \quad .25 \quad .25]$$

The population constant is

$$\begin{aligned}\boldsymbol{l}'_1\mathbf{\Theta}^* &= \boldsymbol{\mu}'+1/2(\boldsymbol{\alpha}_1+\boldsymbol{\alpha}_2)'+1/2(\boldsymbol{\beta}_1+\boldsymbol{\beta}_2)'+1/4(\boldsymbol{\gamma}_{11}+\boldsymbol{\gamma}_{12}+\boldsymbol{\gamma}_{21}+\boldsymbol{\gamma}_{22})' \\ &= \boldsymbol{\mu}'+\boldsymbol{\alpha}'_{\cdot}+\boldsymbol{\beta}'_{\cdot}+\boldsymbol{\gamma}'_{\cdot\cdot}\end{aligned}$$

A second parameter of interest is the comparison of A_1 groups (11 and 12) with A_2 groups (21 and 22). The contrast weights are the average of the first two rows of **A** minus the last two rows. That is,

$$\mathbf{l}'_2 = [0 \quad 1 \quad -1 \quad 0 \quad 0 \quad .5 \quad .5 \quad -.5 \quad -.5]$$

The second alternate parameter is

$$\mathbf{l}'_2\mathbf{\Theta}^* = (\boldsymbol{\alpha}_1 - \boldsymbol{\alpha}_2)' + (\boldsymbol{\gamma}_{1\cdot} - \boldsymbol{\gamma}_{2\cdot})'$$

If the interactions for A_1 and A_2 are equal, then the second parameter estimates the difference $\boldsymbol{\alpha}_1 - \boldsymbol{\alpha}_2$. If not, then the A main-effect contrast is *confounded* with interactions.

A third parameter is the comparison of B_1 with B_2 (groups 11 and 21 with 12 and 22). The contrast weights are the averages of the first and third rows of **A** minus the average of the second and fourth. That is,

$$\mathbf{l}'_3 = [0 \quad 0 \quad 0 \quad 1 \quad -1 \quad .5 \quad -.5 \quad .5 \quad -.5]$$

The third alternate parameter is

$$\mathbf{l}'_3\mathbf{\Theta}^* = (\boldsymbol{\beta}_1 - \boldsymbol{\beta}_2)' + (\boldsymbol{\gamma}_{\cdot 1} - \boldsymbol{\gamma}_{\cdot 2})'$$

Again, if the mean interactions are equal, then the third parameter estimates the difference of the two treatment effects. If the interactions are not equal, then the difference of the means for B_1 and B_2 is not the simple difference of treatment effects, but is confounded with interaction as well.

A final parameter is the interaction contrast, with

$$\mathbf{l}'_4 = [0 \quad 0 \quad 0 \quad 0 \quad 0 \quad 1 \quad -1 \quad -1 \quad 1]$$

$\mathbf{l}'_4$ is the sum of the first and last rows of **A** minus the sum of the second and third. The parameter is

$$\mathbf{l}'_4\mathbf{\Theta}^* = (\boldsymbol{\gamma}_{11} - \boldsymbol{\gamma}_{12})' - (\boldsymbol{\gamma}_{21} - \boldsymbol{\gamma}_{22})'$$

If the difference of interactions $\boldsymbol{\gamma}_{11} - \boldsymbol{\gamma}_{12}$ is the same as the difference $\boldsymbol{\gamma}_{21} - \boldsymbol{\gamma}_{22}$, then we shall say that there is no interaction, for the cell means can be "explained" by a simpler main-effects model. In this case, interaction does not confound the A and B main-effect contrasts.

The complete contrast matrix is

$$\mathbf{L} = \begin{bmatrix} 1 & .5 & .5 & .5 & .5 & .25 & .25 & .25 & .25 \\ 0 & 1 & -1 & 0 & 0 & .5 & .5 & -.5 & -.5 \\ 0 & 0 & 0 & 1 & -1 & .5 & -.5 & .5 & -.5 \\ 0 & 0 & 0 & 0 & 0 & 1 & -1 & -1 & 1 \end{bmatrix}$$

and

$$\mathbf{\Theta} = \begin{bmatrix} \boldsymbol{\mu}' + \boldsymbol{\alpha}'_{\cdot} + \boldsymbol{\beta}'_{\cdot} + \boldsymbol{\gamma}'_{\cdot\cdot} \\ (\boldsymbol{\alpha}_1 - \boldsymbol{\alpha}_2)' + (\boldsymbol{\gamma}_{1\cdot} - \boldsymbol{\gamma}_{2\cdot})' \\ (\boldsymbol{\beta}_1 - \boldsymbol{\beta}_2)' + (\boldsymbol{\gamma}_{\cdot 1} - \boldsymbol{\gamma}_{\cdot 2})' \\ (\boldsymbol{\gamma}_{11} - \boldsymbol{\gamma}_{12})' - (\boldsymbol{\gamma}_{21} - \boldsymbol{\gamma}_{22})' \end{bmatrix} \begin{array}{l} \text{Constant} \\ A \text{ main effect} \\ B \text{ main effect} \\ AB \text{ interaction} \end{array}$$

The reparameterized model matrix is

$$\mathbf{K}=\mathbf{AL}'(\mathbf{LL}')^{-1}=\begin{bmatrix}1 & .5 & .5 & .25\\ 1 & .5 & -.5 & -.25\\ 1 & -.5 & .5 & -.25\\ 1 & -.5 & -.5 & .25\end{bmatrix}$$

The least-squares estimate of $\mathbf{\Theta}$ is

$$\hat{\mathbf{\Theta}}=(\mathbf{K}'\mathbf{DK})^{-1}\mathbf{K}'\mathbf{DY}.$$

$$=\begin{bmatrix}2.32 & 2.60\\ -.98 & -.78\\ -1.95 & -2.04\\ -1.44 & -1.75\end{bmatrix}\begin{matrix}\text{Constant}\\ A\text{ main effect}\\ B\text{ main effect}\\ AB\text{ interaction}\end{matrix}$$

$$\quad\; y_1 \qquad y_2$$

The mean for A_1 is lower than the mean for A_2 for both variates (.98 on y_1, .78 on y_2). The B differences are larger, with mean B_1 about 2 points lower than mean B_2 on both variates. The differences among interactions also appear large by comparison. We may test these statistically to see if they contribute to between-group variation on the criteria. In particular, the low means of group 11 alone seem to contribute to the interaction contrast.

7.4 THE SELECTION OF CONTRASTS

Once an experiment has been designed and the analysis model and hypotheses are known, the particular contrasts to be estimated and/or tested can be constructed. The contrast weights form the rows of a contrast matrix **L**, which defines linear functions of the analysis-of-variance effects. The particular contrasts are chosen according to the design of the study and to the questions and hypotheses that are posed. Therefore, it is impossible to impose statistical rules for their selection.

Several examples of contrasts are given in Section 7.3. More are provided at the end of this chapter in the context of actual research studies. It often happens that the contrasts of interest to researchers can be categorized into general contrast "types." A number of these are discussed here.

It is convenient to describe contrast vectors through a symbolic notation that conveys both the form of the reparameterization as well as the particular effects involved. The symbolic representation of contrasts obviates constructing long and perhaps complex weight vectors, and can be used to improve the convenience and accuracy of computer analyses. One such notation has been employed by Bock (1963), which is based upon the formulation of Kurkjian and Zelen (1962). The notation is discussed here, first for designs with only one classification factor. Contrast vectors for two-way or many-way designs, and for designs with nested effects, can be represented as combinations of effects for the separate classification factors.

One-way Designs

Assume a one-way analysis-of-variance model with a levels of the classification factor. The model is $\mathbf{Y.} = \mathbf{A}\boldsymbol{\Theta}^* + \mathbf{E.}$, with

$$\mathbf{A} = [\mathbf{1}_a, \mathbf{I}_a] \qquad \text{and} \qquad \boldsymbol{\Theta}^* = \begin{bmatrix} \boldsymbol{\mu}' \\ \boldsymbol{\alpha}_1' \\ \boldsymbol{\alpha}_2' \\ \vdots \\ \boldsymbol{\alpha}_a' \end{bmatrix} \tag{7.4.1}$$

where $\mathbf{1}_a$ is an a-element unit vector; $\mathbf{I}_a$ is the $a \times a$ identity matrix. Each row of $\boldsymbol{\Theta}^*$ has p elements, corresponding to the effect for the p separate outcome measures. (For simplicity, it may help to assume $p = 1$).

Represent the contrast matrix for the factor having a levels as $\mathbf{L}_a$. $\mathbf{L}_a$ premultiplies $\boldsymbol{\Theta}^*$ to create no more than a linear combinations of the effects in the alternate parameter matrix $\boldsymbol{\Theta} = \mathbf{L}_a\boldsymbol{\Theta}^*$. In the usual one-way analysis-of-variance model, there are $a+1$ parameters, so $\mathbf{L}_a$ is of the order $a \times (a+1)$. Each row of $\mathbf{L}_a$ consists of a set of weights that multiply the parameters in $\boldsymbol{\Theta}^*$ to produce one of the alternate parameters.

Almost universally in behavioral research, the first parameter is a population constant, which reflects both the scale of the measures and the overall response level of the population(s) sampled. As a function of the rows of the model matrix, the corresponding vector of $\mathbf{L}_a$ is the mean of all rows of $\mathbf{A}$. Inspection of $\mathbf{A}$ reveals that the mean of its rows is the vector

$$\begin{bmatrix} 1 & \frac{1}{a} & \frac{1}{a} & \cdots & \frac{1}{a} \end{bmatrix} \tag{7.4.2}$$

We shall denote the constant term as the "zeroth" effect, and symbolize the corresponding row of the contrast matrix as L0.

The remaining $(a-1)$ vectors are denoted L1, L2, ..., L$(a-1)$. Thus the contrast matrix $\mathbf{L}_a$ has the form

$$\mathbf{L}_a = \begin{bmatrix} \text{L0} \\ \text{L1} \\ \text{L2} \\ \vdots \\ \text{L}(a-1) \end{bmatrix} \tag{7.4.3}$$

L1 through L$(a-1)$, like L0, each represent an entire vector, with $a+1$ elements.

Except for the first vector, the rows of $\mathbf{L}_a$ define contrasts among the parameters and all have zero as the first element. The reader may note that this was true for the examples of the preceding section. We shall primarily concern ourselves with the $(a-1) \times a$ final submatrix of $\mathbf{L}_a$ defining the contrasts among the α_j. The sum of the elements of each row of the submatrix is zero, by the definition of a contrast.

For example, a contrast matrix for the four-level design is given by Eq. 7.3.8.

That is,

$$\mathbf{L}_4 = \begin{bmatrix} 1 & 1/4 & 1/4 & 1/4 & 1/4 \\ 0 & 1 & 0 & 0 & -1 \\ 0 & 0 & 1 & 0 & -1 \\ 0 & 0 & 0 & 1 & -1 \end{bmatrix} \begin{matrix} \text{L0} \\ \text{L1} \\ \text{L2} \\ \text{L3} \end{matrix} \tag{7.4.4}$$

The submatrix that describes the contrasts among the parameters consists of the vectors L1, L2, and L3, omitting the first element. That is,

$$\begin{bmatrix} 1 & 0 & 0 & -1 \\ 0 & 1 & 0 & -1 \\ 0 & 0 & 1 & -1 \end{bmatrix} \begin{matrix} \text{L1} \\ \text{L2} \\ \text{L3} \end{matrix} \tag{7.4.5}$$

The first contrast is $\boldsymbol{\alpha}_1 - \boldsymbol{\alpha}_4$. If the mean vector in subclass j is $\boldsymbol{\mu}_j = \boldsymbol{\mu} + \boldsymbol{\alpha}_j$, then L1 is equivalently $\boldsymbol{\mu}_1 - \boldsymbol{\mu}_4$, or the comparison of the respective population means.

Various sorts of contrasts among means are employed in behavioral research. Many of those most frequently used form selective subsets of those possible. One such subset is the set of *deviation contrasts*, whereby each of $a-1$ parameters, α_j, is contrasted to $\alpha.$, the mean of all α_j. The parameters estimated are of the form $\alpha_j - \alpha.$ or $\mu_j - \mu$. The contrast submatrix for deviation contrasts is of the form

$$\mathbf{L}_{D_a} = \begin{bmatrix} 1-\frac{1}{a} & -\frac{1}{a} & -\frac{1}{a} & \cdots & -\frac{1}{a} & -\frac{1}{a} \\ -\frac{1}{a} & 1-\frac{1}{a} & -\frac{1}{a} & \cdots & -\frac{1}{a} & -\frac{1}{a} \\ \vdots & & & & & \vdots \\ -\frac{1}{a} & -\frac{1}{a} & -\frac{1}{a} & \cdots & 1-\frac{1}{a} & -\frac{1}{a} \end{bmatrix} \begin{matrix} \text{D1} \\ \text{D2} \\ \vdots \\ \text{D}(a-1) \end{matrix} \tag{7.4.6}$$

The subscript D denotes that the contrasts are of the deviation type; a indicates the number of levels of the design factor. The contrast vectors themselves may be represented by the codes D1, D2, . . . , D($a-1$). D0, not seen in the contrast submatrix, is again the mean of all rows of the model matrix, and is identical to L0 of Eq. 7.4.2.

As an example, let $a=4$ for a one-way design having four levels. The alternate parameters to be estimated are $\boldsymbol{\alpha}_1 - \boldsymbol{\alpha}.$, $\boldsymbol{\alpha}_2 - \boldsymbol{\alpha}.$, and $\boldsymbol{\alpha}_3 - \boldsymbol{\alpha}.$. In addition to the constant term, or L0, the matrix has the contrast submatrix $\mathbf{L}_{D_4}$. That is,

$$\mathbf{L}_{D_4} = \begin{bmatrix} 3/4 & -1/4 & -1/4 & -1/4 \\ -1/4 & 3/4 & -1/4 & -1/4 \\ -1/4 & -1/4 & 3/4 & -1/4 \end{bmatrix} \begin{matrix} \text{D1} \\ \text{D2} \\ \text{D3} \end{matrix} \tag{7.4.7}$$

The row vectors are represented by D1, D2, and D3, respectively. The complete contrast matrix is

$$\mathbf{L}_4 = \left[\begin{array}{c|cccc} 1 & 1/4 & 1/4 & 1/4 & 1/4 \\ \hline 0 & & & & \\ 0 & & \mathbf{L}_{D_4} & & \\ 0 & & & & \end{array}\right]\begin{array}{l} \text{D0} \\ \text{D1} \\ \text{D2} \\ \text{D3} \end{array} \tag{7.4.8}$$

With $\mathbf{\Theta}^*$ defined by Eq. 7.4.1, then

$$\begin{aligned} \mathbf{\Theta} &= \mathbf{L}_4\mathbf{\Theta}^* \\ &= \begin{bmatrix} \boldsymbol{\mu}' + \boldsymbol{\alpha}'_. \\ \boldsymbol{\alpha}'_1 - \boldsymbol{\alpha}'_. \\ \boldsymbol{\alpha}'_2 - \boldsymbol{\alpha}'_. \\ \boldsymbol{\alpha}'_3 - \boldsymbol{\alpha}'_. \end{bmatrix} \end{aligned} \tag{7.4.9}$$

The set of deviation contrasts corresponds most closely to the "traditional" terms in the analysis-of-variance model, assuming $\boldsymbol{\alpha}_j = \boldsymbol{\mu}_j - \boldsymbol{\mu}$. The final or missing estimate, $\hat{\boldsymbol{\mu}}_4 - \hat{\boldsymbol{\mu}}$, may be obtained as minus the sum of the other three estimates. Deviation contrasts may be employed when there is no particular order to the groups in the design and when it is useful to estimate the simple terms in the analysis-of-variance model (μ, α_j, β_k, γ_{jk}, and so on).

A second set of contrasts is appropriate when $a-1$ group effects are compared with a control or comparison group. These comprise the set of *simple contrasts*, and will be represented by the code letter C. The contrast submatrix of $\mathbf{L}_a$, for simple contrasts, is

$$\mathbf{L}_{Ca} = \begin{bmatrix} 1 & 0 & 0 & \cdots & -1 \\ 0 & 1 & 0 & \cdots & -1 \\ \vdots & & & & \vdots \\ 0 & 0 & 0 & \cdots 1 & -1 \end{bmatrix}\begin{array}{l} \text{C1} \\ \text{C2} \\ \vdots \\ \text{C}(a-1) \end{array} \tag{7.4.10}$$

In Eq. 7.4.10 all subclass effects are compared with the mean of the last group.

For the one-way situation with four levels of the design factor, $\mathbf{L}_{C_4}$ is

$$\mathbf{L}_{C_4} = \begin{bmatrix} 1 & 0 & 0 & -1 \\ 0 & 1 & 0 & -1 \\ 0 & 0 & 1 & -1 \end{bmatrix}\begin{array}{l} \text{C1} \\ \text{C2} \\ \text{C3} \end{array} \tag{7.4.11}$$

C0, representing the constant term, is the same as L0 or D0 in Eq. 7.4.2. The reparameterized model has parameter matrix $\mathbf{\Theta}$, given by

$$\mathbf{\Theta} = \begin{bmatrix} \boldsymbol{\mu}' + \boldsymbol{\alpha}'_. \\ \boldsymbol{\alpha}'_1 - \boldsymbol{\alpha}'_4 \\ \boldsymbol{\alpha}'_2 - \boldsymbol{\alpha}'_4 \\ \boldsymbol{\alpha}'_3 - \boldsymbol{\alpha}'_4 \end{bmatrix} \tag{7.4.12}$$

Letting $\boldsymbol{\alpha}_j = \boldsymbol{\mu}_j - \boldsymbol{\mu}$, it can be seen that the three contrasts are simple comparisons of population means, $\boldsymbol{\mu}_j - \boldsymbol{\mu}_4$. The convention for symbolic coding will be that the contrast number *omitted* from the set will be the index of the common comparison group. Thus, in the four-level example, the codes C1, C3, C4, will represent the comparison of $\boldsymbol{\alpha}_1$, $\boldsymbol{\alpha}_3$, and $\boldsymbol{\alpha}_4$, with $\boldsymbol{\alpha}_2$, respectively. That is,

$$\mathbf{L}_{C_4} = \begin{bmatrix} 1 & -1 & 0 & 0 \\ 0 & -1 & 1 & 0 \\ 0 & -1 & 0 & 1 \end{bmatrix} \begin{matrix} \text{C1} \\ \text{C3} \\ \text{C4} \end{matrix} \tag{7.4.13}$$

Two additional types of contrasts have the property of orthogonality. Their employment in balanced, or equal-N, designs lends simplicity to the analysis. These are the set of *Helmert contrasts* and the *orthogonal polynomial contrasts*. Through Helmert contrasts, each group effect, $\boldsymbol{\alpha}_j$, is contrasted with the mean of succeeding group effects, in a given order. The contrast submatrix of $\mathbf{L}_a$ has the form

$$\mathbf{L}_{H_a} = \begin{bmatrix} 1 & -\frac{1}{a-1} & -\frac{1}{a-1} & \cdots & -\frac{1}{a-1} & -\frac{1}{a-1} \\ 0 & 1 & -\frac{1}{a-2} & \cdots & -\frac{1}{a-2} & -\frac{1}{a-2} \\ \vdots & & & & & \vdots \\ 0 & 0 & 0 & \cdots & 1 & -1 \end{bmatrix} \begin{matrix} \text{H1} \\ \text{H2} \\ \vdots \\ \text{H}(a-1) \end{matrix} \tag{7.4.14}$$

Helmert contrasts for a five-level factor would be H1, H2, H3, and H4.

$$\mathbf{L}_{H_5} = \begin{bmatrix} 1 & -1/4 & -1/4 & -1/4 & -1/4 \\ 0 & 1 & -1/3 & -1/3 & -1/3 \\ 0 & 0 & 1 & -1/2 & -1/2 \\ 0 & 0 & 0 & 1 & -1 \end{bmatrix} \begin{matrix} \text{H1} \\ \text{H2} \\ \text{H3} \\ \text{H4} \end{matrix} \tag{7.4.15}$$

Although Helmert contrasts may be applied to any design, they are of particular value when there is an order underlying the subgroup definition. As can be seen from Eq. 7.4.15, the Helmert contrasts may be used to compare sequentially ordered group means in a regular fashion. It can also be seen that all Helmert contrasts are orthogonal to one another.

When experimental groups are defined by an underlying quantitative *metric* (for example, age, dosage, time elapsed) it may be of value to determine whether group means differ as a function of the values of the underlying independent variable. For example, physical growth may increase proportionally to a simple polynomial function of age over, say, a five-year period. Or recall of simple learned material may decrease in a manner directly proportional to time elapsed since learning, in 15-minute intervals. In these and similar instances, experimental groups represent discrete conditions on a measured independent variable (for example, 1, 2, 3, 4, 5 years of age; 5, 10, 15 cc drug dosage; 0, 15, 30, 45-minute delay to recall). To determine whether group means differ according to a polynomial function of these numeric values, *orthogonal polynomial contrasts* may be employed.

The contrast weights for orthogonal polynomials are determined through the row-wise orthonormalization of a polynomial matrix in the original metric.

That is, let the scale underlying the group variable have values $x_1, x_2, x_3, \ldots, x_a$. Then the contrast matrix is the row-wise orthogonal factor of **X**, where

$$\mathbf{X} = \begin{bmatrix} x_1^{\,0} & x_2^{\,0} & \cdots & x_a^{\,0} \\ x_1^{\,1} & x_2^{\,1} & \cdots & x_a^{\,1} \\ \vdots & & & \vdots \\ x_1^{\,a-1} & x_2^{\,a-1} & \cdots & x_a^{\,a-1} \end{bmatrix} \tag{7.4.16}$$

The first row of **X** has all unities; the second has the original values of the metric, or the scale underlying the group-membership variable. The following rows define polynomials of increasing degrees of complexity.

If group j has mean outcome score $y_{\cdot j}$, then the reparameterized, or polynomial, model is

$$\begin{aligned} y_{\cdot j} &= \theta_1 + \theta_2 x_j + \theta_3 x_j^2 + \cdots + \theta_a x_j^{a-1} + \epsilon_{\cdot j} \\ &= \sum_{k=0}^{a-1} \theta_{k+1} x_j^{k} + \epsilon_{\cdot j} \end{aligned} \tag{7.4.17}$$

x_j is the value of the independent variable common to observations in group j. Its powers comprise one column of **X** in 7.4.16. The θ_i are the coefficients of the powers of x_j, in the reparameterized model. These are the elements of $\boldsymbol{\theta}$; θ_1 is a constant term which absorbs scaling factors in y. To test for overall group-mean differences, all $a-1$ terms in $\boldsymbol{\theta}$ excluding θ_1 may be tested for nullity (as with any of the contrast reparameterizations). To test for differences proportional to particular polynomials in x, individual coefficients θ_i may be tested. When p is greater than one, $\boldsymbol{\Theta}$ has a column with the polynomial coefficients for each outcome measure.

The symbolic representation of orthogonal polynomials has contrast code P. The set of weights for the contrast submatrix is symbolically represented P1, . . . , P($a-1$),

$$\mathbf{L}_{P_a} = \begin{bmatrix} \text{P1} \\ \text{P2} \\ \vdots \\ \text{P}(a-1) \end{bmatrix} \tag{7.4.18}$$

DeLury (1950) has tabled $\mathbf{L}_{P_a}$ from $a=2$ to $a=26$, for the case where values of the metric are evenly spaced (proportional to 1, 2, 3, . . . , $a-1$, a). For example, if there are two groups, we can only test for a simple linear difference of group means. The contrast weights are

$$\mathbf{L}_{P_2} = [-1 \quad 1]\,\text{P1} \tag{7.4.19a}$$

The vector is represented symbolically as P1. The test of significance is the same as any contrast between $y_{\cdot 1}$ and $y_{\cdot 2}$.

If there are three groups, the contrast weights for linear and quadratic differences among the means are

$$\mathbf{L}_{P_3} = \begin{bmatrix} -1 & 0 & 1 \\ 1 & -2 & 1 \end{bmatrix} \begin{matrix} \text{P1} \\ \text{P2} \end{matrix} \tag{7.4.19b}$$

It can be seen that the P1 weights increase in even intervals, for three groups having means $y_{\cdot 1}, y_{\cdot 2}$, and $y_{\cdot 3}$. This contrast is significant if the group means increase (or decrease) in a monotonic fashion, proportionally to the metric, or to the numbers 1, 2, 3. The P2 weights describe a second-degree or parabolic curve. This contrast is significant if $y_{\cdot 2}$ is significantly off a straight line connecting points $y_{\cdot 1}$ and $y_{\cdot 3}$.

To test for overall mean differences (H_0: $\mu_1 = \mu_2 = \mu_3$), the two-degree-of-freedom test of both contrasts is conducted. This yields the same result as the test of any two contrasts among the three groups. However, to test the complexity of the curve separating the means, separate tests are conducted of linear P1, and of additional variation attributable to quadratic P2. If P2 is significant, *both* linear and quadratic effects are maintained in the model. Not only do group means describe a parabola, but the slope of the line upon which the parabola rests may be non-zero (see Figures 7.4.10, 7.4.11).

When there are four groups, the weights for linear, quadratic, and cubic differences among the means are

$$\mathbf{L}_{P_4} = \begin{bmatrix} -3 & -1 & 1 & 3 \\ 1 & -1 & -1 & 1 \\ -1 & 3 & -3 & -1 \end{bmatrix} \begin{matrix} \text{P1} \\ \text{P2} \\ \text{P3} \end{matrix} \tag{7.4.19c}$$

Again, each successive contrast vector describes a more complex curve than the one preceding. Since each vector has been orthogonalized from those preceding it, rejection of H_0 for any contrast requires that all simpler terms be included in the model as well. Frequently, significant terms which describe complex curves are difficult to interpret. This implies only that the mean outcomes are not easily explained as multiples of the metric values. Some other contrasts may be better to describe differences among the groups.

It can be seen that the rows of $\mathbf{L}_{P_a}$ are orthogonal. They may also be normalized to unit length. The entire contrast matrix is

$$\mathbf{L}_4 = \begin{bmatrix} 1 & 1/4 \quad 1/4 \quad 1/4 \quad 1/4 \\ 0 & \\ 0 & L_{P_4} \\ 0 & \end{bmatrix} \begin{matrix} \text{P0} \\ \text{P1} \\ \text{P2} \\ \text{P3} \end{matrix} \tag{7.4.20}$$

Tabled orthogonal polynomial weights are based on an underlying independent variable with equal intervals. That is, the *treatment* difference between groups one and two must be the same as that between groups two and three, and so on. In practice, the treatment (time, dosage, etc.) is not always alloted in equal intervals. General computational algorithms such as those in the MULTIVARIANCE program may be used instead of tables to generate weights for any metric. The same symbolic representation is still employed.

Bases for One-way Designs

After a set of alternate parameters is chosen, the alternate model matrix may be determined, and used for further analysis. The construction of the alternate model matrix, or basis, is given by Eqs. 7.3.5 and 7.3.6. That is,

$$\mathbf{K} = \mathbf{A}\mathbf{L}'(\mathbf{L}\mathbf{L}')^{-1} \tag{7.4.21}$$

Since **K** multiplies the contrast matrix **L**, there is one column of the basis for each alternate parameter—that is, a column for each row of **L**. We may represent the columns of **K** symbolically using the same notation as for the contrast vectors.

For example, the simple contrast matrix for the one-way design (Eq. 7.3.8), is

$$\mathbf{L} = \begin{bmatrix} 1 & 1/4 & 1/4 & 1/4 & 1/4 \\ 0 & 1 & 0 & 0 & -1 \\ 0 & 0 & 1 & 0 & -1 \\ 0 & 0 & 0 & 1 & -1 \end{bmatrix} \begin{matrix} \text{C0} \\ \text{C1} \\ \text{C2} \\ \text{C3} \end{matrix} \tag{7.4.22}$$

The resulting basis is given by Eq. 7.3.10. Its columns may be referred to as basis vectors C0, C1, C2, and C3.

$$\mathbf{K} = \begin{bmatrix} 1.00 & .75 & -.25 & -.25 \\ 1.00 & -.25 & .75 & -.25 \\ 1.00 & -.25 & -.25 & .75 \\ 1.00 & -.25 & -.25 & -.25 \end{bmatrix} \tag{7.4.23}$$
$$\qquad \text{C0} \quad \text{C1} \quad \text{C2} \quad \text{C3}$$

Any real problem will undoubtedly require evaluation of the basis by computer. However, there are several aspects of constructing **K** that are useful to us. First, the basis may be constructed without reference to the model matrix **A**. Bock (1963) has shown that for any single design factor, the basis may be alternately constructed by

$$\mathbf{K}_a = [\mathbf{1}, \mathbf{K}_{C_a}] \tag{7.4.24}$$

where

$$\mathbf{K}_{C_a} = \mathbf{L}'_{C_a}(\mathbf{L}_{C_a}\mathbf{L}'_{C_a})^{-1} \tag{7.4.25}$$

(using simple contrasts as an example). $\mathbf{L}_{C_a}$ is the $(a-1)\times a$ contrast submatrix of $\mathbf{L}_a$; **1** is an a-element unit vector.

For example, $\mathbf{L}_{C_a}$, from Eq. 7.4.22, is

$$\mathbf{L}_{C_4} = \begin{bmatrix} 1 & 0 & 0 & -1 \\ 0 & 1 & 0 & -1 \\ 0 & 0 & 1 & -1 \end{bmatrix}$$

and

$$\mathbf{K}_{C_4} = \mathbf{L}'_{C_4}(\mathbf{L}_{C_4}\mathbf{L}'_{C_4})^{-1}$$
$$= \begin{bmatrix} .75 & -.25 & -.25 \\ -.25 & .75 & -.25 \\ -.25 & -.25 & .75 \\ -.25 & -.25 & -.25 \end{bmatrix}$$

where $\mathbf{K}$ of Eq. 7.4.23 is $\mathbf{K}_{C_4}$ preceded by a four-element unit vector.

Further, the basis for any given contrast type follows a regular pattern. It may be constructed without Eq. 7.4.21, knowing only the type of contrast, and number of levels, *a*. Thus, for most regular designs, a basis matrix necessary for estimation may be generated from the symbolic contrast codes, without the development of **A** or **L**. The MULTIVARIANCE program utilizes these regularities to avoid constructing unnecessary and potentially large matrices. For arbitrary contrasts that do not conform to the regular patterns, **K** is found from Eqs. 7.4.24 and 7.4.25.

The vectors comprising the basis are an intermediate computation in the analysis-of-variance model. It is not essential that the researcher be able to compute them. The basis vectors are not themselves contrast vectors, but fairly complex functions of the contrasts. Thus the reader will want to be aware of the function of the basis in the analysis-of-variance model. Beyond that it is necessary only to understand and be able to interpret the symbolic contrast codes. The following extensions plus the examples in Chapter 8 exemplify a variety of applications of the symbolic codes.

Higher-order Designs

For sampling designs of more than one factor, the model matrices and bases can be constructed from the corresponding matrices for the separate dimensions of classification. For example, inspection of the model matrix for the 2×3 crossed design in Eq. 7.1.12 reveals that **A** may be generated by means of Kronecker products of model matrices for the separate design factors. Let the model matrix for the two-level factor alone be $\mathbf{A}_2$. That is,

$$\mathbf{A}_2 = \begin{bmatrix} 1 & 1 & 0 \\ 1 & 0 & 1 \end{bmatrix} \quad (A \text{ factor})$$
$$= [\mathbf{1}_2, \quad \mathbf{I}_2] \tag{7.4.26}$$

where $\mathbf{1}_2$ denotes a two-element unit vector; $\mathbf{I}_2$ is the 2×2 identity matrix. The parameters are μ, α_1, and α_2. For the three-level factor alone, the model matrix is

$$\mathbf{A}_3 = \begin{bmatrix} 1 & 1 & 0 & 0 \\ 1 & 0 & 1 & 0 \\ 1 & 0 & 0 & 1 \end{bmatrix} \quad (B \text{ factor})$$
$$= [\mathbf{1}_3, \quad \mathbf{I}_3] \tag{7.4.27}$$

for parameters μ, β_1, β_2, and β_3.

The 6×12 model matrix **A** for the two-way design, including interactions, is a matrix of Kronecker products of the sections of $\mathbf{A}_2$ and $\mathbf{A}_3$. For example, the vector of all unities in **A** is the product $\mathbf{1}_2 \otimes \mathbf{1}_3$; the two vectors for the α effects are the products $\mathbf{I}_2 \otimes \mathbf{1}_3$; the columns for β effects are the products $\mathbf{1}_2 \otimes \mathbf{I}_3$; the interaction vectors are $\mathbf{I}_2 \otimes \mathbf{I}_3$. Juxtaposing these results, we have

$$\mathbf{A} = [\mathbf{1}_2 \otimes \mathbf{1}_3 \mid \mathbf{I}_2 \otimes \mathbf{1}_3 \mid \mathbf{1}_2 \otimes \mathbf{I}_3 \mid \mathbf{I}_2 \otimes \mathbf{I}_3]$$

$$= \left[\begin{array}{c|cc|ccc|cccccc} 1 & 1 & 0 & 1 & 0 & 0 & 1 & 0 & 0 & 0 & 0 & 0 \\ 1 & 1 & 0 & 0 & 1 & 0 & 0 & 1 & 0 & 0 & 0 & 0 \\ 1 & 1 & 0 & 0 & 0 & 1 & 0 & 0 & 1 & 0 & 0 & 0 \\ 1 & 0 & 1 & 1 & 0 & 0 & 0 & 0 & 0 & 1 & 0 & 0 \\ 1 & 0 & 1 & 0 & 1 & 0 & 0 & 0 & 0 & 0 & 1 & 0 \\ 1 & 0 & 1 & 0 & 0 & 1 & 0 & 0 & 0 & 0 & 0 & 1 \end{array}\right] \quad (7.4.28)$$

The columns of **A** are the columns of the Kronecker product $\mathbf{A}_2 \otimes \mathbf{A}_3$, except for their order.

Construction of model matrices for three-way and higher-order designs may be accomplished through extended application of the Kronecker product operator. The main-effects model matrix for a three-factor crossed design, having *a* levels of factor *A*, *b* levels of *B*, and *c* levels of *C*, is

$$\mathbf{A} = [\mathbf{1}_a \otimes \mathbf{1}_b \otimes \mathbf{1}_c \mid \mathbf{I}_a \otimes \mathbf{1}_b \otimes \mathbf{1}_c \mid \mathbf{1}_a \otimes \mathbf{I}_b \otimes \mathbf{1}_c \mid \mathbf{1}_a \otimes \mathbf{1}_b \otimes \mathbf{I}_c]$$

The matrix of Eq. 7.1.13a is an example, with $a = b = c = 2$.

In a similar fashion, the model matrix *after reparameterization* for a multifactor design may be constructed from bases for the individual design factors. For example, the basis for the 2×3 crossed design of Eq. 7.3.13a can be obtained from one-way bases. Deviation contrasts $\alpha_j - \alpha.$ and $\beta_k - \beta.$ were selected for both factors. The one-way contrast matrices are

$$\mathbf{L}_2 = \begin{bmatrix} 1 & 1/2 & 1/2 \\ 0 & 1/2 & -1/2 \end{bmatrix} \begin{matrix} \text{D0} \\ \text{D1} \end{matrix} \quad (A \text{ factor}) \quad (7.4.29)$$

and

$$\mathbf{L}_3 = \begin{bmatrix} 1 & 1/3 & 1/3 & 1/3 \\ 0 & 2/3 & -1/3 & -1/3 \\ 0 & -1/3 & 2/3 & -1/3 \end{bmatrix} \begin{matrix} \text{D0} \\ \text{D1} \\ \text{D2} \end{matrix} \quad (B \text{ factor}). \quad (7.4.30)$$

From these and the separate model matrices (or by Eq. 7.4.24) we obtain bases

$$\mathbf{K}_2 = \begin{bmatrix} 1 & 1 \\ 1 & -1 \end{bmatrix} \quad (A \text{ factor}) \quad (7.4.31)$$
$$\begin{matrix} \text{D0} & \text{D1} \end{matrix}$$

and

$$\mathbf{K}_3 = \begin{bmatrix} 1 & 1 & 0 \\ 1 & 0 & 1 \\ 1 & -1 & -1 \end{bmatrix} \quad (B \text{ factor}) \quad (7.4.32)$$
$$\begin{matrix} \text{D0} & \text{D1} & \text{D2} \end{matrix}$$

The equal-element vector corresponding to the constant term for each factor is the "zeroth" effect, D0 (or C0, H0, and so on). The equal-element vector in the total 6×4 basis **K** is the product $\mathbf{1}_2 \otimes \mathbf{1}_3$ or, in symbolic notation, D0⊗D0 (one vector from $\mathbf{K}_2$, one from $\mathbf{K}_3$).

The basis vector for the *A* main effect is the product of vector D1 for the *A* factor and D0 for the *B*; that is,

$$\text{D1} \otimes \text{D0} = \begin{bmatrix} 1 \\ 1 \\ 1 \\ -1 \\ -1 \\ -1 \end{bmatrix}$$

The *B* effect has two degrees of freedom. The basis vectors corresponding to the two *B*-effect contrasts are the Kronecker products of the D0 vector for factor *A*, and the two effects (D1 and D2) for *B*. The entire basis in Eq. 7.3.13a is formed by juxtaposing these products. That is,

$$\mathbf{K} = \begin{bmatrix} 1 & 1 & 1 & 0 \\ 1 & 1 & 0 & 1 \\ 1 & 1 & -1 & -1 \\ 1 & -1 & 1 & 0 \\ 1 & -1 & 0 & 1 \\ 1 & -1 & -1 & -1 \end{bmatrix} \qquad (7.4.33)$$

$$\text{D0}\otimes\text{D0} \quad \text{D1}\otimes\text{D0} \quad \text{D0}\otimes\text{D1} \quad \text{D0}\otimes\text{D2}$$

Should interaction terms be included in the model, the corresponding basis vectors for the two degrees of freedom would be the products D1⊗D1 and D1⊗D2.

$$\text{D1}\otimes\text{D1 is} \begin{bmatrix} 1 \\ 0 \\ -1 \\ -1 \\ 0 \\ 1 \end{bmatrix} \qquad \text{D1}\otimes\text{D2 is} \begin{bmatrix} 0 \\ 1 \\ -1 \\ 0 \\ -1 \\ 1 \end{bmatrix}$$

In every case it is necessary to maintain the order of factors (that is, a column of $\mathbf{K}_2$ is consistently the prefactor). If some subclasses have no observations, the corresponding rows of **Y.**, **E.**, and the complete **K** may be deleted, leaving $J_0 < J$ rows.

The following example is adapted from Bock (1965; pp. 77–78).* Consider a 2×3×3 (*A*×*B*×*C*) completely crossed design. Linear and quadratic polynomial effects are desired across levels of *B*, and simple contrasts among the levels of *A* and *C*. The separate contrast matrices are:

$$\mathbf{L}_2 = \begin{bmatrix} 1 & 1/2 & 1/2 \\ 0 & 1 & -1 \end{bmatrix} \begin{matrix} \text{C0} \\ \text{C1} \end{matrix} \quad (A \text{ factor})$$

*Material reprinted by permission, from *Proceedings of IBM Scientific Symposium on Statistics, October, 1963.* ©1965 by International Business Machines Corporation.

$$\mathbf{L}_3 = \begin{bmatrix} 1 & 1/3 & 1/3 & 1/3 \\ 0 & -1 & 0 & 1 \\ 0 & 1 & -2 & 1 \end{bmatrix} \begin{matrix} \text{P0} \\ \text{P1} \\ \text{P2} \end{matrix} \quad (B \text{ factor})$$

$$\mathbf{L}_3 = \begin{bmatrix} 1 & 1/3 & 1/3 & 1/3 \\ 0 & 1 & 0 & -1 \\ 0 & 0 & 1 & -1 \end{bmatrix} \begin{matrix} \text{C0} \\ \text{C1} \\ \text{C2} \end{matrix} \quad (C \text{ factor})$$

The bases that result are

$$\mathbf{K}_2 = \begin{bmatrix} 1 & 1/2 \\ 1 & -1/2 \end{bmatrix} \quad \mathbf{K}_3 = \begin{bmatrix} 1 & -1/2 & 1/6 \\ 1 & 0 & -1/3 \\ 1 & 1/2 & 1/6 \end{bmatrix} \quad \mathbf{K}_3 = \begin{bmatrix} 1 & 2/3 & -1/3 \\ 1 & -1/3 & 2/3 \\ 1 & -1/3 & -1/3 \end{bmatrix}$$

C0 C1 (*A* factor)   P0 P1 P2 (*B* factor)   C0 C1 C2 (*C* factor)

The complete model is rank 18. The basis for the entire design is constructed as Kronecker products of the vectors of the separate matrices. The value of the products themselves is not of major importance. However, the reader should be familiar with the symbolic notation from which they are generated. The effects and symbolic vectors denoting the products are given in Table 7.4.1.

Table 7.4.1 Source Listing and Symbolic Vectors for 2×3×3 Factorial Design

Source	*Degrees of Freedom*	*Symbolic Vector*
Constant	1	C0 ⊗ P0 ⊗ C0
$A_1 - A_2$	1	C1 ⊗ P0 ⊗ C0
B: Linear	1	C0 ⊗ P1 ⊗ C0
Quadratic	1	C0 ⊗ P2 ⊗ C0
C: $C_1 - C_3$	1	C0 ⊗ P0 ⊗ C1
$C_2 - C_3$	1	C0 ⊗ P0 ⊗ C2
AB: *A*×linear *B*	1	C1 ⊗ P1 ⊗ C0
A×quadratic *B*	1	C1 ⊗ P2 ⊗ C0
AC	2	C1 ⊗ P0 ⊗ C1
		C1 ⊗ P0 ⊗ C2
BC	4	C0 ⊗ P1 ⊗ C1
		C0 ⊗ P1 ⊗ C2
		C0 ⊗ P2 ⊗ C1
		C0 ⊗ P2 ⊗ C2
ABC	4	C1 ⊗ P1 ⊗ C1
		C1 ⊗ P1 ⊗ C2
		C1 ⊗ P2 ⊗ C1
		C1 ⊗ P2 ⊗ C2
Between groups	$I = 2 \times 3 \times 3 = 18$	

Each vector of **K** is an 18-element Kronecker product of one vector from each of the separate one-way bases. For example, the $A\times$ linear B basis vector is

$$\text{C1}\otimes\text{P1}\otimes\text{C0}=\begin{bmatrix}1/2\\-1/2\end{bmatrix}\otimes\begin{bmatrix}-1/2\\0\\1/2\end{bmatrix}\otimes\begin{bmatrix}1\\1\\1\end{bmatrix}$$

$$=[-1/4 \quad -1/4 \quad -1/4 \quad 0 \quad 0 \quad 0 \quad 1/4 \quad 1/4 \quad 1/4 \quad 1/4 \quad 1/4 \quad 1/4 \quad 0 \quad 0 \quad 0 \quad -1/4 \quad -1/4 \quad -1/4]'$$

The 18×18 complete basis may be substituted in Eq. 7.3.4 to obtain estimates of each effect in the reparameterized model.

The number of vectors in each Kronecker product is equal to the number of factors in the sampling design. That is, for a four-factor design, each basis vector is the product of four smaller vectors from the one-way matrices. The total number of **K** vectors corresponds to the "degrees of freedom between groups," if we include one for the overall population constant. The degrees of freedom, in turn, are restricted to being no greater than the number of groups in the design with at least one observation ($l\leqslant J$).

Sample Problem 4, the essay grading study, yields an $A\times B\times C\times D$ ($2\times 2\times 2\times 4$) factorial arrangement. The four-level factor is to be reparameterized to deviation-type contrasts. The symbolic representation of the basis vectors is given in Table 7.4.2. Each vector in the basis has 32 elements, corresponding to the 32 subclasses in the design, and is a function of four smaller vectors. As before, each column vector of the basis represents a single effect, or single degree of freedom between groups.

Bases for nested designs may be constructed by employing the identity matrix as a factor in the Kronecker products. For example, consider the two-treatment situation, with two classes assigned to treatment one, and three to treatment two. The model is given by Eq. 7.1.14. That is,

$$y_{\cdot ij}=\mu+\alpha_j+b_{i(j)}+\epsilon_{\cdot ij}$$

The treatment factor, A, has two levels; classes, B, has at most three levels for any treatment. The model matrix is

$$\mathbf{A}=\begin{bmatrix}1&1&0&1&0&0&0&0\\1&1&0&0&1&0&0&0\\1&0&1&0&0&1&0&0\\1&0&1&0&0&0&1&0\\1&0&1&0&0&0&0&1\end{bmatrix} \tag{7.4.34}$$

with parameters

$$[\boldsymbol{\theta}^*]'=[\mu \quad \alpha_1 \quad \alpha_2 \quad b_{1(1)} \quad b_{2(1)} \quad b_{1(2)} \quad b_{2(2)} \quad b_{3(2)}]$$

A may be constructed as the Kronecker product of matrices for the two-level treatment factor, and a three-level class factor, treating the design as crossed. The third row of the model matrix for the complete crossed design is

Table 7.4.2 Source Listing and Symbolic Vectors for 2×2×2×4 Factorial Design

Source	*Degrees of Freedom*	*Symbolic Vector*
Constant	1	C0 ⊗ C0 ⊗ C0 ⊗ D0
A	1	C1 ⊗ C0 ⊗ C0 ⊗ D0
B	1	C0 ⊗ C1 ⊗ C0 ⊗ D0
C	1	C0 ⊗ C0 ⊗ C1 ⊗ D0
D	3	C0 ⊗ C0 ⊗ C0 ⊗ D1
		C0 ⊗ C0 ⊗ C0 ⊗ D2
		C0 ⊗ C0 ⊗ C0 ⊗ D3
AB	1	C1 ⊗ C1 ⊗ C0 ⊗ D0
AC	1	C1 ⊗ C0 ⊗ C1 ⊗ D0
AD	3	C1 ⊗ C0 ⊗ C0 ⊗ D1
		C1 ⊗ C0 ⊗ C0 ⊗ D2
		C1 ⊗ C0 ⊗ C0 ⊗ D3
BC	1	C0 ⊗ C1 ⊗ C1 ⊗ D0
BD	3	C0 ⊗ C1 ⊗ C0 ⊗ D1
		C0 ⊗ C1 ⊗ C0 ⊗ D2
		C0 ⊗ C1 ⊗ C0 ⊗ D3
CD	3	C0 ⊗ C0 ⊗ C1 ⊗ D1
		C0 ⊗ C0 ⊗ C1 ⊗ D2
		C0 ⊗ C0 ⊗ C1 ⊗ D3
ABC	1	C1 ⊗ C1 ⊗ C1 ⊗ D0
ABD	3	C1 ⊗ C1 ⊗ C0 ⊗ D1
		C1 ⊗ C1 ⊗ C0 ⊗ D2
		C1 ⊗ C1 ⊗ C0 ⊗ D3
ACD	3	C1 ⊗ C0 ⊗ C1 ⊗ D1
		C1 ⊗ C0 ⊗ C1 ⊗ D2
		C1 ⊗ C0 ⊗ C1 ⊗ D3
BCD	3	C0 ⊗ C1 ⊗ C1 ⊗ D1
		C0 ⊗ C1 ⊗ C1 ⊗ D2
		C0 ⊗ C1 ⊗ C1 ⊗ D3
ABCD	3	C1 ⊗ C1 ⊗ C1 ⊗ D1
		C1 ⊗ C1 ⊗ C1 ⊗ D2
		C1 ⊗ C1 ⊗ C1 ⊗ D3
Between groups $I = 2\times 2\times 2\times 4 = 32$		

deleted, as there is no third class under the first treatment condition. The rank of the model is five.

Bases for the two separate factors, assuming simple contrasts for both, are

$$\mathbf{K}_2 = \begin{bmatrix} 1 & 1/2 \\ 1 & -1/2 \end{bmatrix} \quad (A \text{ factor})$$

$$\begin{matrix} \text{C0} & \text{C1} \end{matrix}$$

and

$$\mathbf{K}_3 = \begin{bmatrix} 1 & 2/3 & -1/3 \\ 1 & -1/3 & -1/3 \\ 1 & -1/3 & 2/3 \end{bmatrix} \quad (B \text{ factor})$$
$$\quad \text{C0} \quad \text{C1} \quad \text{C3}$$

The reparameterized model matrix for an entire six-group crossed design has C0⊗C0 for the constant term, and C1⊗C0 for the treatment contrast. Both products assume that the $\mathbf{K}_2$ vector is the prefactor.

In order to contrast levels of *B* for only the first treatment (that is, classes in treatment one), we may introduce an alternate basis for factor *A*.

$$\mathbf{I}_2 = \begin{bmatrix} 1 & 0 \\ 0 & 1 \end{bmatrix}$$
$$\text{I1} \quad \text{I2}$$

The columns of the identity matrix are symbolically represented as I1 and I2, respectively. The product I1⊗C1 is

$$[2/3 \quad -1/3 \quad -1/3 \quad 0 \quad 0 \quad 0]$$

I1⊗C1 has nonzero elements only in the first three positions, or corresponding to the classes under treatment one. I1⊗C3 cannot be estimated since C3 denotes the comparison of group 3 with group 2, and there is no class 3 under treatment one.

We may estimate two contrasts among classes under treatment two, however. These are the column products I2⊗C1, and I2⊗C3. The complete basis is

$$\mathbf{K} = \begin{bmatrix} 1 & 1/2 & 2/3 & 0 & 0 \\ 1 & 1/2 & -1/3 & 0 & 0 \\ 1 & 1/2 & -1/3 & 0 & 0 \\ 1 & -1/2 & 0 & 2/3 & -1/3 \\ 1 & -1/2 & 0 & -1/3 & -1/3 \\ 1 & -1/2 & 0 & -1/3 & 2/3 \end{bmatrix} \qquad (7.4.35)$$
$$\text{C0⊗C0} \quad \text{C1⊗C0} \quad \text{I1⊗C1} \quad \text{I2⊗C1} \quad \text{I2⊗C3}$$

The third row of **K** may be deleted, since there is no third class under the first experimental condition. The resulting matrix **K** is 5×5 and of rank five, since the product I1⊗C3 was omitted. Note especially that the omission of the effect was made by considering the *contrast* weights, and the fact that the particular contrast would involve a nonexistent group mean. Inspection of the basis vectors would not accomplish the same purpose. The basis elements do not have an easily seen correspondence to the contrasts.

We may extend the use of Kronecker products for nested designs, by considering Sample Problem 5, the programmed instruction experiment. The experiment involves a sex-by-experimental-groups fixed design, with classes randomly assigned to experimental conditions. There are 19 classes nested within the experimental group and 18 within the control group. Sex is crossed with experimental groups and classes. The measures gathered from each class are mean scores, for boys and for girls separately.

The model for the mean outcome of one sex group in one class is given by Eq. 7.1.34. For reparameterizing to contrasts, we may consider the design as if it were an incomplete 2×19×2 crossed design (conditions×classes×sex), with only 18 classes under the control condition. This will result in two empty groups, since there will be no observations for males or females in the missing class.

The contrast matrices for both two-level factors, experimental groups and sex, may be the usual 2×3 matrices. That is,

$$\mathbf{L}_2 = \begin{bmatrix} 1 & 1/2 & 1/2 \\ 0 & 1 & -1 \end{bmatrix} \begin{matrix} \text{C0} \\ \text{C1} \end{matrix}$$

In addition, we shall employ the columns of a 2×2 identity matrix to allow us to estimate between-class effects separately for each experimental condition. Since classes comprise a random effect, particular group comparisons are not of interest. Any arbitrary contrasts may be selected. For exemplary purposes, we shall use deviation contrast parameters for classes, D0, D1, . . . , D18.

Each column of the reparameterized model matrix, **K**, has 76 elements. The last two elements, corresponding to the two missing groups, may be deleted. Assuming design factors in the order: conditions–classes–sex, the symbolic representation for the constant term is C0⊗D0⊗C0. The single degrees of freedom for "experimental groups," for "sex," and for the "groups×sex interaction" are represented by C1 ⊗ D0 ⊗ C0, C0 ⊗ D0 ⊗ C1, and C1 ⊗ D0 ⊗ C1, respectively. These constitute all the fixed effects in the model.

To obtain tests or variance estimates for the "classes" and "sex×classes" random effects, we may wish to include additional columns in the basis for one or both sources of variation. There is no "experimental groups×classes" or "sex×groups×classes" interaction, since the same class is not observed under both treatment conditions. That is, classes are nested within experimental groups.

The Kronecker products for the 18 degrees of freedom, or 18 contrasts among 19 classes *within* the first experimental condition, are the products I1⊗D1⊗C0, I1⊗D2⊗C0, . . . , I1⊗D18⊗C0. Those for the 17 degrees of freedom among 18 classes within the second experimental (control) condition are I2⊗ D1 ⊗ C0, I2⊗ D2⊗ C0, . . . , I2⊗ D17⊗ C0. Together these constitute the 35 degrees of freedom for the classes-within-conditions random effect.

Group or class means should comprise the unit of analysis in most studies of class teaching methods, counseling groups, family interaction, and so on. (See Glass, 1968; Raths, 1967.) It may not be necessary to estimate variation among subjects within groups. Subjects in these instances are not responding independently of one another, nor are they responding under varying experimental conditions, times of day, settings, and so forth. Further, variation among subjects is not the appropriate error term or denominator mean square for any of the fixed effects in the model. These effects are usually of greatest concern. Thus, in the example, we will not estimate the variance among students of a particular sex–class group. We may consider instead that each cell in the design has only a single vector observation, the vector mean for the sex group within the particular class.

With no within-group variance to estimate, the only remaining source of variation in the example is the random "sex×classes within conditions" interaction. This may be obtained like the "classes" random effect—that is, by estimating specific interaction contrasts. Or the interaction sum of products may be found by subtracting variation due to all other sources from the total sum of squares and cross products. Should we choose to code the interaction effects, the Kronecker products for sex-by-classes are I1⊗D1⊗C1, I1⊗D2⊗C1, . . . , I1⊗D18⊗C1, for the experimental group, and I2⊗D1⊗C1, I2⊗D2⊗C1, . . . , I2⊗D17⊗C1, for the control. However, this approach would entail much unnecessary additional computation.

Further examples of the use of the symbolic representation and the use of the Kronecker products may be found in Bock (1965), in the examples of this chapter, and in the instructions for the use of the MULTIVARIANCE program. The symbolic conventions for the program are identical to those here, with the exception that commas (,) replace the Kronecker operator (⊗). Additionally, the program allows for deleting the letter codes from all contrasts but the first, and for generating multiple vectors from a single symbolic code.

Interpretation of Contrast Weights

The reparameterized analysis-of-variance model is $\mathbf{y.}=\mathbf{K}\boldsymbol{\theta}+\boldsymbol{\epsilon}.$, where $\boldsymbol{\theta}=\mathbf{L}\boldsymbol{\theta}^*$. Each term in the sample matrix $\hat{\boldsymbol{\theta}}$ estimates a particular contrast among the original parameters. The magnitude, direction, and standard error of each term conveys the information necessary to the interpretation of group-mean differences. That is, from the elements of $\hat{\boldsymbol{\theta}}$, we have the actual number of score points separating population means, and the direction of the difference (which group is highest, lowest). The standard error also reveals the precision of estimation, as well as the relative size of the group-mean differences.

A contrast estimate will tend to be large if the parameters differ as specified by the contrast weights, and small if there are no differences among parameters or if the differences are not in the direction specified by the contrast weights. For example, if a contrast vector is $\boldsymbol{l}' = [0 \quad 1 \quad -1/2 \quad -1/2]$, for parameters $[\boldsymbol{\theta}^*]' = [\mu \quad \alpha_1 \quad \alpha_2 \quad \alpha_3]$, then

$$\boldsymbol{l}'\boldsymbol{\theta}^* = \alpha_1 - \frac{\alpha_2+\alpha_3}{2}$$

$\boldsymbol{l}'\boldsymbol{\theta}^*$ is maximal (in absolute value) when α_1 is very different from $(\alpha_2+\alpha_3)/2$, regardless of α_2 or α_3. As the parameters depart from that pattern, $\boldsymbol{l}'\boldsymbol{\theta}^*$ will diminish, and estimates of $\boldsymbol{l}'\boldsymbol{\theta}^*$ will tend to be smaller in magnitude. Note that the sign reflects only the direction of difference—that is, whether α_1 is above or below $(\alpha_2+\alpha_3)/2$. Thus a difference of $-k$ points is as revealing as one of $+k$ points.

For any common one-way design, contrasts among parameters are also contrasts among subclass means. For example, the one-way fixed model is

$$\begin{aligned} y_{ij} &= \mu+\alpha_j+\epsilon_{ij} \\ &= \mu_j+\epsilon_{ij} \end{aligned} \qquad (7.4.36)$$

Any contrast among α_j is also a contrast among μ_j. As an example, the difference $\alpha_1-\alpha_2$ is

$$\begin{aligned}\alpha_1-\alpha_2&=(\mu_1-\mu)-(\mu_2-\mu)\\&=\mu_1-\mu_2\end{aligned}\tag{7.4.37}$$

Generally, for any J weights l_j that multiply the α_j and sum to zero,

$$\begin{aligned}\sum_j l_j\alpha_j&=\sum_j l_j(\mu_j-\mu)\\&=\sum_j l_j\mu_j-\mu\sum_j l_j\\&=\sum_j l_j\mu_j\end{aligned}\tag{7.4.38}$$

Thus each contrast may be interpreted as a set of weights applied to group means. The resulting effects are simple weighted mean differences.

Let us assume a one-way five-group design, with simple contrasts C0, C2, C3, C4, and C5. The contrast matrix is

$$\mathbf{L}=\begin{bmatrix}1 & 1/5 & 1/5 & 1/5 & 1/5 & 1/5\\0 & -1 & 1 & 0 & 0 & 0\\0 & -1 & 0 & 1 & 0 & 0\\0 & -1 & 0 & 0 & 1 & 0\\0 & -1 & 0 & 0 & 0 & 1\end{bmatrix}\begin{matrix}\text{C0}\\\text{C2}\\\text{C3}\\\text{C4}\\\text{C5}\end{matrix}\tag{7.4.39}$$

The final five *columns* of $\mathbf{L}$ multiply the α_j parameters, and are thus the weights for subclass means. If we represent the design by means of a block diagram, the design and contrasts are as shown in Figure 7.4.1. From such a diagram it is easily seen that the estimate in $\hat{\boldsymbol{\theta}}$ corresponding to C0, is the average (weighted by N_j) of the subclass means. The estimate corresponding to C1 is the simple weighted difference of the mean for group 2 and the mean for group 1. The estimate will be large if the two group means are very different, and small if their values are close. Block diagrams such as Figure 7.4.1, with any set of contrast weights, provide a guide and simple method for examining exactly the mean differences involved in any term of $\boldsymbol{\theta}$.

The technique can also be employed to clarify the meaning of single interaction contrasts. In most statistical treatises, interaction effects are not clearly

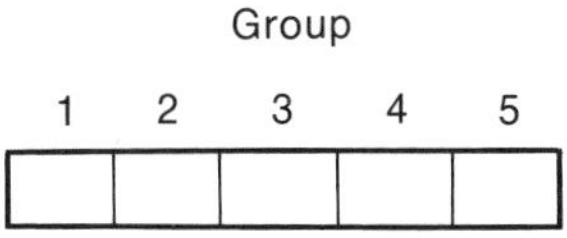

Group 1	2	3	4	5	
1/5	1/5	1/5	1/5	1/5	C0
−1	1	0	0	0	C2
−1	0	1	0	0	C3
−1	0	0	1	0	C4
−1	0	0	0	1	C5

Figure 7.4.1

explicated, and only "omnibus" tests of significance are presented. Yet interaction effects may also be understood in terms of comparisons among means, in two-way or higher-order designs.

Consider a 2×2 ($A \times B$) factorial arrangement, with effects C0 and C1 for each dimension of classification. The block diagram can be represented as in Figure 7.4.2. Here the contrast weights are written for both factors. The A main-

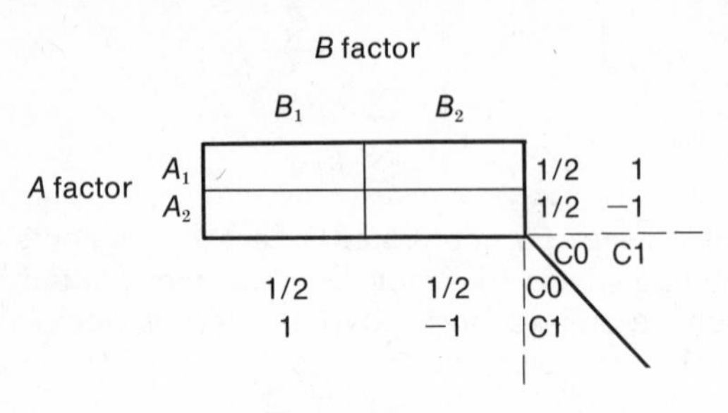

Figure 7.4.2

effect contrast is C1⊗C0 (assuming factor A is first). Multiplying the C1 weights for A, element by element, by the C0 weights for B, and inserting the products in the corresponding cells, we obtain Figure 7.4.3. The A effect is the comparison of the average of all subclasses under A_1, with the average of all under A_2. In terms of means, the contrast to be estimated is

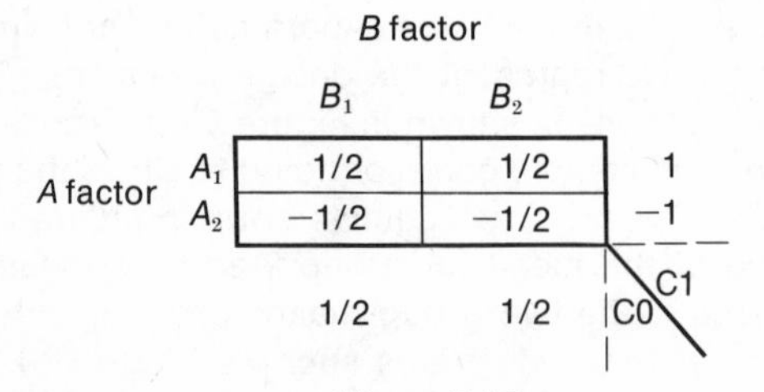

Figure 7.4.3

$$\frac{1}{2}(\mu_{11}+\mu_{12})-\frac{1}{2}(\mu_{21}+\mu_{22}) = \mu_{1\cdot}-\mu_{2\cdot}$$

Similarly, for the B main effect the weights are formed from the product C0⊗C1. These provide an estimate of

$$\frac{1}{2}(\mu_{11}+\mu_{21})-\frac{1}{2}(\mu_{12}+\mu_{22}) = \mu_{\cdot 1}-\mu_{\cdot 2}$$

Interactions may also be explicated in this manner. The interaction contrast is C1⊗C1 (see Figure 7.4.4). It can be seen that the interaction contrast estimates $(\mu_{11}-\mu_{12})-(\mu_{21}-\mu_{22})$. If the estimate is large, it indicates that the *difference* of the means of B_1 and B_2 for A_1 is not equal to the difference of the means

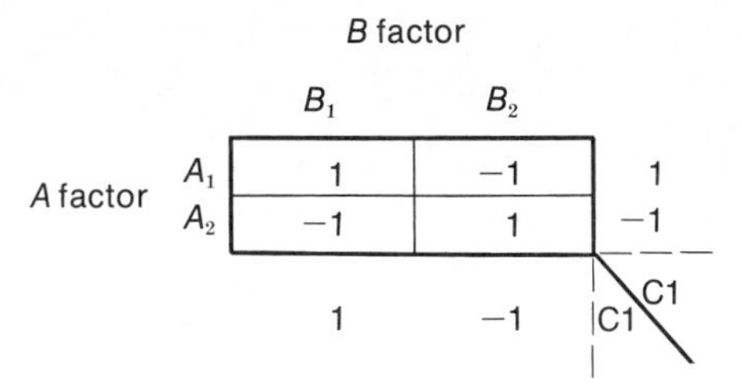

Figure 7.4.4

of B_1 and B_2 for A_2. The comparison of differences of levels of one factor across levels of a second factor is the interaction effect of the two design factors.

Interactions of factors having more than two levels may be depicted in similar fashion. Consider the $2\times3\times3$ ($A\times B\times C$) design having the effects listed in Table 7.4.1. Any one of the main-effect contrast vectors may be seen by collapsing across other factors of classification. For example, the C main effect $C0\otimes P0\otimes C1$ may be seen from a diagram of just this factor alone, as shown in Figure 7.4.5. The contrast is $1\mu_{..1}-1\mu_{..3}$. Or, in terms of individual subclasses,

$$\frac{1}{6}(\mu_{111}+\mu_{121}+\mu_{131}+\mu_{211}+\mu_{221}+\mu_{231})-\frac{1}{6}(\mu_{113}+\mu_{123}+\mu_{133}+\mu_{213}+\mu_{223}+\mu_{233})$$

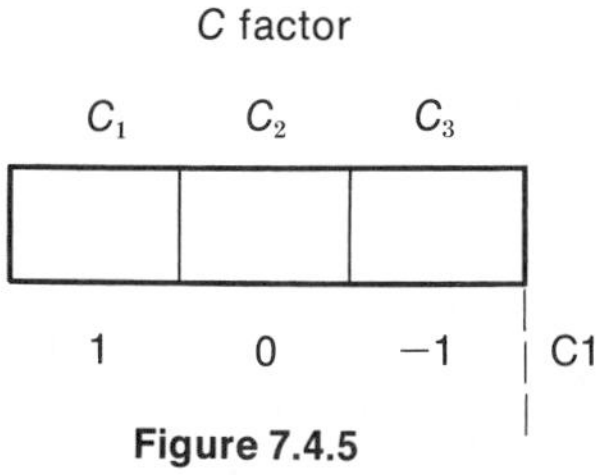

C factor

C_1 C_2 C_3

1 0 −1 | C1

Figure 7.4.5

The $A\times$linear B interaction effect, $C1\otimes P1\otimes C0$, may be diagrammed by collapsing across C, as shown in Figure 7.4.6. The weight differences of A_1 and A_2, across levels of B, form a regular pattern. The effect will estimate the extent to which the *differences* of the A_1 and A_2 means are large for B_1, smaller

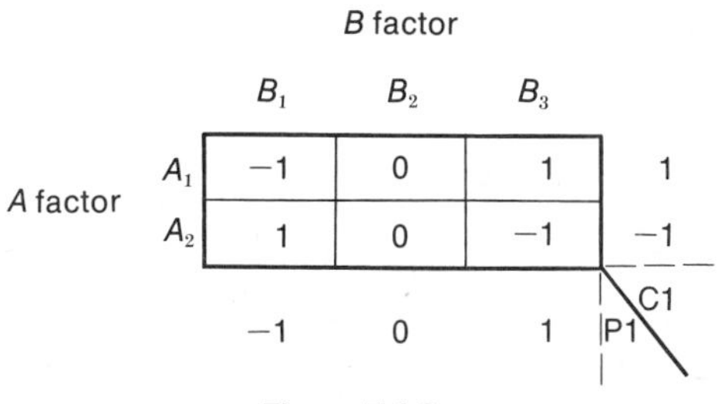

Figure 7.4.6

for B_2, and smaller still for B_3; that is, the extent to which the differences of mean A_1 and mean A_2 fall on a straight line across levels of B. Similarly, C1 ⊗ P2 ⊗ C0 provides a set of weights for determining the extent to which the differences of the A_1 and A_2 means fall in parabolic fashion across levels of B.

The $A \times C$ interaction has two degrees of freedom. The second contrast is C1 ⊗ P0 ⊗ C2, yielding weights as shown in Figure 7.4.7. This interaction contrast is a comparison of the means $\mu_{1\cdot 2}$ and $\mu_{2\cdot 3}$, with the means $\mu_{1\cdot 3}$ and $\mu_{2\cdot 2}$. The corresponding term in $\hat{\boldsymbol{\theta}}$ is an estimate of the extent to which the difference of A_1 and A_2 is larger for C_2 than for C_3.

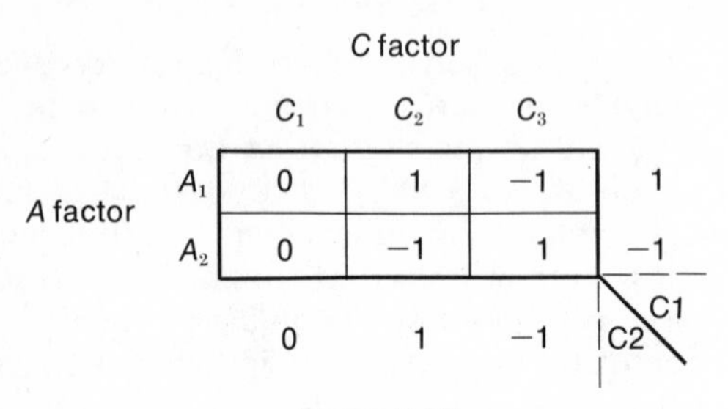

Figure 7.4.7

Any main-effect contrast may also be viewed as graphed points to be fit to sample data. For example, in a one-way three-level design with contrasts C1 and C2, the contrast weights may be depicted as in Figure 7.4.8. The weights for C1 are [1 0 −1] and for C2 are [0 1 −1]. C1 may be viewed as a "hypothesis" set of points across subclass means. To the extent that μ_1 and μ_3 differ in the manner specified by the points for C1, the corresponding estimate

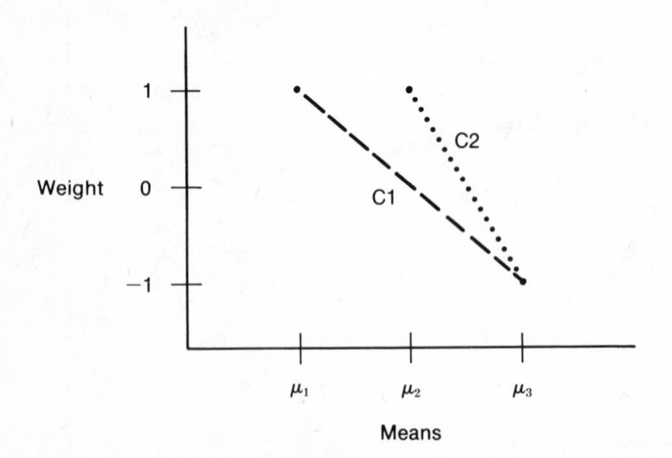

Figure 7.4.8

in $\hat{\boldsymbol{\theta}}$ will be maximal. If the two means are equal in magnitude, the estimate of $\mu_1 - \mu_3$, or fit to the line, will be reduced.

For a four-level factor with Helmert contrasts, the weight vectors for H1, H2, and H3 are $[1 \; -1/3 \; -1/3 \; -1/3]$, $[0 \; 1 \; -1/2 \; -1/2]$, and $[0 \; 0 \; 1 \; -1]$. These may be graphed as in Figure 7.4.9. The estimate of each effect can be

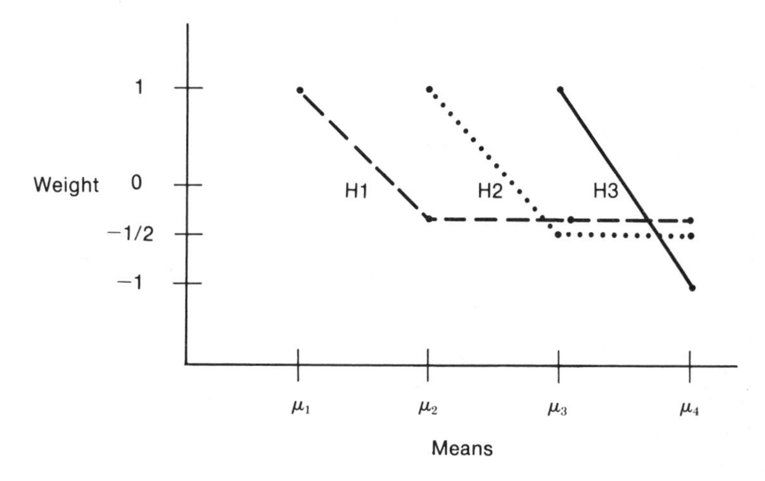

Figure 7.4.9

viewed both as a weighted comparison of means, and as reflecting the extent to which the means differ in accordance with the respective graph points. So, for example, for H2, sample means of $\hat{\mu}_2 = 8$, $\hat{\mu}_3 = 2$, and $\hat{\mu}_4 = 2$ will yield a maximum fit for the contrast with the estimated value of 6. Deviations from the hypothesized pattern may either increase or decrease the estimate, but will affect other contrasts to a greater extent. For example, if the mean for group 4 were to be $\hat{\mu}_4 = 1$ instead of $\hat{\mu}_4 = 2$, the estimate for H2 would become 6.5, while that for H3 would go from 0 to 1.

Orthogonal polynomial contrasts describe curves of successively increasing complexity. For a four-level factor, the weights P1, P2, and P3 may be graphed as in Figure 7.4.10. The estimate corresponding to P1 will be maximal when all four means are proportionately larger (or smaller), in the specified order; that is, when they fall on the P1 line, with either positive or negative slope. If μ_1 and μ_4 tend to differ from μ_2 and μ_3, while within these pairs the means are equal, the estimate for P2 will be maximal.

If, instead, the four means do not conform to any single pattern, they may be described by nonzero functions of several of the weight vectors. For example, a learning curve with time-point means of 5, 12, 16, and 17, will be reflected in both the P1 contrast (for the monotonic increasing trend) *and* the estimate for P2. The P2 reflects the parabolic trend of decreasing acceleration over time. That is, the entire curve may be viewed as a parabola resting upon the line of weights P1. This may be graphed as in Figure 7.4.11.

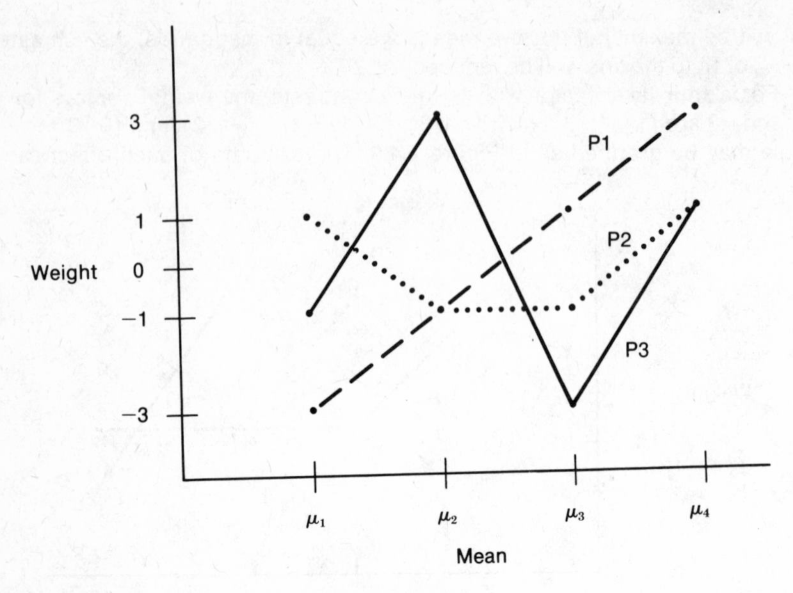

Figure 7.4.10

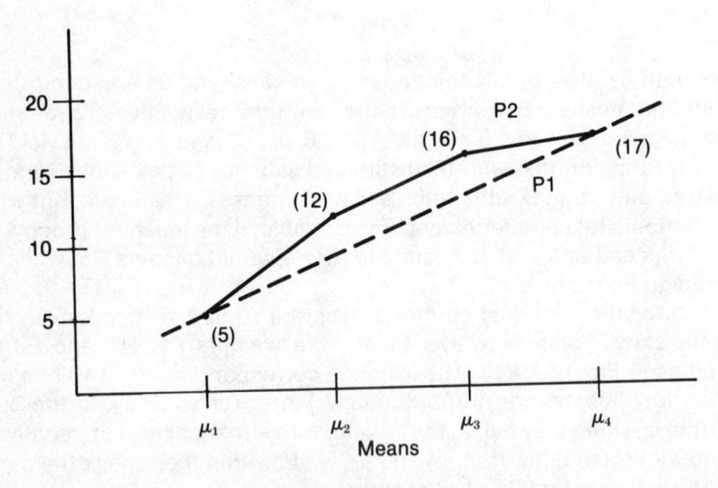

Figure 7.4.11

CHAPTER 8

Analysis of Variance: Estimation

The multivariate analysis-of-variance model is

$$\mathbf{Y.} = \mathbf{A}\boldsymbol{\Theta}^* + \mathbf{E.} \tag{8.0.1}$$

$\mathbf{Y.}$ is the $J \times p$ matrix of means for J groups of observations on p outcome variables. $\mathbf{A}$ is the $J \times m$ model matrix. $\boldsymbol{\Theta}^*$ is the $m \times p$ matrix of unknown analysis-of-variance parameters, or effects, with one column of effects for each criterion variable. $\mathbf{E.}$ is the $J \times p$ matrix of mean errors, with distribution

$$\mathbf{E.} \sim \mathcal{N}_{Jp}(\mathbf{0}, \mathbf{D}^{-1} \otimes \boldsymbol{\Sigma}) \tag{8.0.2}$$

$\mathbf{D}$ is the $J \times J$ diagonal matrix of subclass frequencies. $\boldsymbol{\Sigma}$ is the $p \times p$ matrix of variances and covariances of the criterion measures. J is the total number of groups in the design and may result from crossing two or more sampling factors; for example, in an $a \times b$ two-way model, J is the product ab. When $J - J_0$ subclasses have no observations, rows of $\mathbf{Y.}$, $\mathbf{A}$, $\mathbf{E.}$, and $\mathbf{D}$ may be eliminated corresponding to the null groups.

Unique estimates of all terms in $\boldsymbol{\Theta}^*$ cannot be obtained, since the columns of $\mathbf{A}$ are linear functions of one another. The maximum number of estimable parameters is J, the number of groups or the total degrees of freedom among means. Equation 8.0.1 can be reparameterized to full rank by defining l ($\leq J$) linear combinations of the parameters that are estimable. l is the *rank of the model for significance testing*. Since we usually define as many parameters as we have degrees of freedom, in most situations $l = J$.

The weights defining the linear combinations form the rows of an $l \times m$ contrast matrix $\mathbf{L}$, of rank l. The alternate parameters are

$$\boldsymbol{\Theta} = \mathbf{L}\boldsymbol{\Theta}^* \tag{8.0.3}$$

$\boldsymbol{\Theta}$ is $l \times p$ and contains the alternate parameters (contrasts) to be estimated. Each column of $\boldsymbol{\Theta}$ is the set of contrasts for one criterion measure.

When $\boldsymbol{\Theta}$ replaces $\boldsymbol{\Theta}^*$ in Eq. 8.0.1, a model matrix for the new parameters must also replace $\mathbf{A}$. The reparameterized model matrix, or basis for the design, is the $J \times l$ matrix $\mathbf{K}$, which satisfies $\mathbf{A} = \mathbf{KL}$. The model is reparameterized from

Eq. 8.0.1 to

$$\mathbf{Y.} = \mathbf{KL}\boldsymbol{\Theta}^* + \mathbf{E.}$$
$$= \mathbf{K}\boldsymbol{\Theta} + \mathbf{E.} \tag{8.0.4}$$

L is chosen from the hypotheses of the research. **K** is constructed from **L** by

$$\mathbf{K} = \mathbf{AL}'(\mathbf{LL}')^{-1} \tag{8.0.5}$$

Alternatively, **K** may be constructed directly from **L** or by Kronecker products (for crossed designs), as described in Section 7.4. Note only that **K** defines the independent variables for analysis of variance and, like **A**, is unaffected by the number of criterion measures.

Although the basis provides no useful interpretive information, its construction is essential for the estimation of $\boldsymbol{\Theta}$. Once the model is reparameterized to Eq. 8.0.4, its form is identical to the full-rank regression model, and may be solved by least-squares regression procedures. $\boldsymbol{\Theta}$ in Eq. 8.0.4 is identical in function to the regression weights $\mathbf{B}$. **K** is the full-rank model matrix, like the matrix of regression predictors **X**. In fact, the entire analysis of variance may be performed through regression formulas and programs. Rows of **K** are employed as values of the predictor variables and are appended to the outcome vector for each subject. The procedure is referred to as coding "dummy variables" for regression analysis. The estimated regression weights will be identically the contrast values for $\boldsymbol{\Theta}$.

8.1 POINT ESTIMATION

The least-squares estimation of $\boldsymbol{\Theta}$ follows directly from the minimization of tr $(\hat{\mathbf{E}}.'\mathbf{D}\hat{\mathbf{E}}.)$ in the sample, as presented in Section 7.2. When the model is reparameterized to full-rank form, as in Eq. 8.0.4, the normal equations are obtained from Eq. 7.2.11, with **K** and $\boldsymbol{\Theta}$ in place of **A** and $\boldsymbol{\Theta}^*$, respectively. The least-squares estimate is obtained by solving

$$(\mathbf{K}'\mathbf{DK})\hat{\boldsymbol{\Theta}} = \mathbf{K}'\mathbf{DY.} \tag{8.1.1}$$

Premultiplying both sides of Eq. 8.1.1 by $(\mathbf{K}'\mathbf{DK})^{-1}$, we obtain

$$(\mathbf{K}'\mathbf{DK})^{-1}\mathbf{K}'\mathbf{DK}\hat{\boldsymbol{\Theta}} = (\mathbf{K}'\mathbf{DK})^{-1}\mathbf{K}'\mathbf{DY.}$$

and

$$\hat{\boldsymbol{\Theta}} = (\mathbf{K}'\mathbf{DK})^{-1}\mathbf{K}'\mathbf{DY.} \tag{8.1.2}$$

$\hat{\boldsymbol{\Theta}}$ contains l *least-squares estimates of effects* for each of the criterion measures. For example, in Chapter 7 we reparameterized a one-way four-group model to simple contrasts of each group with the last (Eq. 7.3.9). Let $k = \mu + 1/4\Sigma_j\alpha_j$. The estimated $4 \times p$ matrix is:

$$\hat{\boldsymbol{\Theta}} = \begin{bmatrix} \hat{k}^{(1)} & \hat{k}^{(2)} & \cdots & \hat{k}^{(p)} \\ (\hat{\alpha}_1 - \hat{\alpha}_4)^{(1)} & (\hat{\alpha}_1 - \hat{\alpha}_4)^{(2)} & \cdots & (\hat{\alpha}_1 - \hat{\alpha}_4)^{(p)} \\ (\hat{\alpha}_2 - \hat{\alpha}_4)^{(1)} & (\hat{\alpha}_2 - \hat{\alpha}_4)^{(2)} & \cdots & (\hat{\alpha}_2 - \hat{\alpha}_4)^{(p)} \\ (\hat{\alpha}_3 - \hat{\alpha}_4)^{(1)} & (\hat{\alpha}_3 - \hat{\alpha}_4)^{(2)} & \cdots & (\hat{\alpha}_3 - \hat{\alpha}_4)^{(p)} \end{bmatrix} \tag{8.1.3}$$

In the 2×3 crossed design (Eq. 7.3.13a), with effects $k=\mu+\alpha.+\beta.$, $\alpha_1-\alpha.$, $\beta_1-\beta.$, and $\beta_2-\beta.$, the form of $\hat{\mathbf{\Theta}}$ is

$$\hat{\mathbf{\Theta}}=\begin{bmatrix} \hat{k}^{(1)} & \hat{k}^{(2)} & \cdots & \hat{k}^{(p)} \\ (\hat{\alpha}_1-\hat{\alpha}.)^{(1)} & (\hat{\alpha}_1-\hat{\alpha}.)^{(2)} & \cdots & (\hat{\alpha}_1-\hat{\alpha}.)^{(p)} \\ (\hat{\beta}_1-\hat{\beta}.)^{(1)} & (\hat{\beta}_1-\hat{\beta}.)^{(2)} & \cdots & (\hat{\beta}_1-\hat{\beta}.)^{(p)} \\ (\hat{\beta}_2-\hat{\beta}.)^{(1)} & (\hat{\beta}_2-\hat{\beta}.)^{(2)} & \cdots & (\hat{\beta}_2-\hat{\beta}.)^{(p)} \end{bmatrix} \tag{8.1.4}$$

Each column contains exactly the estimated effects for a single outcome variable; that is, it contains those that would be obtained for the single measure if it were the only criterion.

The terms of $\hat{\mathbf{\Theta}}$ are the estimated mean differences for each of the measures. Together with an estimate of their precision, they provide all the descriptive data necessary for interpreting the analysis-of-variance outcomes. The magnitude of the estimate, plus the sign, reveals the degree to which the groups differ and in which direction. The only requisite to their interpretation is knowledge of the specific contrasts estimated by each term. By comparison, "strength of effect" or proportion of explained variation measures are not generally valid in fixed-effects models.

Each row of the matrix $\hat{\mathbf{\Theta}}$ represents a single contrast or single degree of freedom between groups. There are at most as many contrasts as the total between-groups degrees of freedom J, also the total number of groups (or J_0 if some groups have no observations). For purposes of significance testing, we may test the nullity of any one contrast (one row of $\mathbf{\Theta}$), or of multiple contrasts. For example, a simultaneous test of the last three rows of $\mathbf{\Theta}$ for the one-way model (Eq. 8.1.3) is a test that all four group mean vectors are equal (H_0: $\boldsymbol{\alpha}_1=\boldsymbol{\alpha}_2=\boldsymbol{\alpha}_3=\boldsymbol{\alpha}_4$). Test of the two β-effects in the two-way model (Eq. 8.1.4) is the test that the three means for factor B are equal (H_0: $\boldsymbol{\beta}_1=\boldsymbol{\beta}_2=\boldsymbol{\beta}_3$). These simultaneous tests yield the common "omnibus" results for multiple-degree-of freedom main-effect and interaction hypotheses. Under the general model, tests can also be conducted on individual contrasts or on subsets of the contrasts among means.

Example

The estimation of terms for the two-way data of Table 3.3.2 is presented in Section 7.3. The matrices of means and frequencies are

$$\mathbf{Y.}=\begin{bmatrix} .50 & .75 \\ 3.17 & 3.67 \\ 2.20 & 2.40 \\ 3.43 & 3.57 \end{bmatrix}\begin{matrix}\text{Group 11}\\ \text{Group 12}\\ \text{Group 21}\\ \text{Group 22}\end{matrix} \qquad \mathbf{D}=\begin{bmatrix} 4 & & & (\text{Zero}) \\ & 6 & & \\ & & 5 & \\ (\text{Zero}) & & & 7 \end{bmatrix}$$
$$\qquad y_1 \quad y_2$$

The analysis-of-variance model is

$$\mathbf{y}'_{\cdot jk}=\boldsymbol{\mu}'+\boldsymbol{\alpha}'_j+\boldsymbol{\beta}'_k+\boldsymbol{\gamma}'_{jk}+\boldsymbol{\epsilon}'_{\cdot jk}$$

with $j=1, 2$ and $k=1, 2$. There are four groups of subjects; the rank of the model matrix is four. The alternate parameters are

$$\Theta = \begin{bmatrix} \mu' + \alpha'_{.} + \beta'_{.} + \gamma'_{..} \\ (\alpha_1 - \alpha_2)' + (\gamma_{1\cdot} - \gamma_{2\cdot})' \\ (\beta_1 - \beta_2)' + (\gamma_{\cdot 1} - \gamma_{\cdot 2})' \\ (\gamma_{11} - \gamma_{12})' - (\gamma_{21} - \gamma_{22})' \end{bmatrix} \begin{matrix} \text{Constant} \\ A \text{ main effect} \\ B \text{ main effect} \\ AB \text{ interaction} \end{matrix}$$

The basis is

$$\mathbf{K} = \begin{bmatrix} 1 & .5 & .5 & .25 \\ 1 & .5 & -.5 & -.25 \\ 1 & -.5 & .5 & -.25 \\ 1 & -.5 & -.5 & .25 \end{bmatrix}$$

The estimate of Θ is

$$\hat{\Theta} = (\mathbf{K}'\mathbf{D}\mathbf{K})^{-1} \quad \mathbf{K}'\mathbf{D}\mathbf{Y}.$$

$$= \begin{bmatrix} .047 & & & (\text{Symmetric}) \\ .009 & .190 & & \\ .018 & .007 & .190 & \\ .007 & .070 & .037 & .760 \end{bmatrix} \begin{bmatrix} 56.0 & 62.0 \\ -7.0 & -6.0 \\ -15.0 & -16.0 \\ -1.0 & -1.5 \end{bmatrix}$$

$$= \begin{bmatrix} 2.32 & 2.60 \\ -.98 & -.78 \\ -1.95 & -2.04 \\ -1.44 & -1.75 \end{bmatrix} \begin{matrix} \text{Constant} \\ A \text{ main effect} \\ B \text{ main effect} \\ AB \text{ interaction} \end{matrix}$$

$$\qquad y_1 \qquad y_2$$

The elements estimate effects for separate criterion measures. For example,

$$[(\hat{\alpha}_1 - \hat{\alpha}_2) + (\hat{\gamma}_{1\cdot} - \hat{\gamma}_{2\cdot})]^{(1)} = -.98 \quad (y_1)$$

$$[(\hat{\alpha}_1 - \hat{\alpha}_2) + (\hat{\gamma}_{1\cdot} - \hat{\gamma}_{2\cdot})]^{(2)} = -.78 \quad (y_2)$$

If interactions are all equal, then these are the simple $\hat{\alpha}_1 - \hat{\alpha}_2$ estimates.

Properties of $\hat{\Theta}$

The elements of $\hat{\Theta}$ are estimated under a *simultaneous* least-squares procedure. That is, they provide best estimates given the particular number and selection of effects to be estimated. The order of effects is of no consequence. However, the addition or deletion of terms will generally affect the estimates of all remaining parameters. Each parameter is estimated given, or eliminating, all others. If subclass frequencies are unequal, *or* if nonorthogonal contrasts are chosen, then the number of parameters estimated will affect all of their numerical values. Under completely orthogonal conditions (equal-N_j, orthogonal contrasts), the estimates are independent and will not change with the inclusion or removal of other independent effects.

We may examine a simple orthogonal case. Consider a one-way design with four levels, and twelve observations per subclass. With Helmert contrasts, the orthogonality is maintained and the estimation of effects through matrix operations may be expressed through scalars. If either orthogonality condition were violated, however, the demonstration would be more complex. The model matrix, contrast matrix, and basis are

$$\mathbf{A}=\begin{bmatrix}1&1&0&0&0\\1&0&1&0&0\\1&0&0&1&0\\1&0&0&0&1\end{bmatrix}$$

$$\mathbf{L}=\begin{bmatrix}1&1/4&1/4&1/4&1/4\\0&1&-1/3&-1/3&-1/3\\0&0&1&-1/2&-1/2\\0&0&0&1&-1\end{bmatrix}\begin{matrix}\text{H0}\\\text{H1}\\\text{H2}\\\text{H3}\end{matrix}$$

and

$$\mathbf{K}=\mathbf{AL}'(\mathbf{LL}')^{-1}$$

$$=\begin{bmatrix}1&3/4&0&0\\1&-1/4&2/3&0\\1&-1/4&-1/3&1/2\\1&-1/4&-1/3&-1/2\end{bmatrix}$$
$$\begin{matrix}\text{H0}&\text{H1}&\text{H2}&\text{H3}\end{matrix}$$

The diagonal matrix of subclass frequencies is

$$\mathbf{D}=\text{diag}\,(12, 12, 12, 12)$$

The estimates for one outcome measure are

$$\hat{\boldsymbol{\theta}}=(\mathbf{K}'\mathbf{DK})^{-1}\mathbf{K}'\mathbf{Dy}.$$

$$=\begin{bmatrix}48&0&0&0\\0&9&0&0\\0&0&8&0\\0&0&0&6\end{bmatrix}^{-1}\begin{bmatrix}12(y_{\cdot 1}+y_{\cdot 2}+y_{\cdot 3}+y_{\cdot 4})\\3(3y_{\cdot 1}-y_{\cdot 2}-y_{\cdot 3}-y_{\cdot 4})\\4(2y_{\cdot 2}-y_{\cdot 3}-y_{\cdot 4})\\6(y_{\cdot 3}-y_{\cdot 4})\end{bmatrix}$$

$$=\begin{bmatrix}1/4\sum_j y_{\cdot j}\\y_{\cdot 1}-1/3(y_{\cdot 2}+y_{\cdot 3}+y_{\cdot 4})\\y_{\cdot 2}-1/2(y_{\cdot 3}+y_{\cdot 4})\\y_{\cdot 3}-y_{\cdot 4}\end{bmatrix}\begin{matrix}\text{H0}\\\text{H1}\\\text{H2}\\\text{H3}\end{matrix} \tag{8.1.5}$$

Were the number of variates to be greater than one, $\hat{\boldsymbol{\Theta}}$ would have the same function in each row but a separate column for each additional measure.

The elements of $\hat{\boldsymbol{\theta}}$ are simple and obvious combinations of the observed group means. If nonorthogonal contrasts were selected, or if the elements of **D** were not equal, **K′DK** would not be diagonal, and the linear functions of the means would be significantly more complex. In particular, the diagonality of **K′DK** assures that only the single scaling constant (1/48, 1/9, 1/8, 1/6) multiplies each effect in **K′Dy.**. With nondiagonal **K′DK**, elements would also multiply **K′Dy.**, which are functions of effects *other than* the single one being estimated. Under nonorthogonal conditions, each effect is a linear function of all of the means or of all other effects as well.

Let us examine the distribution of the estimate $\hat{\boldsymbol{\Theta}}$. Since elements are linear functions of the rows of **Y.**, we shall first examine the distribution of the mean matrix. According to the assumption of Eq. 8.0.2, $\mathbf{E.} \sim \mathcal{N}(\mathbf{0}, \mathbf{D}^{-1} \otimes \boldsymbol{\Sigma})$. From this we may obtain the expectation and covariance matrix of **Y.**; the expectation is

$$\begin{aligned} \mathcal{E}(\mathbf{Y.}) &= \mathcal{E}(\mathbf{K}\boldsymbol{\Theta} + \mathbf{E.}) \\ &= \mathbf{K}\boldsymbol{\Theta} \end{aligned} \tag{8.1.6}$$

and the covariance matrix is

$$\begin{aligned} \mathcal{V}(\mathbf{Y.}) &= \mathcal{E}[\mathbf{Y.} - \mathcal{E}(\mathbf{Y.})][\mathbf{Y.} - \mathcal{E}(\mathbf{Y.})]' \\ &= \mathcal{E}[(\mathbf{Y.} - \mathbf{K}\boldsymbol{\Theta})(\mathbf{Y.} - \mathbf{K}\boldsymbol{\Theta})'] \\ &= \mathcal{E}(\mathbf{E.E.}') \\ &= \mathcal{V}(\mathbf{E.}) \\ &= \mathbf{D}^{-1} \otimes \boldsymbol{\Sigma} \end{aligned} \tag{8.1.7}$$

The mean observations $\mathbf{y}'_{.j}$, like the mean errors, are independently distributed with variance–covariance matrix $(1/N_j)\boldsymbol{\Sigma}$.

These expressions may be used to determine the properties of $\hat{\boldsymbol{\Theta}}$. $\hat{\boldsymbol{\Theta}}$ is an unbiased estimate of $\boldsymbol{\Theta}$, since

$$\begin{aligned} \mathcal{E}(\hat{\boldsymbol{\Theta}}) &= \mathcal{E}[(\mathbf{K}'\mathbf{D}\mathbf{K})^{-1}\mathbf{K}'\mathbf{D}\mathbf{Y.}] \\ &= (\mathbf{K}'\mathbf{D}\mathbf{K})^{-1}\mathbf{K}'\mathbf{D}\mathcal{E}(\mathbf{Y.}) \\ &= (\mathbf{K}'\mathbf{D}\mathbf{K})^{-1}\mathbf{K}'\mathbf{D}\mathbf{K}\boldsymbol{\Theta} \\ &= \boldsymbol{\Theta} \end{aligned} \tag{8.1.8}$$

The variance–covariance matrix of the elements of $\hat{\boldsymbol{\Theta}}$ is

$$\begin{aligned} \mathcal{V}(\hat{\boldsymbol{\Theta}}) &= \mathcal{V}[(\mathbf{K}'\mathbf{D}\mathbf{K})^{-1}\mathbf{K}'\mathbf{D}\mathbf{Y.}] \\ &= (\mathbf{K}'\mathbf{D}\mathbf{K})^{-1}\mathbf{K}'\mathbf{D}\mathcal{V}(\mathbf{Y.})\mathbf{D}'\mathbf{K}(\mathbf{K}'\mathbf{D}\mathbf{K})^{-1} \\ &= (\mathbf{K}'\mathbf{D}\mathbf{K})^{-1}\mathbf{K}'\mathbf{D}[\mathbf{D}^{-1} \otimes \boldsymbol{\Sigma}]\mathbf{D}'\mathbf{K}(\mathbf{K}'\mathbf{D}\mathbf{K})^{-1} \\ &= (\mathbf{K}'\mathbf{D}\mathbf{K})^{-1} \otimes \boldsymbol{\Sigma} \\ &= \mathbf{G} \otimes \boldsymbol{\Sigma} \end{aligned} \tag{8.1.9}$$

The covariance matrix of the ith *row* of $\hat{\boldsymbol{\Theta}}$ (that is, $\hat{\boldsymbol{\theta}}'_i$) is the $p \times p$ matrix $[g_{ii}\boldsymbol{\Sigma}]$. $[g_{ii}]$ is the ii diagonal element of $(\mathbf{K}'\mathbf{D}\mathbf{K})^{-1}$. That is, estimates of a single contrast for different variables are interdependent and to an extent proportional to the covariance of the respective measures. Generally, mean contrasts for multiple variables are not independent, and multivariate test criteria should be employed.

The variance–covariance matrix of the *k*th *column* of elements in $\hat{\boldsymbol{\Theta}}$ (that is, $\hat{\boldsymbol{\theta}}_k$) is

$$\mathscr{V}(\hat{\boldsymbol{\theta}}_k) = \sigma_k^2(\mathbf{K}'\mathbf{D}\mathbf{K})^{-1} \tag{8.1.10}$$

σ_k^2 is the variance of criterion measure y_k. The diagonal elements of Eq. 8.1.10 are the variances of the l contrasts for one criterion measure; the square roots are the standard errors.

$$\sigma_{\hat{\theta}_{ik}} = \sigma_k\sqrt{g_{ii}} \tag{8.1.11}$$

where $\hat{\theta}_{ik}$ is the estimate of contrast i for criterion measure y_k.

G or $(\mathbf{K}'\mathbf{D}\mathbf{K})^{-1}$ may be nondiagonal (nonzero covariances), indicating that the contrasts in $\hat{\boldsymbol{\theta}}_k$ are not independent. That is in general mean contrasts, even for a single criterion, are interdependent. This complicates significance testing, since tests on various effects are also not independent.

If **G** is not diagonal, the terms in $\hat{\boldsymbol{\Theta}}$ change if contrasts are added or deleted or if the selection of contrasts is altered. Nondiagonal **G** may result from one or both of two conditions: nonorthogonal contrasts in **L** or unequal elements in **D** (that is, unequal subclass frequencies). Contrasts may be rendered independent by selecting only orthogonal contrasts, and by restricting cell frequencies to being equal. This situation can be solved with scalar algebra, as presented in most texts. Solutions under the general linear model, while more complex, do not place the stringent requirements upon research design.

If rows of the contrast matrix **L** are orthogonal, the orthogonality of $\mathbf{K} = \mathbf{A}\mathbf{L}'(\mathbf{L}\mathbf{L}')^{-1}$ is maintained. $\mathbf{L}\mathbf{L}'$ is diagonal, and multiplication by $(\mathbf{L}\mathbf{L}')^{-1}$ constitutes only a rescaling of the contrast vectors. Since construction of **K** involves appending a unit vector to a subset of the scaled contrast vectors (see Eq. 7.4.24), **K** is likewise orthogonal. Contrariwise, the nonorthogonality of **L** will in general destroy the orthogonality of the basis.

If elements of **D** are not equal, **G** will generally be nondiagonal, even with orthogonal **K**. For example, assume a two-group design with two observations per group. Then

$$\mathbf{K} = \begin{bmatrix} 1 & 1 \\ 1 & -1 \end{bmatrix} \quad \text{and} \quad \mathbf{D} = \begin{bmatrix} 2 & 0 \\ 0 & 2 \end{bmatrix}$$

The variance–covariance matrix of the estimated grand mean and mean difference has

$$(\mathbf{K}'\mathbf{D}\mathbf{K}) = \begin{bmatrix} 4 & 0 \\ 0 & 4 \end{bmatrix}$$

and

$$\sigma^2(\mathbf{K}'\mathbf{D}\mathbf{K})^{-1} = \sigma^2 \begin{bmatrix} 1/4 & 0 \\ 0 & 1/4 \end{bmatrix}$$

With equal N_j, the estimated constant term and mean difference are uncorrelated.

If we introduce a single additional observation into the second group,

$$\mathbf{D} = \begin{bmatrix} 2 & 0 \\ 0 & 3 \end{bmatrix}$$

Then

$$(\mathbf{K'DK}) = \begin{bmatrix} 5 & -1 \\ -1 & 5 \end{bmatrix}$$

and

$$\sigma^2(\mathbf{K'DK})^{-1} = \frac{\sigma^2}{24}\begin{bmatrix} 5 & 1 \\ 1 & 5 \end{bmatrix}$$

The two effects are interdependent, with covariance $\sigma^2/24$.

The reason for the nonzero covariance can be more plainly seen if we write basis vectors for all observations, rather than only for means. In the two-group example with $N_1 = N_2 = 2$, the basis vectors are orthogonal. That is,

$$\mathbf{K} = \begin{bmatrix} 1 & 1 \\ 1 & 1 \\ 1 & -1 \\ 1 & -1 \end{bmatrix}$$

With an additional observation in group two, each vector takes on an additional element, to destroy the orthogonality. That is,

$$\mathbf{K} = \begin{bmatrix} 1 & 1 \\ 1 & 1 \\ 1 & -1 \\ 1 & -1 \\ 1 & -1 \end{bmatrix}$$

The inner product is -1.

Since one or both sources of nonorthogonality may be present in a particular research design, a general orthogonal solution is necessary. Then the source of nonorthogonality is of little consequence. The need to discard observations or to restrict contrasts to those that are orthogonal is obviated. We will perform tests of significance on elements of $\boldsymbol{\Theta}$ by transforming $\hat{\boldsymbol{\Theta}}$ to a matrix with independent rows. In a completely orthogonal arrangement (equal N_j, orthogonal contrasts), the rows of $\hat{\boldsymbol{\Theta}}$ are independent, and the transformation involves only a simple rescaling.

The matrix $\mathbf{G} = (\mathbf{K'DK})^{-1}$ in Eq. 8.1.10 is the matrix of *variance–covariance factors* among the estimates. Its elements are proportional to the variances and covariances by the constant factor σ_k^2. $\mathbf{G}$ or $\sigma_k^2\mathbf{G}$ may be reduced to correlational form in the usual manner. Let $\mathbf{D}_G = \text{diag}\,(\mathbf{G})$, then

$$\mathbf{R}_G = \mathbf{D}_G^{-1/2}\mathbf{G}\mathbf{D}_G^{-1/2} \tag{8.1.12}$$

$\mathbf{R}_G$ are the *correlations among the estimates* for any one criterion measure. The correlations provide a standardized measure of the extent to which the contrasts are interdependent and would change with the addition or deletion of other effects. That is, the elements are measures of the degree of nonorthogonality of the design.

Example

The variance–covariance factors among the estimates for the data of Table 3.3.2 are

$$\mathbf{G}=(\mathbf{K}'\mathbf{D}\mathbf{K})^{-1}=\begin{bmatrix} .047 & & & \text{(Symmetric)} \\ .009 & .190 & & \\ .018 & .007 & .190 & \\ .007 & .070 & .037 & .760 \end{bmatrix}\begin{matrix}\text{Constant}\\ A \text{ main effect}\\ B \text{ main effect}\\ AB \text{ interaction}\end{matrix}$$

$$\begin{matrix}\text{Constant} & A & B & AB\end{matrix}$$

The variance–covariance matrix is $(\mathbf{K}'\mathbf{D}\mathbf{K})^{-1}$ times the constant multiplier σ_k^2 for variable y_k alone. When σ_k^2 is estimated, we may estimate the covariance matrix and the precision of $\hat{\mathbf{\Theta}}$.

The correlations among the estimates are the same with or without σ_k^2. The constant multiplier drops out in the computations. The diagonal matrix of variances is

$$\mathbf{D}_G=\text{diag}\,(.047,\quad .190,\quad .190,\quad .760)$$

The correlations are

$$\mathbf{R}_G=\begin{bmatrix} 1.000 & & & \text{(Symmetric)} \\ .097 & 1.000 & & \\ .185 & .034 & 1.000 & \\ .034 & .185 & .097 & 1.000 \end{bmatrix}\begin{matrix}\text{Constant}\\ A \text{ main effect}\\ B \text{ main effect}\\ AB \text{ interaction}\end{matrix}$$

$$\begin{matrix}\text{Constant} & A & B & AB\end{matrix}$$

The inequality among subclass frequencies has introduced small positive correlations among all the estimates. If the interactions were not estimated, we would expect the constant estimate to change slightly, the *B* contrast to a somewhat larger extent, and the *A* contrast still more. Nevertheless, none of the intercorrelations is particularly large.

Conditions for the Estimation of $\mathbf{\Theta}$

The conditions for estimating $\mathbf{\Theta}$ depend upon the conditions for the selection of contrasts in Section 7.3. In order for $\mathbf{\Theta}$ to be estimable by Eq. 8.1.2, the product $\mathbf{K}'\mathbf{D}\mathbf{K}$ must be of full rank so that it may be inverted. $\mathbf{K}$ is $J\times I$ and the gramian $\mathbf{K}'\mathbf{D}\mathbf{K}$ is $I\times I$. The first condition is that I cannot exceed J. The maximum number of estimable contrasts, including one for the constant term, is the number of groups of observations, or the total degrees of freedom among means. *Fewer* than J effects may be estimated.

Further, no column of $\mathbf{K}$ can be exactly a linear function of other columns. This condition restricts the contrasts estimated to those values not completely determined by others in $\mathbf{\Theta}$. For example, having estimated $\alpha_1-\alpha_2$ and $\alpha_2-\alpha_3$, we could not include a vector for $\alpha_1-\alpha_3$ in the contrast matrix. The corresponding vector of **K** would be a simple function of the preceding two vectors. Contrasts need not be orthogonal, however.

If an element of **D** is zero, then the rank of $(\mathbf{K}'\mathbf{D}\mathbf{K})$ will be restricted further. One between-group degree of freedom is "lost" for each empty subclass in the sampling design. If the complete design has J groups of observations but only J_0 $(<J)$ groups have one or more subjects, the maximum degrees of freedom among means is restricted to J_0. The particular contrasts which may not be estimated are determined by examination of the sampling design (see Sample Problem 3, the dental calculus study).

$\hat{\mathbf{\Theta}}$ is not restricted in any manner by the correlations among criterion measures. Each column of $\hat{\mathbf{\Theta}}$ comprises a single set of univariate estimates for the corresponding y-variate, and does not depend upon other columns.

8.2 ESTIMATING DISPERSIONS

The variance–covariance matrix of $\hat{\mathbf{\Theta}}$ is given by Eq. 8.1.9. That is,

$$\begin{aligned}\mathscr{V}(\hat{\mathbf{\Theta}}) &= (\mathbf{K}'\mathbf{D}\mathbf{K})^{-1} \otimes \mathbf{\Sigma} \\ &= \mathbf{G} \otimes \mathbf{\Sigma}\end{aligned} \tag{8.2.1}$$

For any one criterion measure, we may extract a diagonal element of $\mathbf{\Sigma}$ to obtain the variance–covariance matrix of the corresponding column of $\hat{\mathbf{\Theta}}$. For y_k,

$$\mathscr{V}(\hat{\boldsymbol{\theta}}_k) = \sigma_k{}^2(\mathbf{K}'\mathbf{D}\mathbf{K})^{-1} \tag{8.2.2}$$

$\mathbf{K}'\mathbf{D}\mathbf{K}$ is determined by the analysis-of-variance model. $\mathbf{\Sigma}$ may be estimated from sample data. The estimate is used to describe the intercorrelations among the criterion measures and to provide interval estimates and tests on elements or sections of $\mathbf{\Theta}$.

The estimate of the $p \times p$ covariance matrix is provided by the sums of squares and cross products of the residuals, or discrepancies of the observations and the model. The total sum of products of the observed scores is

$$\begin{aligned}\mathbf{S}_T &= \textstyle\sum_j \sum_i \mathbf{y}_{ij}\mathbf{y}_{ij}' \\ &= \mathbf{Y}'\mathbf{Y}\end{aligned} \tag{8.2.3}$$

where **Y** is the $N \times p$ data matrix; $\mathbf{S}_T$ has N degrees of freedom.

The sum of products due to the model (between groups) is

$$\begin{aligned}\mathbf{S}_B &= (\mathbf{K}\hat{\mathbf{\Theta}})'\mathbf{D}\mathbf{K}\hat{\mathbf{\Theta}} \\ &= \hat{\mathbf{\Theta}}'\mathbf{K}'\mathbf{D}\mathbf{K}\hat{\mathbf{\Theta}}\end{aligned} \tag{8.2.4}$$

The center matrix **D** is necessary since we have defined **K** as the basis for the means, while the total and residual sums of products include variation among subjects. That is, each mean is weighted by the number of subjects it represents. $\mathbf{S}_B$ is the weighted sum of products of l linear functions of the observations and has l degrees of freedom.

The residual sum of products is the difference

$$\mathbf{S}_E = \mathbf{S}_T - \mathbf{S}_B$$
$$= \mathbf{Y}'\mathbf{Y} - \hat{\boldsymbol{\Theta}}'\mathbf{K}'\mathbf{D}\mathbf{K}\hat{\boldsymbol{\Theta}} \quad (8.2.5)$$

$\mathbf{S}_E$ is the *error sum of squares and cross products*. The *error degrees of freedom* are $n_e = N - l$.

The unbiased maximum likelihood estimate of the variance–covariance matrix is

$$\hat{\boldsymbol{\Sigma}} = \frac{1}{n_e}\mathbf{S}_E$$
$$= \frac{1}{N-l}(\mathbf{Y}'\mathbf{Y} - \hat{\boldsymbol{\Theta}}'\mathbf{K}'\mathbf{D}\mathbf{K}\hat{\boldsymbol{\Theta}}) \quad (8.2.6)$$

Each diagonal element of $\hat{\boldsymbol{\Sigma}}$ is $\hat{\sigma}_k^2$, the sample variance of one criterion measure, given the model parameters. Each off-diagonal element is the sample covariance of two outcome measures.

In the most common situation, l is equal to J and $\hat{\boldsymbol{\Sigma}}$ has a simpler form. This occurs whenever all between-group degrees of freedom are specified in the model (the maximum J or J_0 if there are empty groups). In this case all main effect and interactions are included in $\boldsymbol{\Theta}$. The *only* residual variation is then the within-group sum of squares and cross products, or the sum of products of the individual scores deviated from their separate subclass means.

Algebraically, when $l = J$ the basis is square and can itself be inverted. Then

$$\mathbf{S}_B = \hat{\boldsymbol{\Theta}}'\mathbf{K}'\mathbf{D}\mathbf{K}\hat{\boldsymbol{\Theta}}$$
$$= \mathbf{Y}_{.}'\mathbf{D}\mathbf{K}(\mathbf{K}'\mathbf{D}\mathbf{K})^{-1}\mathbf{K}'\mathbf{D}\mathbf{K}(\mathbf{K}'\mathbf{D}\mathbf{K})^{-1}\mathbf{K}'\mathbf{D}\mathbf{Y}_{.}$$
$$= \mathbf{Y}_{.}'\mathbf{D}\mathbf{K}\mathbf{K}^{-1}\mathbf{D}^{-1}(\mathbf{K}')^{-1}\mathbf{K}'\mathbf{D}\mathbf{Y}_{.}$$
$$= \mathbf{Y}_{.}'\mathbf{D}\mathbf{Y}_{.}$$

and

$$\mathbf{S}_E = \mathbf{Y}'\mathbf{Y} - \mathbf{Y}_{.}'\mathbf{D}\mathbf{Y}_{.} \quad (8.2.7)$$

In terms of data vectors, $\mathbf{S}_E$ is

$$\mathbf{S}_E = \sum_{j=1}^{J}\left[\sum_{i=1}^{N_j}\mathbf{y}_{ij}\mathbf{y}_{ij}'\right] - \sum_{j=1}^{J}N_j\mathbf{y}_{\cdot j}\mathbf{y}_{\cdot j}'$$
$$= \sum_{j=1}^{J}\left[\sum_{i=1}^{N_j}\mathbf{y}_{ij}\mathbf{y}_{ij}' - N_j\mathbf{y}_{\cdot j}\mathbf{y}_{\cdot j}'\right]$$
$$= \sum_{j=1}^{J}\sum_{i=1}^{N_j}(\mathbf{y}_{ij} - \mathbf{y}_{\cdot j})(\mathbf{y}_{ij} - \mathbf{y}_{\cdot j})' \quad (8.2.7a)$$

where $\mathbf{y}_{ij}$ is the $p \times 1$ vector observation for subject i in subclass j and $\mathbf{y}_{\cdot j}$ is the vector mean for subclass j. That is,

$$\mathbf{y}_{\cdot j} = \frac{1}{N_j}\Sigma_i\,\mathbf{y}_{ij}$$

When $\mathbf{S}_E$ has the form of Eq. 8.2.7, it is identically the sum of J sum-of-products matrices for the separate groups, each adjusted to the subclass mean vector. These are pooled to obtain the *common within-group sum of products*, under the assumption that $\boldsymbol{\Sigma}$ is the same for all subgroups of observations. Let $\mathbf{S}_{w_j}$ be the sum of products of mean deviations for subclass j. That is,

$$\mathbf{S}_{w_j} = \sum_{i=1}^{N_j} (\mathbf{y}_{ij} - \mathbf{y}_{\cdot j})(\mathbf{y}_{ij} - \mathbf{y}_{\cdot j})' \tag{8.2.8}$$

Then Eq. 8.2.7a becomes

$$\mathbf{S}_E = \sum_{j=1}^{J} \mathbf{S}_{w_j} = \mathbf{S}_W \tag{8.2.9}$$

The degrees of freedom for $\mathbf{S}_E$ are the within-group degrees of freedom,

$$\sum_{j=1}^{J} (N_j - 1) = N - J$$

J_0 replaces J if there are empty subclasses.

Whenever there are real or hypothesized differences among the mean vectors $\mathbf{y}_{\cdot j}$, the within-group matrices $\mathbf{S}_{w_j}$ and $\mathbf{S}_E$ provide the only estimates of random variation that are not confounded with fixed mean differences. The diagonal elements of $\mathbf{S}_E$ are the usual analysis-of-variance within-group sums of squares for each of the p measures.

The within-group variance–covariance matrix is

$$\hat{\boldsymbol{\Sigma}} = \frac{1}{N-J} \mathbf{S}_E \tag{8.2.10}$$

The variances or diagonal elements of $\hat{\boldsymbol{\Sigma}}$ are the within-group mean squares for the p outcome measures. $\hat{\boldsymbol{\Sigma}}$ may be reduced to correlational form in the usual manner. This provides correlations among the y-variables which are not inflated, or deflated, by mean differences (see Section 3.3).

Regardless of the form of $\hat{\boldsymbol{\Sigma}}$, the population correlations among the criteria may be estimated from random variation about the model. Let $\boldsymbol{\Delta}$ be a diagonal matrix of only the variances from $\boldsymbol{\Sigma}$. That is,

$$\begin{aligned} \boldsymbol{\Delta} &= \text{diag}\,(\boldsymbol{\Sigma}) \\ &= \text{diag}\,(\sigma_1^2, \sigma_2^2, \ldots, \sigma_p^2) \end{aligned} \tag{8.2.11}$$

The standard deviations are

$$\boldsymbol{\Delta}^{1/2} = \text{diag}\,(\sigma_1, \sigma_2, \ldots, \sigma_p) \tag{8.2.11a}$$

The $p \times p$ matrix of correlations among the criteria are

$$\mathcal{R} = \boldsymbol{\Delta}^{-1/2} \boldsymbol{\Sigma} \boldsymbol{\Delta}^{-1/2} \tag{8.2.12}$$

Substituting $\hat{\boldsymbol{\Sigma}}$ for $\boldsymbol{\Sigma}$ in Eqs. 8.2.11 and 8.2.12 yields the sample matrix $\hat{\mathcal{R}}$. A correction for bias in $\hat{\mathcal{R}}$ is given by Olkin (1966). If the sample consists of subgroups with different vector means, the within-group correlations should be interpreted instead of correlations obtained by treating all subjects as members of a single population.

In the univariate case, $\hat{\boldsymbol{\Sigma}}$ is the scalar residual variance of the outcome measure. That is, when $p=1$,

$$\hat{\boldsymbol{\Sigma}}=\hat{\sigma}^2$$
$$=\frac{1}{N-l}(\mathbf{y}'\mathbf{y}-\hat{\boldsymbol{\theta}}'\mathbf{K}'\mathbf{D}\mathbf{K}\hat{\boldsymbol{\theta}}) \tag{8.2.13}$$

where $\mathbf{y}$ is the $N\times 1$ observational vector and $\hat{\boldsymbol{\theta}}$ is the single column of estimated parameters. Further, if $l=J$, then

$$\hat{\sigma}^2=\frac{1}{N-J}\sum_j\sum_i(y_{ij}-y_{\cdot j})^2 \tag{8.2.14}$$

This is the usual within-group variance or mean square, and comprises one diagonal element of $\boldsymbol{\Sigma}$ in Eq. 8.2.10.

Example

The total sum of cross products for the 22 observations of Table 3.3.2 is given in Section 3.3 as

$$\mathbf{S}_T=\begin{bmatrix}184 & 195\\ 195 & 212\end{bmatrix}\begin{matrix}y_1\\ y_2\end{matrix}$$
$$\begin{matrix}y_1 & y_2\end{matrix}$$

In the two-way analysis-of-variance model, we have $l=J=4$. $\mathbf{K}$ is square and

$$\mathbf{S}_B=\mathbf{Y}_{\cdot}'\mathbf{D}\mathbf{Y}_{\cdot}=\begin{bmatrix}167.65 & 183.18\\ 183.18 & 201.00\end{bmatrix}\begin{matrix}y_1\\ y_2\end{matrix}$$
$$\begin{matrix}y_1 & y_2\end{matrix}$$

$\mathbf{S}_E$ is the within-group sum of products:

$$\mathbf{S}_E=\mathbf{S}_W=\begin{bmatrix}16.35 & 11.72\\ 11.72 & 11.00\end{bmatrix}\begin{matrix}y_1\\ y_2\end{matrix}$$
$$\begin{matrix}y_1 & y_2\end{matrix}$$

The error degrees of freedom are $n_e=22-4=18$. The error covariance matrix is

$$\hat{\boldsymbol{\Sigma}}=\frac{1}{18}\mathbf{S}_E=\begin{bmatrix}.91 & .65\\ .65 & .61\end{bmatrix}\begin{matrix}y_1\\ y_2\end{matrix}$$
$$\begin{matrix}y_1 & y_2\end{matrix}$$

The within-group mean squares for y_1 and y_2 are .91 and .61, respectively. The correlation of y_1 and y_2 is

$$\hat{\rho}_{12}=\frac{.65}{\sqrt{.91(.61)}}=.85$$

The two variates have a high positive association.

Given the estimate of Σ, we may substitute in Eq. 8.2.2 to obtain the standard errors of $\hat{\Theta}$. The variances of the elements in one column of $\hat{\Theta}$ are the diagonal elements of Eq. 8.2.2. For contrast *i* in column *k*, the sample variance of the single estimate is

$$\hat{\sigma}_{\hat{\theta}_{ik}}{}^2 = \hat{\sigma}_k{}^2 g_{ii} \qquad (8.2.15)$$

where g_{ii} is the *ii* diagonal element of $\mathbf{G} = (\mathbf{K}'\mathbf{D}\mathbf{K})^{-1}$. $\hat{\sigma}_k{}^2$ is the variance of y_k, from $\hat{\Sigma}$.

The standard error of $\hat{\theta}_{ik}$ is

$$\hat{\sigma}_{\hat{\theta}_{ik}} = \hat{\sigma}_k \sqrt{g_{ii}} \qquad (8.2.16)$$

The standard errors may be expressed as an $l \times p$ matrix, having the sample standard error of $\hat{\theta}_{ik}$ in the *ik* position. Let **d** be a *p*-element vector of standard deviations from $\hat{\Sigma}$. That is,

$$\mathbf{d}' = [\hat{\sigma}_1 \ \hat{\sigma}_2 \ \cdots \ \hat{\sigma}_p] \qquad (8.2.17)$$

Define **g** as the *l*-element vector of square roots of the diagonal elements of $\mathbf{G} = (\mathbf{K}'\mathbf{D}\mathbf{K})^{-1}$. That is,

$$\mathbf{g}' = [\sqrt{g_{11}} \ \sqrt{g_{22}} \ \cdots \ \sqrt{g_{ll}}]. \qquad (8.2.18)$$

The matrix of sample standard errors is

$$\mathbf{H} = \mathbf{g}\mathbf{d}' = \begin{bmatrix} \mathbf{h}'_1 \\ \mathbf{h}'_2 \\ \vdots \\ \mathbf{h}'_l \end{bmatrix} \qquad (8.2.19)$$

The *i*th row of **H**, $\mathbf{h}'_i$, contains the standard errors for the *p* elements of the same row of $\hat{\Theta}$. That is,

$$\mathbf{h}'_i = [\hat{\sigma}_{\hat{\theta}_{i1}} \ \hat{\sigma}_{\hat{\theta}_{i2}} \ \cdots \ \hat{\sigma}_{\hat{\theta}_{ip}}]$$

The elements of **H** may be employed in the construction of confidence intervals about the elements of Θ. Under the assumption of normally distributed **Y**., $[\hat{\theta}_{ik} - \theta_{ik}]/\hat{\sigma}_{\hat{\theta}_{ik}}$ follows a *t* distribution with $N-l$ degrees of freedom. The $1-\alpha$ interval estimate of θ_{ik} is

$$\hat{\theta}_{ik} - ch_{ik} \leq \theta_{ik} \leq \hat{\theta}_{ik} + ch_{ik} \qquad (8.2.20)$$

or

$$\theta_{ik}\text{:} \ \hat{\theta}_{ik} \pm ch_{ik} \qquad (8.2.20a)$$

where $c = t_{N-l,\alpha/2}$ is the upper $100\alpha/2$ percentage point of *t* with $N-l$ degrees of freedom, and h_{ik} is the standard error $\hat{\sigma}_{\hat{\theta}_{ik}}$.

Intervals may also be drawn on entire rows of Θ, in the form of *p* simultaneous intervals for one effect or contrast, on all measures. Let $\boldsymbol{\theta}'_i$ be the $(1 \times p)$ *i*th row of Θ and $\hat{\boldsymbol{\theta}}'_i$ be the corresponding estimate. The *p* intervals in vector form, are obtained by adding and subtracting a multiple of $\mathbf{h}'_i$ from the estimate $\hat{\boldsymbol{\theta}}'_i$.

$$\boldsymbol{\theta}'_i\text{: } \hat{\boldsymbol{\theta}}'_i \pm k\mathbf{h}'_i \tag{8.2.21}$$

where

$$k=\sqrt{\frac{(N-I)p}{N-I-p+1}F_{p,N-I-p+1,\alpha}} \tag{8.2.21a}$$

k is a function of the 100α upper percentage point of the F distribution, with p and $N-I-p+1$ degrees of freedom. The multiplier k assures that the confidence level for every one of the p separate intervals in the vector is *at least* $1-\alpha$. It can be easily seen that when $p=1$, the interval is the same as that specified by expression 8.2.20. With an increased number of variables k also increases, yielding wider intervals for each measure. That is, the intervals for individual variates must be wider than Eq. 8.2.20 to assure $1-\alpha$ confidence for the entire set.

Intervals on rows of $\boldsymbol{\Theta}$ are a special case of intervals on linear combinations of the rows. Linear combinations of rows of $\boldsymbol{\Theta}$ are $\mathbf{v}'\boldsymbol{\Theta}$, with $\mathbf{v}$ being any arbitrary weight vector. In expression 8.2.21, $\mathbf{v}$ is a column of an identity matrix, and $\mathbf{v}'\boldsymbol{\Theta} = \boldsymbol{\theta}'_i$. If other linear compounds are of interest, it is necessary to obtain the covariance matrix of the composite, $\mathbf{v}'\hat{\boldsymbol{\Theta}}$.

$$\begin{aligned}\mathscr{V}(\mathbf{v}'\hat{\boldsymbol{\Theta}}) &= \mathbf{v}'\mathscr{V}(\hat{\boldsymbol{\Theta}})\mathbf{v} \\ &= \mathbf{v}'[(\mathbf{K}'\mathbf{D}\mathbf{K})^{-1}\otimes \boldsymbol{\Sigma}]\mathbf{v} \\ &= [\mathbf{v}'(\mathbf{K}'\mathbf{D}\mathbf{K})^{-1}\mathbf{v}]\boldsymbol{\Sigma} \\ &= w\boldsymbol{\Sigma}\end{aligned} \tag{8.2.22}$$

Substituting the sample value for $\boldsymbol{\Sigma}$, the estimated variances of the linear composite for each of the p measures are the diagonal elements of $w\hat{\boldsymbol{\Sigma}}$. The standard errors may be put in vector form. Express the square roots of the diagonal of $\hat{\boldsymbol{\Sigma}}$ as a vector $\mathbf{d}'$, as in Eq. 8.2.17. The standard errors comprise the $1\times p$ vector,

$$\mathbf{h}' = \sqrt{w}\,\mathbf{d}' \tag{8.2.23}$$

The $1-\alpha$ interval estimate of $\mathbf{v}'\boldsymbol{\Theta}$ is

$$\mathbf{v}'\boldsymbol{\Theta}\text{: } \mathbf{v}'\hat{\boldsymbol{\Theta}} \pm k\mathbf{h}' \tag{8.2.24}$$

where k is defined by Eq. 8.2.21a. The confidence level is *at least* $1-\alpha$ for each of the p intervals in the vector. This procedure for interval estimation directly parallels the procedure for regression, which is presented in Section 4.4.

Example

The estimate $\hat{\boldsymbol{\Theta}}$ for the 2×2 bivariate crossed design is given in Section 8.1. The variance–covariance factors among the estimates are

$$\mathbf{G} = \begin{bmatrix} .047 & & \text{(Symmetric)} & \\ .009 & .190 & & \\ .018 & .007 & .190 & \\ .007 & .070 & .037 & .760 \end{bmatrix} \begin{matrix} \text{Constant} \\ A \text{ main effect} \\ B \text{ main effect} \\ AB \text{ interaction} \end{matrix}$$

$$\begin{matrix} \text{Constant} & A & B & AB \end{matrix}$$

The estimated variances are $\hat{\sigma}_1^2 = .91$ and $\hat{\sigma}_2^2 = .61$. Each is estimated with $n_e = 18$ degrees of freedom. The vector of standard deviations is

$$\mathbf{d}' = [\sqrt{.908} \quad \sqrt{.611}] = [.953 \quad .782]$$

The square roots of the diagonal elements of **G**, in vector form, are

$$\mathbf{g}' = [.218 \quad .436 \quad .436 \quad .871]$$

The standard errors are

$$\mathbf{H} = \begin{bmatrix} .21 & .17 \\ .42 & .34 \\ .42 & .34 \\ .83 & .68 \end{bmatrix} \begin{matrix} \text{Constant} \\ A \text{ main effect} \\ B \text{ main effect} \\ AB \text{ interaction} \end{matrix}$$
$$\qquad y_1 \quad y_2$$

Let us extract the A main-effect contrasts from $\hat{\mathbf{\Theta}}$. The means for the first level of the A factor, minus the means for the second level are

$$\hat{\boldsymbol{\theta}}'_2 = [-.98 \quad -.78]$$

The corresponding standard errors are

$$\mathbf{h}'_2 = [.42 \quad .34]$$

A .95 confidence interval on θ_{21} alone requires $t_{18,.025} = 2.101$. The interval is

$$-.98 - 2.101(.42) \leq \theta_{21} \leq -.98 + 2.101(.42)$$

or

$$-1.85 \leq \theta_{21} \leq -.11$$

We are convinced (with .95 confidence) that the population mean for A_1 is below that for A_2, on y_1 alone.

To draw a simultaneous interval on the two elements of $\boldsymbol{\theta}'_2$ we require $F_{2,17,.05} = 3.59$. The .95 bivariate interval has constant

$$k = \sqrt{\frac{(22-4)2}{22-4-2+1} 3.59} = 2.76$$

The lower limit to the interval is

$$[-.98 \quad -.78] - 2.76[.42 \quad .34] = [-2.13 \quad -1.72]$$

The upper limit is

$$[-.98 \quad -.78] + 2.76[.42 \quad .34] = [.16 \quad .16]$$

The interval for θ_{21} alone is wider, to assure *at least* .95 confidence for both terms. For both variables together we cannot be certain that the population mean for A_1 is below the mean for A_2. Both separate intervals contain zero. A multivariate test of significance is necessary to decide if there are real group-mean differences.

8.3 PREDICTED MEANS AND RESIDUALS

The estimates $\hat{\mathbf{\Theta}}$ and their standard errors provide all the data necessary to interpret the fixed effects in analysis-of-variance models. $\hat{\mathbf{\Theta}}$ also contains the information necessary to test hypotheses about between-group differences, although the tests may be complicated by the nonindependence of the rows of $\hat{\mathbf{\Theta}}$.

As an interpretive device, subclass means as *predicted* or *estimated* through the model, may provide direct insight into the effects in the data. It is often useful to estimate subsets of terms in the model and to use those terms alone to predict the mean outcomes.

For example, consider an $A \times B$ two-way fixed-effects factorial arrangement, with a levels of factor A and b levels of B. The p-variate mean model is

$$\mathbf{y}_{\cdot jk} = \boldsymbol{\mu} + \boldsymbol{\alpha}_j + \boldsymbol{\beta}_k + \boldsymbol{\gamma}_{jk} + \boldsymbol{\epsilon}_{\cdot jk} \tag{8.3.1}$$

All terms are $p \times 1$ vectors.

If all terms including interactions are non-null, then the only estimate of $\mathbf{y}_{\cdot jk}$ is the sum of all the effects. Represent the estimated vector mean by $\hat{\mathbf{y}}_{\cdot jk}$. Then

$$\hat{\mathbf{y}}_{\cdot jk} = \hat{\boldsymbol{\mu}} + \hat{\boldsymbol{\alpha}}_j + \hat{\boldsymbol{\beta}}_k + \hat{\boldsymbol{\gamma}}_{jk} \tag{8.3.2}$$

The predicted $\hat{\mathbf{y}}_{\cdot jk}$ is of course equal to the observed sample mean $\mathbf{y}_{\cdot jk}$. The terms in Eq. 8.3.2 exhaust all possible sources of variation in the vector mean.

Should some terms be taken to be zero, by assumption or by hypothesis tests, it may be desirable to omit them from the model and to predict means from those that remain. Two purposes are served. One, the means predicted under the smaller model are generally easier to interpret. This occurs by the elimination of random sources of variation distinguishing one vector from another. The resulting means are estimated with smaller standard error, since fewer components are summed than in Eq. 8.3.2.

Two, comparison of means estimated under models of alternate sizes, or of estimated and observed means, can generally lend insight into the effects *omitted* from the larger model. The examination of residuals is a useful device for the discovery of unusual treatment effects, or of subclasses of observations which conform particularly well, or particularly poorly, to the model underlying the data.

To complete the example, assume that we discover that neither the $\hat{\boldsymbol{\beta}}_k$ nor the $\hat{\boldsymbol{\gamma}}_{jk}$ differ significantly from zero. We may remove these terms from the model, to obtain best estimates of those that remain and to predict the mean outcomes from them. The predicted means are

$$\hat{\mathbf{y}}_{\cdot jk} = \hat{\boldsymbol{\mu}} + \hat{\boldsymbol{\alpha}}_j \tag{8.3.3}$$

Predicted $\hat{y}_{\cdot jk}$ for any variate will differ from one level of A to another. They do not differ across levels of B, however, nor will A mean differences vary across

B. In this manner, the predicted means provide a clearer illustration of specific effects of importance than do the observed means.

The number of degrees of freedom in the prediction model is *c*, the *rank of the model for estimation*. In Eq. 8.3.2, *c* is equal to the product $J=ab$ [1 for μ, plus $a-1$ for α_j, plus $b-1$ for β_k, plus $(a-1)(b-1)$ for γ_{jk}]. It is also equal to *l*, the rank of the complete model or the rank of the model for significance testing. In Eq. 8.3.3, the rank of the model for estimation is $c=a$ (1 for μ, plus $a-1$ for α_j). The rank of the model for estimation can be no greater than the rank of the full model *l*, and is usually less. When $c=l=J$, as in Eq. 8.3.2, the model is a trivial one since *J* subclass means are predicted through an equal number of more complex parameters.

The differences between the observed and estimated means are the *mean residuals*. For the model of Eq. 8.3.3 these are

$$\begin{aligned}\mathbf{y}_{\cdot jk}-\hat{\mathbf{y}}_{\cdot jk} &= [\hat{\boldsymbol{\mu}}+\hat{\boldsymbol{\alpha}}_j+\hat{\boldsymbol{\beta}}_k+\hat{\boldsymbol{\gamma}}_{jk}]-[\hat{\boldsymbol{\mu}}+\hat{\boldsymbol{\alpha}}_j]\\ &= \hat{\boldsymbol{\beta}}_k+\hat{\boldsymbol{\gamma}}_{jk}\end{aligned} \tag{8.3.4}$$

The residuals, estimated in separate components ($\hat{\boldsymbol{\beta}}$, $\hat{\boldsymbol{\gamma}}$) or together, can indicate factors operating in the data that are not described by the model. In more complex models, the interpretive facilitation may be even greater, as the number of extraneous sources of variation excluded from the model increases. Single interactions or complex terms in the model that are nonzero may be understood by the comparison of predicted means under models including and excluding the specific term of interest.

In designs having subclasses without observations, the reduced-rank model can be used to predict the missing means (see Sample Problem 3, dental calculus reduction). Suppose there were no subjects in the second *B* group at the first *A* level. The mean predicted by Eq. 8.3.3 would still be the mean for all groups at the first level of *A*; that is, $\hat{\mathbf{y}}_{\cdot 12}=\hat{\boldsymbol{\mu}}+\hat{\boldsymbol{\alpha}}_1$. The expression does not require either a $\boldsymbol{\beta}$ or $\boldsymbol{\gamma}$ estimate. Under a "main-effect" model, $\hat{\mathbf{y}}_{\cdot 12}=\hat{\boldsymbol{\mu}}+\hat{\boldsymbol{\alpha}}_1+\hat{\boldsymbol{\beta}}_2$, the estimates can still be obtained as long as there are *any* observations at the second *B* level. These observations make the estimation of $\boldsymbol{\beta}_2$, and then $\mathbf{y}_{\cdot 12}$, possible. However, $\boldsymbol{\gamma}_{12}$ would not be estimable. For the estimates $\hat{\mathbf{y}}_{\cdot 12}$ to be valid, it is necessary to assume that the group mean $\mathbf{y}_{\cdot 12}$ follows the same model as vectors for other subclasses, with no unique interaction. Residuals for null subclasses cannot be obtained.

The predicted means for *all* subclasses can be obtained in matrix form. The degrees of freedom in the model for estimation is *c*; this is also the number of columns of the basis or rows of $\boldsymbol{\Theta}$ in the estimation model. Let $\mathbf{K}_c$ be leading *c* columns of $\mathbf{K}$, corresponding to the terms to be included in the estimation model. Then the $c\times p$ matrix of estimated effects is

$$\hat{\boldsymbol{\Theta}}_c=(\mathbf{K}_c'\mathbf{D}\mathbf{K}_c)^{-1}\mathbf{K}_c'\mathbf{D}\mathbf{Y}. \tag{8.3.5}$$

Since rows of $\hat{\boldsymbol{\Theta}}$ are generally interdependent, $\hat{\boldsymbol{\Theta}}_c$ may differ from the leading rows of the $l\times p$ matrix $\hat{\boldsymbol{\Theta}}$. The variance–covariance matrix of $\hat{\boldsymbol{\Theta}}_c$ is $\mathscr{V}(\hat{\boldsymbol{\Theta}}_c)=(\mathbf{K}_c'\mathbf{D}\mathbf{K}_c)^{-1}\otimes\boldsymbol{\Sigma}$.

The matrix of means predicted through the rank-c model is

$$\hat{\mathbf{Y}}_{\cdot} = \mathbf{K}_c \hat{\boldsymbol{\Theta}}_c \tag{8.3.6}$$

When $c = l = J$, $\mathbf{K}_c$ is square and Eq. 8.3.6 reduces to the trivial form $\hat{\mathbf{Y}}_{\cdot} = \mathbf{Y}_{\cdot}$. When $c < J$, the estimated and observed means differ by the terms that are omitted from $\mathbf{K}_c$ and $\hat{\boldsymbol{\Theta}}_c$. $\hat{\mathbf{Y}}_{\cdot}$ is of order $J \times p$, even when some subclasses have no observations.

Under the general arbitrary-N model, each *predicted* mean equally represents a particular subpopulation. The rows of $\hat{\mathbf{Y}}_{\cdot}$ may be averaged without respect to N_j to obtain estimates of row and column means. These are not biased by disproportionate sample sizes. For example, in a 2×3 ($A \times B$) crossed design, the matrix of predicted means has row vectors $\hat{\mathbf{y}}'_{\cdot jk}$. The estimate of the population mean for the first level of A is the simple average,

$$\hat{\mathbf{y}}'_{\cdot 1 \cdot} = \frac{\hat{\mathbf{y}}'_{\cdot 11} + \hat{\mathbf{y}}'_{\cdot 12} + \mathbf{y}'_{\cdot 13}}{3} \tag{8.3.7}$$

$\hat{\mathbf{y}}_{\cdot 1 \cdot}$ does not depend on the number of observations in the groups, even if there are one or more null subclasses. The same unweighted averaging may be employed across any dimensions of classification, to obtain the *combined estimated means* for row, column, or interaction effects.

From Eqs. 8.1.6 and 8.1.7, the expectation and covariance matrix of $\mathbf{Y}_{\cdot}$ are $\mathscr{E}(\mathbf{Y}_{\cdot}) = \mathbf{K}\boldsymbol{\Theta}$ and $\mathscr{V}(\mathbf{Y}_{\cdot}) = \mathbf{D}^{-1} \otimes \boldsymbol{\Sigma}$, respectively. The expectation of the predicted means is

$$\begin{aligned} \mathscr{E}(\hat{\mathbf{Y}}_{\cdot}) &= \mathscr{E}(\mathbf{K}_c \hat{\boldsymbol{\Theta}}_c) \\ &= \mathbf{K}_c \boldsymbol{\Theta}_c \end{aligned} \tag{8.3.8}$$

The covariance matrix is

$$\begin{aligned} \mathscr{V}(\hat{\mathbf{Y}}_{\cdot}) &= \mathscr{V}(\mathbf{K}_c \hat{\boldsymbol{\Theta}}_c) \\ &= \mathbf{K}_c \mathscr{V}(\hat{\boldsymbol{\Theta}}_c) \mathbf{K}'_c \\ &= \mathbf{K}_c [(\mathbf{K}'_c \mathbf{D} \mathbf{K}_c)^{-1} \otimes \boldsymbol{\Sigma}] \mathbf{K}'_c \\ &= \mathbf{K}_c (\mathbf{K}'_c \mathbf{D} \mathbf{K}_c)^{-1} \mathbf{K}'_c \otimes \boldsymbol{\Sigma} \\ &= \mathbf{Q} \otimes \boldsymbol{\Sigma} \end{aligned} \tag{8.3.9}$$

Although the observed means are independent across subclasses, the predicted means are not. The covariance matrix of the kth column of $\hat{\mathbf{Y}}_{\cdot}$ for one criterion measure is

$$\mathscr{V}(\hat{\mathbf{y}}_{\cdot k}) = \sigma_k^2 [\mathbf{K}_c (\mathbf{K}'_c \mathbf{D} \mathbf{K}_c)^{-1} \mathbf{K}'_c] = \sigma_k^2 \mathbf{Q} \tag{8.3.10}$$

In general, the matrix is nondiagonal and predicted means are interrelated.

The diagonal elements of Eq. 8.3.10 are the variances of the predicted means; the square roots are the standard errors. The standard error of the predicted mean in group j on variate k is $\sigma_k \sqrt{q_{jj}}$. Substituting the sample standard deviation for σ_k provides an estimate of the standard error, which may be used to draw confidence intervals on particular predicted values. The standard error of the mean predicted from a model of rank c ($< J$) is always smaller than the standard error of the corresponding observed mean $\sigma_k / \sqrt{N_j}$.

The estimated mean residuals are the $J \times p$ matrix

$$\hat{\mathbf{E}}. = \mathbf{Y}. - \hat{\mathbf{Y}}. \quad (8.3.11)$$

The residuals may be standardized to a common metric by dividing each element by the standard deviation of the corresponding variable. The *standardized residuals* are

$$\hat{\mathbf{E}}.^* = \hat{\mathbf{E}}.\hat{\mathbf{\Delta}}^{-1/2} \quad (8.3.12)$$

$\hat{\mathbf{\Delta}}$ is the $p \times p$ diagonal matrix of variances from $\hat{\mathbf{\Sigma}}$, or $\hat{\mathbf{\Delta}} = \text{diag}\,(\hat{\mathbf{\Sigma}})$. $\hat{\mathbf{\Delta}}^{-1/2}$ is the diagonal matrix of inverse standard deviations. The conversion to $\hat{\mathbf{E}}.^*$ facilitates comparing the residuals across variates.

The residuals may be further standardized to mean zero and unit variance, to assure comparability across subclasses with different N_j's. This requires the expectation and covariance matrix of $\hat{\mathbf{E}}.$. The expected value of each residual is zero. The covariance matrix is

$$\begin{aligned}
\mathscr{V}(\hat{\mathbf{E}}.) &= \mathscr{V}(\mathbf{Y}. - \hat{\mathbf{Y}}.) \\
&= \mathscr{V}(\mathbf{Y}. - \mathbf{K}_c\hat{\mathbf{\Theta}}_c) \\
&= \mathscr{V}(\mathbf{Y}. - \mathbf{K}_c[\mathbf{K}_c'\mathbf{D}\mathbf{K}_c]^{-1}\mathbf{K}_c'\mathbf{D}\mathbf{Y}.) \\
&= \mathscr{V}(\mathbf{I} - \mathbf{Q}\mathbf{D})\mathbf{Y}. \\
&= (\mathbf{I} - \mathbf{Q}\mathbf{D})\mathscr{V}(\mathbf{Y}.)(\mathbf{I} - \mathbf{Q}\mathbf{D})' \\
&= (\mathbf{I} - \mathbf{Q}\mathbf{D})\mathbf{D}^{-1}(\mathbf{I} - \mathbf{Q}\mathbf{D})' \otimes \mathbf{\Sigma} \\
&= (\mathbf{D}^{-1} - \mathbf{Q}) \otimes \mathbf{\Sigma}
\end{aligned} \quad (8.3.13)$$

Like the estimated means, the estimated residuals are not independent across subclasses, to the extent that $\mathbf{Q} = \mathbf{K}_c(\mathbf{K}_c'\mathbf{D}\mathbf{K}_c)^{-1}\mathbf{K}_c'$ is nondiagonal.

The standard errors of the elements of $\hat{\mathbf{E}}.$ are the square roots of the diagonal elements of Eq. 8.3.13. The standard error of $\hat{\epsilon}_{\cdot jk}$ for group j and variate k is

$$\sigma_{\hat{\epsilon}_{\cdot jk}} = \sigma_k \sqrt{\frac{1}{N_j} - q_{jj}} \quad (8.3.14)$$

q_{jj} is the jj diagonal element of $\mathbf{Q}$ and is never greater than $1/N_j$. σ_k is the standard deviation of the variate y_k from $\mathbf{\Sigma}$. Substituting the sample value for $\mathbf{\Sigma}$ in Eqs. 8.3.13 and 8.3.14 yields the estimate of the standard error ($\hat{\sigma}_{\hat{\epsilon}_{\cdot jk}}$).

Under the assumption of normal $\epsilon_{\cdot jk}$, the $1-\alpha$ confidence interval on $\epsilon_{\cdot jk}$ is

$$\epsilon_{\cdot jk}\colon\ \hat{\epsilon}_{\cdot jk} \pm t_{N-l,\alpha/2}(\hat{\sigma}_{\hat{\epsilon}_{\cdot jk}}) \quad (8.3.15)$$

$t_{N-l,\alpha/2}$ is the $100\alpha/2$ upper percentage point of the t distribution with $N-l$ degrees of freedom. The null hypothesis may be tested that $\epsilon_{\cdot jk}$ is zero, by direct comparison of the ratio $\hat{\epsilon}_{\cdot jk}/(\hat{\sigma}_{\hat{\epsilon}_{\cdot jk}})$ to the critical t-value. H_0 is rejected if the critical value is exceeded.

A Simple Case

Consider the situation in which no between-group differences have been found, and the model best fitting the data has only a population scale constant.

That is, assume that $\hat{\mathbf{y}}_{\cdot jk} = \hat{\boldsymbol{\mu}}$. The basis $\mathbf{K}_1$ is the J-element unit vector, $\mathbf{1}$, and the predicted means are

$$\hat{\mathbf{Y}}. = \mathbf{K}_1\hat{\boldsymbol{\Theta}}_1 = \mathbf{1}\hat{\boldsymbol{\mu}}'$$

$$= \begin{bmatrix} \hat{\mu}^{(1)} & \hat{\mu}^{(2)} & \cdots & \hat{\mu}^{(p)} \\ \hat{\mu}^{(1)} & \hat{\mu}^{(2)} & \cdots & \hat{\mu}^{(p)} \\ \vdots & & & \vdots \\ \hat{\mu}^{(1)} & \hat{\mu}^{(2)} & \cdots & \hat{\mu}^{(p)} \end{bmatrix} \tag{8.3.16}$$

The variance–covariance factors are

$$\mathbf{Q} = \mathbf{K}_1(\mathbf{K}_1'\mathbf{D}\mathbf{K}_1)^{-1}\mathbf{K}_1 = \mathbf{1}\frac{1}{N}\mathbf{1}'$$

$$= \frac{1}{N}\begin{bmatrix} 1 & 1 & \cdots & 1 \\ 1 & 1 & \cdots & 1 \\ \vdots & & & \vdots \\ 1 & 1 & \cdots & 1 \end{bmatrix} \tag{8.3.17}$$

The variances for variate k are all σ_k^2/N, and are smaller than the variance of the observed mean σ_k^2/N_j since $N = \Sigma_j N_j$.

The estimated residuals are the differences

$$\hat{\mathbf{E}}. = \mathbf{Y}. - \hat{\mathbf{Y}}. = \mathbf{Y}. - \mathbf{1}\hat{\boldsymbol{\mu}}' \tag{8.3.18}$$

Each residual is the simple difference of an observed mean and the grand mean of all observations for the particular variate. The $J \times J$ matrix of sample variances and covariances of residuals for all groups on one outcome measure is

$$\hat{\sigma}_k^2(\mathbf{D}^{-1} - \mathbf{Q}) = \hat{\sigma}_k^2\left(\mathbf{D}^{-1} - \frac{1}{N}\mathbf{1}\mathbf{1}'\right)$$

$$= \hat{\sigma}_k^2 \begin{bmatrix} \frac{1}{N_1} - \frac{1}{N} & -\frac{1}{N} & -\frac{1}{N} & \cdots & -\frac{1}{N} \\ -\frac{1}{N} & \frac{1}{N_2} - \frac{1}{N} & -\frac{1}{N} & \cdots & -\frac{1}{N} \\ \vdots & & & & \vdots \\ -\frac{1}{N} & -\frac{1}{N} & -\frac{1}{N} & \cdots & \frac{1}{N_J} - \frac{1}{N} \end{bmatrix} \tag{8.3.19}$$

The standard error for the mean residual in group j is

$$\hat{\sigma}_{\hat{\epsilon}_{\cdot jk}} = \hat{\sigma}_k \sqrt{\frac{1}{N_j} - \frac{1}{N}} \tag{8.3.19a}$$

The term can be employed to test the departure of the particular residual from zero. The standard error of the mean residual will tend to be smaller as N_j or q_{jj} (subtracted from $1/N_j$) becomes larger. The residuals have maximum precision when the number of subjects in the group and the number of terms in the model are large.

Example

The observed means and frequencies for the data of Table 3.3.2 are

$$\mathbf{Y.} = \begin{bmatrix} .50 & .75 \\ 3.17 & 3.67 \\ 2.20 & 2.40 \\ 3.43 & 3.57 \end{bmatrix} \begin{matrix} \text{Group 11} \\ \text{Group 12} \\ \text{Group 21} \\ \text{Group 22} \end{matrix} \qquad \mathbf{D} = \begin{bmatrix} 4 & & & \text{(Zero)} \\ & 6 & & \\ & & 5 & \\ \text{(Zero)} & & & 7 \end{bmatrix}$$
$$\quad y_1 \quad y_2$$

The within-group standard deviations are $\hat{\sigma}_1 = .953$ and $\hat{\sigma}_2 = .782$.

Assume that both A and B main effects are significant to the model but the interaction is not. We shall estimate means based on a rank-three model,

$$\hat{\mathbf{y}}_{\cdot jk} = \hat{\boldsymbol{\mu}} + \hat{\boldsymbol{\alpha}}_j + \hat{\boldsymbol{\beta}}_k$$

The first three columns of the basis, for the constant and the A and B main effects, are

$$\mathbf{K}_3 = \begin{bmatrix} 1 & .5 & .5 \\ 1 & .5 & -.5 \\ 1 & -.5 & .5 \\ 1 & -.5 & -.5 \end{bmatrix}$$
$$\text{Constant} \quad A \quad B$$

The least-squares estimates of the first three effects alone are

$$\hat{\boldsymbol{\Theta}}_3 = (\mathbf{K}_3'\mathbf{D}\mathbf{K}_3)^{-1}\mathbf{K}_3'\mathbf{D}\mathbf{Y}.$$

$$= \begin{bmatrix} 2.34 & 2.61 \\ -.85 & -.62 \\ -1.88 & -1.96 \end{bmatrix} \begin{matrix} \text{Constant} \\ A \text{ main effect} \\ B \text{ main effect} \end{matrix}$$
$$y_1 \quad y_2$$

These values differ slightly from the corresponding elements of $\hat{\boldsymbol{\Theta}}$ in Section 8.1, since the interactions have been deleted.

The predicted means are

$$\hat{\mathbf{Y}}. = \mathbf{K}_3\hat{\boldsymbol{\Theta}}_3 = \begin{bmatrix} .97 & 1.32 \\ 2.85 & 3.28 \\ 1.82 & 1.94 \\ 3.70 & 3.90 \end{bmatrix} \begin{matrix} \text{Group 11} \\ \text{Group 12} \\ \text{Group 21} \\ \text{Group 22} \end{matrix}$$
$$y_1 \quad y_2$$

The estimated mean for all subjects at the first level of the A factor is $(.97+2.85)/2 = 1.91$ for y_1, and $(1.32+3.28)/2 = 2.30$ for y_2. The means in

$\hat{\mathbf{Y}}.$ do not appear to be close to those of $\mathbf{Y}.$. The residuals are

$$\hat{\mathbf{E}}. = \mathbf{Y}. - \hat{\mathbf{Y}}. = \begin{bmatrix} -.47 & -.57 \\ .32 & .38 \\ .38 & .46 \\ -.27 & -.33 \end{bmatrix} \begin{matrix} \text{Group 11} \\ \text{Group 12} \\ \text{Group 21} \\ \text{Group 22} \end{matrix}$$

$$\qquad\qquad y_1 \qquad y_2$$

The largest residuals appear for group 11, having mean observed scores very different from the other groups. Since $\hat{\mathbf{E}}.$ contains only the interaction effects, it appears that there may be a statistically significant interaction.

The standard error of $\hat{\epsilon}_{\cdot 12} = -.57$ is

$$\hat{\sigma}_2 \sqrt{\frac{1}{N_{11}} - q_{11}}$$

The (1, 1) diagonal element of $\mathbf{Q} = \mathbf{K}_3(\mathbf{K}_3'\mathbf{D}\mathbf{K}_3)^{-1}\mathbf{K}_3'$ is $q_{11} = .168$. The standard error is

$$.782 \sqrt{\frac{1}{4} - .168} = .224$$

The predicted and observed means differ by about 2 1/2 standard errors. The large difference suggests that the mean for group 11 is being affected by important factors not included in the main-effect model.

8.4 SAMPLE PROBLEMS

Sample Problem 2 – Word Memory Experiment

The data for the four-treatment word memory problem may be analyzed by comparing mean recall scores across experimental conditions. For this, we may apply a one-way bivariate analysis-of-variance model. The number of words recalled and the proportion of word categories reconstructed are the outcome measures.

The mean model is

$$\mathbf{y}_{\cdot j}' = \boldsymbol{\mu}' + \boldsymbol{\alpha}_j' + \boldsymbol{\epsilon}_{\cdot j}'$$

All terms are 1×2 row vectors. The matrix model for all groups is

$$\mathbf{Y}. = \mathbf{A}\boldsymbol{\Theta}^* + \mathbf{E}.$$

$\mathbf{Y}.$ and $\mathbf{E}.$ are each 4×2 matrices. The model matrix and parameters are defined as in the preceding sections.

$$\mathbf{A} = \begin{bmatrix} 1 & 1 & 0 & 0 & 0 \\ 1 & 0 & 1 & 0 & 0 \\ 1 & 0 & 0 & 1 & 0 \\ 1 & 0 & 0 & 0 & 1 \end{bmatrix}$$

and

$$[\Theta^*]' = [\mu \quad \alpha_1 \quad \alpha_2 \quad \alpha_3 \quad \alpha_4]$$

The data for all 48 observations are listed in the Appendix. The first observation has scores on the dependent variables, of 50 and 1, respectively. The second of these scores is the ratio of categories reconstructed to categories possible—that is, 10/10. In addition, each observation has six time measures, to be employed for covariance analysis.

The basic descriptive data for the problem are the matrix mean, the diagonal matrix of subclass frequencies, and the pooled within-group variance–covariance and correlation matrices. The means and frequencies are

$$\mathbf{Y.} = \begin{bmatrix} 39.83 & .97 \\ 42.17 & .94 \\ 40.00 & 1.00 \\ 36.25 & .97 \end{bmatrix} \begin{matrix} \text{Condition 1} \\ \text{Condition 2} \\ \text{Condition 3} \\ \text{Condition 4} \end{matrix}$$
$$\begin{matrix} \text{Words} & \text{Categories} \end{matrix}$$

and

$$\mathbf{D} = \text{diag}\,(12, 12, 12, 12)$$

The sum-of-product matrices for the four groups, adjusted to the group vector means, are

$$\mathbf{S}_{w_1} = \begin{bmatrix} 547.67 & 2.94 \\ 2.94 & .02 \end{bmatrix} \qquad \mathbf{S}_{w_2} = \begin{bmatrix} 505.67 & 6.62 \\ 6.62 & .13 \end{bmatrix}$$

$$\mathbf{S}_{w_3} = \begin{bmatrix} 222.00 & 0.0 \\ 0.0 & 0.0 \end{bmatrix} \qquad \mathbf{S}_{w_4} = \begin{bmatrix} 210.25 & 2.30 \\ 2.30 & .07 \end{bmatrix}$$

On inspection, the within-group matrices may appear not to be homogeneous. To maintain the example, we will ignore possible differences and pool to obtain a common estimate of Σ. The pooled within-group sum-of-products matrix is

$$\mathbf{S}_W = \sum_{j=1}^{4} \mathbf{S}_{w_j}$$
$$= \begin{bmatrix} 1485.58 & 11.85 \\ 11.85 & .22 \end{bmatrix} \begin{matrix} \text{Words} \\ \text{Categories} \end{matrix}$$
$$\begin{matrix} \text{Words} & \text{Categories} \end{matrix}$$

$\mathbf{S}_W$ may equivalently be obtained from the total sum of products and the subclass means. That is,

$$\mathbf{S}_W = \mathbf{Y}'\mathbf{Y} - \mathbf{Y}'_{.}\mathbf{D}\mathbf{Y}.$$
$$= \begin{bmatrix} 76831.00 & 1850.90 \\ 1850.90 & 45.29 \end{bmatrix} - \begin{bmatrix} 75345.42 & 1839.05 \\ 1839.05 & 45.07 \end{bmatrix}$$

The within-group covariance matrix is

$$\mathbf{V}_W = \hat{\Sigma} = \frac{1}{N-J}\mathbf{S}_W$$

$$= \frac{1}{48-4} \begin{bmatrix} 1485.58 & 11.85 \\ 11.85 & .22 \end{bmatrix}$$

$$= \begin{bmatrix} 33.76 & .27 \\ .27 & .005 \end{bmatrix} \begin{matrix} \text{Words} \\ \text{Categories} \end{matrix}$$

$$\begin{matrix} \text{Words} & \text{Categories} \end{matrix}$$

The diagonal elements, $s_1^2 = 33.76$, and $s_2^2 = .005$, are the within-group variances or mean squares for the two measures.

The within-group standard deviations are

$$s_1 = \sqrt{33.76} = 5.81 \quad \text{Words}$$
$$s_2 = \sqrt{.005} = .07 \quad \text{Categories}$$

These may be included as the elements of a diagonal matrix, $\mathbf{D}_W^{1/2}$, which is inverted to obtain the within-group intercorrelations. That is,

$$\mathbf{R}_W = \mathbf{D}_W^{-1/2} \mathbf{V}_W \mathbf{D}_W^{-1/2}$$

$$= \begin{bmatrix} 1/5.81 & 0 \\ 0 & 1/.07 \end{bmatrix} \begin{bmatrix} 33.76 & .27 \\ .27 & .005 \end{bmatrix} \begin{bmatrix} 1/5.81 & 0 \\ 0 & 1/.07 \end{bmatrix}$$

$$= \begin{bmatrix} 1.00 & .65 \\ .65 & 1.00 \end{bmatrix} \begin{matrix} \text{Words} \\ \text{Categories} \end{matrix}$$

$$\begin{matrix} \text{Words} & \text{Categories} \end{matrix}$$

The correlation of the two measures is high positive, $r_{12} = .65$.

In general, mean differences on the two measures do not appear large. There is a noticeable ceiling effect for the second outcome variable, with all subjects in treatment group 3 obtaining a perfect score of 5, or 100 percent. Between-group differences are not consistent. Although more words were recalled in group 2, fewer categories were reconstructed than in the other groups; however, differences on one or both variates may be nonsignificant.

To test the hypotheses of the effect of structure upon word recall, three specific mean contrasts are of interest. These are the comparisons of groups 1 and 2, groups 2 and 3, and groups 3 and 4, respectively. The contrast matrix is

$$\mathbf{L} = \begin{bmatrix} 1 & .25 & .25 & .25 & .25 \\ 0 & 1 & -1 & 0 & 0 \\ 0 & 0 & 1 & -1 & 0 \\ 0 & 0 & 0 & 1 & -1 \end{bmatrix} \begin{matrix} \text{L0} \\ \text{L1} \\ \text{L2} \\ \text{L3} \end{matrix}$$

The row vectors L0, L1, L2, and L3 are not orthogonal. The alternate parameters are

$$\mathbf{\Theta} = \begin{bmatrix} \boldsymbol{\mu}' + 1/4 \sum_j \boldsymbol{\alpha}_j' \\ \boldsymbol{\alpha}_1' - \boldsymbol{\alpha}_2' \\ \boldsymbol{\alpha}_2' - \boldsymbol{\alpha}_3' \\ \boldsymbol{\alpha}_3' - \boldsymbol{\alpha}_4' \end{bmatrix}$$

Each difference is a two-element vector, having the contrast value for words and categories, respectively.

The basis, necessary for estimating $\mathbf{\Theta}$, is

$$\mathbf{K} = \mathbf{AL}'(\mathbf{LL}')^{-1}$$

$$= \begin{bmatrix} 1.00 & .75 & .50 & .25 \\ 1.00 & -.25 & .50 & .25 \\ 1.00 & -.25 & -.50 & .25 \\ 1.00 & -.25 & -.50 & -.75 \end{bmatrix}$$

$$\begin{matrix} \text{L0} & \text{L1} & \text{L2} & \text{L3} \end{matrix}$$

The parameter estimates are

$$\hat{\mathbf{\Theta}} = (\mathbf{K}'\mathbf{DK})^{-1}\mathbf{K}'\mathbf{DY}.$$

$$= \begin{bmatrix} 39.56 & .97 \\ -2.33 & .03 \\ 2.17 & -.06 \\ 3.75 & .03 \end{bmatrix} \begin{matrix} \mu' + 1/4 \sum_j \alpha_j' \\ \alpha_1' - \alpha_2' \\ \alpha_2' - \alpha_3' \\ \alpha_3' - \alpha_4' \end{matrix}$$

$$\begin{matrix} \text{Words} & \text{Categories} \end{matrix}$$

The standard errors of the estimated effects are the square roots of the diagonal elements of $(\mathbf{K}'\mathbf{DK})^{-1} \otimes \mathbf{\Sigma}$. These may be expressed as a column and row vector, respectively. The variance–covariance factors of the estimates are

$$\mathbf{G} = (\mathbf{K}'\mathbf{DK})^{-1} = \begin{bmatrix} .0208 & & & \text{(Symmetric)} \\ 0 & .1667 & & \\ 0 & -.0833 & .1667 & \\ 0 & 0 & -.0833 & .1667 \end{bmatrix} \begin{matrix} \text{L0} \\ \text{L1} \\ \text{L2} \\ \text{L3} \end{matrix}$$

$$\begin{matrix} \text{L0} & \text{L1} & \text{L2} & \text{L3} \end{matrix}$$

Since all N_j's are equal, the negative off-diagonal covariance factors are due exclusively to the nonorthogonality of contrast vectors.

The diagonal elements of $(\mathbf{K}'\mathbf{DK})^{-1}$ are proportional to the variances of the contrasts. In this particular instance, the three contrasts are simple mean differences. For example, $\hat{\theta}_{21} = y_{\cdot 1}^{(1)} - y_{\cdot 2}^{(1)} = -2.33$ for the first criterion measure. From univariate theory, the estimated variance of a difference of means is

$$s_1^2\left(\frac{1}{N_1} + \frac{1}{N_2}\right)$$

Since $N_1 = N_2 = 12$, we can see that this is exactly the value s_1^2 times the second diagonal element of $(\mathbf{K}'\mathbf{DK})^{-1}$. That is,

$$s_1^2\left(\frac{1}{N_1} + \frac{1}{N_2}\right) = s_1^2\left(\frac{1}{12} + \frac{1}{12}\right)$$

$$= s_1^2(.1667)$$

The standard error of the difference is the square root, $s_1\sqrt{.1667}$.

All standard errors may be expressed in matrix form by defining

$$\mathbf{g} = \begin{bmatrix} \sqrt{g_{11}} \\ \sqrt{g_{22}} \\ \sqrt{g_{33}} \\ \sqrt{g_{44}} \end{bmatrix} = \begin{bmatrix} \sqrt{.0208} \\ \sqrt{.1667} \\ \sqrt{.1667} \\ \sqrt{.1667} \end{bmatrix} = \begin{bmatrix} .144 \\ .408 \\ .408 \\ .408 \end{bmatrix}$$

and

$$\mathbf{d}' = [s_1 \quad s_2] = [5.81 \quad .07]$$

The matrix of standard errors is

$$\mathbf{H} = \mathbf{gd}'$$

$$= \begin{bmatrix} .84 & .01 \\ 2.37 & .03 \\ 2.37 & .03 \\ 2.37 & .03 \end{bmatrix} \begin{matrix} \boldsymbol{\mu}' + 1/4 \sum_j \boldsymbol{\alpha}_j' \\ \boldsymbol{\alpha}_1' - \boldsymbol{\alpha}_2' \\ \boldsymbol{\alpha}_2' - \boldsymbol{\alpha}_3' \\ \boldsymbol{\alpha}_3' - \boldsymbol{\alpha}_4' \end{matrix}$$

Words Categories

To draw a confidence interval on any single element, we require $t_{\nu,\alpha/2}$. With $\alpha = .05$, and $\nu = N - I = 44$, the tabled t value is 2.02. The .95 interval estimate of θ_{21} is

$$-2.33 - 2.02(2.37) \leqslant \theta_{21} \leqslant -2.33 + 2.02(2.37)$$

or

$$-7.12 \leqslant \theta_{21} \leqslant 2.46$$

The point estimate is negative. Our "single best guess" is that α_2 exceeds α_1 for the first outcome measure. The estimate of the difference is -2.33. That is, on the average, treatment 2 increased word recall by about 2 1/3 words over treatment condition 1. The standard error and interval estimate provide further information. In particular, since the interval includes zero, we may not conclude that there is a "significant difference" in treatment means, in favor of treatment 2. We may not conclude that information regarding a hierarchical structure was more beneficial to recall than was a lesser degree of information. At this level of specificity, the major hypothesis of the study is not supported.

Inspection of the remaining estimates and standard errors shows few effects which, *in isolation*, appear significant. Contrasts other than those chosen may be significant, however. For example, $\hat{\alpha}_2^{(1)} - \hat{\alpha}_3^{(1)} = 2.17$ and $\hat{\alpha}_3^{(1)} - \hat{\alpha}_4^{(1)} = 3.75$. The difference $\hat{\alpha}_2^{(1)} - \hat{\alpha}_4^{(1)}$ of 5.92 points is larger, and in the expected direction. A joint test of the three contrasts, for one or both variates, may support the major hypothesis of the study. This is discussed in the following sections.

For comparison purposes, let us draw an interval on the second row of $\boldsymbol{\Theta}$, $(\boldsymbol{\alpha}_1' - \boldsymbol{\alpha}_2')$, as in expression 8.2.21 or more generally in expression 8.2.24. Let $\mathbf{v}' = [0 \quad 1 \quad 0 \quad 0]$. The estimate is identically the second row of the matrix,

$$\mathbf{v}'\hat{\boldsymbol{\Theta}} = [-2.33 \qquad .03]$$

Words Categories

The estimated covariance matrix of the differences is

$$[\mathbf{v}'(\mathbf{K}'\mathbf{D}\mathbf{K})^{-1}\mathbf{v}]\hat{\boldsymbol{\Sigma}} = .1667\begin{bmatrix} 33.76 & .270 \\ & .27 & .005 \end{bmatrix}$$

$$= \begin{bmatrix} 5.630 & .045 \\ .045 & .001 \end{bmatrix} \begin{matrix} \text{Words} \\ \text{Categories} \end{matrix}$$
$$\quad \text{Words} \quad \text{Categories}$$

The standard errors are $\sqrt{5.63}$ and $\sqrt{.001}$, respectively, or

$$\mathbf{h}' = [2.37 \quad .03]$$
$$\text{Words} \quad \text{Categories}$$

$\mathbf{h}'$ is equivalent to the multiplier $\sqrt{.1667}$ times the vector of standard deviations, $\mathbf{d}' = [5.81 \quad .07]$. Also, $\mathbf{h}'$ is identical to the second row of $\mathbf{H}$, due to the simple form of $\mathbf{v}$.

The vector interval requires $F_{p,N-l-p+1,\alpha}$. With $p=2$, $N=48$, $l=4$, and $\alpha=.05$, $F_{2,43,.05}=3.22$. Then

$$k = \sqrt{\frac{(48-4)2}{48-4-2+1}3.22} = 2.57$$

For just the number of words recalled,

$$-2.33 - 2.57(2.37) \leq \theta_{21} \leq -2.33 + 2.57(2.37)$$

or

$$-8.42 \leq \theta_{21} \leq 3.76$$

This is wider than the previous interval drawn on θ_{21}, as the confidence is now at least .95 for the second variate, categories, as well as for the words measure.

The rank of the model for estimation has been assumed to be $c=4$. Since $c=J$, the predicted and observed means are equal, and the mean residuals are null. Should tests of significance indicate that some of the terms in $\boldsymbol{\Theta}$ are null, we may wish to reduce the model rank and predict means from the remaining nonzero effects. The estimate of $\boldsymbol{\Theta}$ for those effects remaining will be altered, since the three contrast vectors are not orthogonal.

From inspection of the data, it appears that the major hypothesis of the study is not supported. No effect in $\boldsymbol{\Theta}$ exceeds twice its standard error, and the direction of the effects is not consistent. In particular, the "categories" variable shows little variation among subjects or groups. We suspect that the measure does not add any discrimination among experimental conditions.

Sample Problem 3—Dental Calculus Reduction

The dentifrice study has $J=10$ groups, representing the crossing of two years of experimentation with five experimental conditions. Experimental conditions one and two are controls, whereas three, four, and five represent three different experimental agents.

The mean model for all ten subclasses is

$$\mathbf{Y}. = \mathbf{A}\boldsymbol{\Theta}^* + \mathbf{E}.$$

$\mathbf{Y}.$ and $\mathbf{E}.$ are each 10×6, with a column for each of the six tooth measures. The complete model matrix and parameters are given by Eqs. 7.1.29 and 7.1.30. The 10×10 diagonal matrix of subclass frequencies is given in Eq. 7.1.31. Since groups (1,5), (2,2), and (2,4) have no observations, rows of $\mathbf{Y}.$, $\mathbf{A}$, $\mathbf{D}$, and $\mathbf{E}.$ corresponding to the three null subclasses are omitted as in Eqs. 7.1.32 and 7.1.33. The maximal rank of $\mathbf{A}$ is reduced from $J = 10$ to $J_0 = 7$, the number of subclasses with observations. The first (or α) main effect is years; the second (or β) effect is treatments.

The observed means for the ten groups are

$$\mathbf{Y}. = \begin{bmatrix} .75 & 2.25 & 3.75 & 4.13 & 2.25 & .88 \\ 1.33 & 1.78 & 3.11 & 3.33 & 2.56 & 1.56 \\ .43 & .86 & 1.29 & 1.57 & 1.00 & .43 \\ 1.00 & .80 & 2.00 & 1.20 & .60 & .00 \\ - & - & - & - & - & - \\ .68 & 1.57 & 2.71 & 2.75 & 1.57 & .71 \\ - & - & - & - & - & - \\ .54 & .79 & 2.08 & 1.71 & .96 & .67 \\ - & - & - & - & - & - \\ .23 & .42 & .77 & 1.31 & .65 & .19 \end{bmatrix} \begin{matrix} \left.\begin{matrix} \text{Control 1} \\ \text{Control 2} \\ \text{Agent 1} \\ \text{Agent 2} \\ \text{Agent 3} \end{matrix}\right\} \text{Year 1} \\ \left.\begin{matrix} \text{Control 1} \\ \text{Control 2} \\ \text{Agent 1} \\ \text{Agent 2} \\ \text{Agent 3} \end{matrix}\right\} \text{Year 2} \end{matrix}$$

Columns: Right canine, Right lateral incisor, Right central incisor, Left central incisor, Left lateral incisor, Left canine

The frequencies are

$$\mathbf{D} = \text{diag}\,(8, 9, 7, 5, 0, 28, 0, 24, 0, 26)$$

The within-groups variance–covariance matrix, given in Section 3.4, is

$$\mathbf{V}_W = \hat{\boldsymbol{\Sigma}} = \begin{bmatrix} 1.38 & & & & & \text{(Symmetric)} \\ 1.02 & 2.62 & & & & \\ .81 & 2.18 & 4.24 & & & \\ 1.07 & 2.60 & 4.31 & 6.19 & & \\ .74 & 1.67 & 2.43 & 3.49 & 3.09 & \\ .91 & 1.01 & 1.12 & 1.30 & 1.21 & 1.58 \end{bmatrix} \begin{matrix} \text{Right canine} \\ \text{Right lateral incisor} \\ \text{Right central incisor} \\ \text{Left central incisor} \\ \text{Left lateral incisor} \\ \text{Left canine} \end{matrix}$$

Columns: Right canine, Right lateral incisor, Right central incisor, Left central incisor, Left lateral incisor, Left canine

The within-group variances, or mean squares, are the diagonal elements.

The rank of the entire model matrix, or "rank of the model for significance testing" is $l=J_0=7$. Thus we will reparameterize and estimate seven linear combinations of the 18 effects in $\mathbf{\Theta}^*$. These may be obtained by first considering each main effect in isolation. For the two-level year factor, the model matrix is

$$\mathbf{A}_2 = \begin{bmatrix} 1 & 1 & 0 \\ 1 & 0 & 1 \end{bmatrix} = [\mathbf{1}_2, \quad \mathbf{I}_2]$$

The parameters are $\boldsymbol{\mu}$, $\boldsymbol{\alpha}_1$ and $\boldsymbol{\alpha}_2$. The contrast matrix is

$$\mathbf{L}_2 = \begin{bmatrix} 1 & .5 & .5 \\ 0 & 1 & -1 \end{bmatrix} \begin{matrix} \text{C0} & \text{Constant} \\ \text{C1} & \text{Years} \end{matrix}$$

The basis for just this factor is

$$\mathbf{K}_2 = \mathbf{A}_2\mathbf{L}_2'(\mathbf{L}_2\mathbf{L}_2')^{-1} = \begin{bmatrix} 1 & .5 \\ 1 & -.5 \end{bmatrix}$$
$$\begin{matrix} \text{C0} & \text{C1} \end{matrix}$$

For the experimental conditions factor alone, the model matrix is

$$\mathbf{A}_5 = [\mathbf{1}_5, \quad \mathbf{I}_5]$$

The parameters, in addition to $\boldsymbol{\mu}$, are $\boldsymbol{\beta}_1$ and $\boldsymbol{\beta}_2$ for the control groups and $\boldsymbol{\beta}_3$, $\boldsymbol{\beta}_4$, and $\boldsymbol{\beta}_5$ for the three experimental agents.

To compare treatments for the unusual design structure, unique contrasts must be constructed. The first three contrasts are the mean comparisons for agents 1, 2, and 3, respectively, with the mean of the two control conditions. The final contrast is the comparison of the two control-group vector means (expected to prove nonsignificant). The contrast matrix is

$$\mathbf{L}_5 = \begin{bmatrix} 1 & .2 & .2 & .2 & .2 & .2 \\ 0 & -.5 & -.5 & 1 & 0 & 0 \\ 0 & -.5 & -.5 & 0 & 1 & 0 \\ 0 & -.5 & -.5 & 0 & 0 & 1 \\ 0 & 1 & -1 & 0 & 0 & 0 \end{bmatrix} \begin{matrix} \text{L0} & \text{Constant} \\ \text{L1} & \text{Agent 1} \\ \text{L2} & \text{Agent 2} \\ \text{L3} & \text{Agent 3} \\ \text{L4} & \text{Controls} \end{matrix}$$

The basis is

$$\mathbf{K}_5 = \begin{bmatrix} 1 & -.2 & -.2 & -.2 & .5 \\ 1 & -.2 & -.2 & -.2 & -.5 \\ 1 & .8 & -.2 & -.2 & 0 \\ 1 & -.2 & .8 & -.2 & 0 \\ 1 & -.2 & -.2 & .8 & 0 \end{bmatrix}$$
$$\begin{matrix} \text{L0} & \text{L1} & \text{L2} & \text{L3} & \text{L4} \end{matrix}$$

The complete basis for the population constant, the three active-agent contrasts, the contrast of the two controls, the year contrast, and the single estimable interaction, may be formed as Kronecker products of the columns of

$\mathbf{K}_2$ and $\mathbf{K}_5$. Assuming that the products are computed with the $\mathbf{K}_2$ (year) vector as the prefactor, the 10×7 basis is

$$\mathbf{K}=\begin{bmatrix} 1 & -.2 & -.2 & -.2 & .5 & .5 & -.1 \\ 1 & -.2 & -.2 & -.2 & -.5 & .5 & -.1 \\ 1 & .8 & -.2 & -.2 & 0 & .5 & .4 \\ 1 & -.2 & .8 & -.2 & 0 & .5 & -.1 \\ 1 & -.2 & -.2 & .8 & 0 & .5 & -.1 \\ 1 & -.2 & -.2 & -.2 & .5 & -.5 & .1 \\ 1 & -.2 & -.2 & -.2 & -.5 & -.5 & .1 \\ 1 & .8 & -.2 & -.2 & 0 & -.5 & -.4 \\ 1 & -.2 & .8 & -.2 & 0 & -.5 & .1 \\ 1 & -.2 & -.2 & .8 & 0 & -.5 & .1 \end{bmatrix}$$

$$\text{C0}\otimes\text{L0} \quad \text{C0}\otimes\text{L1} \quad \text{C0}\otimes\text{L2} \quad \text{C0}\otimes\text{L3} \quad \text{C0}\otimes\text{L4} \quad \text{C1}\otimes\text{L0} \quad \text{C1}\otimes\text{L1}$$

Parallel to the reduction of the matrix of means, the fifth, seventh and ninth rows of **K** may be eliminated, leaving the basis for extant groups as a square 7×7 matrix.

We note that C1⊗L1 is the only estimable interaction. The control and experimental agent 1 are the only two experimental conditions having observations in both years. The sampling diagram is given in Figure 8.4.1. Cells with X's

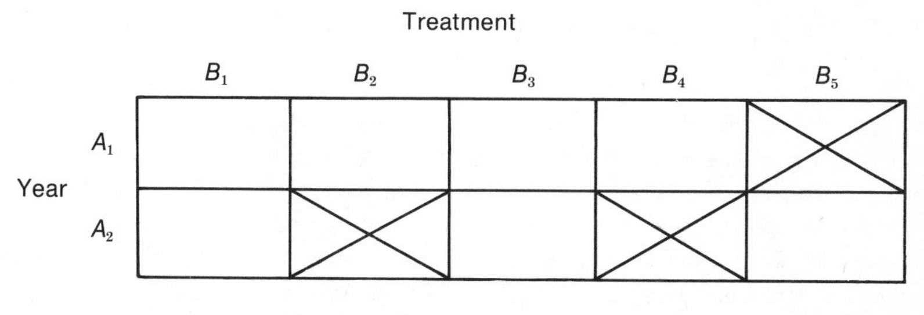

Figure 8.4.1

have no observations. If we write the weights for the interaction C1⊗L1 as in Section 7.4, we obtain the diagram of Figure 8.4.2. No estimate that depends

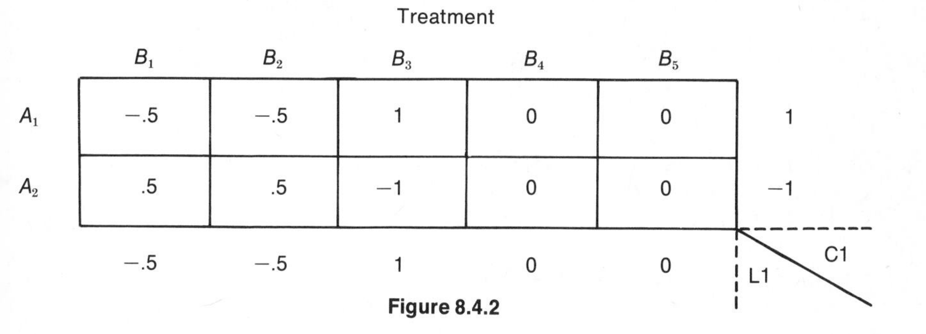

Figure 8.4.2

upon a null subclass is involved in the contrast. Although cell (2,2) has no observations, the mean for cell (2,1) and (2,2) may be estimated from cell (2,1) alone. Any other interaction of $\mathbf{L}_2$ and $\mathbf{L}_5$ contrasts is dependent upon other combinations of null-group means and cannot be obtained.

Other sampling arrangements create other inestimable effects. For example, if the design had no observations in either B_2 group, the diagram would be as shown in Figure 8.4.3. Two degrees of freedom between groups are "lost" for the two empty groups. However, one of the inestimable effects is a B main-effect contrast. No comparison with B_2 is possible; the B degrees of freedom are three rather than four. In addition, one interaction contrast cannot be estimated.

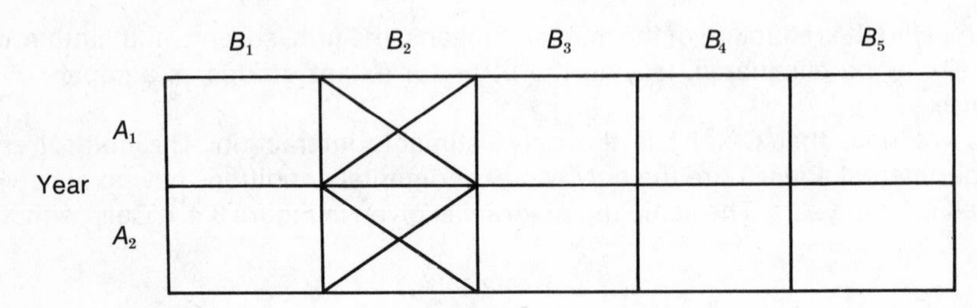

Figure 8.4.3

The rank of the full model for significance testing is $l=7$. All effects that may contribute to criterion variation must be considered. However, it is hypothesized (and later verified) that only the first four effects are essential to the model. That is, the control contrast and the years and interaction contrasts are all null, and may be deleted from the model. We will obtain "best" estimates of only the remaining terms; the rank of the model for estimation is $c=4$ (one degree of freedom to estimate the constant term, plus three for the active-agent contrasts). The terms to be estimated comprise the 4×6 matrix $\mathbf{\Theta}_4$.

$$\mathbf{\Theta}_4=\begin{bmatrix} \mathbf{k}' \\ \boldsymbol{\beta}_3'-1/2(\boldsymbol{\beta}_1'+\boldsymbol{\beta}_2') \\ \boldsymbol{\beta}_4'-1/2(\boldsymbol{\beta}_1'+\boldsymbol{\beta}_2') \\ \boldsymbol{\beta}_5'-1/2(\boldsymbol{\beta}_1'+\boldsymbol{\beta}_2') \end{bmatrix} \begin{matrix} \text{C0}\otimes\text{L0} & \text{Constant} \\ \text{C0}\otimes\text{L1} & \text{Agent 1} \\ \text{C0}\otimes\text{L2} & \text{Agent 2} \\ \text{C0}\otimes\text{L3} & \text{Agent 3} \end{matrix}$$

The least-squares estimate of $\mathbf{\Theta}_4$ is

$$\hat{\mathbf{\Theta}}_4=(\mathbf{K}_4'\mathbf{D}\mathbf{K}_4)^{-1}\mathbf{K}_4'\mathbf{D}\mathbf{Y}.$$

$\mathbf{K}_4$ is the first four columns of $\mathbf{K}$. Then

$$
\hat{\boldsymbol{\Theta}}_4 = \begin{bmatrix} .68 & 1.10 & 2.13 & 2.08 & 1.20 & .53 \\ -.31 & -.93 & -1.07 & -1.43 & -.92 & -.30 \\ .18 & -.93 & -.98 & -1.91 & -1.29 & -.91 \\ -.59 & -1.31 & -2.21 & -1.80 & -1.24 & -.72 \end{bmatrix} \begin{matrix} \mathbf{k}' \\ \boldsymbol{\beta}_3' - 1/2(\boldsymbol{\beta}_1' + \boldsymbol{\beta}_2') \\ \boldsymbol{\beta}_4' - 1/2(\boldsymbol{\beta}_1' + \boldsymbol{\beta}_2') \\ \boldsymbol{\beta}_5' - 1/2(\boldsymbol{\beta}_1' + \boldsymbol{\beta}_2') \end{matrix}
$$

Right canine, Right lateral incisor, Right central incisor, Left central incisor, Left lateral incisor, Left canine

Let $\mathbf{g}$ be the 4×1 vector of square roots of the diagonal of $(\mathbf{K}_4'\mathbf{D}\mathbf{K}_4)^{-1}$ and $\mathbf{d}'$ the 1×6 vector of standard deviations from $\hat{\boldsymbol{\Sigma}}$. Then the standard errors are

$$
\begin{aligned}
\mathbf{H} &= \mathbf{g}\mathbf{d}' \\
&= \begin{bmatrix} .12 \\ .23 \\ .47 \\ .25 \end{bmatrix} [1.17 \quad 1.62 \quad 2.06 \quad 2.49 \quad 1.76 \quad 1.26] \\
&= \begin{bmatrix} .14 & .19 & .25 & .30 & .21 & .15 \\ .27 & .38 & .48 & .58 & .41 & .29 \\ .55 & .76 & .97 & 1.17 & .83 & .59 \\ .29 & .40 & .51 & .61 & .43 & .31 \end{bmatrix} \begin{matrix} \mathbf{k}' \\ \boldsymbol{\beta}_3' - 1/2(\boldsymbol{\beta}_1' + \boldsymbol{\beta}_2') \\ \boldsymbol{\beta}_4' - 1/2(\boldsymbol{\beta}_1' + \boldsymbol{\beta}_2') \\ \boldsymbol{\beta}_5' - 1/2(\boldsymbol{\beta}_1' + \boldsymbol{\beta}_2') \end{matrix}
\end{aligned}
$$

Right canine, Right lateral incisor, Right central incisor, Left central incisor, Left lateral incisor, Left canine

Inspection of $\hat{\boldsymbol{\Theta}}_4$ reveals that, with only one exception, all comparisons with the controls are negative. For all three experimental agents, mean calculus scores were lower than in the two control groups. For example, agent 3 ($\boldsymbol{\beta}_5$), which appears the most effective, has contrast values ranging from $-.59$ to -2.21, for the right canine and the right central incisor, respectively.

A test of any one contrast may be obtained by dividing the estimate by the respective standard error. The resulting statistic is referred to a table of the t distribution, with 100 degrees of freedom ($N - J = 107 - 7$). For example, with $\alpha = .01$, the critical t-value for the one-sided alternative is -2.36. For the comparison of agent 3 with the control, this value is exceeded for all teeth but the canines (that is, $-.59/.29 > -2.36$ and $-.72/.31 > -2.36$).

We might expect that a multivariate test of the agent effect would show significance, with the canines contributing no useful between-group variation. It appears that the only teeth to demonstrate effectiveness are those with a higher degree of calculus formation. Although the standard errors of the contrasts for agents 1 and 3 are similar, the mean differences are larger for agent 3, probably the most effective in reducing calculus formation.

Means estimated from the rank-four model may be obtained for all groups, by employing the first four columns of **K**. These are

$$\hat{\mathbf{Y}}_{\cdot} = \mathbf{K}_4\hat{\mathbf{\Theta}}_4$$

$$= \begin{bmatrix} .82 & 1.73 & 2.98 & 3.11 & 1.89 & .91 \\ .82 & 1.73 & 2.98 & 3.11 & 1.89 & .91 \\ .52 & .81 & 1.90 & 1.68 & .97 & .61 \\ 1.00 & .80 & 2.00 & 1.20 & .60 & .00 \\ .23 & .42 & .77 & 1.31 & .65 & .19 \\ .82 & 1.73 & 2.98 & 3.11 & 1.89 & .91 \\ .82 & 1.73 & 2.98 & 3.11 & 1.89 & .91 \\ .52 & .81 & 1.90 & 1.68 & .97 & .61 \\ 1.00 & .80 & 2.00 & 1.20 & .60 & .00 \\ .23 & .42 & .77 & 1.31 & .65 & .19 \end{bmatrix} \begin{matrix} \left.\begin{matrix} \text{Control 1} \\ \text{Control 2} \\ \text{Agent 1} \\ \text{Agent 2} \\ \text{Agent 3} \end{matrix}\right\} \text{Year 1} \\ \left.\begin{matrix} \text{Control 1} \\ \text{Control 2} \\ \text{Agent 1} \\ \text{Agent 2} \\ \text{Agent 3} \end{matrix}\right\} \text{Year 2} \end{matrix}$$

Columns: Right canine, Right lateral incisor, Right central incisor, Left central incisor, Left lateral incisor, Left canine

These means have a patterned simplicity, since all rows have been generated as linear functions of four rows of $\hat{\mathbf{\Theta}}_4$. The elements of $\hat{\mathbf{Y}}_{\cdot}$ are obtained by summing only a subset of all possible components, eliminating those hypothesized or known to be null. In particular, the control contrast $\hat{\boldsymbol{\beta}}_1-\hat{\boldsymbol{\beta}}_2$ reflects only random variation and is among those eliminated. The resulting estimates of population means for the two control groups are identical. Since year effects are also judged to be null, the difference reflects only random variation and is not included in the estimates. As a result, the estimates for years 1 and 2 are identical. Finally, elimination of nonsignificant interactions produces a particularly simple pattern of means, free from random components that add complexity to the comparison of specific groups.

The predicted means are more efficiently estimated than the observed means, which contain all components. The estimated variance–covariance matrix of $\mathbf{Y}_{\cdot}$ is $\mathbf{D}^{-1}\otimes\hat{\mathbf{\Sigma}}$. For example, the mean calculus score for the right canine in the first control group for year 1, $y_{\cdot 11}{}^{(1)}$, has variance

$$\frac{1}{N_1}\hat{\sigma}_1{}^2 = \frac{1}{8}(1.38) = .172$$

The standard error is $\sqrt{.172} = .415$. The variance–covariance matrix of $\hat{\mathbf{Y}}_{\cdot}$ is $\mathbf{K}_4(\mathbf{K}_4'\mathbf{D}\mathbf{K}_4)^{-1}\mathbf{K}_4'\otimes\hat{\mathbf{\Sigma}} = \mathbf{Q}\otimes\hat{\mathbf{\Sigma}}$. The variance of $\hat{y}_{\cdot 11}{}^{(1)}$ is the product of $\hat{\sigma}_1{}^2$ and the leading element of $\mathbf{Q}$. This is approximately $(1/45)1.38 = .031$. The standard error is $\sqrt{.031} = .175$.

Under the general model with arbitrary N, the estimated means may be combined across subclasses without weighting by the N_j. Let us obtain means for the five treatment conditions, combined across years of experimentation.

Averaging means for the two years in this example will yield the same means as we have for each year, since the two are identical. The reader may wish to compare the "combined estimated means" from one half of $\hat{\mathbf{Y}}.$ with the "combined observed means" of Table 3.4.1. The observed values are confounded by the inclusion of all effects, of which some are nonsignificant, and by undue weighting for the larger groups (for example, control 1, year 2; agent 1, year 2).

In $\hat{\mathbf{Y}}.$ vector means have been estimated for null subclasses. These groups are assumed to follow the same model as those with data. For example, the estimated means for agent 2 in the second year of experimentation, $\hat{\mathbf{y}}'_{\cdot 24}$ are valid as long as the observation of that treatment combination would not alter the mean effectiveness of agent 2, of agents in year 2, or introduce a nonzero interaction.

Mean residuals, $\mathbf{Y}.-\hat{\mathbf{Y}}.$, may be obtained for the $J_0=7$ groups having observations. These include the mean differences of the two controls, year differences, and interactions. It is useful to inspect these terms to identify unmodeled effects of possible interest. For the example, these are

$$\hat{\mathbf{E}}. = \mathbf{Y}.-\hat{\mathbf{Y}}.$$

$$= \begin{bmatrix} -.07 & .52 & .77 & 1.01 & .36 & -.04 \\ .51 & .04 & .13 & .22 & .67 & .64 \\ -.09 & .05 & -.62 & -.11 & .03 & -.18 \\ .00 & .00 & .00 & .00 & .00 & .00 \\ -.14 & -.16 & -.26 & -.36 & -.32 & -.20 \\ .03 & -.01 & .18 & .03 & -.01 & .05 \\ .00 & .00 & .00 & .00 & .00 & .00 \end{bmatrix} \begin{array}{l} \left.\begin{array}{l} \text{Control 1} \\ \text{Control 2} \\ \text{Agent 1} \\ \text{Agent 2} \end{array}\right\} \text{Year 1} \\ \left.\begin{array}{l} \text{Control 1} \\ \text{Agent 1} \\ \text{Agent 3} \end{array}\right\} \text{Year 2} \end{array}$$

Columns: Right canine, Right lateral incisor, Right central incisor, Left central incisor, Left lateral incisor, Left canine

The residuals may be put in standard metric by dividing by variable standard deviations. A more useful metric is to divide each by its own standard error, yielding zero-mean, unit-variance statistics, which individually follow a t distribution. Residual degrees of freedom are $N-J_0=107-7=100$.

The estimated variance–covariance matrix of $\hat{\mathbf{E}}.$ is $[\mathbf{D}^{-1}-\mathbf{Q}]\otimes\hat{\mathbf{\Sigma}}$. The standard errors are the square roots of the diagonal elements. For example, the standard error of the mean residual for the right canine in the first control, for year 1, $e_{\cdot 11}^{(1)}$, is

$$\sqrt{1.38(1/8-1/45)} = .376$$

The original residual is $-.07$. The t-value is $-.07/.376=-.19$, and does not exceed the critical value of t_{100} at $\alpha=.05$. The effects eliminated for this tooth alone are seen to reflect only random variation ($t_{100,\,.025}=1.98$).

Dividing all the residuals by their respective standard errors, we have:

	Right canine	Right lateral incisor	Right central incisor	Left central incisor	Left lateral incisor	Left canine
Year 1 Control 1	−.19	1.00	1.17	1.27	.64	−.09
Year 1 Control 2	1.46	.09	.22	.30	1.27	1.72
Year 1 Agent 1	−.22	.09	−.90	−.13	.06	−.44
Year 1 Agent 2	.00	.00	.00	.00	.00	.00
Year 2 Control 1	−1.05	−.86	−1.10	−1.25	−1.56	−1.35
Year 2 Agent 1	.22	−.09	.90	.13	−.06	.44
Year 2 Agent 3	.00	.00	.00	.00	.00	.00

None exceeds the critical *t*-value, although the rows corresponding to the controls exhibit some residuals of moderate magnitude. Together, these may throw some doubt upon the assumption that the control-2 agent was truly nonactive, or that control vector means are identical.

Unfortunately, residuals for behavioral data are seldom so small or regular as those demonstrated here. Although they tend to confirm the fit of the model in this instance, in other situations they are useful to identify a lack of fit instead.

Sample Problem 4 – Essay Grading Study

The essay study has 32 experimental conditions; these represent all combinations of information provided teachers, concerning characteristics of the pupil-author. Eight combinations result from subjects being informed that pupil-authors were Negro or white, male or female, and of high or low ability. Four different essay pairs were employed as stimuli; each pair was scored by some teachers under each information condition. Each teacher-subject rated two essays (on two topics) supposedly written by the same pupil-author. The subclass frequencies, and mean teacher ratings under all 32 conditions, for both essay topics, are given in Table 8.4.1.

The number of observations per group ranges from 1 to 6, with a total N of 112. Each subject has two outcome scores, which are themselves the sums of nine item responses. For comparative purposes in significance testing, we may wish to create a third score, as the sum of these two. Since the means for the sum are the sums of the separate mean ratings, they are not included here.

The data matrix for the entire sample, $\mathbf{Y}$, is of order 112×2. The total sum of products for the two essay topics is

$$\mathbf{S}_T = \mathbf{Y}'\mathbf{Y} = \begin{bmatrix} 251969 & 262323 \\ 262323 & 300707 \end{bmatrix}$$

Table 8.4.1 Frequencies and Mean Essay Ratings for Teachers under Different Information Conditions*

Group (j)	Information Given: Race	Information Given: Sex	Information Given: Ability	Essay Pair	Number of Teachers (N_j)	Mean Ratings: Essay Topic I†	Mean Ratings: Essay Topic II‡
1	Negro	Male	High	1	4	44.25	34.50
2				2	3	53.33	59.67
3				3	3	47.00	67.67
4				4	3	40.33	47.67
5			Low	1	3	37.33	28.33
6				2	4	39.50	58.50
7				3	3	47.00	70.00
8				4	3	34.33	35.67
9		Female	High	1	4	61.50	44.75
10				2	3	46.00	68.67
11				3	4	61.25	56.75
12				4	3	49.67	49.00
13			Low	1	6	41.17	33.33
14				2	3	35.00	41.00
15				3	4	43.75	47.75
16				4	4	47.75	46.50
17	White	Male	High	1	5	56.20	56.80
18				2	3	39.33	53.00
19				3	3	59.67	70.67
20				4	3	52.33	54.00
21			Low	1	5	45.80	45.00
22				2	3	43.00	63.67
23				3	4	41.25	56.00
24				4	5	48.00	44.80
25		Female	High	1	1	10.00	10.00
26				2	4	40.00	39.25
27				3	3	59.00	61.33
28				4	2	39.00	43.00
29			Low	1	4	37.25	29.25
30				2	4	30.75	47.25
31				3	3	48.00	60.00
32				4	3	41.67	33.67

*Range of possible ratings is from 9 to 90 points.
†My favorite school subject.
‡What I think about.

Adjusting to separate subclass mean vectors, the within-groups sum of products is

$$\mathbf{S}_W = \mathbf{S}_T - \mathbf{Y}_{.}'\mathbf{D}\mathbf{Y}_{.}$$

$$= \begin{bmatrix} 13877.68 & 8475.37 \\ 8475.37 & 17429.10 \end{bmatrix} \begin{matrix} \text{Essay topic I} \\ \text{Essay topic II} \end{matrix}$$

$$\begin{matrix} \text{Essay topic I} & \text{Essay topic II} \end{matrix}$$

$\mathbf{Y}_{.}$ is the 32×2 matrix mean, and $\mathbf{D}$ the order-32 diagonal matrix of subclass frequencies, both from Table 8.4.1.

The estimate of error variation is obtained by dividing by the degrees of freedom, $N-J=112-32=80$.

$$\mathbf{V}_W=\hat{\Sigma}=\frac{1}{80}\mathbf{S}_W$$

$$=\begin{bmatrix}173.47 & 105.94\\ 105.94 & 217.86\end{bmatrix}\begin{matrix}\text{Essay topic I}\\ \text{Essay topic II}\end{matrix}$$

$$\begin{matrix}\text{Essay} & \text{Essay}\\ \text{topic I} & \text{topic II}\end{matrix}$$

The variances, or within-group mean squares, are 173.47 and 217.86 for the two essay topics. If there are group-mean differences, these mean squares are valid estimates of the σ_k^2, whereas estimates not adjusting to separate vector means will be biased. The sample standard deviations for the two outcome measures are $s_1=\sqrt{173.47}=13.17$, and $s_2=\sqrt{217.86}=14.76$, respectively.

We may obtain the correlation matrix of the outcome measures by expressing the standard deviations in diagonal matrix form $\mathbf{D}_W{}^{1/2}$. Then

$$\mathbf{R}_W=\mathbf{D}_W{}^{-1/2}\mathbf{V}_W\mathbf{D}_W{}^{-1/2}$$

$$=\begin{bmatrix}1/13.17 & 0\\ 0 & 1/14.76\end{bmatrix}\begin{bmatrix}173.47 & 105.94\\ 105.94 & 217.86\end{bmatrix}\begin{bmatrix}1/13.17 & 0\\ 0 & 1/14.76\end{bmatrix}$$

$$=\begin{bmatrix}1.00 & .54\\ .54 & 1.00\end{bmatrix}\begin{matrix}\text{Essay topic I}\\ \text{Essay topic II}\end{matrix}$$

$$\begin{matrix}\text{Essay} & \text{Essay}\\ \text{topic I} & \text{topic II}\end{matrix}$$

The two essay topics share a moderate amount of variation, but are far from perfectly intercorrelated ($r_{12}=.54$). Maintaining the two separate measures for analysis appears necessary.

The complete four-way analysis-of-variance mean model is

$$\mathbf{y}_{\boldsymbol{\cdot}jklm}=\boldsymbol{\mu}+\boldsymbol{\alpha}_j+\boldsymbol{\beta}_k+\boldsymbol{\gamma}_l+\boldsymbol{\delta}_m+(\boldsymbol{\alpha\beta})_{jk}+(\boldsymbol{\alpha\gamma})_{jl}+(\boldsymbol{\alpha\delta})_{jm}+(\boldsymbol{\beta\gamma})_{kl}+(\boldsymbol{\beta\delta})_{km}+(\boldsymbol{\gamma\delta})_{lm}$$
$$+(\boldsymbol{\alpha\beta\gamma})_{jkl}+(\boldsymbol{\alpha\beta\delta})_{jkm}+(\boldsymbol{\alpha\gamma\delta})_{jlm}+(\boldsymbol{\beta\gamma\delta})_{klm}+(\boldsymbol{\alpha\beta\gamma\delta})_{jklm}+\boldsymbol{\epsilon}_{\boldsymbol{\cdot}jklm}$$

All terms are 2×1 vectors. Terms of the form $(\boldsymbol{\alpha\beta})_{jk}$, $(\boldsymbol{\beta\gamma\delta})_{klm}$, or $(\boldsymbol{\alpha\beta\gamma\delta})_{jklm}$ do not indicate the product of main effects, but rather the interactions of the respective treatment conditions. $\boldsymbol{\alpha}$ is the race effect; $\boldsymbol{\beta}$, sex; $\boldsymbol{\gamma}$, ability; and $\boldsymbol{\delta}$, essay pair.

The entire model matrix **A** has 32 rows for the 32 subclasses, and 135 columns for all main-effect and interaction parameters. The rank of **A** for significance testing is $l=J=32$. This is the sum of all main-effect and interaction degrees of freedom, including one for the constant. The residual or within-group covariance matrix has $112-32=80$ degrees of freedom.

For exemplary purposes, let us concern ourselves with only the constant, the four main effects, and the race×sex interaction. These terms have proven through further analysis to be statistically significant. The model matrix for just these terms is the 32×15 matrix,

$$
\mathbf{A} = \begin{bmatrix}
1 & 1 & 0 & 1 & 0 & 1 & 0 & 1 & 0 & 0 & 0 & 1 & 0 & 0 & 0 \\
1 & 1 & 0 & 1 & 0 & 1 & 0 & 0 & 1 & 0 & 0 & 1 & 0 & 0 & 0 \\
1 & 1 & 0 & 1 & 0 & 1 & 0 & 0 & 0 & 1 & 0 & 1 & 0 & 0 & 0 \\
1 & 1 & 0 & 1 & 0 & 1 & 0 & 0 & 0 & 0 & 1 & 1 & 0 & 0 & 0 \\
1 & 1 & 0 & 1 & 0 & 0 & 1 & 1 & 0 & 0 & 0 & 1 & 0 & 0 & 0 \\
1 & 1 & 0 & 1 & 0 & 0 & 1 & 0 & 1 & 0 & 0 & 1 & 0 & 0 & 0 \\
1 & 1 & 0 & 1 & 0 & 0 & 1 & 0 & 0 & 1 & 0 & 1 & 0 & 0 & 0 \\
1 & 1 & 0 & 1 & 0 & 0 & 1 & 0 & 0 & 0 & 1 & 1 & 0 & 0 & 0 \\
1 & 1 & 0 & 0 & 1 & 1 & 0 & 1 & 0 & 0 & 0 & 0 & 1 & 0 & 0 \\
1 & 1 & 0 & 0 & 1 & 1 & 0 & 0 & 1 & 0 & 0 & 0 & 1 & 0 & 0 \\
1 & 1 & 0 & 0 & 1 & 1 & 0 & 0 & 0 & 1 & 0 & 0 & 1 & 0 & 0 \\
1 & 1 & 0 & 0 & 1 & 1 & 0 & 0 & 0 & 0 & 1 & 0 & 1 & 0 & 0 \\
1 & 1 & 0 & 0 & 1 & 0 & 1 & 1 & 0 & 0 & 0 & 0 & 1 & 0 & 0 \\
1 & 1 & 0 & 0 & 1 & 0 & 1 & 0 & 1 & 0 & 0 & 0 & 1 & 0 & 0 \\
1 & 1 & 0 & 0 & 1 & 0 & 1 & 0 & 0 & 1 & 0 & 0 & 1 & 0 & 0 \\
1 & 1 & 0 & 0 & 1 & 0 & 1 & 0 & 0 & 0 & 1 & 0 & 1 & 0 & 0 \\
1 & 0 & 1 & 1 & 0 & 1 & 0 & 1 & 0 & 0 & 0 & 0 & 0 & 1 & 0 \\
1 & 0 & 1 & 1 & 0 & 1 & 0 & 0 & 1 & 0 & 0 & 0 & 0 & 1 & 0 \\
1 & 0 & 1 & 1 & 0 & 1 & 0 & 0 & 0 & 1 & 0 & 0 & 0 & 1 & 0 \\
1 & 0 & 1 & 1 & 0 & 1 & 0 & 0 & 0 & 0 & 1 & 0 & 0 & 1 & 0 \\
1 & 0 & 1 & 1 & 0 & 0 & 1 & 1 & 0 & 0 & 0 & 0 & 0 & 1 & 0 \\
1 & 0 & 1 & 1 & 0 & 0 & 1 & 0 & 1 & 0 & 0 & 0 & 0 & 1 & 0 \\
1 & 0 & 1 & 1 & 0 & 0 & 1 & 0 & 0 & 1 & 0 & 0 & 0 & 1 & 0 \\
1 & 0 & 1 & 1 & 0 & 0 & 1 & 0 & 0 & 0 & 1 & 0 & 0 & 1 & 0 \\
1 & 0 & 1 & 0 & 1 & 1 & 0 & 1 & 0 & 0 & 0 & 0 & 0 & 0 & 1 \\
1 & 0 & 1 & 0 & 1 & 1 & 0 & 0 & 1 & 0 & 0 & 0 & 0 & 0 & 1 \\
1 & 0 & 1 & 0 & 1 & 1 & 0 & 0 & 0 & 1 & 0 & 0 & 0 & 0 & 1 \\
1 & 0 & 1 & 0 & 1 & 1 & 0 & 0 & 0 & 0 & 1 & 0 & 0 & 0 & 1 \\
1 & 0 & 1 & 0 & 1 & 0 & 1 & 1 & 0 & 0 & 0 & 0 & 0 & 0 & 1 \\
1 & 0 & 1 & 0 & 1 & 0 & 1 & 0 & 1 & 0 & 0 & 0 & 0 & 0 & 1 \\
1 & 0 & 1 & 0 & 1 & 0 & 1 & 0 & 0 & 1 & 0 & 0 & 0 & 0 & 1 \\
1 & 0 & 1 & 0 & 1 & 0 & 1 & 0 & 0 & 0 & 1 & 0 & 0 & 0 & 1
\end{bmatrix}
$$

The parameters are

$$[\boldsymbol{\Theta}^*]' = [\boldsymbol{\mu} \quad \boldsymbol{\alpha}_1 \quad \boldsymbol{\alpha}_2 \quad \boldsymbol{\beta}_1 \quad \boldsymbol{\beta}_2 \quad \boldsymbol{\gamma}_1 \quad \boldsymbol{\gamma}_2 \quad \boldsymbol{\delta}_1 \quad \boldsymbol{\delta}_2 \quad \boldsymbol{\delta}_3 \quad \boldsymbol{\delta}_4 \quad (\boldsymbol{\alpha\beta})_{11} \quad (\boldsymbol{\alpha\beta})_{12} \quad (\boldsymbol{\alpha\beta})_{21} \quad (\boldsymbol{\alpha\beta})_{22}]$$

The rank of the model for estimation, including just these terms, is $c = 8$. This is the between-group degrees of freedom for this subset of effects (1 for estimating $\boldsymbol{\mu}$, plus 1 for $\boldsymbol{\alpha}$, 1 for $\boldsymbol{\beta}$, 1 for $\boldsymbol{\gamma}$, 3 for $\boldsymbol{\delta}$, and 1 for $\boldsymbol{\alpha\beta}$).

Let us develop the contrast matrix for all the effects in **A** simultaneously. The row of **L** corresponding to the constant term is the average of all rows of **A**. That is,

$$\boldsymbol{l}'_1 = [1 \quad .5 \quad .5 \quad .5 \quad .5 \quad .5 \quad .5 \quad .25 \quad .25 \quad .25 \quad .25 \quad .25 \quad .25 \quad .25 \quad .25]$$

For the contrast $\boldsymbol{\alpha}_1 - \boldsymbol{\alpha}_2$, we can subtract the average of rows 17 through 32, from the average of rows 1 through 16. That is,

$$\boldsymbol{l}'_2 = [0 \quad 1 \quad -1 \quad 0 \quad 0 \quad 0 \quad 0 \quad 0 \quad 0 \quad 0 \quad 0 \quad .5 \quad .5 \quad -.5 \quad -.5]$$

We note that the α main effect is confounded with $(\alpha\beta)$ interaction terms. Only if the interaction proves to be nonsignificant will the α main-effect estimates be unconfounded. Similarly, the row of **L** for $\beta_1-\beta_2$ is the average of rows 1 through 8 plus 17 through 24, minus the average of the remaining sixteen. That is,

$$l'_3 = [0 \;\; 0 \;\; 0 \;\; 1 \;\; -1 \;\; 0 \;\; 0 \;\; 0 \;\; 0 \;\; 0 \;\; 0 \;\; .5 \;\; -.5 \;\; .5 \;\; -.5]$$

The β main-effect estimates also involve $(\alpha\beta)$ interaction terms. The row of **L** for $\gamma_1-\gamma_2$ is the average of **A** rows 1 through 4, 9 through 12, 17 through 20, and 25 through 28, minus the average of the other sixteen. That is,

$$l'_4 = [0 \;\; 0 \;\; 0 \;\; 0 \;\; 0 \;\; 1 \;\; -1 \;\; 0 \;\; 0 \;\; 0 \;\; 0 \;\; 0 \;\; 0 \;\; 0 \;\; 0]$$

The γ main-effect estimates are not confounded with $(\alpha\beta)$ interactions. However, the unequal cell frequencies may introduce interdependencies between α, β, and γ estimates.

For the different essay pairs, used primarily as a control variable, the type of contrast employed is not of much significance. For deviation contrasts, $\delta_m-\delta.$ $(m=1, 2, 3)$, the rows of the contrast matrix are the average of the eight rows having δ_m minus the average of all 32 rows. The three vectors are

$$\begin{bmatrix} l'_5 \\ l'_6 \\ l'_7 \end{bmatrix} = \begin{bmatrix} 0 & 0 & 0 & 0 & 0 & 0 & 0 & .75 & -.25 & -.25 & -.25 & 0 & 0 & 0 & 0 \\ 0 & 0 & 0 & 0 & 0 & 0 & 0 & -.25 & .75 & -.25 & -.25 & 0 & 0 & 0 & 0 \\ 0 & 0 & 0 & 0 & 0 & 0 & 0 & -.25 & -.25 & .75 & -.25 & 0 & 0 & 0 & 0 \end{bmatrix}$$

Finally, the interaction contrast $(\alpha\beta)_{11}-(\alpha\beta)_{12}-[(\alpha\beta)_{21}-(\alpha\beta)_{22}]$ may be obtained by including in **L** a vector that is the average of rows 1 through 8 of **A**, plus the average of 25 through 32, minus the averages of 9 through 16, and 17 through 24. The resultant contrast vector is

$$l'_8 = [0 \;\; 0 \;\; 0 \;\; 0 \;\; 0 \;\; 0 \;\; 0 \;\; 0 \;\; 0 \;\; 0 \;\; 0 \;\; 1 \;\; -1 \;\; -1 \;\; 1]$$

Although the α and β main effects are confounded with the interaction, the interaction term is not confounded with main effects. Again, however, unequal subclass frequencies may induce interdependencies among all of the estimates.

The basis for the eight effects may be obtained from **L** by juxtaposing the eight row vectors, and solving for **K** by Eq. 8.0.5. Or the basis vectors may be generated as Kronecker products of basis vectors for the individual main effects. For example, for all three two-level factors (A, B, C), the one-way basis is

$$\mathbf{K}_2 = \begin{bmatrix} 1 & .5 \\ 1 & -.5 \end{bmatrix}$$
$$\quad\;\; \text{C0} \quad \text{C1}$$

For the essay factor (D), the basis is

$$\mathbf{K}_4 = \begin{bmatrix} 1 & 1 & 0 & 0 \\ 1 & 0 & 1 & 0 \\ 1 & 0 & 0 & 1 \\ 1 & -1 & -1 & -1 \end{bmatrix}$$
$$\quad\;\; \text{D0} \quad \text{D1} \quad \text{D2} \quad \text{D3}$$

The 32×8 basis has vectors that are the Kronecker products of three $\mathbf{K}_2$ vectors and one $\mathbf{K}_4$ vector, in that order. The products are the first eight effects listed in Table 7.4.2; namely,

1. $C0 \otimes C0 \otimes C0 \otimes D0$ (Constant)
2. $C1 \otimes C0 \otimes C0 \otimes D0$ (Race)
3. $C0 \otimes C1 \otimes C0 \otimes D0$ (Sex)
4. $C0 \otimes C0 \otimes C1 \otimes D0$ (Ability)
5. $C0 \otimes C0 \otimes C0 \otimes D1$ (Essay pair 1)
6. $C0 \otimes C0 \otimes C0 \otimes D2$ (Essay pair 2)
7. $C0 \otimes C0 \otimes C0 \otimes D3$ (Essay pair 3)
8. $C1 \otimes C1 \otimes C0 \otimes D0$ (Race×sex)

The leading $c = 8$ vectors of the reparametrized model matrix are

$$\mathbf{K}_8 = \begin{bmatrix}
1 & .5 & .5 & .5 & 1 & 0 & 0 & .25 \\
1 & .5 & .5 & .5 & 0 & 1 & 0 & .25 \\
1 & .5 & .5 & .5 & 0 & 0 & 1 & .25 \\
1 & .5 & .5 & .5 & -1 & -1 & -1 & .25 \\
1 & .5 & .5 & -.5 & 1 & 0 & 0 & .25 \\
1 & .5 & .5 & -.5 & 0 & 1 & 0 & .25 \\
1 & .5 & .5 & -.5 & 0 & 0 & 1 & .25 \\
1 & .5 & .5 & -.5 & -1 & -1 & -1 & .25 \\
1 & .5 & -.5 & .5 & 1 & 0 & 0 & -.25 \\
1 & .5 & -.5 & .5 & 0 & 1 & 0 & -.25 \\
1 & .5 & -.5 & .5 & 0 & 0 & 1 & -.25 \\
1 & .5 & -.5 & .5 & -1 & -1 & -1 & -.25 \\
1 & .5 & -.5 & -.5 & 1 & 0 & 0 & -.25 \\
1 & .5 & -.5 & -.5 & 0 & 1 & 0 & -.25 \\
1 & .5 & -.5 & -.5 & 0 & 0 & 1 & -.25 \\
1 & .5 & -.5 & -.5 & -1 & -1 & -1 & -.25 \\
1 & -.5 & .5 & .5 & 1 & 0 & 0 & -.25 \\
1 & -.5 & .5 & .5 & 0 & 1 & 0 & -.25 \\
1 & -.5 & .5 & .5 & 0 & 0 & 1 & -.25 \\
1 & -.5 & .5 & .5 & -1 & -1 & -1 & -.25 \\
1 & -.5 & .5 & -.5 & 1 & 0 & 0 & -.25 \\
1 & -.5 & .5 & -.5 & 0 & 1 & 0 & -.25 \\
1 & -.5 & .5 & -.5 & 0 & 0 & 1 & -.25 \\
1 & -.5 & .5 & -.5 & -1 & -1 & -1 & -.25 \\
1 & -.5 & -.5 & .5 & 1 & 0 & 0 & .25 \\
1 & -.5 & -.5 & .5 & 0 & 1 & 0 & .25 \\
1 & -.5 & -.5 & .5 & 0 & 0 & 1 & .25 \\
1 & -.5 & -.5 & .5 & -1 & -1 & -1 & .25 \\
1 & -.5 & -.5 & -.5 & 1 & 0 & 0 & .25 \\
1 & -.5 & -.5 & -.5 & 0 & 1 & 0 & .25 \\
1 & -.5 & -.5 & -.5 & 0 & 0 & 1 & .25 \\
1 & -.5 & -.5 & -.5 & -1 & -1 & -1 & .25
\end{bmatrix}$$

The parameters are

$$\Theta_8' = [\mathbf{k} \quad \alpha_1-\alpha_2+\{(\alpha\beta)_{1\cdot}-(\alpha\beta)_{2\cdot}\} \quad \beta_1-\beta_2+\{(\alpha\beta)_{\cdot 1}-(\alpha\beta)_{\cdot 2}\} \quad \gamma_1-\gamma_2$$

Constant — Race — Sex — Ability

$$\delta_1-\delta_\cdot \quad \delta_2-\delta_\cdot \quad \delta_3-\delta_\cdot \quad (\alpha\beta)_{11}-(\alpha\beta)_{12}-\{(\alpha\beta)_{21}-(\alpha\beta)_{22}\}]$$

Essay pair 1 — Essay pair 2 — Essay pair 3 — Race×sex

The variance–covariance factors of the estimates are

$$\mathbf{G}=(\mathbf{K}_8'\mathbf{D}\mathbf{K}_8)^{-1}$$

$$= 10^{-3}\times\begin{bmatrix} 9.16 & & & & & & & (\text{Symmetric}) \\ -.44 & 36.30 \\ -.45 & 4.03 & 36.36 \\ 1.62 & -1.55 & -1.62 & 36.22 \\ -.98 & -1.05 & -1.04 & .74 & 24.88 \\ .01 & 1.21 & 1.23 & -1.01 & -8.46 & 28.02 \\ .23 & -.25 & .96 & -.95 & -8.11 & -9.51 & 27.56 \\ 3.75 & -2.02 & -2.07 & -.10 & 5.58 & -7.92 & .34 & 147.38 \end{bmatrix}$$

The estimates of effects are

$$\hat{\Theta}_8=\mathbf{G}\mathbf{K}_8'\mathbf{D}\mathbf{Y}_\cdot=\begin{bmatrix} 45.31 & 49.09 \\ .74 & .22 \\ .99 & 7.90 \\ 8.12 & 5.74 \\ -.31 & -11.04 \\ -4.37 & 4.75 \\ 5.12 & 11.24 \\ -12.75 & -11.80 \end{bmatrix}\begin{matrix}\text{Constant}\\ \text{Race}\\ \text{Sex}\\ \text{Ability}\\ \text{Essay pair 1}\\ \text{Essay pair 2}\\ \text{Essay pair 3}\\ \text{Race}\times\text{sex}\end{matrix}$$

Essay topic I — Essay topic II

The standard errors of the elements are the products of the standard deviations for the two essays and the square roots of the diagonal elements of **G**. As a product of vectors, these are

$$\mathbf{H}=\mathbf{g}\mathbf{d}'=\begin{bmatrix}\sqrt{.00916}\\ \sqrt{.03630}\\ \sqrt{.03636}\\ \sqrt{.03622}\\ \sqrt{.02488}\\ \sqrt{.02802}\\ \sqrt{.02756}\\ \sqrt{.14738}\end{bmatrix}[13.17 \quad 14.76]$$

$$
= \begin{bmatrix} 1.26 & 1.41 \\ 2.51 & 2.81 \\ 2.51 & 2.81 \\ 2.51 & 2.81 \\ 2.08 & 2.33 \\ 2.20 & 2.47 \\ 2.19 & 2.45 \\ 5.06 & 5.67 \end{bmatrix} \begin{matrix} \text{Constant} \\ \text{Race} \\ \text{Sex} \\ \text{Ability} \\ \text{Essay 1} \\ \text{Essay 2} \\ \text{Essay 3} \\ \text{Race} \times \text{sex} \end{matrix}
$$

Essay topic I   Essay topic II

The contrast estimates and standard errors provide direct information on the effects in the data. First, it is clear that the individual essays are quite different. The estimates of essay effects vary from +11.24 to −11.04, with the two topics and four essay pairs showing few consistencies. For the first topic, "my favorite school subject," the first (almost randomly chosen) composition received scores averaging .31 below the mean of all essays (that is, $\hat{\delta}_1^{(1)} - \hat{\delta}.^{(1)} = -.31$). The second and third compositions received ratings averaging 4.36 points below and 5.12 points above the mean of all four stimuli, respectively. Though not estimated, $\hat{\delta}_4^{(1)} - \hat{\delta}.^{(1)}$ is $-(-.31 - 4.36 + 5.12) = -.45$ point. Thus the four compositions on topic I, and even more so on topic II, represent differing writing styles and qualities. Across essay pairs, this is an expected and desired experimental condition. Yet, for any one pair of compositions, it is possible that the credibility of the stimulus is threatened if a teacher notes that two essays supposedly written by the same pupil are of very different quality.

The ability effect is consistent. When the teachers believed that the essays were written by high-potential students, they rated them 8.12 and 5.74 points, on the average, above the ratings given low-potential students. The standard errors are 2.51 and 2.81 for the two ability contrasts. Both ratios of contrast to standard error exceed the .05 critical t value with 80 degrees of freedom. Before concluding that this effect is significant and without exception, a multivariate test criterion should be applied to the pair of differences. Also tests of the interaction terms should be conducted. These will assure that the ability differences are not an artifact of one or more exceptional essays or experimental conditions. These tests are discussed in Chapter 9.

The contrasts of essay scores for black and white pupils are both positive (blacks having a higher average), but small. The mean differences of .74 and .22 point for the two essay topics, respectively, do not appear to be significantly different from zero. The standard errors are relatively large (2.51 and 2.81).

Both sex contrasts are positive, but only one is large. On the average, males were rated .99 point higher than females on essay topic I, with a standard error of 2.51. For essay topic II, males received an average of 7.90 points more than females. The standard error is 2.81. This effect in isolation exceeds the .05 critical t value with 80 degrees of freedom; that is, $7.90/2.81 > 1.99$. Since there is not consistency for both essays, we shall seek further information including the results of multivariate significance tests, before deciding whether the effect is significant.

The interaction effect of race and sex is large with respect to the standard errors and is in the same direction for both essay topics. The difference of male and female means for Negroes is much smaller than the difference for whites. To clarify the nature of the interaction, we can predict the matrix of means from the rank-8 model. These are combined across ability and essay levels to yield means for each combination of race and sex.

The complete matrix of predicted means is 32×2, and is

$$\hat{\mathbf{Y}}. = \mathbf{K}_8\hat{\mathbf{\Theta}}_8$$

The residuals are the differences of observed and predicted means ($\mathbf{Y}.-\hat{\mathbf{Y}}.$). In this case the residuals consist of all estimable interaction terms, with the exception of race×sex. The residuals have been converted to t statistics by dividing each by its standard error. These are presented, together with the predicted means, in Table 8.4.2.

The predicted means may be combined across subclasses, without respect to the N_j, to yield means for combinations of effects. For example, the mean rating given male Negro authors on the first essay topic is 42.99, or (46.74+42.68+52.17+46.60+38.62+34.56+44.05+38.48)/8. The means for all race-sex combinations are

	Male	Female
Negro	42.99	48.37
White	48.62	41.26

Essay topic I

	Male	Female
Negro	50.20	48.20
White	55.88	42.08

Essay topic II

It may be of interest, or necessary, to compute sex differences and standard errors for males and females separately. However, at least one trend is apparent from the tables. For pupil-authors thought to be black, the average ratings of males and females are 5.38 and 2.00 points apart, but in opposite directions for the two essay topics. By imprecise judgmental criteria, these differences appear comparatively small. Further, if the differences were random, they could well be expected to be in opposite directions. For pupils thought to be white, however, large rating differences are observed for both essay topics (7.36 and 13.80 mean points), consistently in favor of males. The teachers appear to hold very different expectations for white girls and boys, but do not distinguish when rating blacks. Girls, from whom better products are expected, are punished for average work. Questions are raised concerning additional factors, such as the teachers' own race and sex-group membership, as well as the influence of their expectations upon the pupils' actual achievement.

A number of specific hypotheses may be drawn from inspection of the residuals. Only one value exceeds the 1.99 critical value, however. This is the mean residual for essay topic I in experimental subclass 25. The raw residual for the group is $10.00-45.01=-35.01$ with a standard error of 12.61. The .95 interval estimate of $\epsilon_{\cdot 2211}$ is -35.01 ± 1.99 (12.61), or from -60.11 to -9.91. The interval does not include zero, and probably reflects an effect other than random variation. Paralleling this, the group shows a large but nonsignificant residual for the second essay topic. Inspection of the raw data and subclass means re-

Table 8.4.2 Predicted Mean Essay Ratings, and Residuals as *t* Statistics, for Teachers under Different Information Conditions

Group	Information Given			Essay	Essay Topic I*		Essay Topic II†	
	Race	Sex	Ability	Pair	Mean	Residual	Mean	Residual
1	Negro	Male	High	1	46.74	−.45	42.04	−1.21
2				2	42.68	1.59	57.83	.24
3				3	52.17	−.77	64.31	.45
4				4	46.60	−.94	48.13	−.06
5			Low	1	38.62	−.19	36.29	−1.05
6				2	34.56	.90	52.08	1.04
7				3	44.05	.44	58.57	1.53
8				4	38.48	−.62	42.38	−.90
9		Female	High	1	52.13	1.65	40.04	.74
10				2	48.07	−.31	55.82	1.71
11				3	57.56	.66	62.31	−.89
12				4	51.99	−.35	46.13	.38
13			Low	1	44.00	−.66	34.29	−.20
14				2	39.95	−.74	50.08	−1.21
15				3	49.43	−1.01	56.56	−1.40
16				4	43.87	.69	40.38	.97
17	White	Male	High	1	52.37	.79	47.72	1.67
18				2	48.31	−1.34	63.51	−1.40
19				3	57.80	.28	69.99	.09
20				4	52.23	.01	53.81	.03
21			Low	1	44.25	.31	41.98	.55
22				2	40.19	.42	57.76	.78
23				3	49.68	−1.51	64.25	−1.32
24				4	44.11	.81	48.07	−.61
25		Female	High	1	45.01	−2.78	33.92	−1.69
26				2	40.95	−.17	49.71	−1.69
27				3	50.44	1.29	56.19	.69
28				4	44.88	−.69	40.01	.32
29			Low	1	36.89	.07	28.17	.17
30				2	32.83	−.37	43.96	.53
31				3	42.32	.85	50.45	1.28
32				4	36.75	.74	34.26	−.08

*My favorite school subject.
†What I think about.

veals that only one observation was recorded for the subclass. More specifically, subject number 88 (see data listing in the Appendix), responded with a rating of 1 on eight of nine scales for both essays, and did not provide any of the additional information requested. It would appear that the subject was not a serious participant in the study. His scores may be omitted from further analyses. All effects may be reestimated with one fewer observation. Failure to omit the observation may result in other spurious results, such as a single significant high-order interaction.

CHAPTER 9

Analysis of Variance: Tests of Significance

Variation and covariation in the criterion variables may be partitioned into components attributable to the analysis-of-variance model and a residual. Or the variation may be attributed to components representing particular mean differences. Test criteria are applied to determine whether individual contrasts or "omnibus" main effects and interactions explain observed variation in the outcome measures. When there is more than a single criterion score, a multivariate test statistic is appropriate.

The estimation of individual mean contrasts is discussed in the preceding chapters. Those estimates provide the starting point for tests of significance. Unlike most statistical treatises, planned contrasts are discussed prior to "overall" significance tests. Results for omnibus hypotheses of the sort H_0: $\mu_1 = \mu_2 = \cdots = \mu_J$ are obtained by pooling sums of products for $J-1$ independent contrasts among the group means.

The analysis-of-variance mean model is

$$\mathbf{Y.} = \mathbf{A}\boldsymbol{\Theta}^* + \mathbf{E.} \tag{9.0.1}$$

The reparameterized model is

$$\mathbf{Y.} = \mathbf{K}\boldsymbol{\Theta} + \mathbf{E.} \tag{9.0.2}$$

$\mathbf{Y.}$ and $\mathbf{E.}$ are each $J \times p$; $\mathbf{K}$ is the $J \times l$ basis for the parameters in $\boldsymbol{\Theta}$. $\boldsymbol{\Theta} = \mathbf{L}\boldsymbol{\Theta}^*$ is the $l \times p$ matrix of parameters to be estimated from the sample. l is the number of mean contrasts in the complete model or the *rank of the model for significance testing*, satisfying $l \leq J$. In this chapter we are concerned with testing the nullity of some or all of the contrasts in $\boldsymbol{\Theta}$.

After the model has been reparameterized to full rank, the form is mathematically identical to the full-rank regression model, $\mathbf{Y} = \mathbf{XB} + \mathbf{E}$. The distributional assumptions made under the two models are also identical. Specifically, the model matrices, $\mathbf{X}$ and $\mathbf{K}$, are fixed and error-free, and are of rank equal to the number of columns. Rows of $\mathbf{E}$ (observations), are assumed to be independent with expectation zero and identical covariance matrices. The common covariance matrix $\boldsymbol{\Sigma}$ is arbitrary and may exhibit any pattern of intercorrelations among the criterion measures. For interval estimation and tests of significance, we assume further that the random errors are drawn from a multivariate normal population.

Algebraically the models are the same. The distinction of the two is primarily one of convenience. The analysis-of-variance model explicitly defines subclass membership of the observations through the use of subscripts. It is usually employed in *group-comparison* research, whenever the independent variables are defined by membership in experimental or naturally occurring subpopulations. By comparison, if the independent variables consist of a range of scores on *measured* variables, the regression model is perhaps more convenient to apply. Either analysis may be applied to either sort of data (using "dummy variables") with identical results.

The distinction of the analysis-of-variance and regression models is *not* the ability to interpret causal relationships. These may be implied when the experimental setting involves the random assignment of subjects to conditions, and when the manipulation of the experimental treatment is controlled. Either statistical model may be applied. Without the two essential experimental considerations, both models will provide only measures of association, or correlation, of the independent and dependent variables. Analysis of variance is valuable in comparing means of naturally occurring or intact groups, even when causal relationships cannot be determined.

The significance-testing procedures of this chapter parallel those in Chapter 5 for the regression model. The reader may wish to follow the material in the earlier chapter, which is presented in greater detail. The role of a single predictor variable in the regression model is supplanted by that of a particular contrast among means in analysis of variance.

9.1 SEPARATING THE SOURCES OF VARIATION

The least-squares estimate of $\boldsymbol{\Theta}$ in Eq. 9.0.2 is given by Eq. 8.1.2. That is,

$$\hat{\boldsymbol{\Theta}} = (\mathbf{K}'\mathbf{D}\mathbf{K})^{-1}\mathbf{K}'\mathbf{D}\mathbf{Y}. \tag{9.1.1}$$

$\mathbf{D}$ is the diagonal matrix of subclass frequencies $\mathbf{D} = \text{diag}\,[N_1, N_2, \ldots, N_J]$. Each row of $\hat{\boldsymbol{\Theta}}$ is a single contrast among means for the p criterion measures, and corresponds to one degree of freedom between groups. In total there are l rows, each of which is the product of one row of the contrast matrix $\mathbf{L}$ and the original parameters $\boldsymbol{\Theta}^*$.

A hypothesis about one contrast involves a single row of $\boldsymbol{\Theta}$ and is tested from the corresponding row of $\hat{\boldsymbol{\Theta}}$. A hypothesis involving multiple effects or multiple degrees of freedom among groups involves two or more rows of $\boldsymbol{\Theta}$, and is tested from the corresponding rows of $\hat{\boldsymbol{\Theta}}$. Usually we have a series of tests involving sections of $\boldsymbol{\Theta}$. For example, in an $a \times b$ crossed design, we may wish to test the nullity of $a-1$ rows of $\boldsymbol{\Theta}$ containing the A contrasts, $b-1$ rows with the B contrasts, and $(a-1)(b-1)$ rows with interaction contrasts. These provide tests of overall A and B mean differences and of interaction.

Hypothesis tests about $\boldsymbol{\Theta}$ require sum-of-squares and cross-products matrices that reflect the relative importance of the effects to the model. The partition of sums of products into components for the model and residual is given by Eqs. 8.2.3 to 8.2.5. The total sum of products of observed scores is the $p \times p$ matrix $\mathbf{S}_T = \mathbf{Y}'\mathbf{Y}$, with N degrees of freedom. The sum of products due to the model is $\mathbf{S}_B = \hat{\mathbf{\Theta}}'\mathbf{K}'\mathbf{D}\mathbf{K}\hat{\mathbf{\Theta}}$ with l degrees of freedom. The error sum of products is $\mathbf{S}_E = \mathbf{S}_T - \mathbf{S}_B$, with $n_e = N - l$ degrees of freedom. When $l = J$, and all estimable between-group effects are included in the model, $\mathbf{S}_E$ is the pooled within-group sum of products ($\mathbf{S}_E = \mathbf{S}_W$), with $N - J$ degrees of freedom. The population variance–covariance matrix is estimated by $\hat{\mathbf{\Sigma}} = \mathbf{S}_E / n_e$.

In general, multiple tests using rows of $\hat{\mathbf{\Theta}}$ are not valid. The sum of products of the rows of $\hat{\mathbf{\Theta}}$ do not exhaust all the between-group variation. That is,

$$\hat{\mathbf{\Theta}}'\hat{\mathbf{\Theta}} \neq \mathbf{S}_B$$

The matrix estimate may be employed only to conduct tests or draw intervals upon one or a small number of elements. Further, rows of $\hat{\mathbf{\Theta}}$ are not independent. Statistical error rates for tests upon multiple rows may be increased manyfold. This can be seen by inspecting the covariance matrix of one column of $\hat{\mathbf{\Theta}}$. Let $\hat{\boldsymbol{\theta}}_k$ be the kth column of estimates, for criterion y_k. Then the covariance matrix of the estimates is given by Eq. 8.2.2. That is,

$$\mathscr{V}(\hat{\boldsymbol{\theta}}_k) = \sigma_k^2(\mathbf{K}'\mathbf{D}\mathbf{K})^{-1} \tag{9.1.2}$$

Estimates are interdependent to the extent that the covariances, or off-diagonal terms of $(\mathbf{K}'\mathbf{D}\mathbf{K})^{-1}$ are nonzero.

Should $\mathbf{L}$ be row-wise orthogonal (so that $\mathbf{K}$ will be orthogonal by columns), *and* $\mathbf{D}$ have equal elements, the rows of $\hat{\mathbf{\Theta}}$ will be independent. Sums of squares and products may then be obtained directly from these rows. If *either* orthogonality condition is violated, the sums of products will not be independent and will not sum to the correct total between-group sum of squares and cross products.

The orthogonality condition is highly artificial. It does not often conform either to the experimental situation or to the research goals. A general nonorthogonal solution provides an analysis tool consistent with the research design. If the conditions of orthogonality are met, the general model may still be applied. In the special case of orthogonal contrasts and equal N_j the computations are simplified. The general model will produce the solution more commonly derived through scalars or vectors, rather than matrix manipulation.

The general solution involves a second reparameterization of the analysis-of-variance model to a basis matrix with orthogonal columns. This is precisely the reparameterization to orthogonality in the regression model (see Section 5.1). That is, rather than estimating $\mathbf{\Theta}$ we estimate a function of $\mathbf{\Theta}$ that would be obtained if $\mathbf{K}'\mathbf{D}\mathbf{K}$ were diagonal.

Let $\mathbf{T}$ be the triangular Cholesky factor of $\mathbf{K}'\mathbf{D}\mathbf{K}$, such that

$$\mathbf{K}'\mathbf{D}\mathbf{K} = \mathbf{T}\mathbf{T}' \tag{9.1.3}$$

Then the transformed effects to be estimated are $\mathbf{T}'\mathbf{\Theta}$. $\mathbf{K}'\mathbf{D}\mathbf{K}$ and $\mathbf{T}'$ are both $l \times l$, and $\mathbf{T}'\mathbf{\Theta}$ is $l \times p$. Like $\mathbf{\Theta}$, there is one row for each effect in the model and one column for each criterion variable. Since $\mathbf{\Theta}$ contains p separate sets of contrasts for separate measures y_k, $\mathbf{T}'\mathbf{\Theta}$ also contains p separate sets of transformed effects.

The estimate of $\mathbf{T}'\boldsymbol{\Theta}$ is the $l \times p$ matrix

$$\mathbf{U} = \widehat{\mathbf{T}'\boldsymbol{\Theta}} = \mathbf{T}'\hat{\boldsymbol{\Theta}} \tag{9.1.4}$$

Let us inspect the properties of the transformed estimates and then observe the effects of the reparameterization upon the original model.

The expectation of $\mathbf{U}$ is

$$\begin{aligned}\mathscr{E}(\mathbf{U}) &= \mathscr{E}(\mathbf{T}'\hat{\boldsymbol{\Theta}}) \\ &= \mathbf{T}'\mathscr{E}(\hat{\boldsymbol{\Theta}}) \\ &= \mathbf{T}'\boldsymbol{\Theta}\end{aligned} \tag{9.1.5}$$

$\mathbf{U}$ is an unbiased estimate of the population matrix $\mathbf{T}'\boldsymbol{\Theta}$, since $\mathbf{K}'\mathbf{DK}$ and thus $\mathbf{T}$ are matrices of fixed constants. The variance–covariance matrix of $\mathbf{U}$ is

$$\begin{aligned}\mathscr{V}(\mathbf{U}) &= \mathbf{T}'\mathscr{V}(\hat{\boldsymbol{\Theta}})\mathbf{T} \\ &= \mathbf{T}'[(\mathbf{K}'\mathbf{DK})^{-1} \otimes \boldsymbol{\Sigma}]\mathbf{T} \\ &= \mathbf{T}'(\mathbf{TT}')^{-1}\mathbf{T} \otimes \boldsymbol{\Sigma} \\ &= \mathbf{I} \otimes \boldsymbol{\Sigma}\end{aligned} \tag{9.1.6}$$

The variance–covariance matrix of one column of $\mathbf{U}$ is

$$\mathscr{V}(\mathbf{u}_k) = \sigma_k{}^2\mathbf{I} \tag{9.1.6a}$$

If Eq. 9.1.6a is compared with Eq. 9.1.2 it can be seen that unlike $\hat{\boldsymbol{\Theta}}$, rows of $\mathbf{U}$ are independent of one another. $\mathbf{U}$ is the matrix of *orthogonal estimates* or *semipartial regression coefficients*. Although $(\mathbf{K}'\mathbf{DK})^{-1}$ may be nondiagonal, the off-diagonal covariance terms in $\mathbf{I}$ are identically zero. $\mathbf{U}$ is the same order as $\hat{\boldsymbol{\Theta}}$ and estimates the same functions. However, the contrast estimates in $\mathbf{U}$ have the additional property of independence in a predetermined order.

Rows of $\mathbf{U}$, like those of $\hat{\boldsymbol{\Theta}}$, have an arbitrary variance–covariance matrix, $\boldsymbol{\Sigma}$. Values of the same contrast for p measures are still intercorrelated.

If the design is completely orthogonal, with diagonal $\mathbf{K}'\mathbf{DK}$, $\mathbf{T}$ will also be diagonal and $\mathbf{U}$ will be a simple rescaling of the rows of $\hat{\boldsymbol{\Theta}}$. In the general case, $\mathbf{T}$ is a nondiagonal matrix and performs a more complex transformation. The estimate $\mathbf{U}$ is

$$\begin{aligned}\mathbf{U} &= \mathbf{T}'\hat{\boldsymbol{\Theta}} \\ &= \mathbf{T}'(\mathbf{K}'\mathbf{DK})^{-1}\mathbf{K}'\mathbf{DY}. \\ &= \mathbf{T}'(\mathbf{TT}')^{-1}\mathbf{K}'\mathbf{DY}. \\ &= \mathbf{T}^{-1}\mathbf{K}'\mathbf{DY}.\end{aligned} \tag{9.1.7}$$

$\mathbf{T}^{-1}$ is the Cholesky factor of $(\mathbf{K}'\mathbf{DK})^{-1}$. Thus it is the specific transformation that premultiplies $\mathbf{K}'$ to yield an orthonormal matrix with respect to the metric $\mathbf{D}$. That is,

$$\begin{aligned}\mathbf{U} &= \mathbf{T}^{-1}\mathbf{K}'\mathbf{DY}. \\ &= [\mathbf{K}^*]'\mathbf{DY}.\end{aligned} \tag{9.1.8}$$

$\mathbf{K}^*$ is columnwise orthonormal, satisfying $[\mathbf{K}^*]'\mathbf{D}\mathbf{K}^* = \mathbf{I}$. The computations for the MULTIVARIANCE program are performed according to Eq. 9.1.8, with $\mathbf{K}$ orthonormalized by the modified Gram–Schmidt procedure.

Equation 9.1.8 may also be written as

$$\mathbf{U} = [(\mathbf{K}^*)'\mathbf{D}\mathbf{K}^*]^{-1}(\mathbf{K}^*)'\mathbf{D}\mathbf{Y}. \tag{9.1.8a}$$

The term in brackets is simply an identity product. Comparison of Eq. 9.1.8a with 9.1.1 shows us that $\mathbf{U}$ is exactly the least-squares estimate of effects, computed from orthonormal $\mathbf{K}$ rather than from the original basis. $\mathbf{U}$ serves the same function as $\hat{\boldsymbol{\Theta}}$, if the basis is first orthonormalized by columns. Just as $\hat{\boldsymbol{\Theta}}$ is the estimate of $\boldsymbol{\Theta}$ in $\mathbf{Y}. = \mathbf{K}\boldsymbol{\Theta} + \mathbf{E}.$, $\mathbf{U}$ is the estimate of $\mathbf{T}'\boldsymbol{\Theta}$ in

$$\mathbf{Y}. = \mathbf{K}^*\mathbf{T}'\boldsymbol{\Theta} + \mathbf{E}. \tag{9.1.9}$$

The reparameterization involves factoring the basis into the orthonormal basis and an upper triangular matrix. That is,

$$\mathbf{K} = \mathbf{K}^*\mathbf{T}' \tag{9.1.10}$$

The orthonormalization is performed in a particular order of columns or effects. Thus, the *order* of contrasts in $\mathbf{K}$ and $\boldsymbol{\Theta}$ plays a role in testing multiple consecutive hypotheses. Each column of $\mathbf{K}^*$ is computed to be orthogonal to preceding columns. Each row of $\mathbf{U}$ is the estimate of the corresponding term in $\boldsymbol{\Theta}$, eliminating or holding constant all *preceding* effects. The sums of squares and cross products of rows of $\mathbf{U}$ are the sums of products for particular contrasts, eliminating all preceding contrasts.

Represent the ith row of $\mathbf{U}$ as $\mathbf{u}'_i$, where $\mathbf{u}'_i$ is the $1 \times p$ vector containing the estimates of the ith contrast, independent of contrasts 1 through $i-1$. The orthogonal estimates may be represented by rows. That is,

$$\mathbf{U} = \begin{bmatrix} \mathbf{u}'_1 \\ \mathbf{u}'_2 \\ \vdots \\ \mathbf{u}'_l \end{bmatrix} \tag{9.1.11}$$

The sum of squares and cross products for the ith contrast, eliminating preceding effects, is the $p \times p$ matrix $\mathbf{u}_i\mathbf{u}'_i$. To examine $\mathbf{u}_i\mathbf{u}'_i$ and its expectation we need to partition $\mathbf{T}$, the Cholesky factor of $\mathbf{K}'\mathbf{D}\mathbf{K}$. Let the rows of $\mathbf{T}'$ be $\mathbf{t}'_i$ and the rows of $\boldsymbol{\Theta}$ be $\boldsymbol{\theta}'_i$. Then the orthogonal effects $\mathbf{T}'\hat{\boldsymbol{\Theta}}$ estimate population matrix $\mathbf{T}'\boldsymbol{\Theta}$,

$$\mathbf{T}'\boldsymbol{\Theta} = \begin{bmatrix} \mathbf{t}'_1 \\ \mathbf{t}'_2 \\ \mathbf{t}'_3 \\ \vdots \\ \mathbf{t}'_l \end{bmatrix} \begin{bmatrix} \boldsymbol{\theta}'_1 \\ \boldsymbol{\theta}'_2 \\ \boldsymbol{\theta}'_3 \\ \vdots \\ \boldsymbol{\theta}'_l \end{bmatrix} = \begin{bmatrix} t_{11} & t_{12} & t_{13} & \cdots & t_{1l} \\ 0 & t_{22} & t_{23} & \cdots & t_{2l} \\ 0 & 0 & t_{33} & \cdots & t_{3l} \\ \vdots & & & & \vdots \\ 0 & 0 & 0 & \cdots & t_{ll} \end{bmatrix} \begin{bmatrix} \boldsymbol{\theta}'_1 \\ \boldsymbol{\theta}'_2 \\ \boldsymbol{\theta}'_3 \\ \vdots \\ \boldsymbol{\theta}'_l \end{bmatrix}$$

$$= \begin{bmatrix} t_{11}\boldsymbol{\theta}'_1 + t_{12}\boldsymbol{\theta}'_2 + t_{13}\boldsymbol{\theta}'_3 + \cdots + t_{1l}\boldsymbol{\theta}'_l \\ \mathbf{0}' \quad + t_{22}\boldsymbol{\theta}'_2 + t_{23}\boldsymbol{\theta}'_3 + \cdots + t_{2l}\boldsymbol{\theta}'_l \\ \mathbf{0}' \quad + \quad \mathbf{0}' \quad + t_{33}\boldsymbol{\theta}'_3 + \cdots + t_{3l}\boldsymbol{\theta}'_l \\ \vdots \qquad\qquad\qquad\qquad \vdots \\ \mathbf{0}' \quad + \quad \mathbf{0}' \quad + \quad \mathbf{0}' \quad + \cdots + t_{ll}\boldsymbol{\theta}'_l \end{bmatrix} \tag{9.1.12}$$

Each row of $\mathbf{T}'\boldsymbol{\Theta}$ is the product of a row of $\mathbf{T}'$ and the entire matrix $\boldsymbol{\Theta}$. The ith row of $\mathbf{U}$ is $\mathbf{u}'_i = \mathbf{t}'_i\hat{\boldsymbol{\Theta}}$, with expectation $\mathbf{t}'_i\boldsymbol{\Theta}$ and variance–covariance matrix $\boldsymbol{\Sigma}$. The expectation of the sum of products of $\mathbf{u}'_i$ is

$$\mathscr{E}(\mathbf{u}_i\mathbf{u}'_i) = \boldsymbol{\Theta}'\mathbf{t}_i\mathbf{t}'_i\boldsymbol{\Theta} + \boldsymbol{\Sigma} \tag{9.1.13}$$

The partition of sums of squares and cross products is presented in Table 9.1.1. Each product $\mathbf{u}_i\mathbf{u}'_i$ is a $p \times p$ matrix of squares and products for the ith row of $\boldsymbol{\Theta}$, eliminating preceding effects. Tests of significance involve determining whether some or all of the $\mathbf{u}_i\mathbf{u}'_i$ with fixed components $\boldsymbol{\Theta}$ are large, relative to the residual lacking the fixed components.

The sum of the $\mathbf{u}_i\mathbf{u}'_i$ for all effects is

$$\begin{aligned} \sum_{i=1}^{l} \mathbf{u}_i\mathbf{u}'_i &= \mathbf{U}'\mathbf{U} \\ &= \hat{\boldsymbol{\Theta}}'\mathbf{T}\mathbf{T}'\hat{\boldsymbol{\Theta}} \\ &= \hat{\boldsymbol{\Theta}}'\mathbf{K}'\mathbf{D}\mathbf{K}\hat{\boldsymbol{\Theta}} \\ &= \mathbf{S}_B \end{aligned} \tag{9.1.14}$$

The sums of products of rows of $\mathbf{U}$, unlike rows of $\hat{\boldsymbol{\Theta}}$, are a complete partition of the variation due to the model, or between groups. In the transformation to orthogonal parameters the total sum of products has not been altered. Instead, variation has been attributed to the sources in the model, in a specified step-wise order.

Table 9.1.1 Partition of Sums of Products for Rank-l Multivariate Analysis of Variance

Source	*Degrees of Freedom*	*Squares and Cross Products*	*Expected Squares and Products*
$\boldsymbol{\theta}'_1$	1	$\mathbf{u}_1\mathbf{u}'_1$	$\boldsymbol{\Theta}'\mathbf{t}_1\mathbf{t}'_1\boldsymbol{\Theta}+\boldsymbol{\Sigma}$
$\boldsymbol{\theta}'_2$, eliminating $\boldsymbol{\theta}'_1$	1	$\mathbf{u}_2\mathbf{u}'_2$	$\boldsymbol{\Theta}'\mathbf{t}_2\mathbf{t}'_2\boldsymbol{\Theta}+\boldsymbol{\Sigma}$
$\boldsymbol{\theta}'_3$, eliminating $\boldsymbol{\theta}'_1$ and $\boldsymbol{\theta}'_2$	1	$\mathbf{u}_3\mathbf{u}'_3$	$\boldsymbol{\Theta}'\mathbf{t}_3\mathbf{t}'_3\boldsymbol{\Theta}+\boldsymbol{\Sigma}$
$\vdots$	$\vdots$	$\vdots$	$\vdots$
$\boldsymbol{\theta}'_l$, eliminating $\boldsymbol{\theta}'_1, \boldsymbol{\theta}'_2, \ldots, \boldsymbol{\theta}'_{l-1}$	1	$\mathbf{u}_l\mathbf{u}'_l$	$\boldsymbol{\Theta}'\mathbf{t}_l\mathbf{t}'_l\boldsymbol{\Theta}+\boldsymbol{\Sigma}$
$\boldsymbol{\Theta}$	l	$\sum_{i=1}^{l} \mathbf{u}_i\mathbf{u}'_i = \mathbf{U}'\mathbf{U}$	$\boldsymbol{\Theta}'\mathbf{K}'\mathbf{D}\mathbf{K}\boldsymbol{\Theta}+l\boldsymbol{\Sigma}$
Residual	$n_e = N-l$	$\mathbf{S}_E = \mathbf{Y}'\mathbf{Y}-\mathbf{U}'\mathbf{U}$	$(N-l)\boldsymbol{\Sigma}$
Total	N	$\mathbf{S}_T = \mathbf{Y}'\mathbf{Y}$	

Sums of products and degrees of freedom for adjacent contrasts may be combined to test hypotheses about overall main effects and interactions, or about two or more contrasts simultaneously. The complete sum of products for any main effect, in a particular order, has the same value regardless of the type of contrasts chosen.

The sum of products of one or more rows of **U**, employed to test a particular hypothesis, is the *sum of products for hypothesis,* $\mathbf{S}_H$, with degrees of freedom n_h. If there is more than one such matrix, an additional subscript is added to distinguish one matrix and degrees of freedom from another—that is, $\mathbf{S}_{H_j}$ and n_{h_j}.

For example, consider a 2×3 crossed design, with the model reparameterized to deviation contrasts for main effects and interactions. In the complete model $\hat{\mathbf{\Theta}}$ and **U** each has six rows, with effects for the constant, *A*, *B*, and interaction, in that order. The contrast parameters are represented symbolically as

D0⊗D0	Constant
D1⊗D0	*A* main effect
D0⊗D1	*B* main effect
D0⊗D2	*B* main effect
D1⊗D1	*AB* interaction
D1⊗D2	*AB* interaction

The orthogonal estimates comprise a 6×*p* matrix, with one row for each column of **K**. That is,

$$\mathbf{U} = [\mathbf{K}^*]'\mathbf{DY}.$$

$$= \begin{bmatrix} \mathbf{u}'_1 \\ \mathbf{u}'_2 \\ \mathbf{u}'_3 \\ \mathbf{u}'_4 \\ \mathbf{u}'_5 \\ \mathbf{u}'_6 \end{bmatrix} \begin{matrix} \text{Constant} \\ A \text{ main effect, eliminating constant} \\ \left.\begin{matrix} \\ \\ \end{matrix}\right\} B \text{ main effects, eliminating constant and } A \\ \left.\begin{matrix} \\ \\ \end{matrix}\right\} AB \text{ interactions, eliminating constant, } A\text{, and } B \end{matrix} \tag{9.1.15}$$

The partition of sums of squares and cross products for main effects and interaction is given in Table 9.1.2. Each $p \times p$ sum of products for hypothesis, $\mathbf{S}_{H_j}$, contains the *p* univariate sums of squares in the diagonal positions. Each is exactly the sum of squares that would be obtained if performing the analysis for that particular criterion variable alone. In addition, the off-diagonal positions contain the between-group sums of cross products of every pair of criterion variables. These reflect the intercorrelations among the measures and need be considered in conducting multivariate significance tests.

Tests of significance are obtained by determining whether the terms of $\mathbf{S}_{H_j}$ are large compared with those of the residual $\mathbf{S}_E$. One test criterion is based upon the comparison of the "generalized variance" or determinant of $\mathbf{S}_E$ with that of $\mathbf{S}_E+\mathbf{S}_{H_j}$. If the two are about the same, we conclude that the $\mathbf{t}'_j\mathbf{\Theta}$ components do not have a noticeable effect and are null. If the generalized variance of the residuals in $\mathbf{S}_E$ is much smaller than that of $\mathbf{S}_E+\mathbf{S}_{H_j}$, we conclude the reverse, that $\mathbf{t}'_j\mathbf{\Theta}$ are nonnull and of importance. In this case we reject the null hypothesis.

able 9.1.2 Partition of Sums of Products for 2×3 Fixed-effects Crossed Design

Source	Degrees of Freedom	Sum of Products	Mean Products	Expected Sum of Products
onstant	$n_{h_1}=1$	$\mathbf{S}_{H_1}=\mathbf{u}_1\mathbf{u}'_1$	$\mathbf{M}_{H_1}=\mathbf{S}_{H_1}/1$	$\mathbf{\Theta}'\mathbf{t}_1\mathbf{t}'_1\mathbf{\Theta}+\mathbf{\Sigma}$
, eliminating constant	$n_{h_2}=1$	$\mathbf{S}_{H_2}=\mathbf{u}_2\mathbf{u}'_2$	$\mathbf{M}_{H_2}=\mathbf{S}_{H_2}/1$	$\mathbf{\Theta}'\mathbf{t}_2\mathbf{t}'_2\mathbf{\Theta}+\mathbf{\Sigma}$
, eliminating *A* and constant	$n_{h_3}=2$	$\mathbf{S}_{H_3}=\mathbf{u}_3\mathbf{u}'_3+\mathbf{u}_4\mathbf{u}'_4$	$\mathbf{M}_{H_3}=\mathbf{S}_{H_3}/2$	$\mathbf{\Theta}'\mathbf{t}_3\mathbf{t}'_3\mathbf{\Theta}+\mathbf{\Theta}'\mathbf{t}_4\mathbf{t}'_4\mathbf{\Theta}+2\mathbf{\Sigma}$
B, eliminating *A*, *B*, and constant	$n_{h_4}=2$	$\mathbf{S}_{H_4}=\mathbf{u}_5\mathbf{u}'_5+\mathbf{u}_6\mathbf{u}'_6$	$\mathbf{M}_{H_4}=\mathbf{S}_{H_4}/2$	$\mathbf{\Theta}'\mathbf{t}_5\mathbf{t}'_5\mathbf{\Theta}+\mathbf{\Theta}'\mathbf{t}_6\mathbf{t}'_6\mathbf{\Theta}+2\mathbf{\Sigma}$
etween groups	$n_b=6$	$\mathbf{S}_B=\mathbf{S}_{H_1}+\mathbf{S}_{H_2}+\mathbf{S}_{H_3}+\mathbf{S}_{H_4}$ $=\mathbf{U}'\mathbf{U}$	$\mathbf{M}_B=\mathbf{S}_B/6$	$\mathbf{\Theta}'\mathbf{T}\mathbf{T}'\mathbf{\Theta}+6\mathbf{\Sigma}$
ithin groups	$n_e=N-6$	$\mathbf{S}_E=\mathbf{S}_T-\mathbf{S}_B$ $=\mathbf{Y}'\mathbf{Y}-\mathbf{U}'\mathbf{U}$	$\mathbf{M}_E=\mathbf{S}_E/n_e$ $=\hat{\mathbf{\Sigma}}$	$(N-6)\mathbf{\Sigma}$
otal	N	$\mathbf{S}_T=\mathbf{Y}'\mathbf{Y}$		

In Table 9.1.2, $\mathbf{u}_3\mathbf{u}'_3$ and $\mathbf{u}_4\mathbf{u}'_4$ have been pooled to obtain tests of significance of the overall two-degree-of-freedom *B* main effect. It is also possible to obtain independent tests of the two separate contrasts. This is accomplished by not summing the two matrices and considering each separately. Overall or "omnibus" test statistics can obscure specific results that are hypothesized to exist in the data. Specific planned contrasts will yield different results depending upon the contrast type and order. However, the sum $\mathbf{u}_3\mathbf{u}'_3+\mathbf{u}_4\mathbf{u}'_4$ is the total of all orthogonal *B* sources of variation, eliminating the constant and the *A* main effect. This total is constant, regardless of the type of contrasts chosen.

Each sum-of-products matrix may be divided by its degrees of freedom to obtain the $p\times p$ matrix of *mean squares and cross products* (**M**). $\mathbf{M}_{H_j}$ contains the univariate mean squares between groups for each of the criterion variables in the diagonal positions. The error mean-squares-and-products matrix in the example is simply the within-group variance–covariance matrix, with the variance estimates on the diagonal. The covariance matrix is not restriced and may reveal any pattern of association among criterion variables. It may also be reduced to standardized form to estimate the variable intercorrelations.

The error term for analysis of variance depends upon the particular model and effects being tested. The most common is the pooled within-group variance–covariance matrix employed in fixed-effects factorial designs. The matrix is $\mathbf{S}_E=\mathbf{S}_W=\mathbf{Y}'\mathbf{Y}-\mathbf{Y}'_{\cdot}\mathbf{D}\mathbf{Y}_{\cdot}$ (see Eq. 8.2.7). The degrees of freedom are $n_e=N-J$, where J is the total number of subclasses. Should some groups have no observations, J_0, the number of groups with at least one subject, replaces J.

A second class of error terms is the *residual*, after fitting a given model to the data. This has the form $\mathbf{S}_E=\mathbf{Y}'\mathbf{Y}-\mathbf{U}'\mathbf{U}$ where **U** contains the contribution of l defined sources of variation, to the model. The residual is estimated with $n_e=N-l$ degrees of freedom. For example, in a one-observation-per-subclass design, a basis may be constructed for only main effects. The "residual" is then the interaction sum of products. However, if there are replications within cells, and all possible between-cell variation is not included in the basis, the residual is all remaining between-cell variation, plus within-cell variation. Should all J sources of between-group variation be contained in the basis, the "residual" is identically the within-group sum of products (see Eqs. 8.2.7–8.2.9). For example, in Table 9.1.2 the maximum rank of the model is $J=6$. Since six contrasts are estimated, the residual $\mathbf{S}_E$ is identically the within-groups matrix $\mathbf{S}_E=\mathbf{S}_W$.

A third class of error terms shall be designated *special effects*. Here the sum of products for error is the sum of one or more products $\mathbf{u}_i\mathbf{u}'_i$, as estimated through the model. For example, in Sample Problem 5, on programmed instruction effects, experimental conditions and sex are fixed effects. Classes are random, nested within conditions but crossed with sex. There is no within-cell replication since there is only one testing of each sex group in each class. The interaction of sex and classes may be omitted from the basis and designated "residual," providing the error term for the sex and sex×conditions effects.

The error term for the experimental conditions main effect is classes nested within conditions. This effect is included in the basis. Thus we may designate the final 35 rows of $\mathbf{U}$ (the 35 degrees of freedom for classes effects) as a "special effects" error. Then $n_e=35$ and $\mathbf{U}_E$ is the final $35\times p$ submatrix of $\mathbf{U}$. The error sum of products is

$$\mathbf{S}_E=\mathbf{U}_E'\mathbf{U}_E \tag{9.1.16}$$

It is always possible to obtain one sum-of-products matrix by subtraction. This might be, for example, $\mathbf{S}_E$ in Table 9.1.1 or

$$\mathbf{S}_{H_4}=\mathbf{S}_T-\mathbf{S}_E-\sum_{j=1}^{3}\mathbf{S}_{H_j}$$

in Table 9.1.2. If n_h is large, subtracting to obtain sums of products can obviate orthonormalizing a potentially large basis. However, no specific contrasts within the effect can be estimated.

Tests of significance are conducted in the order opposite from the order of elimination in orthonormalizing $\mathbf{K}$. The significance of the last contrast, or set of contrasts, using the last rows of $\mathbf{U}$ is determined first. If these are not significant, the next-to-last hypothesis is tested, using earlier rows of $\mathbf{U}$. The procedure continues until a significant effect is encountered.

Once significant effects are found, all preceding terms of $\mathbf{U}$ are confounded with those effects. This can be seen in expression 9.1.12. For example, if we find that $\boldsymbol{\theta}'_l$ is zero (null hypothesis accepted), then the $\boldsymbol{\theta}'_l$ term disappears from all earlier rows of $\mathbf{U}$. If $\boldsymbol{\theta}'_l$ is nonzero, then all earlier terms are confounded with some nonzero $\boldsymbol{\theta}'_l$ effect. When this is the case, $\boldsymbol{\theta}'_l$ must be ordered ahead of the other terms in $\mathbf{K}$ and $\boldsymbol{\Theta}$. $\mathbf{K}$ is reorthonormalized to obtain unconfounded tests of the other terms, eliminating $\boldsymbol{\theta}'_l$. Further consideration is given to the order of effects, in the following sections.

Some Simple Cases

When subclass frequencies are equal and contrasts are orthogonal, the sums of products between groups are simple functions of rows of $\hat{\boldsymbol{\Theta}}$. Consider a 2×2 fixed-effects crossed design, with two observations per group; that is, $\mathbf{D}=\text{diag}\,(2, 2, 2, 2)$.

The contrasts and basis for main effects and interaction are symbolically represented as C0 $\otimes$ C0 (constant), C1 $\otimes$ C0 (*A* main-effect contrast), C0 $\otimes$ C1 (*B* main-effect contrast), and C1 $\otimes$ C1 (interaction). These are

$$\mathbf{L}=\begin{bmatrix} 1 & .5 & .5 & .5 & .5 & .25 & .25 & .25 & .25 \\ 0 & 1 & -1 & 0 & 0 & .5 & .5 & -.5 & -.5 \\ 0 & 0 & 0 & 1 & -1 & .5 & -.5 & .5 & -.5 \\ 0 & 0 & 0 & 0 & 0 & 1 & -1 & -1 & 1 \end{bmatrix}\begin{matrix}\text{Constant} \\ A\text{ main effect} \\ B\text{ main effect} \\ AB\text{ interaction}\end{matrix} \tag{9.1.17}$$

and

$$\mathbf{K}=\begin{bmatrix} 1 & .5 & .5 & .25 \\ 1 & .5 & -.5 & -.25 \\ 1 & -.5 & .5 & -.25 \\ 1 & -.5 & -.5 & .25 \end{bmatrix} \tag{9.1.18}$$
$$\begin{matrix}\text{Constant} & A & B & AB\end{matrix}$$

The orthogonal basis and triangular factor (Cholesky factor of $\mathbf{K}'\mathbf{D}\mathbf{K}$) are

$$\mathbf{K}^*=\begin{bmatrix} \sqrt{8}/8 & \sqrt{2}/4 & \sqrt{2}/4 & \sqrt{2}/4 \\ \sqrt{8}/8 & \sqrt{2}/4 & -\sqrt{2}/4 & -\sqrt{2}/4 \\ \sqrt{8}/8 & -\sqrt{2}/4 & \sqrt{2}/4 & -\sqrt{2}/4 \\ \sqrt{8}/8 & -\sqrt{2}/4 & -\sqrt{2}/4 & \sqrt{2}/4 \end{bmatrix} \tag{9.1.19}$$
$$\begin{matrix}\text{Constant} & A & B & AB\end{matrix}$$

and

$$\mathbf{T}'=\begin{bmatrix} \sqrt{8} & 0 & 0 & 0 \\ 0 & \sqrt{2} & 0 & 0 \\ 0 & 0 & \sqrt{2} & 0 \\ 0 & 0 & 0 & \sqrt{2}/2 \end{bmatrix} \tag{9.1.20}$$

Since $\mathbf{T}'$ is diagonal, $\mathbf{U}=\mathbf{T}'\hat{\mathbf{\Theta}}$ is the same as $\hat{\mathbf{\Theta}}$ but with rows multiplied by $[t_{ii}]$. Equivalently,

$$\mathbf{U}=[\mathbf{K}^*]'\mathbf{D}\mathbf{Y}.$$
$$=\begin{bmatrix} \sqrt{8}/8 & \sqrt{8}/8 & \sqrt{8}/8 & \sqrt{8}/8 \\ \sqrt{2}/4 & \sqrt{2}/4 & -\sqrt{2}/4 & -\sqrt{2}/4 \\ \sqrt{2}/4 & -\sqrt{2}/4 & \sqrt{2}/4 & -\sqrt{2}/4 \\ \sqrt{2}/4 & -\sqrt{2}/4 & -\sqrt{2}/4 & \sqrt{2}/4 \end{bmatrix}\begin{bmatrix} 2 & & & (\text{Zero}) \\ & 2 & & \\ & & 2 & \\ (\text{Zero}) & & & 2 \end{bmatrix}\begin{bmatrix} \mathbf{y}'_{\cdot 11} \\ \mathbf{y}'_{\cdot 12} \\ \mathbf{y}'_{\cdot 21} \\ \mathbf{y}'_{\cdot 22} \end{bmatrix}$$

$$=\begin{bmatrix} \dfrac{\sqrt{8}}{4}\sum_j\sum_k \mathbf{y}'_{\cdot jk} \\ \dfrac{\sqrt{2}}{2}\sum_k(\mathbf{y}'_{\cdot 1k}-\mathbf{y}'_{\cdot 2k}) \\ \dfrac{\sqrt{2}}{2}\sum_j(\mathbf{y}'_{\cdot j1}-\mathbf{y}'_{\cdot j2}) \\ \dfrac{\sqrt{2}}{2}(\mathbf{y}'_{\cdot 11}+\mathbf{y}'_{\cdot 22}-\mathbf{y}'_{\cdot 12}-\mathbf{y}'_{\cdot 21}) \end{bmatrix}=\begin{bmatrix} \mathbf{u}'_1 \\ \mathbf{u}'_2 \\ \mathbf{u}'_3 \\ \mathbf{u}'_4 \end{bmatrix}\begin{matrix}\text{Constant} \\ A\text{ main effect} \\ B\text{ main effect} \\ AB\text{ interaction}\end{matrix} \tag{9.1.21}$$

The $p \times p$ squares and products for the A main effect are

$$\mathbf{u}_2\mathbf{u}'_2 = 1/2\left[\sum_k (\mathbf{y}_{\cdot 1k}-\mathbf{y}_{\cdot 2k})\right]\left[\sum_k (\mathbf{y}_{\cdot 1k}-\mathbf{y}_{\cdot 2k})'\right]$$
$$= \sum_k 4(\mathbf{y}_{\cdot\cdot k}-\mathbf{y}_{\cdot\cdot\cdot})(\mathbf{y}_{\cdot\cdot k}-\mathbf{y}_{\cdot\cdot\cdot})' \tag{9.1.22}$$

where the number of observations in each level of factor A is four. In the orthogonal case, sums of products for all main effects and interactions may be expressed as simple deviations of level and subclass means, from the overall vector mean $\mathbf{y}_{\cdot\cdot\cdot}$. The reader may wish to verify this for the B contrast and AB interaction.

The orthogonal model is the case most frequently presented in texts (for example, Morrison, 1967; Cooley and Lohnes, 1971). Although the computations under the general linear model are more complex, many of the complexities disappear when subclass frequencies are equal. Use of the general model, on the other hand, facilitates the estimation of contrasts that are not orthogonal, even in equal-N designs. The transformation to $\mathbf{T}'\mathbf{\Theta}$ assures that only sums of squares and products of independent components will be obtained.

In the univariate case, $\mathbf{\Theta}$ is an l-element column vector. Also each row of $\mathbf{U}$ has only a single element. If we assume that the 2×2 example is univariate, the A sum of squares is

$$\mathbf{u}_2\mathbf{u}'_2 = u_2^2$$
$$= \sum_k 4(y_{\cdot\cdot k}-y_{\cdot\cdot\cdot})^2 \tag{9.1.23}$$

This is the usual A sum of squares as obtained through scalar algebra for univariate analysis of variance.

Example

The data of Table 3.3.2 comprise a bivariate 2×2 crossed design with unequal cell frequencies. Thus the orthonormal basis and triangular factor have a more complex form than in Eqs. 9.1.19 and 9.1.20. The basis is $\mathbf{K}$ as given by Eq. 9.1.18; the matrix of subclass frequencies is $\mathbf{D} = \text{diag}\,(4, 6, 5, 7)$.

The Cholesky factor of $\mathbf{K}'\mathbf{DK}$ is

$$\mathbf{T}' = \begin{bmatrix} 4.69 & -.21 & -.43 & 0.00 \\ & 2.34 & -.04 & -.21 \\ & & 2.31 & -.11 \\ \text{(Zero)} & & & 1.15 \end{bmatrix}$$

The Gram-Schmidt orthonormal basis satisfying $[\mathbf{K}^*]'\mathbf{DK}^* = \mathbf{I}$ is

$$\mathbf{K}^* = \begin{bmatrix} .21 & .23 & .26 & .29 \\ .21 & .23 & -.17 & -.19 \\ .21 & -.19 & .26 & -.23 \\ .21 & -.19 & -.18 & .16 \end{bmatrix}$$

The matrix of cell means is

$$\mathbf{Y.} = \begin{bmatrix} .50 & .75 \\ 3.17 & 3.67 \\ 2.20 & 2.40 \\ 3.43 & 3.57 \end{bmatrix} \begin{matrix} \text{Group 11} \\ \text{Group 12} \\ \text{Group 21} \\ \text{Group 22} \end{matrix}$$
$$\quad y_1 \quad\quad y_2$$

The orthogonal estimates are

$$\mathbf{U} = [\mathbf{K}^*]'\mathbf{DY.}$$

$$= \begin{bmatrix} 11.94 & 13.22 \\ -1.91 & -1.36 \\ -4.33 & -4.52 \\ -1.65 & -2.00 \end{bmatrix} \begin{matrix} \text{Constant} \\ A\text{, eliminating constant} \\ B\text{, eliminating constant and } A \\ AB\text{, eliminating constant, } A\text{, and } B \end{matrix}$$
$$\quad y_1 \quad\quad y_2$$

These estimates are mean differences computed to be statistically independent in the order constant, *A*, *B*, *AB*, and to have equal variance–covariance matrices over repeated samplings. Multiplication of $\mathbf{T}'$ and $\mathbf{\Theta}$ from Section 8.1 will yield identical results and may be inspected to see the relationship of $\hat{\mathbf{\Theta}}$ with $\mathbf{U}$.

The sum of products for the constant term is

$$\mathbf{S}_{H_1} = \mathbf{u}_1\mathbf{u}'_1 = \begin{bmatrix} 11.94 \\ 13.22 \end{bmatrix} [11.94 \quad 13.22]$$

$$= \begin{bmatrix} 142.55 & 157.82 \\ 157.82 & 174.73 \end{bmatrix}$$

The sum of products for *A* eliminating the constant is

$$\mathbf{S}_{H_2} = \mathbf{u}_2\mathbf{u}'_2 = \begin{bmatrix} 3.64 & 2.60 \\ 2.60 & 1.86 \end{bmatrix}$$

The diagonal elements of $\mathbf{S}_{H_2}$ are the sums of squares for the *A* main effect for y_1 and y_2 alone. The sum of products for *B*, eliminating *A* and the constant, is

$$\mathbf{S}_{H_3} = \mathbf{u}_3\mathbf{u}'_3 = \begin{bmatrix} 18.75 & 19.56 \\ 19.56 & 20.41 \end{bmatrix}$$

The sum of products for interaction, eliminating all other effects, is

$$\mathbf{S}_{H_4} = \mathbf{u}_4\mathbf{u}'_4 = \begin{bmatrix} 2.72 & 3.30 \\ 3.30 & 4.01 \end{bmatrix}$$

All degrees of freedom are unity ($n_{h_1} = n_{h_2} = n_{h_3} = n_{h_4} = 1$). Each matrix is the squares and products of a single row of $\mathbf{U}$. The mean products matrices are identical to the sums of products.

The error sum of products is the within-groups matrix, computed in Section 8.2. That is,

$$\mathbf{S}_E = \mathbf{S}_W = \begin{bmatrix} 16.35 & 11.72 \\ 11.72 & 11.00 \end{bmatrix}$$

$\mathbf{S}_E$ has $n_e = 18$ degrees of freedom.

The elements of $\mathbf{S}_E$ are compared with those of the $\mathbf{S}_H$ matrices to decide whether each effect contributes to criterion variation. The total sum of squares and products of the original data is

$$\mathbf{S}_T = \begin{bmatrix} 184 & 195 \\ 195 & 212 \end{bmatrix}$$

It is easily verified that the total has been exactly partitioned. That is,

$$\mathbf{S}_T = \mathbf{S}_E + \sum_{j=1}^{4} \mathbf{S}_{H_j} = \mathbf{S}_E + \mathbf{U}'\mathbf{U}$$

9.2 TEST CRITERIA

In this section we use the sums of products developed in Section 9.1 to test the nullity of rows of $\mathbf{\Theta}$. The significance of effects may be tested for all p variates jointly, for each of the criterion measures, and for each measure eliminating preceding measures in a specified order. The test statistics are the multivariate likelihood ratio criterion, univariate F statistics, and "step-down" F statistics, respectively. In addition, Hotelling's T^2 is employed, as a special case of the likelihood criterion, to test multivariate hypotheses concerning a single contrast or single linear combination of effects in $\mathbf{\Theta}$.

All of the test statistics presume the multivariate normality of mean vectors. Subjects are assumed to respond independently of one another, with a common variance–covariance matrix of scores, $\mathbf{\Sigma}$.

There is *no* necessary relationship between the results of multivariate and univariate tests of the same hypothesis. For example, consider vector means for two groups on two variates having their end points at $\mathbf{y}_{\cdot 1}$ and $\mathbf{y}_{\cdot 2}$, as depicted in Figure 9.2.1a. The points around $\mathbf{y}_{\cdot 1}$ and $\mathbf{y}_{\cdot 2}$ represent individual vector observations on the two variates y_1 and y_2. Assuming a zero or negative correlation between variables, the mean difference on y_1 or y_2 alone may not be significant. This would be evidenced by the difference on either variable separately (the length of a or b) being small, relative to within-group dispersion of the variate. By comparison, a multivariate test statistic incorporating both dimensions of variation may yield significant effects. This is evidenced by the length of segment c being longer than either a or b. In addition, within-group variation in the direction of segment c may be smaller than for either y_1 or y_2 alone.

Altering the within-group correlation of y_1 and y_2 may produce the reverse result. Let us assume that group means differ significantly on both y_1 and y_2 alone. Because of the positive correlation of the two, the largest within-group

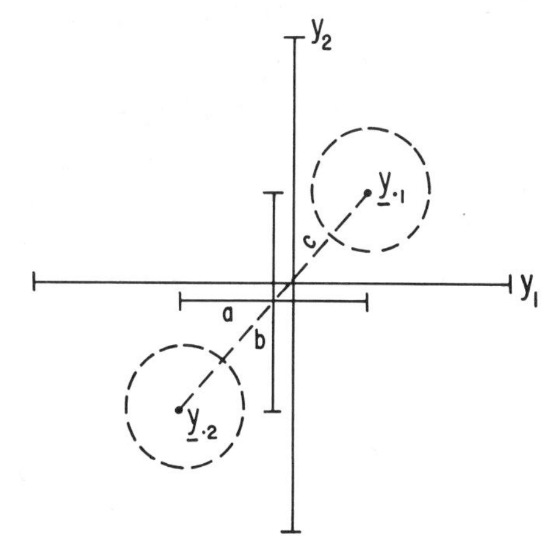

Figure 9.2.1a Multivariate difference significant, not univariate.

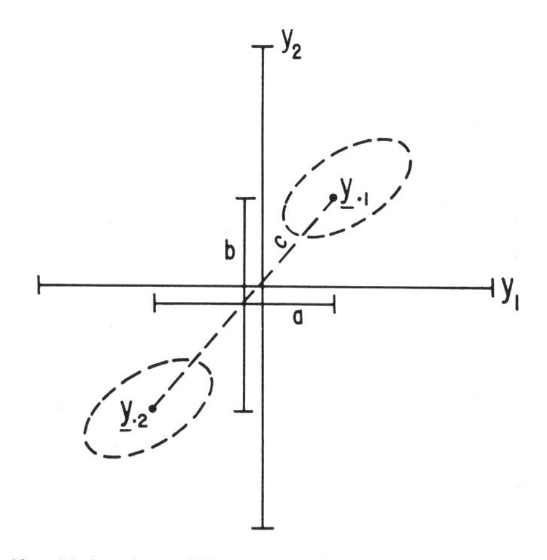

Figure 9.2.1b Univariate differences significant, not multivariate.

dispersion is on the same dimension as the bivariate maximally discriminating line (*c*). This segment, in turn, may not be of sufficient relative length to produce a significant multivariate test statistic.

It is easy to imagine situations in which one or more of a number of univariate results is significant and not the multivariate, or the reverse. Not only may correlations differ, but also the locations of vector means and the variances within groups, as well as the number of groups and measures. The choice of test statistic must follow the design of the research! Whenever variables consist of multiple measures of the same construct, a multivariate test statistic is appropriate for deciding whether or not the hypothesis is supported. Univariate *F* ratios for a single effect are *not* independent, and will tend to compound sampling and decision errors.

If the criterion measures have a theoretical or actual ordering (for example, in terms of complexity, time, or ordered dimensions), then step-down analysis may be appropriate. If it is hypothesized that groups will vary on specifically defined dimensions that are linear combinations of the original measures (for example, factors and discriminant variables), it is more appropriate to transform the data to those dimensions before hypothesis testing. This is accomplished by explicit prior definition of the transformation or, empirically, through "discriminant analysis" techniques. Other test criteria, discussed in Chapter 10, may then be employed.

Hypotheses

The general multivariate analysis-of-variance hypothesis is that one or more rows of $\boldsymbol{\Theta}$ are null for all p measures. Let $\boldsymbol{\Theta}_h$ be a section of $\boldsymbol{\Theta}$ having n_h rows. Each row is a particular mean contrast with p elements, and corresponds to a single degree of freedom between groups. Then the null hypothesis is that the particular contrasts are zero for all measures, or

$$H_0\colon \boldsymbol{\Theta}_h = \mathbf{0} \tag{9.2.1}$$

The alternate is that the contrasts are not zero for one or more measures.

For example, in the one-way four-group design of the word memory experiment (Sample Problem 2), the rows of $\boldsymbol{\Theta}$ are two-element vectors. The four rows are the constant $\mathbf{k}'$ and the three differences $\boldsymbol{\alpha}_1'-\boldsymbol{\alpha}_2'$, $\boldsymbol{\alpha}_2'-\boldsymbol{\alpha}_3'$, and $\boldsymbol{\alpha}_3'-\boldsymbol{\alpha}_4'$, respectively. We may test the nullity of one, two, or all three of these contrasts. For example, the test of

$$H_0\colon \boldsymbol{\alpha}_3-\boldsymbol{\alpha}_4=\mathbf{0} \tag{9.2.2}$$

is equivalent to testing that $\boldsymbol{\alpha}_3 = \boldsymbol{\alpha}_4$, or that the last row of $\boldsymbol{\Theta}$ is null. Also, Eq. 9.2.2 becomes $H_0\colon \boldsymbol{\mu}_3 = \boldsymbol{\mu}_4$ if we let $\boldsymbol{\mu}_j = \boldsymbol{\mu}+\boldsymbol{\alpha}_j$. Equation 9.2.2 is *not* equivalent to $H_0\colon \boldsymbol{\alpha}_3 = \boldsymbol{\alpha}_4 = \mathbf{0}$, however. Under the reparameterization to simple contrasts, the $\boldsymbol{\alpha}_j$ only need be equal, not necessarily zero, to accept H_0. The test of 9.2.2 requires only the estimates from the corresponding last row of $\hat{\boldsymbol{\Theta}}$ or $\mathbf{U}$.

We may also test the nullity of all three final rows of $\boldsymbol{\Theta}$. The hypothesis is

$$H_0\colon \boldsymbol{\alpha}_1=\boldsymbol{\alpha}_2=\boldsymbol{\alpha}_3=\boldsymbol{\alpha}_4 \tag{9.2.3}$$

The alternative is that one or more of the vectors is not equal to the others. Equivalently, Eq. 9.2.3 becomes $H_0\colon \boldsymbol{\mu}_1=\boldsymbol{\mu}_2=\boldsymbol{\mu}_3=\boldsymbol{\mu}_4$ if we let $\boldsymbol{\alpha}_j=\boldsymbol{\mu}_j-\boldsymbol{\mu}$.

The test of Eq. 9.2.3 is the three-degree-of-freedom test of equality of the four vector means, or the nullity of all contrasts among the four groups. The hypothesis is of the identical form as Eq. 9.2.1 if $\boldsymbol{\Theta}_h$ is the last $n_h = 3$ rows of $\boldsymbol{\Theta}$. Each hypothesis is an extension of its univariate counterpart. In order for the multivariate hypothesis to be accepted, however, the data must be supportive for all p measures.

Consider the 2×3 main-effects crossed design with rows $\mathbf{k}' = \boldsymbol{\mu}'+\boldsymbol{\alpha}'_{.}+\boldsymbol{\beta}'_{.}$, $\boldsymbol{\alpha}_1'-\boldsymbol{\alpha}'_{.}$, $\boldsymbol{\beta}_1'-\boldsymbol{\beta}'_{.}$, and $\boldsymbol{\beta}_2'-\boldsymbol{\beta}'_{.}$, respectively. The hypothesis that all β-effects are equal is

$$H_0\colon \boldsymbol{\beta}_1=\boldsymbol{\beta}_2=\boldsymbol{\beta}_{.} \tag{9.2.4}$$

or that $\boldsymbol{\mu}_{.1}=\boldsymbol{\mu}_{.2}=\boldsymbol{\mu}_{.3}$. The hypothesis is that the final $n_h=2$ rows of $\boldsymbol{\Theta}$ are zero.

H_0 is tested from the final two rows of $\hat{\boldsymbol{\Theta}}$ or $\mathbf{U}$. Again, only under the unnecessary assumption that $\Sigma_k \boldsymbol{\beta}_k = \mathbf{0}$ is H_0 equivalent to the test that $\boldsymbol{\beta}_k = \mathbf{0}$.

We may separately test only the second row of $\boldsymbol{\Theta}$ for the hypothesis that

$$H_0\colon \boldsymbol{\alpha}_1 = \boldsymbol{\alpha}. \tag{9.2.5}$$

or that $\boldsymbol{\mu}_{1\cdot} = \boldsymbol{\mu}_{2\cdot}$ for all outcome variables. The one-degree-of-freedom test requires the second row of the estimates $\hat{\boldsymbol{\Theta}}$ or $\mathbf{U}$. If both hypotheses 9.2.4 and 9.2.5 are accepted, we may wish to test that the overall population constant is zero, or

$$H_0\colon \mathbf{k} = \mathbf{0} \tag{9.2.6}$$

Generally, in social science research the origins of measurement scales are arbitrary, and hypothesis 9.2.6 is not of concern. However in selected instances, such as when the data are change scores or growth scores, departure from zero mean is meaningful. The hypothesis is tested using only the first row of $\hat{\boldsymbol{\Theta}}$ or $\mathbf{U}$. Equation 9.2.6 is identical to the simple hypothesis H_0: $\boldsymbol{\mu} = \mathbf{0}$, if there are no α or β effects (one group of observations).

In like fashion, interaction contrasts may comprise further rows of $\boldsymbol{\Theta}$ and may individually or jointly be tested for departure from zero. *Unlike main effects*, interactions are departures from the simpler (main-effect) model. If the interactions are accepted as equal, they are also identically zero.

Specific research problems usually involve testing a sequence of hypotheses about main effects and interactions, or about multiple specific contrasts. The following sections present test criteria for a single hypothesis. The effects of order and testing multiple hypotheses are discussed following the test criteria; the sample problems discussed in Section 9.3 provide further illustration.

The multivariate null hypothesis is given by Eq. 9.2.1. $\boldsymbol{\Theta}$ may be assumed partitioned into the final n_h rows to be tested and the leading $l-n_h$ rows, not under scrutiny. That is,

$$\boldsymbol{\Theta} = \begin{bmatrix} \boldsymbol{\Theta}_0 \\ \hline \boldsymbol{\Theta}_h \end{bmatrix} \begin{matrix} l-n_h \text{ rows} \\ \\ n_h \text{ rows} \end{matrix} \tag{9.2.7a}$$
$$p \text{ columns}$$

where n_h represents the *degrees of freedom for hypothesis*. $\boldsymbol{\Theta}$ is estimated by Eq. 9.1.1. The final n_h rows of the estimate are $\hat{\boldsymbol{\Theta}}_h$. The orthogonal estimates $\mathbf{U}$ (Eq. 9.1.4) may be likewise partitioned. $\mathbf{U}_h$ is the final $n_h \times p$ submatrix of $\mathbf{U}$ corresponding to the n_h effects, *eliminating* effects 1 through $l-n_h$. That is,

$$\mathbf{U} = \begin{bmatrix} \mathbf{U}_0 \\ \hline \mathbf{U}_h \end{bmatrix} \begin{matrix} l-n_h \text{ rows} \\ \\ n_h \text{ rows} \end{matrix} \tag{9.2.7b}$$
$$p \text{ columns}$$

The sum of products for hypothesis is the sum of squares and cross products of the n_h rows of $\mathbf{U}$,

$$\begin{aligned} \mathbf{S}_H &= \sum_{i=l-n_h+1}^{l} \mathbf{u}_i \mathbf{u}'_i \\ &= \mathbf{U}'_h \mathbf{U}_h \end{aligned} \tag{9.2.8}$$

The error sum of squares and cross products may have any of the forms discussed in Section 9.1. The matrix is represented as $\mathbf{S}_E$ with n_e degrees of freedom. Mean squares and cross products for hypothesis and error, respectively, are

$$\mathbf{M}_H = \frac{\mathbf{S}_H}{n_h} \tag{9.2.9a}$$

and

$$\hat{\mathbf{\Sigma}} = \mathbf{M}_E = \frac{\mathbf{S}_E}{n_e} \tag{9.2.9b}$$

Equations 9.2.8 through 9.2.9b are all $p \times p$ symmetric matrices.

Likelihood Ratio Criterion

The likelihood ratio criterion provides a multivariate statistic for testing H_0 with any values of p and n_h. The same criterion for testing H_0 for the regression model is presented in Chapter 5. Substitution of $\mathbf{\Theta}$ for $\mathbf{B}$ and $\mathbf{K}$ for $\mathbf{X}$ yields parallel results for the analysis-of-variance model.

The assumption for the use of the likelihood ratio criterion is that the mean errors are distributed independently in multivariate normal form with expectation $\mathbf{0}$ and variance–covariance matrix $\mathbf{\Sigma}/N_j$. $\mathbf{\Sigma}$ may have any arbitrary form as long as it is nonsingular, with $|\mathbf{\Sigma}| > 0$. This restriction requires that (a) there must be at least as many degrees of freedom for error as criterion measures, that is, $n_e \geqslant p$; and (b) no dependent variable can be exactly expressible as a linear combination of other variates. If the degrees of freedom are too few, either the number of observations must be increased or the number of variates decreased. Variables that are linearly dependent occur, for example, when both subtest and total test scores are included in a single analysis or when the variables are percentage scores that sum to 100 for each subject. In either case, at least one of the variables may be omitted from the analysis; its inclusion yields only redundant information. Or variables may be analyzed in subsets that do not individually contain the dependencies. All other aspects of the analysis (that is, estimation of effects) may be completed with the entire set of measures.

The likelihood ratio is a measure of the extent to which the data are less likely to have arisen from a population described by the model when H_0 is true than when H_0 is false. It is derived by evaluating the likelihood function for the multivariate normal distribution under two models. One model is $\mathbf{Y}. = \mathbf{K\Theta} + \mathbf{E}.$, as in Eq. 9.0.2. The other model is $\mathbf{Y}. = \mathbf{K}_0\mathbf{\Theta}_0 + \mathbf{E}._0$, where $\mathbf{K}_0$ and $\mathbf{\Theta}_0$ are the leading $l - n_h$ effects in $\mathbf{K}$ and $\mathbf{\Theta}$, respectively. The effects in $\mathbf{\Theta}_h$ are omitted. If the likelihood of the first model is sufficiently greater in the sample, then we conclude that the terms in $\mathbf{\Theta}_h$ are important and we reject H_0. The first model with $\mathbf{\Theta}_h$ provides a better description of the data. If the likelihoods of the two models are similar, then the smaller model is maintained and H_0 is supported.

The likelihood ratio statistic is a comparison of residual variation under the two models. Under the first model, $\mathbf{\Sigma}$ is the variance–covariance matrix of the residuals and $|\mathbf{\Sigma}|$ is a multivariate or generalized dispersion measure. Under the second model, the variance–covariance matrix of the residuals is $\mathbf{\Sigma}_0$ and $|\mathbf{\Sigma}_0|$ is the generalized dispersion measure. If the terms omitted in the second model are significant, then $|\mathbf{\Sigma}_0|$ will be much larger than $|\mathbf{\Sigma}|$, since important sources of variation have been attributed to the residual. If the terms omitted in the second model are not significant, then their estimates only reflect additional random variation. $|\boldsymbol{\Sigma}_0|$ will not be much different from $|\boldsymbol{\Sigma}|$.

The likelihood ratio statistic is

$$\Lambda = \frac{|\hat{\boldsymbol{\Sigma}}|}{|\hat{\boldsymbol{\Sigma}}_0|} \tag{9.2.10}$$

The smaller the value of Λ, the more inclined we are to reject H_0.

Simple transformations of Λ follow well-known distributional forms. For large N, Bartlett (1947) has shown that

$$\chi^2 = -m \log_e \Lambda \tag{9.2.11}$$

follows a chi-square distribution, with $n_h p$ degrees of freedom. The multiplier is

$$m = [n_e - (p+1-n_h)/2] \tag{9.2.11a}$$

where n_e is the error degrees of freedom, usually $N-J$. H_0 is rejected with $1-\alpha$ confidence if χ^2 exceeds the 100α upper percentage point of the χ^2 distribution with $n_h p$ degrees of freedom. Otherwise H_0 is maintained. Note that smaller values of Λ yield larger χ^2 results.

A more accurate approximation for the distribution of Λ is an F transformation given by Rao (1952). The test statistic is

$$F = \frac{1-\Lambda^{1/s}}{\Lambda^{1/s}} \cdot \frac{ms+1-n_h p/2}{n_h p} \tag{9.2.12}$$

where

$$s = \left(\frac{p^2 n_h^2 - 4}{p^2 + n_h^2 - 5} \right)^{1/2} \tag{9.2.12a}$$

m is the same as defined for the chi-square test (Eq. 9.2.11a). Using Rao's transformation, H_0 is rejected with confidence $1-\alpha$ if F exceeds the 100α upper percentage point of the F distribution with $n_h p$ and $ms+1-n_h p/2$ degrees of freedom. Like the χ^2, a smaller value of Λ results in a larger F statistic. Since s becomes indeterminate with $n_h p = 2$, setting s to unity in such situations will provide a correct test statistic.

For accuracy, especially in smaller problems, the F transformation (Eq. 9.2.12) should be employed in preference to the χ^2 transform (Eq. 9.2.11). In the special case when either p or n_h is 1 or 2, the F statistic of Eq. 9.2.12 exactly follows the corresponding F distribution. When the degrees of freedom are fractional, rounding to the next lowest integer value will provide the conservative test.

Λ may be computed for any sum of products for hypothesis $\mathbf{S}_H$, with $n_h \geq 1$ degrees of freedom, and error sum of products $\mathbf{S}_E$. Expression 9.2.10 is equivalently

$$\Lambda = \frac{|\mathbf{S}_E|}{|\mathbf{S}_E + \mathbf{S}_H|} \tag{9.2.13}$$

The likelihood ratio can be obtained directly from the sum-of-products partitions. Both $|\mathbf{S}_E|$ and $|\mathbf{S}_E + \mathbf{S}_H|$ may be found by factoring the matrices into triangular factors by the method of Cholesky. The determinant is obtained from the factors. For example, let $\mathbf{S}_E = \mathbf{T}_E\mathbf{T}'_E$, such that $\mathbf{T}_E$ is the Cholesky factor. The determinant is

$$|\mathbf{S}_E| = |\mathbf{T}_E|\,|\mathbf{T}'_E| = \prod_{k=1}^{p} [t_e]_{kk}{}^2 \tag{9.2.14}$$

Then

$$\log|\mathbf{S}_E| = 2\sum_{k=1}^{p} \log\,[t_e]_{kk} \tag{9.2.15}$$

Parallel forms may be followed for $\mathbf{S}_E + \mathbf{S}_H$.

Hummel and Sligo (1971) have shown that a realistic error rate is maintained if the multivariate test statistic is used for a single decision about H_0. A significant multivariate result may be followed by a small number of univariate tests to determine which variates show the greatest and/or smallest mean differences.

Example

We shall use the data of Table 3.3.2 to test the significance of the interaction effect. The null hypothesis is

$$H_0\colon \boldsymbol{\theta}'_4 = \mathbf{0}' \qquad \text{or} \qquad H_0\colon \gamma_{11} - \gamma_{12} = \gamma_{21} - \gamma_{22}$$

The sum of products for interaction, eliminating the constant and main effects, is given in Section 9.1. That is,

$$\mathbf{S}_{H_4} = \mathbf{u}_4\mathbf{u}'_4 = \begin{bmatrix} 2.72 & 3.30 \\ 3.30 & 4.01 \end{bmatrix} \begin{matrix} y_1 \\ y_2 \end{matrix}$$
$$\qquad\qquad\qquad\quad y_1 \qquad y_2$$

There is $n_{h_4} = 1$ degree of freedom for interaction. The error sum of products is

$$\mathbf{S}_E = \begin{bmatrix} 16.35 & 11.72 \\ 11.72 & 11.00 \end{bmatrix} \begin{matrix} y_1 \\ y_2 \end{matrix}$$
$$\qquad\qquad y_1 \qquad y_2$$

having $n_e = 18$ degrees of freedom. The determinants are

$$|\mathbf{S}_E| = 16.35(11.00) - 11.72^2 = 42.45$$

$$|\mathbf{S}_E + \mathbf{S}_{H_4}| = 19.07(15.01) - 15.02^2 = 60.50$$

The likelihood ratio statistic is

$$\Lambda = \frac{42.45}{60.50} = .702$$

The multiplier for the F transformation is

$$m = [18 - (2+1-1)/2] = 17$$

Since $n_{h_4}p = 2$, s is not computed but set to unity by substitution.

The F transformation is

$$F = \frac{1-.702^1}{.702^1} \cdot \frac{17(1)+1-(2)/2}{2} = 3.61$$

with 2 and 17 degrees of freedom. The .01 critical F value is not exceeded (the .05 value is exceeded) and H_0 is maintained. The final row of $\mathbf{\Theta}$ is null for both variates. Since the hypothesis is the only possible *interaction* contrast, we shall consider the individual interaction terms γ_{jk} to be zero.

Hotelling's T^2

The T^2 statistic (Hotelling, 1931) is a specialization of the likelihood ratio statistic to a single vector mean, or a single linear composite of mean vectors. T^2 can be employed in place of the likelihood ratio test whenever the degrees of freedom for hypothesis is $n_h = 1$. The test of significance from Λ or T^2 will yield identical results. The T^2 statistic is a generalization of Student's t to multiple criterion measures; when $p=1$, T^2 is identically the square of t, or F with one degree of freedom in the numerator.

For the most general form of T^2, let $\mathbf{M}$ be a $J \times p$ matrix mean for J populations of observations on p variates. Assume that observations in each group are independently normally distributed, with expectation $\boldsymbol{\mu}_j'$ (the jth row of $\mathbf{M}$) and $p \times p$ covariance matrix $\mathbf{\Sigma}$.

The null hypothesis is

$$H_0\text{: } \mathbf{v}'\mathbf{M} = \boldsymbol{\tau}' \tag{9.2.16}$$

Equation 9.2.16 asserts that a particular linear combination of the rows of $\mathbf{M}$ is equal to a specified $1 \times p$ vector $\boldsymbol{\tau}'$. The alternative hypothesis is that the two vectors are not equal, for one or more elements.

To test Eq. 9.2.16, we draw a random sample of N_j observations from population j ($j = 1, 2, \ldots, J$). Let $\mathbf{y}_{ij}$ be the $p \times 1$ vector observation for subject i in group j. The total number of observations is $N = \Sigma_j N_j$. The sample vector mean for group j is

$$\mathbf{y}'_{\boldsymbol{\cdot} j} = \frac{1}{N_j} \Sigma_i \mathbf{y}'_{ij} \tag{9.2.17}$$

Row vectors $\mathbf{y}'_{\boldsymbol{\cdot} j}$ are juxtaposed in the $J \times p$ sample mean matrix $\mathbf{Y.}$ to estimate $\mathbf{M}$ ($\mathbf{Y.} = \hat{\mathbf{M}}$). Over repeated samplings, $\mathbf{Y.}$ is an unbiased estimate, with $\mathscr{E}(\mathbf{Y.}) = \mathbf{M}$. Let $\mathbf{D}$ be a $J \times J$ diagonal matrix of cell frequencies, $\mathbf{D} = \text{diag}$ $(N_1, N_2, \ldots, N_J)$. Then the covariance matrix of $\mathbf{Y.}$ over repeated samplings is

$$\mathscr{V}(\mathbf{Y.}) = \mathbf{D}^{-1} \otimes \mathbf{\Sigma} \tag{9.2.18}$$

Rows of $\mathbf{Y.}$ are independent. The variance–covariance matrix of a row of means $\mathbf{y}'_{\boldsymbol{\cdot} j}$ is $(1/N_j)\mathbf{\Sigma}$.

The form of the covariance matrix is arbitrary; the p variates may have any pattern of intercorrelations. The estimate of $\mathbf{\Sigma}$ is provided by the pooled within-group variation of observations about the subclass means. Let **Y** be the entire $N \times p$ observation matrix. Then

$$
\begin{aligned}
\hat{\boldsymbol{\Sigma}} &= \mathbf{S}_W \\
&= \frac{1}{N-J} \sum_j \sum_i (\mathbf{y}_{ij} - \mathbf{y}_{\cdot j})(\mathbf{y}_{ij} - \mathbf{y}_{\cdot j})' \\
&= \frac{1}{N-J} \left[\sum_j \left(\sum_i \mathbf{y}_{ij}\mathbf{y}'_{ij} - N_j \mathbf{y}_{\cdot j}\mathbf{y}'_{\cdot j} \right) \right] \\
&= \frac{1}{N-J} (\mathbf{Y}'\mathbf{Y} - \mathbf{Y}'_{\cdot}\mathbf{D}\mathbf{Y}_{\cdot})
\end{aligned}
\tag{9.2.19}
$$

To test H_0 (Eq. 9.2.16) we require an estimate of $\mathbf{v}'\mathbf{M}$ and of the covariance matrix of the product. The estimate of $\mathbf{v}'\mathbf{M}$ is the same linear function of the sample means,

$$\widehat{\mathbf{v}'\mathbf{M}} = \mathbf{v}'\mathbf{Y}_{\cdot} \tag{9.2.20}$$

The covariance matrix of $\mathbf{v}'\mathbf{Y}_{\cdot}$ is

$$
\begin{aligned}
\mathscr{V}(\mathbf{v}'\mathbf{Y}_{\cdot}) &= \mathbf{v}'\mathscr{V}(\mathbf{Y}_{\cdot})\mathbf{v} \\
&= \mathbf{v}'(\mathbf{D}^{-1} \otimes \boldsymbol{\Sigma})\mathbf{v} \\
&= [\mathbf{v}'\mathbf{D}^{-1}\mathbf{v}]\boldsymbol{\Sigma}
\end{aligned}
\tag{9.2.21}
$$

The covariance matrix of a linear combination of means is a scalar function of $\boldsymbol{\Sigma}$.

Hotelling's statistic is

$$T^2 = \frac{1}{\mathbf{v}'\mathbf{D}^{-1}\mathbf{v}} (\mathbf{v}'\mathbf{Y}_{\cdot} - \boldsymbol{\tau}')\hat{\boldsymbol{\Sigma}}^{-1}(\mathbf{v}'\mathbf{Y}_{\cdot} - \boldsymbol{\tau}')' \tag{9.2.22}$$

T^2 follows the T^2 distribution, with parameters p and $N-J-p+1$. Tables of T^2 are given in Jensen and Howe (1968). H_0 is rejected with confidence $1-\alpha$ if T^2 exceeds the 100α upper percentage point of $T^2_{p,N-J-p+1}$. T^2 may also be referred to tables of the F distribution, using the transformation given by expression 5.2.27. n_e is replaced by $N-J$ for analysis-of-variance applications.

One-group case: The T^2 statistic is appropriate in a number of familiar situations. If there is only a single group of observations, we may use T^2 to test that the population vector mean is equal to a vector of constants. The null hypothesis is

$$H_0: \boldsymbol{\mu} = \boldsymbol{\tau} \tag{9.2.23}$$

This has the form of Eq. 9.2.16, with $\boldsymbol{\mu}'$ a $1 \times p$ vector, and **v** the unit scalar, $v = 1$.

The general form of T^2 is given by Eq. 9.2.22. $\mathbf{y}'_{\cdot}$ is the $1 \times p$ sample vector mean and **D** a scalar equal to the number of subjects, N. The test statistic is

$$T^2 = N(\mathbf{y}_{\cdot} - \boldsymbol{\tau})'\hat{\boldsymbol{\Sigma}}^{-1}(\mathbf{y}_{\cdot} - \boldsymbol{\tau}) \tag{9.2.24}$$

The sample covariance matrix (Eq. 9.2.19) for one group is

$$\hat{\boldsymbol{\Sigma}} = \frac{1}{N-1} \sum_{i=1}^{N} (\mathbf{y}_i - \mathbf{y}_{\cdot})(\mathbf{y}_i - \mathbf{y}_{\cdot})' \tag{9.2.25}$$

H_0 is rejected if

$$T^2 \geqslant \frac{p(N-1)}{N-p} F_{p,N-p,\alpha}$$

It can be seen that when $p=1$, T^2 is the square of the t statistic for H_0: $\mu=\tau$. Equation 9.2.24 simplifies to

$$T^2 = \frac{(y_{\cdot}-\tau)^2}{\hat{\sigma}^2/N}$$

Example

Two multiple-choice tests were administered to $N=11$ students. Test 1 consisted of 10 four-choice items, with the chance response level of 2.5 items correct. Test 2 consisted of 20 five-choice items with chance response level of 4 correct. The researcher wished to determine whether actual responses differed from the chance level.

The observed means on the two tests are $y_{\cdot}^{(1)}=3.2$ and $y_{\cdot}^{(2)}=8$. The sample variance–covariance matrix for the two tests is

$$\hat{\mathbf{\Sigma}} = \begin{bmatrix} 1.44 & .30 \\ .30 & 1.69 \end{bmatrix}$$

Substituting in Eq. 9.2.24,

$$T^2 = 11[3.2-2.5 \quad 8-4]\hat{\mathbf{\Sigma}}^{-1}\begin{bmatrix} 3.2-2.5 \\ 8-4 \end{bmatrix} = 104.14$$

The .05 critical F value, with 2 and 9 degrees of freedom, is 4.26. The critical value of T^2 is

$$\frac{2(10)}{9}(4.26) = 9.47$$

H_0 is rejected. The subjects responded above chance level.

Two-group case: When there are $J=2$ groups of subjects, we may wish to test that the vector means are equal. The null hypothesis is

$$H_0\colon \boldsymbol{\mu}_1 = \boldsymbol{\mu}_2$$

or

$$H_0\colon \boldsymbol{\mu}_1 - \boldsymbol{\mu}_2 = \mathbf{0} \tag{9.2.26}$$

Equation 9.2.26 has the form of 9.2.16, where $\mathbf{M}$ is $2\times p$, $\mathbf{v}' = [1 \quad -1]$, and $\boldsymbol{\tau}' = [0 \quad 0]$.

Assume that $\mathbf{y}_{\cdot 1}$ and $\mathbf{y}_{\cdot 2}$ are sample vector means for the two groups, based on N_1 and N_2 observations, respectively. $\mathbf{Y}_{\cdot}$ is $2\times p$, with row vectors $\mathbf{y}_{\cdot 1}'$ and $\mathbf{y}_{\cdot 2}'$. $\mathbf{D}$ is 2×2 with diagonal elements N_1 and N_2. The sample covariance matrix for two groups is

$$\hat{\boldsymbol{\Sigma}}=\frac{1}{N-2}\sum_{j=1}^{2}\sum_{i=1}^{N_j}(\mathbf{y}_{ij}-\mathbf{y}_{\cdot j})(\mathbf{y}_{ij}-\mathbf{y}_{\cdot j})' \tag{9.2.27}$$

where N is the total N_1+N_2.

If the general form (Eq. 9.2.22) is applied, the test statistic is

$$T^2=\left\{[1 \quad -1]\begin{bmatrix}N_1 & 0\\ 0 & N_2\end{bmatrix}^{-1}\begin{bmatrix}1\\ -1\end{bmatrix}\right\}^{-1}(\mathbf{y}_{\cdot 1}-\mathbf{y}_{\cdot 2})'\,\hat{\boldsymbol{\Sigma}}^{-1}(\mathbf{y}_{\cdot 1}-\mathbf{y}_{\cdot 2})$$

$$=\frac{N_1N_2}{N_1+N_2}(\mathbf{y}_{\cdot 1}-\mathbf{y}_{\cdot 2})'\hat{\boldsymbol{\Sigma}}^{-1}(\mathbf{y}_{\cdot 1}-\mathbf{y}_{\cdot 2}) \tag{9.2.28}$$

We may recognize the univariate form of Eq. 9.2.28 as the square of the t statistic for H_0: $\mu_1=\mu_2$. That is if $p=1$, $\hat{\boldsymbol{\Sigma}}$ is the scalar $\hat{\sigma}^2$, and

$$T^2=\frac{(y_{\cdot 1}-y_{\cdot 2})^2}{\hat{\sigma}_d^{\,2}}$$

where

$$\hat{\sigma}_d^{\,2}=\hat{\sigma}^2\left(\frac{1}{N_1}+\frac{1}{N_2}\right)$$

Row of $\boldsymbol{\Theta}$: T^2 may be used to test the nullity of a single row or linear combination of rows of $\boldsymbol{\Theta}$. Since a single row is a particular linear combination of rows, with $\mathbf{v}$ having one unit element and the remaining elements zeros, we discuss only the general case here.

Suppose we wish to test

$$H_0\colon\ \mathbf{v}'\boldsymbol{\Theta}=\boldsymbol{\tau}' \tag{9.2.29}$$

where $\boldsymbol{\Theta}$ is an $l\times p$ matrix of contrast parameters and $\boldsymbol{\tau}'$ is a $1\times p$ vector of constants, selected according to the research questions. The estimate of $\boldsymbol{\Theta}$ is $\hat{\boldsymbol{\Theta}}=(\mathbf{K}'\mathbf{D}\mathbf{K})^{-1}\mathbf{K}'\mathbf{D}\mathbf{Y}_{\cdot}$, with covariance matrix $(\mathbf{K}'\mathbf{D}\mathbf{K})^{-1}\otimes\boldsymbol{\Sigma}$. The covariance matrix of the linear combination $\mathbf{v}'\hat{\boldsymbol{\Theta}}$ is

$$\begin{aligned}\mathscr{V}(\mathbf{v}'\hat{\boldsymbol{\Theta}})&=\mathbf{v}'\mathscr{V}(\hat{\boldsymbol{\Theta}})\mathbf{v}\\ &=\mathbf{v}'[(\mathbf{K}'\mathbf{D}\mathbf{K})^{-1}\otimes\boldsymbol{\Sigma}]\mathbf{v}\\ &=[\mathbf{v}'(\mathbf{K}'\mathbf{D}\mathbf{K})^{-1}\mathbf{v}]\boldsymbol{\Sigma}\end{aligned} \tag{9.2.30}$$

Let $\hat{\boldsymbol{\Sigma}}$ be an estimate of $\boldsymbol{\Sigma}$, derived under the analysis-of-variance model. The test statistic is

$$T^2=\frac{1}{\mathbf{v}'(\mathbf{K}'\mathbf{D}\mathbf{K})^{-1}\mathbf{v}}(\mathbf{v}'\hat{\boldsymbol{\Theta}}-\boldsymbol{\tau}')\hat{\boldsymbol{\Sigma}}^{-1}(\mathbf{v}'\hat{\boldsymbol{\Theta}}-\boldsymbol{\tau}')' \tag{9.2.31}$$

Note that $\mathbf{K}'\mathbf{D}\mathbf{K}$, the covariance factors of $\hat{\boldsymbol{\Theta}}$, replace $\mathbf{D}$ in the T^2 denominator.

Let n_e be degrees of freedom for estimating $\boldsymbol{\Sigma}$. Then H_0 is rejected if

$$T^2\geqslant\frac{pn_e}{n_e-p+1}F_{p,\,n_e-p+1,\,\alpha} \tag{9.2.32}$$

$F_{p,n_e-p+1,\alpha}$ is the upper 100α percentage point of the F distribution, with p and n_e-p+1 degrees of freedom.

We often test the significance of a vector of contrasts, eliminating preceding effects. The same statistic (Eq. 9.2.31) may be employed with $\mathbf{u}'_i$, one row of $\mathbf{U}$, in place of $\mathbf{v}'\hat{\boldsymbol{\Theta}}$. $\mathbf{I}$ replaces the covariance factors $(\mathbf{K}'\mathbf{DK})^{-1}$, and the premultiplication factor disappears. To test for zero effect, $\boldsymbol{\tau}$ is null. The test statistic is

$$T^2 = \mathbf{u}'_i\hat{\boldsymbol{\Sigma}}^{-1}\mathbf{u}_i \tag{9.2.33}$$

There is a simple correspondence between Λ when $n_h=1$ and Hotelling's T^2 statistic. The relationship of the two is given in Chapter 5 for the regression model. That is,

$$\Lambda = \frac{1}{1+T^2/n_e} \tag{9.2.34}$$

Both Λ and T^2 yield the same (exact) F value for one hypothesis degree of freedom.

Example

Let us use Hotelling's T^2 statistic to test whether the B main effect is significant for the 2×2 crossed design of Table 3.3.2. The null hypothesis is H_0: $\boldsymbol{\beta}_1=\boldsymbol{\beta}_2$. The row of $\mathbf{U}$ for the B contrast, eliminating the constant and A, is given in Section 9.1. That is,

$$\mathbf{u}'_3 = \underset{\quad y_1 \qquad\quad y_2}{[-4.33 \quad -4.52]}$$

The within-group variance–covariance matrix is

$$\hat{\boldsymbol{\Sigma}} = \begin{bmatrix} .91 & .65 \\ .65 & .61 \end{bmatrix}\begin{matrix} y_1 \\ y_2 \end{matrix}$$
$$\qquad y_1 \quad y_2$$

$\hat{\boldsymbol{\Sigma}}$ has $n_e=18$ degrees of freedom.

The T^2 statistic is

$$T^2 = \mathbf{u}'_3\hat{\boldsymbol{\Sigma}}^{-1}\mathbf{u}_3 = 34.49$$

The .01 critical F value, with 2 and 17 degrees of freedom, is 6.11. Transforming T^2 to F, we have

$$F = \frac{17(34.49)}{2(18)} = 16.29$$

F does exceed the critical value, and H_0 is rejected with .99 confidence. There is a significant difference between the vector means for levels of the B main effect. For both variates, the population mean for B_1 is lower than for B_2.

Univariate *F* tests

Multivariate test statistics should form the basis for decision making whenever criterion variables are aspects of the same behavioral construct. However, separate *F* statistics for each of the outcome measures provide useful descriptive data. For any one hypothesis, the largest single-variate *F* ratio is obtained for the variable having the largest between-group difference, relative to within-group variation. Likewise, the smallest single *F* statistic is obtained for the measure least affected by the group membership variables; and so on.

Multiple univariate *F* ratios provide relative strength-of-effect estimates for the outcome measures. They may also facilitate comparing mean differences for transformed and untransformed data, for subtest scores computed in different manners, or for multiple factors or principal components of the same test battery. Separate *F* statistics for variables that are correlated are *not* independent of one another and should not be used as partial tests of multivariate hypotheses.

Hummel and Sligo (1971) compared several interpretive devices for multivariate outcomes. They conclude that the most useful approach is to use a multivariate criterion for the global test. If H_0 is *rejected*, a small number of univariate *F* statistics may be inspected or tested individually, to determine which variables have important group-mean differences.

The general form of the multivariate null hypothesis is given by Eq. 9.2.1. A section of $\boldsymbol{\Theta}$ comprising n_h rows or contrasts, and p columns or measures is hypothesized to be null. Specific instances of H_0 may be

$$H_{0_1}: \boldsymbol{\alpha}_1 = \boldsymbol{\alpha}_2 = \boldsymbol{\alpha}_3 = \boldsymbol{\alpha}_4 \tag{9.2.35a}$$

or

$$H_{0_2}: \boldsymbol{\beta}_1 = \boldsymbol{\beta}_2 = \boldsymbol{\beta}. \tag{9.2.35b}$$

or involve only a single comparison,

$$H_{0_3}: \boldsymbol{\gamma}_1 = \boldsymbol{\gamma}_2 \tag{9.2.35c}$$

Each vector contains the effect for the p separate measures. Univariate results will provide p separate but correlated test statistics, for *each* element of the vectors, respectively. For example, in place of H_{0_1} we may have p univariate hypotheses

$$H_{0_1}: \ \alpha_1{}^{(k)} = \alpha_2{}^{(k)} = \alpha_3{}^{(k)} = \alpha_4{}^{(k)} \tag{9.2.36}$$

for outcomes y_k $(k = 1, 2, \ldots, p)$.

The univariate results are simple by-products of the multivariate sum-of-products matrices. Each hypothesis sum of products, $\mathbf{S}_H$, is the sum of n_h $(\geqslant 1)$ vector products of specified rows of $\mathbf{U}$. $\mathbf{S}_H$ is the sum of products between groups, and has n_h degrees of freedom. Dividing, $\mathbf{S}_H/n_h$ yields $\mathbf{M}_H$, the $p \times p$ matrix of mean squares and products. $\mathbf{M}_H$ has the mean squares between groups, for each variable separately, in the diagonal positions.

The mean squares and products for error are obtained from the sum of products for error, $\mathbf{S}_E$, and the error degrees of freedom, n_e. The $p \times p$ matrix is $\mathbf{M}_E = \mathbf{S}_E/n_e = \hat{\boldsymbol{\Sigma}}$. $\mathbf{M}_E$ has the error mean squares for each variate in the diagonal positions.

Ratios of the diagonal elements of $\mathbf{M}_H$ to those of $\mathbf{M}_E$ follow *F* distributions, with n_h and n_e degrees of freedom. For any pair of matrices, there are p such ratios. That is,

$$F_k = \frac{[m_h]_{kk}}{[m_e]_{kk}} \tag{9.2.37}$$

for $k = 1, 2, \ldots, p$. Each F statistic is a test that $\boldsymbol{\theta}_h^{(k)} = \mathbf{0}$, or that the n_h effects are null for a particular variate.

The univariate F statistics are invariant under permutation of criterion measures. Each is exactly the F statistic that would have been obtained if only a single measure were included in the analysis. The univariate F ratios for various contrasts, like their multivariate counterparts, are subject to the conditions of ordering of effects. In a nonorthogonal design, for tests to be independent across main effects and interactions, an ordered elimination procedure is necessary, whether the number of criterion variates is one or many.

Example

We obtain the multivariate test of the interaction effect for the data of Table 3.3.2, on page 314. The sum of products for interaction, eliminating all else, is

$$\mathbf{S}_{H_4} = \begin{bmatrix} 2.72 & 3.30 \\ 3.30 & 4.01 \end{bmatrix} \qquad n_{h_4} = 1$$

The sum of products for error is

$$\mathbf{S}_E = \begin{bmatrix} 16.35 & 11.72 \\ 11.72 & 11.00 \end{bmatrix} \qquad n_e = 18$$

The mean squares between groups for y_1 and y_2 are identically the sums of squares, since there is only a single degree of freedom. That is,

$$[m_h]_{11} = 2.72 \qquad [m_h]_{22} = 4.01$$

The mean squares within groups are

$$[m_e]_{11} = \frac{16.35}{18} = .91 \quad (y_1)$$

$$[m_e]_{22} = \frac{11.00}{18} = .61 \quad (y_2)$$

The F ratios for the two variates for interaction, eliminating all else, are

$$F_1 = \frac{2.72}{.91} = 3.00 \quad (y_1)$$

$$F_2 = \frac{4.01}{.61} = 6.56 \quad (y_2)$$

Each ratio has 1 and 18 degrees of freedom. Neither exceeds the .01 critical F value. The value for y_2 does exceed the .05 critical value however, and we may suspect that there is some interaction for a small portion of the data.

Step-down Analysis

Step-down tests may be conducted for one or more analysis-of-variance effects, as for regression effects in Section 5.2. The step-down statistic for the criterion variable y_k is identical to the univariate test that is obtained if preceding criteria are eliminated as predictors in a regression model. Step-down analysis is the same as $p-1$ ordered analyses of covariance. The step-down procedure enables the researcher to determine the between-group effect for the first criterion measure; for the second criterion measure, eliminating the first; for the third eliminating the first two; and so on. In this manner it can be determined whether all between-group differences are concentrated in the leading criteria or whether later criteria contribute to group differences, above and beyond earlier measures.

Like the other criteria, the step-down statistics depend upon the $p \times p$ sum of products for hypothesis $\mathbf{S}_H$ and the error sum of products $\mathbf{S}_E$. Assume that $\mathbf{S}_H$ is the sum of squares and products of n_h rows of orthogonal estimates, with n_h (≥ 1) degrees of freedom. $\mathbf{S}_E$ is the residual or error sum of products, estimated with n_e degrees of freedom.

Step-down test statistics are F ratios based upon the conditional variance of each criterion, given preceding measures. These are obtained through the triangular Cholesky factorization of $\mathbf{S}_E$ and of the sum $\mathbf{S} = \mathbf{S}_E + \mathbf{S}_H$. Let us represent these factorizations as

$$\mathbf{S}_E = \mathbf{T}_E \mathbf{T}_E' \tag{9.2.38a}$$

and

$$\mathbf{S} = \mathbf{T}^* [\mathbf{T}^*]' \tag{9.2.38b}$$

$[t_e]_{kk}$ and $[t^*]_{kk}$ are the diagonal elements of $\mathbf{T}_E$ and $\mathbf{T}^*$ respectively.

It is shown in Chapter 2 that the Cholesky factor of a covariance matrix contains the standard deviations of the conditional distributions of the variates, eliminating preceding measures. $[t_e]_{11}^2$ is the error sum of squares for y_1. Each following $[t_e]_{kk}^2$ is the error sum of squares for y_k, given $y_1, y_2, \ldots, y_{k-1}$. Similarly, $[t^*]_{kk}^2$ is the sum of squares between groups plus error for y_k, given the preceding variates. And $[t^*]_{kk}^2 - [t_e]_{kk}^2$ is the sum of squares between groups for y_k, given $y_1, y_2, \ldots, y_{k-1}$.

Dividing the between-group value by its degrees of freedom, n_h, yields the *step-down hypothesis mean square*. Dividing $[t_e]_{kk}^2$ by its degrees of freedom yields the *step-down error mean square*. For each criterion eliminated (as with predictors in regression), error degrees of freedom are reduced by one. Thus the degrees of freedom for $[t_e]_{kk}^2$ are $n_e - k + 1$. This is n_e for $[t_e]_{11}^2$, and one fewer for each subsequent term.

There are p step-down F statistics for any hypothesis of the form H_0: $\mathbf{\Theta}_h = \mathbf{0}$. The kth statistic is the ratio of the two conditional mean squares. That is,

$$\begin{aligned} F_k^* &= \frac{([t^*]_{kk}^2 - [t_e]_{kk}^2)/n_h}{[t_e]_{kk}^2/(n_e - k + 1)} \\ &= \frac{[t^*]_{kk}^2 - [t_e]_{kk}^2}{[t_e]_{kk}^2} \cdot \frac{n_e - k + 1}{n_h} \end{aligned} \tag{9.2.39}$$

The univariate and step-down F statistics for the first variate are identical. F_2^* through F_p^* however, are tests of the between-group effect for y_k, eliminating any portion of the effect that can be attributed to variables preceding y_k in $\mathbf{S}_E$ and $\mathbf{S}_H$. F_k^* is referred to upper percentage points of the F distribution, with n_h and n_e-k+1 degrees of freedom. H_0 is rejected if, and only if, at least one step-down F statistic exceeds its critical value. Step-down analysis is a multivariate procedure that may be used instead of the likelihood ratio criterion. It provides the *only* test criteria, of those discussed here, that are dependent upon the order of the dependent variables.

If there is no logical order (in terms of complexity, time, and so on) inherent in the outcome measures, step-down procedures are of little value, and may yield misleading results. Important criteria should be ordered first, and the variables that are more dubious, more complex, or occurring at later times, be ordered last. In this manner it may be determined whether all significant variation between groups is concentrated in simpler, or earlier, measures.

The final F_p^* is interpreted first, then F_{p-1}^*, F_{p-2}^*, and so on. If a significant F_k^* is encountered, we have no valid test of preceding terms. y_1 through y_k are deemed necessary to the model and H_0 is rejected. Variables may be reordered to test preceding terms, eliminating those already found significant. Assuming a prior logical ordering however, this practice is questionable. Step-down tests of a given hypothesis under alternative orders of variates are not independent, and would tend to inflate decision error rates. Further discussion of step-down tests is given in Section 5.2.

It is possible to assign differing type-I error rates to the p step-down tests. Let α_k be the probability of a type-I error, assigned to the variable y_k alone. The overall probability of falsely rejecting at least one of the p subhypotheses is

$$\alpha = 1 - \prod_{k=1}^{p} (1-\alpha_k) \tag{9.2.40}$$

Differential α_k levels can be selected so that a fixed α for the overall hypothesis is maintained (for example, .05 or .01).

Example

The criteria of Table 3.3.2 are attitude scores before and after an intervening stimulus situation. Let us test for interaction of A and B main effects using step-down tests. This provides an alternative to the likelihood ratio test, illustrated for the same hypothesis.

The error sum of products and its Cholesky factor are

$$\mathbf{S}_E = \begin{bmatrix} 16.35 & 11.72 \\ 11.72 & 11.00 \end{bmatrix} \qquad \mathbf{T}_E = \begin{bmatrix} 4.04 & 0 \\ 2.90 & 1.61 \end{bmatrix}$$

The sum $\mathbf{S}_E+\mathbf{S}_{H_4}$ and its Cholesky factor are

$$\mathbf{S} = \mathbf{S}_E+\mathbf{S}_{H_4} = \begin{bmatrix} 19.07 & 15.02 \\ 15.02 & 15.01 \end{bmatrix} \qquad \mathbf{T}^* = \begin{bmatrix} 4.37 & 0 \\ 3.44 & 1.78 \end{bmatrix}$$

The step-down ratios are

$$F_1^* = \frac{(4.37^2 - 4.04^2)}{4.04^2} \cdot \frac{18-1+1}{1} = 3.00 \quad (y_1)$$

$$F_2^* = \frac{(1.78^2 - 1.61^2)}{1.61^2} \cdot \frac{18-2+1}{1} = 3.77 \quad (y_2, \text{ eliminating } y_1)$$

F_1^* is identical to the univariate ratio for y_1.

Interpreting F_2^* first, the value does not exceed the .01 critical F-value, with 1 and 17 degrees of freedom. Thus we proceed to F_1^*. This value is also not significant (d.f. = 1, 18), and H_0 is accepted.

Note that in computing the likelihood ratio statistic, $|\mathbf{S}_E|$ and $|\mathbf{S}_E + \mathbf{S}_H|$ are required. Both may be accurately obtained through the Cholesky factorization (see Chapter 2). It is a simple matter in programming to obtain both multivariate test criteria simultaneously.

Multiple Hypotheses

In most cases we are concerned with testing a series of consecutive hypotheses. These may involve the various main effects and interactions in factorial designs. Or they may involve several orthogonal planned contrasts among levels of a single factor. The result is that there may be two or more sections of $\mathbf{\Theta}$ to be tested, each involving a hypothesis such as Eq. 9.2.1.

For example, in a 2×3 crossed design, $\mathbf{\Theta}$ consists of one row for the constant, one row for the A contrast, two rows for B contrasts, and two for AB interactions. Each row has p elements. The $6 \times p$ matrix may be diagrammed in partitioned form as follows:

$$\mathbf{\Theta} = \begin{bmatrix} \mathbf{\Theta}_k & (1 \times p) \\ \hline \mathbf{\Theta}_A & (1 \times p) \\ \hline \mathbf{\Theta}_B & (2 \times p) \\ \hline \mathbf{\Theta}_{AB} & (2 \times p) \end{bmatrix} \tag{9.2.41}$$

For each section of $\mathbf{\Theta}$ there is a corresponding section of the matrix of orthogonal estimates $\mathbf{U}$. For the 2×3 example, the sections of $\mathbf{U}$ are

$$\mathbf{U} = \begin{bmatrix} \mathbf{U}_k \\ \hline \mathbf{U}_A \\ \hline \mathbf{U}_B \\ \hline \mathbf{U}_{AB} \end{bmatrix} = \begin{bmatrix} \mathbf{u}'_1 \\ \hline \mathbf{u}'_2 \\ \hline \mathbf{u}'_3 \\ \mathbf{u}'_4 \\ \hline \mathbf{u}'_5 \\ \mathbf{u}'_6 \end{bmatrix} \begin{matrix} \text{Constant} \\ A\text{, eliminating constant} \\ B\text{, eliminating constant and } A \\ \\ AB\text{, eliminating constant, } A\text{, and } B \\ \\ \end{matrix} \tag{9.2.42}$$

The partition is the same as that given by Eq. 9.1.15.

The hypothesis sum-of-products matrices are formed from the rows of **U**. If we were to test a hypothesis about the constant, the sum-of-products matrix is

$$\mathbf{S}_{H_1} = \mathbf{U}_k'\mathbf{U}_k = \mathbf{u}_1\mathbf{u}'_1 \tag{9.2.43a}$$

The degrees of freedom are $n_{h_1} = 1$. For the *A* main effect, the sum of products is

$$\mathbf{S}_{H_2} = \mathbf{U}_A'\mathbf{U}_A = \mathbf{u}_2\mathbf{u}'_2 \tag{9.2.43b}$$

with degrees of freedom $n_{h_2} = 1$. For *B*, eliminating *A*,

$$\mathbf{S}_{H_3} = \mathbf{U}_B'\mathbf{U}_B = \mathbf{u}_3\mathbf{u}'_3 + \mathbf{u}_4\mathbf{u}'_4 \tag{9.2.43c}$$

$\mathbf{S}_{H_3}$ has $n_{h_3} = 2$ degrees of freedom. For interaction,

$$\mathbf{S}_{H_4} = \mathbf{U}_{AB}'\mathbf{U}_{AB} = \mathbf{u}_5\mathbf{u}'_5 + \mathbf{u}_6\mathbf{u}'_6 \tag{9.2.43d}$$

with $n_{h_4} = 2$. To test the specific *B* contrasts, the third and fourth matrices would be $\mathbf{u}_3\mathbf{u}'_3$ and $\mathbf{u}_4\mathbf{u}'_4$, each with one degree of freedom, instead of $\mathbf{S}_{H_3}$.

The additional subscript on $\mathbf{S}_H$ and n_h is necessary to distinguish one effect from another. When there is more than one hypothesis, the subscripted matrix and degrees of freedom are substituted for $\mathbf{S}_H$ and n_h in applying all the test criteria. For example, to test the four multivariate hypotheses, $\mathbf{S}_{H_1}$ through $\mathbf{S}_{H_4}$ are separately employed in place of $\mathbf{S}_H$ in Eq. 9.2.13. The respective n_{h_j} replaces n_h in Eqs. 9.2.11 and 9.2.12.

In the general nonorthogonal model (unequal N_j *or* nonorthogonal contrasts), the orthogonal estimates **U** represent a reparameterization of $\boldsymbol{\Theta}$ to orthogonal independent variables in $\mathbf{K}^*$. Each effect is tested, eliminating all preceding effects in the model. Both the order of placement of effects in $\boldsymbol{\Theta}$ (the "order of elimination") and the order in which the results are interpreted are of consequence.

In general, simple effects and those *known* to be of importance are placed first. The constant term is among these, as are any control variables, blocking variables, and so forth. We test the contribution of other factors, above and beyond those that are deemed necessary in advance of analysis. Complex effects and effects that are the *focus* of the research are placed in later positions. They are tested for their unique contribution to criterion variation, above and beyond the others. In this manner we avoid attributing effectiveness to experimental variables that may be explained just as well by simpler or better-known factors. Thus in the two-way design, *B* is the major factor of concern in the study.

Interactions are complex functions and are ordered last, usually by degree (two-way interactions, then three-way, then four-way, and so on). If interactions do not contribute to criterion variation above and beyond the main effects, they are omitted from the model. The principle of scientific parsimony dictates that the simpler (main-effect) explanation is preferred. Interactions also indicate the interpretability of main effects. If an interaction is significant, it is likely that simpler main-effect explanations will not adequately describe the outcomes. It is particular *combinations* of experimental conditions that are effective. Interactions cannot be meaningfully ordered to precede the main effects they involve; for example, the *AB* interaction cannot precede main effects *A* or *B* in the order of elimination.

The first hypothesis test to be *interpreted* is the last set of effects in $\boldsymbol{\Theta}$, or the last in the order of elimination. In the two-way example, this is H_0: $\boldsymbol{\Theta}_{AB}=\mathbf{0}$. The last terms in the model are the more complex terms (high-order interactions, complex between-group effects). Elimination of these effects from the model is consistent with scientific parsimony. Maintenance of complex effects is an early warning that simpler explanations of the data may not suffice.

Only if H_0 is accepted for the last effect can a valid test be obtained of preceding terms in $\mathbf{U}$. This may be seen in the diagrams of Eq. 9.1.12. If H_0 is accepted for $\boldsymbol{\theta}'_l$, then the row of $\boldsymbol{\Theta}$ is null in the population. The last row of $\hat{\boldsymbol{\Theta}}$ reflects only random variation about expectation $\mathbf{0}'$. All terms $t_{il}\boldsymbol{\theta}'_l$ are zero and disappear from the prior rows of $\mathbf{T}'\boldsymbol{\Theta}$. The preceding row is then $t_{l-1,l-1}\boldsymbol{\theta}'_{l-1}$. Tests of significance applied to this row are tests of *only* $\boldsymbol{\theta}'_{l-1}$.

Similarly, if H_0 is accepted for $\boldsymbol{\theta}'_{l-1}$, then $\boldsymbol{\theta}'_{l-1}$ is null and disappears from rows one through $l-2$ of the product matrix. Only in this case are prior terms in the ordering not confounded $\boldsymbol{\theta}'_{l-1}$ effects; and so on, through $\boldsymbol{\theta}'_1$.

The same situation occurs when multiple rows of $\mathbf{U}$ are tested simultaneously (multiple-degree-of-freedom tests). For example, in the 2×3 design, only if the *AB* interaction is nonsignificant do we have a valid test of the *A* or *B* main effects. Here we jointly test the two rows of $\boldsymbol{\Theta}_{AB}$—that is, $\boldsymbol{\theta}'_5$ and $\boldsymbol{\theta}'_6$. If *B* is nonsignificant, then *A* may also be tested in this order.

If H_0 is rejected for $\boldsymbol{\theta}'_l$ or $\boldsymbol{\theta}'_{l-1}$, all preceding rows of $\mathbf{T}'\boldsymbol{\Theta}$ and $\mathbf{U}$ contain fixed components due to these final rows. Preceding effects are confounded and may not be validly tested in this order. For example, if $\boldsymbol{\Theta}_{AB}$ rows are nonzero, the rows of $\mathbf{U}$ for *A* and *B* main effects have nonzero *AB* components. Tests on $\boldsymbol{\Theta}_A$ or $\boldsymbol{\Theta}_B$ may prove significant *or* nonsignificant, due only to the inclusion of the *AB* terms.

Should tests of preceding terms be of importance, they must be reordered and placed in a position in the basis *following* those that are significant. For example, if the *B* main effect is significant and we wish to test the *A* contrast, we must reorder the *B* contrasts to precede *A* in $\mathbf{K}$ and $\boldsymbol{\Theta}$. $\mathbf{U}$ is reestimated in the new order, and *A* may be tested, eliminating the significant *B* effects. In a three-way design ($A\times B\times C$) we may find the *C* main effect to be significant. To test either the *A* or *B* main effect, the *C* contrast(s) must be ordered ahead of those for *A* and *B*. If *B* is significant and we wish to test *A*, we may require still another ordering, with both *B* and *C* effects ahead of *A*. Interactions should never precede the main effects they involve (for example, the *AC* interaction should not precede either the *A* or *C* main effect, although it may precede *B*).

The number of alternative orders should be kept to a minimum, to avoid compounding statistical error rates. The importance of each main effect should be given careful consideration in establishing an initial order.

Anderson (1962) has shown that under a single ordering of effects, differing α levels may be applied to each test of significance and combined to obtain an overall or experimentwise type-I error rate. If we assign error rate α_j to the hypothesis for $\mathbf{S}_{H_j}$ ($j=1, 2, \ldots, q$), then the probability of falsely rejecting at least one null hypothesis, out of q, is

$$\alpha=1-\prod_{j=1}^{q}(1-\alpha_j) \qquad (9.2.44)$$

Suppose, for example, in the 2×3 crossed design, that we wish to test the three hypotheses H_{0_1}: $\boldsymbol{\Theta}_A = \mathbf{0}$, H_{0_2}: $\boldsymbol{\Theta}_B = \mathbf{0}$, and H_{0_3}: $\boldsymbol{\Theta}_{AB} = \mathbf{0}$. Our decision rule is that only if an effect is nonsignificant will we test preceding terms. That is, only if we accept H_{0_3} will we test H_{0_1} or H_{0_2}, and only if we accept H_{0_2} will we test H_{0_1}. We assign $\alpha_3 = .01$ for H_{0_3}, and $\alpha_2 = .05$ for H_{0_2}. Wishing to keep the experimentwise α at no greater than, say, .08, we decide that α_1 for H_{0_1} must be no greater than .0218, since

$$.08 = 1-(1-.0218)(1-.05)(1-.01)$$

Any value larger than $\alpha_1 = .0218$ will increase the product to greater than .08.

Notes on Estimation and Significance Testing

Under the general linear model, the magnitudes of the estimates in $\hat{\boldsymbol{\Theta}}$ vary according to the number and type of contrasts selected. Only effects that are nonzero in the population should be maintained in the model. The common research procedure is to test the significance of all terms in the model that may contribute to criterion variation (all main effects and interactions that the design permits). Those that are not significant may be omitted, and best estimates may be obtained of those remaining. This procedure usually requires two passes with most computer programs, one for significance testing and another for estimation.

The material of this chapter concerns significance testing. It is assumed that the entire analysis-of-variance model has rank l, or l degrees of freedom (including 1 for the constant). A contrast is estimated corresponding to each degree of freedom. The contribution of every term or set is tested by partitioning the total sum of products into independent components that exhaust all sources of variation. In practice, this testing forms the first stage of the analysis.

Once significance testing has been completed, terms that are not significant may be omitted from the model. The smaller number of terms remaining may be reestimated and used in interpreting trends in the data. The number of degrees of freedom that are maintained is c, the rank of the model for estimation. These c contrasts may be combined to estimate cell means and mean residuals (Section 8.3). The maximum value of c is l, the rank of the model for significance testing.

$\hat{\boldsymbol{\Theta}}_c$ is the $c \times p$ matrix of estimates for the reduced model, after significance testing. Computational forms may follow the testing-estimation procedure. The orthogonal estimates $\mathbf{U}$ may be obtained first for all l effects by $\mathbf{U} = [\mathbf{K}^*]'\mathbf{DY}$. (Eq. 9.1.8). The Cholesky factor of $\mathbf{K}'\mathbf{DK}$ is constructed at the same time as $\mathbf{K}$ is orthonormalized. $\hat{\boldsymbol{\Theta}}_c$ is obtained by the inverse relationship from Eq. 9.1.4. Let $\mathbf{T}_c$ be the leading $c \times c$ submatrix of the Cholesky factor, and $\mathbf{U}_c$ the leading c rows of $\mathbf{U}$. Then

$$\hat{\boldsymbol{\Theta}}_c = (\mathbf{T}_c{}^{-1})'\mathbf{U}_c \qquad (9.2.45)$$

The MULTIVARIANCE program proceeds from l orthogonal estimates to the c estimates in $\hat{\boldsymbol{\Theta}}_c$. Since both parameters are required prior to run time, c may be initially set to zero, to l, or to some other arbitrary value until the tests of significance can be inspected. A second run, with c corrected, will provide the most useful data for interpretation.

9.3 SAMPLE PROBLEMS

Sample Problem 2 – Word Memory Experiment

To test the significance of mean differences in the one-way, four-level word memory example, we must first obtain the orthogonal estimates **U**. All N_j in the problem are equal. Should the contrast vectors be orthogonal, **U** would consist of standardized row vectors of $\hat{\boldsymbol{\Theta}}$. However, the design of the experiment dictates the selection of contrasts $\boldsymbol{\alpha}_1-\boldsymbol{\alpha}_2$, $\boldsymbol{\alpha}_2-\boldsymbol{\alpha}_3$, and $\boldsymbol{\alpha}_3-\boldsymbol{\alpha}_4$. These are not orthogonal, and a matrix transformation of the estimates to independence is necessary.

The original model for the data is

$$\mathbf{y}'_{\cdot j}=\boldsymbol{\mu}'+\boldsymbol{\alpha}'_j+\boldsymbol{\epsilon}'_{\cdot j}$$

All terms are 1×2 vectors, with $j=1, 2, 3, 4$. The rank of the model matrix **A**, and reparameterized model matrix **K**, is $l=4$ (one degree of freedom for the constant, plus three between groups).

The matrix of contrast parameters is

$$\boldsymbol{\Theta}=\begin{bmatrix}\boldsymbol{\mu}'+1/4\sum_j\boldsymbol{\alpha}'_j\\ \boldsymbol{\alpha}'_1-\boldsymbol{\alpha}'_2\\ \boldsymbol{\alpha}'_2-\boldsymbol{\alpha}'_3\\ \boldsymbol{\alpha}'_3-\boldsymbol{\alpha}'_4\end{bmatrix}=\begin{bmatrix}\boldsymbol{\Theta}_0\ (1\times 2)\\ \hline \boldsymbol{\Theta}_A\ (3\times 2)\end{bmatrix}$$

The single null hypothesis for both variates is H_0: $\boldsymbol{\Theta}_A=\mathbf{0}$. Both $\boldsymbol{\Theta}_A$ and $\mathbf{0}$ are 3×2 matrices. H_0 is equivalent to H_0: $\boldsymbol{\alpha}_1=\boldsymbol{\alpha}_2=\boldsymbol{\alpha}_3=\boldsymbol{\alpha}_4$.

We shall orthonormalize the basis by columns to obtain **U**. The matrix of subclass frequencies is $\mathbf{D}=\text{diag}\ (12, 12, 12, 12)$. **K** is given in Section 8.4. The factoring is

$$\mathbf{K}=\mathbf{K}^*\mathbf{T}'$$

or

$$\begin{bmatrix}1.00 & .75 & .50 & .25\\ 1.00 & -.25 & .50 & .25\\ 1.00 & -.25 & -.50 & .25\\ 1.00 & -.25 & -.50 & -.75\end{bmatrix}$$

$$=\begin{bmatrix}.144 & .250 & 0 & 0\\ .144 & -.083 & .236 & 0\\ .144 & -.083 & -.118 & .204\\ .144 & -.083 & -.118 & -.204\end{bmatrix}\begin{bmatrix}6.93 & 0 & 0 & 0\\ 0 & 3.00 & 2.00 & 1.00\\ 0 & 0 & 2.83 & 1.41\\ 0 & 0 & 0 & 2.45\end{bmatrix}$$

The reader may verify that $[\mathbf{K}^*]'\mathbf{D}\mathbf{K}^*=\mathbf{I}$.

The orthogonal estimates are

$$\mathbf{U}=[\mathbf{K}^*]'\mathbf{D}\mathbf{Y}.$$

$$=\begin{bmatrix}.144 & .144 & .144 & .144\\ .250 & -.083 & -.083 & -.083\\ 0 & .236 & -.118 & -.118\\ 0 & 0 & .204 & -.204\end{bmatrix}\begin{bmatrix}12 & 0 & 0 & 0\\ 0 & 12 & 0 & 0\\ 0 & 0 & 12 & 0\\ 0 & 0 & 0 & 12\end{bmatrix}\begin{bmatrix}39.83 & .97\\ 42.17 & .94\\ 40.00 & 1.00\\ 36.25 & .97\end{bmatrix}$$

$$
= \begin{bmatrix} 274.10 & 6.71 \\ 1.08 & -.01 \\ 11.43 & -.12 \\ 9.19 & .08 \end{bmatrix} \begin{matrix} \mathbf{u}'_1 \\ \mathbf{u}'_2 \\ \mathbf{u}'_3 \\ \mathbf{u}'_4 \end{matrix}
$$

Words Categories

If we wished to test that the constant term is equal to a specified vector (that is, H_0: $\boldsymbol{\mu}+1/4\Sigma_j\boldsymbol{\alpha}_j=\boldsymbol{\gamma}$), we would employ $\mathbf{u}'_1$ and obtain the 2×2 matrix of hypothesis squares and products, $\mathbf{S}_H = \mathbf{u}_1\mathbf{u}'_1$. Since the scale of the measures is not of major concern to the study, we shall proceed to test the hypothesis of mean differences.

The vectors of $\mathbf{U}$ containing the independent estimates for the three-degree-of-freedom test are $\mathbf{u}'_2$, $\mathbf{u}'_3$, and $\mathbf{u}'_4$. Each yields a squares and products matrix for one contrast, eliminating preceding effects. For $\boldsymbol{\alpha}_1-\boldsymbol{\alpha}_2$, eliminating the constant, the matrix is

$$
\mathbf{u}_2\mathbf{u}'_2 = \begin{bmatrix} 1.17 & -.01 \\ -.01 & .00 \end{bmatrix}
$$

For $\boldsymbol{\alpha}_2-\boldsymbol{\alpha}_3$, eliminating the constant and $\boldsymbol{\alpha}_1-\boldsymbol{\alpha}_2$, we have

$$
\mathbf{u}_3\mathbf{u}'_3 = \begin{bmatrix} 130.68 & -1.35 \\ -1.35 & .01 \end{bmatrix}
$$

And for $\boldsymbol{\alpha}_3-\boldsymbol{\alpha}_4$, eliminating all others, the squares and products are

$$
\mathbf{u}_4\mathbf{u}'_4 = \begin{bmatrix} 84.38 & .75 \\ .75 & .01 \end{bmatrix}
$$

Each matrix has the contrast sums of squares for the two dependent variables in the diagonal positions. The interdependency of the two measures induces a nonzero sum-of-products off-diagonal element.

To obtain the three-degree-of-freedom test, the hypothesis matrices are pooled to obtain $\mathbf{S}_H$.† That is,

$$
\mathbf{S}_H = \sum_{i=2}^{4} \mathbf{u}_i\mathbf{u}'_i
$$

$$
= \begin{bmatrix} 216.23 & -.61 \\ -.61 & .02 \end{bmatrix} \begin{matrix} \text{Words} \\ \text{Categories} \end{matrix}
$$

Words Categories

†Since the contrasts are not orthogonal, only the last of the set may be tested separately. This is $\boldsymbol{\alpha}_3-\boldsymbol{\alpha}_4$ in the present order, with matrix $\mathbf{u}_4\mathbf{u}'_4$. To test the other contrasts separately, they must be reordered and placed in the last position.

In one-way designs and equal-N crossed designs, the between-group sum of products may be obtained directly from vector means for the subclasses, and the overall vector mean. Since the present example meets both conditions, we observe that the leading element of $\mathbf{S}_H$, the between-group sum of squares for *words*, is equivalent to the univariate value:

$$SS_B = \sum_{j=1}^{4} N_j (y_{\cdot j} - y_{\cdot\cdot})^2$$

In the example, $N_j = 12$ and

$$y_{\cdot\cdot} = \frac{39.83+42.17+40.00+36.25}{4} = 39.56$$

Then

$$\begin{aligned} SS_B &= 12[(39.83-39.56)^2+(42.17-39.56)^2 \\ &\quad +(40-39.56)^2+(36.25-39.56)^2] \\ &= 216.23 \end{aligned}$$

This is precisely the value obtained through matrix operations. By construction of the contrast matrix and basis, however, the result is derived through the estimation of specific contrasts of experimental concern. By expanding the scalars to vectors, sums of cross products as well as sums of squares are obtained simultaneously for p measures (see Morrison, 1967). If subclass frequencies are unequal in crossed designs, then the results may be obtained only through matrix operations. The estimated effects and sums of products are *not* simple functions of observed vector means.

The between-group mean squares and products is $\mathbf{S}_H$ divided by its degrees of freedom, $n_h = 3$. The mean products are

$$\mathbf{M}_H = \frac{1}{3}\mathbf{S}_H = \begin{bmatrix} 72.08 & -.20 \\ -.20 & .01 \end{bmatrix} \begin{matrix} \text{Words} \\ \text{Categories} \end{matrix}$$

Words Categories

The between-group mean squares for the two measures separately are 72.08 and .01. Because of the relationship between the two measures, we obtain a multivariate test of significance, utilizing both mean squares as well as the mean cross product, −.20.

The error sum of products is the within-group matrix, from Section 8.4,

$$\begin{aligned} \mathbf{S}_E &= \mathbf{Y}'\mathbf{Y} - \mathbf{Y}_{\cdot}'\mathbf{D}\mathbf{Y}_{\cdot} \\ &= \begin{bmatrix} 1485.58 & 11.85 \\ 11.85 & .22 \end{bmatrix} \begin{matrix} \text{Words} \\ \text{Categories} \end{matrix} \end{aligned}$$

Words Categories

The degrees of freedom are $n_e = N - J = 44$.

The error mean squares and cross products are

$$\mathbf{M}_E = \frac{1}{44}\mathbf{S}_E = \begin{bmatrix} 33.76 & .270 \\ .27 & .005 \end{bmatrix} \begin{matrix} \text{Words} \\ \text{Categories} \end{matrix}$$

$$\qquad\qquad \text{Words} \quad \text{Categories}$$

To test H_0, we utilize the likelihood ratio criterion,

$$\Lambda = \frac{|\mathbf{S}_E|}{|\mathbf{S}_E + \mathbf{S}_H|}$$

To assess $|\mathbf{S}_E|$, we factor $\mathbf{S}_E$ according to the Cholesky method, obtaining $\mathbf{S}_E = \mathbf{T}_E\mathbf{T}_E'$ (although in a simple case as this we may evaluate $|\mathbf{S}_E|$ directly). The Cholesky factor is

$$\mathbf{T}_E = \begin{bmatrix} 38.54 & 0 \\ .31 & .36 \end{bmatrix}$$

and

$$\begin{aligned} |\mathbf{S}_E| &= |\mathbf{T}_E|^2 \\ &= 38.54^2(.36)^2 \\ &= 190.12 \end{aligned}$$

Similarly, factoring $\mathbf{S}_E + \mathbf{S}_H = \mathbf{T}^*[\mathbf{T}^*]'$, we have

$$\mathbf{S}_E + \mathbf{S}_H = \begin{bmatrix} 1701.81 & 11.24 \\ 11.24 & .24 \end{bmatrix}$$

and

$$\mathbf{T}^* = \begin{bmatrix} 41.25 & 0 \\ .27 & .41 \end{bmatrix}$$

Then

$$|\mathbf{S}_E + \mathbf{S}_H| = 41.25^2(.41)^2 = 287.33$$

The likelihood ratio is

$$\Lambda = \frac{190.12}{287.33} = .662$$

The value is noticeably below unity, and may show a significant effect. Λ may be transformed to an F statistic, with multipliers m and s. That is,

$$\begin{aligned} m &= [n_e - (p+1-n_h)/2] \\ &= [44-(2+1-3)/2] \\ &= 44 \end{aligned}$$

and

$$\begin{aligned} s &= \left(\frac{p^2n_h^2 - 4}{p^2 + n_h^2 - 5}\right)^{1/2} \\ &= \left(\frac{2^2(3^2) - 4}{2^2 + 3^2 - 5}\right)^{1/2} \\ &= 2 \end{aligned}$$

The F transform is

$$F = \frac{1-\Lambda^{1/s}}{\Lambda^{1/s}} \cdot \frac{ms+1-n_h p/2}{n_h p}$$
$$= \frac{1-\sqrt{.662}}{\sqrt{.662}} \cdot \frac{44(2)+1-(3\cdot 2)/2}{3(2)}$$
$$= .23 \cdot \frac{86}{6}$$
$$= 3.29$$

The .05 critical value of the F distribution with 6 and 86 degrees of freedom is 2.2. The observed F-value is larger, and H_0 is rejected.

Before we conclude that the research hypothesis is supported, however, we must inspect the direction of mean differences. According to the original hypothesis, group means are expected to be highest when a maximal amount of structural information is provided the subject. That is, the means were expected to be highest for group 1, and sequentially lower for groups 2, 3, and 4. Inspection of the means **Y.**, reveals that there is no such trend for variable 2, proportion of categories reconstructed.

For the first variate, number of words recalled, the trend exists for groups 2, 3, and 4. Inspection of $\hat{\mathbf{\Theta}}$ (Section 8.4) reveals that the group-1 mean of 39.83 is not significantly higher or lower, than the group-2 mean. The estimated difference $\hat{\alpha}_1^{(1)} - \hat{\alpha}_2^{(1)}$ is -2.33, with standard error 2.37. The t value, $-2.33/2.37$, is not significant. We may conclude that there is some support, although not complete, for the major hypothesis of the study.

It may be of some interest to inspect the F ratios for the separate outcome measures. These are ratios of between-group mean squares to the respective error mean squares. The univariate F statistics are

$$F_1 = \frac{[m_h]_{11}}{[m_e]_{11}} = \frac{72.08}{33.76} = 2.13 \quad \text{Words}$$

and

$$F_2 = \frac{[m_h]_{22}}{[m_e]_{22}} = \frac{.007}{.005} = 1.36 \quad \text{Categories}$$

Each ratio is referred to an F distribution, with $n_h = 3$ and $n_e = 44$ degrees of freedom. Although the two are not independent, neither individually exceeds the .05 critical value of $F_{3,44}$.

Presentation of the analysis for the example should include descriptive matrices **Y.**, **D**, and $\mathbf{R}_W$, as well as $\hat{\mathbf{\Theta}}$ and the corresponding standard errors. If predicted means are obtained from a subset of effects, these should be presented in as simple manner as possible, for each hypothesis. Since all four effects are necessary to the one-way model, predicted means are identical to the observed means and are not obtained here (that is, $c = l = 4$). The analysis-of-variance summary is presented in Table 9.3.1.

The experimental effect is more strongly seen in the number-of-words variable. However, only when the two responses are considered *jointly* do we

Table 9.3.1 Analysis of Variance for Word Memory Experiment

Source	*d.f.*	*Mean Products*		*Multivariate F (d.f.)*	*Univariate F*	
		Words	*Categories*		*Words*	*Categories*
Constant	1	$\begin{bmatrix} 75129.19 & 1839.66 \\ 1839.66 & 45.05 \end{bmatrix}$		—	—	—
Between groups, eliminating constant	3	$\begin{bmatrix} 72.08 & -.20 \\ -.20 & .01 \end{bmatrix}$		3.29* (6, 86)	2.13	1.36
Within groups	44	$\begin{bmatrix} 33.76 & .270 \\ .27 & .005 \end{bmatrix}$				
Total	48					

*Significant at $p < .05$.

see significantly different outcomes with differing degrees of structural information. It does not appear that information regarding the organization of word lists universally increases memory of the words. The directional hypothesis, as forwarded by Mandler and Stephens (1967), has received little support. Further analysis may determine whether the mean differences are altered in direction or magnitude when adjustments are made for varying periods of *time* utilized by the subjects in memorizing the word lists (see *analysis of covariance*).

Sample Problem 3 – Dental Calculus Reduction

The data for the dental calculus study are measured calculus scores on the six anterior teeth of the lower mandible. The results of the study are analyzed by fitting a two-way fixed-effects analysis-of-variance model to the data. The sampling factors are years of experimentation (A), having two levels, and five experimental conditions (B). The total number of cells is $J = 10$.

The experimental conditions are two control agents (groups 1 and 2) and three different anticalculus agents (groups 3, 4, and 5). Three subclasses have no observations, those for condition 5 in year 1, and for conditions 2 and 4 in year 2. The sampling design is diagrammed on page 16. The number of cells having one or more observations is $J_0=7$.

The full model has rank $l = J_0 = 7$. The degrees of freedom are one for the population constant, four for contrasts among experimental conditions, one for the years effect, and one for the conditions-by-years interaction. Three additional interaction degrees of freedom are lost due to the missing cells.

The effect of different anticalculus agents is the most critical to the study. However there are aspects of the design that require inspection *prior* to interpreting agent differences. One, it is necessary to see whether there is an interaction of agents and years, with agents having different effects if administered at different times. If not, it is likely that both the A effect and the $A \times B$ interaction may be deleted from the model. These are ordered last for significance testing so that they may be inspected for significance first, eliminating agent effects. (Note by comparison that if the years effect were assumed or known to be significant, it would have been ordered ahead of the agents effect. Then agents could be tested, eliminating year differences.)

Further, it is necessary to test differences between the two "controls" (experimental conditions 1 and 2) to see whether they are equivalent. Only if they are can they be used together as a single comparison group. The difference between the two controls is the "experimental conditions" contrast ordered last. Its test can be interpreted individually to determine whether control differences add to criterion variation above and beyond other agent effects. If not, the control effect may be deleted and the other agent differences tested without reordering.

$\mathbf{\Theta}$ may be considered as ordered and partitioned into sections corresponding to the various effects:

$$\mathbf{\Theta} = \begin{bmatrix} \mathbf{\Theta}_k \; (1\times 6) \\ \hline \mathbf{\Theta}_B \; (3\times 6) \\ \hline \mathbf{\Theta}_{B*} \; (1\times 6) \\ \hline \mathbf{\Theta}_A \; (1\times 6) \\ \hline \mathbf{\Theta}_{AB} \; (1\times 6) \end{bmatrix} \begin{matrix} \text{Constant} \\ \text{Active agents} \\ \text{Controls} \\ \text{Years} \\ \text{Interaction} \end{matrix}$$

Each column of $\mathbf{\Theta}$ contains the measured calculus contrasts for one of the six mandibular teeth.

The model and basis for the design are constructed in Chapter 8. The years effect is the simple comparison of year 1 with year 2, or symbolically C1. The agents effects are the comparison of agent 1 (group 3) with the average of the two controls (groups 1 and 2), the comparison of agent 2 with the controls, the comparison of agent 3 with the controls, and the difference of the two control means. Since these contrasts do not fit the regular pattern of other contrast types, the rows of **L** are represented as L1, L2, L3, and L4 for the four effects, respectively.

Contrast matrices for the two factors ($\mathbf{L}_2$ and $\mathbf{L}_5$) are constructed and transformed to one-way bases. Kronecker products of one column from $\mathbf{K}_2$ and one from $\mathbf{K}_5$ produce the entire basis for the 10-group design (see Section 8.4). Deleting the fifth, seventh, and ninth rows for empty groups, we have

$$\mathbf{K} = \begin{bmatrix} 1 & -.2 & -.2 & -.2 & .5 & .5 & -.1 \\ 1 & -.2 & -.2 & -.2 & -.5 & .5 & -.1 \\ 1 & .8 & -.2 & -.2 & 0 & .5 & .4 \\ 1 & -.2 & .8 & -.2 & 0 & .5 & -.1 \\ 1 & -.2 & -.2 & -.2 & .5 & -.5 & .1 \\ 1 & .8 & -.2 & -.2 & 0 & -.5 & -.4 \\ 1 & -.2 & -.2 & .8 & 0 & -.5 & .1 \end{bmatrix}$$

$$\begin{matrix} C0\otimes L0 & C0\otimes L1 & C0\otimes L2 & C0\otimes L3 & C0\otimes L4 & C1\otimes L0 & C1\otimes L1 \\ \text{Constant} & \text{Agent 1} & \text{Agent 2} & \text{Agent 3} & \text{Controls} & \text{Years} & \text{Interaction} \end{matrix}$$

Columns do not now sum to zero. However, orthogonalizing from the leading unit vector will assure that the column weights multiplied by the respective N_j will have zero sum.

To obtain the orthogonal estimates, we first orthogonalize **K** with respect to the diagonal matrix of subclass frequencies. The frequencies, eliminating diagonal zeros, are $\mathbf{D} = \text{diag}\,(8, 9, 7, 5, 28, 24, 26)$. The total sample size is $N = 107$. The Gram-Schmidt factorization is

$$\mathbf{K} = \mathbf{K}^*\mathbf{T}' = \begin{bmatrix} .10 & -.06 & -.03 & -.09 & .07 & .23 & -.21 \\ .10 & -.06 & -.03 & -.09 & -.30 & 0 & 0 \\ 10 & .15 & 0 & 0 & 0 & .23 & .24 \\ .10 & -.06 & .43 & 0 & 0 & 0 & 0 \\ .10 & -.06 & -.03 & -.09 & .07 & -.07 & .06 \\ .10 & .15 & 0 & 0 & 0 & -.07 & -.07 \\ .10 & -.06 & -.03 & .16 & 0 & 0 & 0 \end{bmatrix}$$

$$\times \begin{bmatrix} 10.34 & .93 & -1.59 & .44 & 1.31 & -2.37 & -.35 \\ & 4.69 & -.31 & -1.61 & -.83 & -.30 & -1.23 \\ & & 2.16 & -.79 & -.41 & 1.64 & -.33 \\ & & & 4.06 & -1.22 & -1.53 & .31 \\ & & & & 2.68 & -2.09 & .42 \\ & & & & & 3.41 & .91 \\ \text{(Zero)} & & & & & & 1.70 \end{bmatrix}$$

The orthogonal estimates are $\mathbf{U} = [\mathbf{K}^*]'\mathbf{D}\mathbf{Y}_{\cdot\cdot}$ The matrix of observed means for the seven subclasses having observations is

Y. =

		Right canine	Right lateral incisor	Right central incisor	Left central incisor	Left lateral incisor	Left canine
Year 1	Control 1	.75	2.25	3.75	4.13	2.25	.88
	Control 2	1.33	1.78	3.11	3.33	2.56	1.56
	Agent 1	.43	.86	1.29	1.57	1.00	.43
	Agent 2	1.00	.80	2.00	1.20	.60	.00
Year 2	Control 1	.68	1.57	2.71	2.75	1.57	.71
	Agent 1	.54	.79	2.08	1.71	.96	.67
	Agent 3	.23	.42	.77	1.31	.65	.19

The orthogonal estimates are

$$\mathbf{U} = \begin{bmatrix} 6.19 & 11.41 & 21.56 & 22.43 & 13.05 & 6.28 \\ -.54 & -1.96 & -1.20 & -3.24 & -1.94 & .04 \\ .85 & -.98 & -.37 & -2.70 & -1.81 & -1.40 \\ -2.40 & -5.32 & -8.97 & -7.32 & -5.01 & -2.92 \\ -1.71 & -.15 & -.45 & -.75 & -2.24 & -2.16 \\ -.05 & 1.34 & .62 & 2.29 & 1.30 & -.09 \\ -.31 & -1.04 & -3.12 & -2.57 & -1.08 & -.68 \end{bmatrix} = \begin{bmatrix} \mathbf{u}'_1 \\ \mathbf{u}'_2 \\ \mathbf{u}'_3 \\ \mathbf{u}'_4 \\ \mathbf{u}'_5 \\ \mathbf{u}'_6 \\ \mathbf{u}'_7 \end{bmatrix} \begin{matrix} \text{Constant} \\ \text{Agents} \\ \\ \\ \text{Controls} \\ \text{Years} \\ \text{Interaction} \end{matrix}$$

Right canine, Right lateral incisor, Right central incisor, Left central incisor, Left lateral incisor, Left canine

From **U** we are able to derive the sums of squares and cross products for the hypotheses of interest. We are not concerned with the nullity of the constant term, since all subjects show some predisposition to calculus formation. To compare the three active agents with the control (eliminating the constant), the sum-of-products matrix is

$$\mathbf{S}_{H_1} = \mathbf{u}_2\mathbf{u}'_2 + \mathbf{u}_3\mathbf{u}'_3 + \mathbf{u}_4\mathbf{u}'_4$$

$$= \begin{bmatrix} 6.78 & & & & & \text{(Symmetric)} \\ 13.00 & 33.08 & & & & \\ 21.86 & 50.38 & 81.94 & & & \\ 17.03 & 47.94 & 70.50 & 71.41 & & \\ 11.55 & 32.24 & 47.93 & 47.89 & 32.18 & \\ 5.79 & 16.82 & 26.63 & 25.03 & 17.09 & 10.48 \end{bmatrix} \begin{matrix} \text{Right canine} \\ \text{Right lateral incisor} \\ \text{Right central incisor} \\ \text{Left central incisor} \\ \text{Left lateral incisor} \\ \text{Left canine} \end{matrix}$$

Right canine, Right lateral incisor, Right central incisor, Left central incisor, Left lateral incisor, Left canine

$\mathbf{S}_{H_1}$ has $n_{h_1} = 3$ degrees of freedom.

The sum of squares and cross products for comparing the two control groups, eliminating the constant and active-agent effects, is

$$\mathbf{S}_{H_2} = \mathbf{u}_5\mathbf{u}'_5$$

$$= \begin{bmatrix} 2.94 & & & & & \text{(Symmetric)} \\ .26 & .02 & & & & \\ .77 & .07 & .20 & & & \\ 1.28 & .11 & .33 & .56 & & \\ 3.83 & .33 & 1.00 & 1.67 & 5.00 & \\ 3.71 & .32 & .97 & 1.61 & 4.83 & 4.67 \end{bmatrix}$$

$\mathbf{S}_{H_2}$ has $n_{h_2} = 1$ degree of freedom.

The matrices for years (eliminating the constant and all conditions) and for the years-by-agents interaction (eliminating all main effects) are $\mathbf{S}_{H_3} = \mathbf{u}_6\mathbf{u}'_6$ and $\mathbf{S}_{H_4} = \mathbf{u}_7\mathbf{u}'_7$, respectively. These are

$$\mathbf{S}_{H_3} = \begin{bmatrix} .00 & & & & & \text{(Symmetric)} \\ -.07 & 1.80 & & & & \\ -.03 & .83 & .39 & & & \\ -.11 & 3.07 & 1.42 & 5.24 & & \\ -.06 & 1.75 & .81 & 2.99 & 1.70 & \\ .00 & -.11 & -.05 & -.19 & -.11 & .01 \end{bmatrix}$$

and

$$\mathbf{S}_{H_4} = \begin{bmatrix} .10 & & & & & \text{(Symmetric)} \\ .33 & 1.09 & & & & \\ .98 & 3.26 & 9.74 & & & \\ .81 & 2.68 & 8.03 & 6.62 & & \\ .34 & 1.13 & 3.38 & 2.79 & 1.17 & \\ .21 & .71 & 2.12 & 1.75 & .74 & .46 \end{bmatrix}$$

Both n_{h_3} and n_{h_4} are 1.

The error sum of products is given in Section 3.4. $\mathbf{S}_E$ may be obtained either as a residual, subtracting $\mathbf{U}'\mathbf{U}$ from the total $\mathbf{Y}'\mathbf{Y}$, or directly as the within-groups matrix, since all seven between-group effects are included in $\mathbf{K}$. That is,

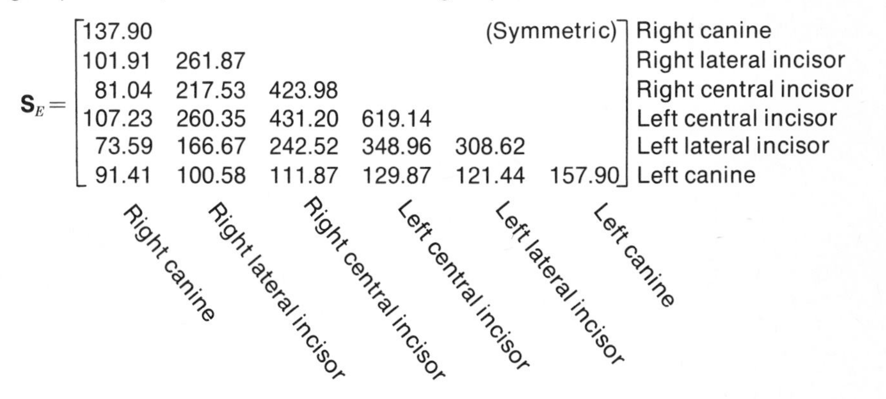

$$\mathbf{S}_E = \begin{bmatrix} 137.90 & & & & & \text{(Symmetric)} \\ 101.91 & 261.87 & & & & \\ 81.04 & 217.53 & 423.98 & & & \\ 107.23 & 260.35 & 431.20 & 619.14 & & \\ 73.59 & 166.67 & 242.52 & 348.96 & 308.62 & \\ 91.41 & 100.58 & 111.87 & 129.87 & 121.44 & 157.90 \end{bmatrix} \begin{matrix} \text{Right canine} \\ \text{Right lateral incisor} \\ \text{Right central incisor} \\ \text{Left central incisor} \\ \text{Left lateral incisor} \\ \text{Left canine} \end{matrix}$$

The error degrees of freedom are $n_e = N - J_0 = 100$. The error mean squares and cross products are $\mathbf{M}_E = \mathbf{S}_E/100$. The six error mean squares are on the diagonal of $\mathbf{M}_E$, that is $\hat{\sigma}_k^2$ $(k = 1, 2, \ldots, 6)$.

The first hypothesis to be tested is that ordered last in the Gram-Schmidt elimination. This is the test of interaction, or H_0: $\mathbf{\Theta}_{AB} = \mathbf{0}$. Equivalently, H_0 is $\gamma_{jk} = \mathbf{0}$ for all (j, k). Only for interactions, however, does equivalence of terms imply that the individual effects are null. The likelihood ratio for interaction is

$$\Lambda = \frac{|\mathbf{S}_E|}{|\mathbf{S}_E + \mathbf{S}_{H_4}|}$$

To obtain $|\mathbf{S}_E|$, we factor $\mathbf{S}_E$ by the Cholesky procedure. The factor is

$$\mathbf{T}_E = \begin{bmatrix} 11.74 & & & & & (\text{Zero}) \\ 8.68 & 13.66 & & & & \\ 6.90 & 11.54 & 15.59 & & & \\ 9.13 & 13.26 & 13.80 & 13.02 & & \\ 6.27 & 8.22 & 6.69 & 6.94 & 10.43 & \\ 7.78 & 2.42 & 1.94 & -.00 & 3.82 & 8.55 \end{bmatrix}$$

The determinant of $\mathbf{S}_E$ is the squared product of the diagonal elements of $\mathbf{T}_E$:

$$|\mathbf{S}_E| = \prod_{k=1}^{6} [t_e]_{kk}^2$$

Since this product is unwieldy, we may instead use natural logarithms. That is,

$$\begin{aligned} \log_e |\mathbf{S}_E| &= 2 \sum_{k=1}^{6} \log_e [t_e]_{kk} \\ &= 2(\log_e 11.74 + \log_e 13.66 + \log_e 15.59 \\ &\quad + \log_e 13.02 + \log_e 10.43 + \log_e 8.55) \\ &= 29.764 \end{aligned}$$

Factoring $\mathbf{S}_E + \mathbf{S}_{H_4}$, the Cholesky factor is

$$\mathbf{T}^* = \begin{bmatrix} 11.75 & & & & & (\text{Zero}) \\ 8.70 & 13.68 & & & & \\ 6.98 & 11.70 & 15.75 & & & \\ 9.20 & 13.37 & 13.88 & 13.03 & & \\ 6.29 & 8.26 & 6.69 & 6.95 & 10.43 & \\ 7.80 & 2.44 & 1.97 & -.00 & 3.81 & 8.55 \end{bmatrix}$$

From $\mathbf{T}^*$,

$$\begin{aligned} \log_e |\mathbf{S}_E + \mathbf{S}_{H4}| &= 2 \sum_{k=1}^{6} \log_e [t^*]_{kk} \\ &= 29.791 \end{aligned}$$

From the two logs,

$$\begin{aligned} \log_e |\mathbf{S}_E| - \log_e |\mathbf{S}_E + \mathbf{S}_{H_4}| &= \log_e \frac{|\mathbf{S}_E|}{|\mathbf{S}_E + \mathbf{S}_{H_4}|} \\ &= 29.764 - 29.791 \\ &= -.027 \end{aligned}$$

The likelihood criterion is

$$\Lambda = e^{-.027} = .973$$

Λ is close to 1 and we suspect that the interaction is not significant.

The *F* transformation is

$$F = \frac{1-\Lambda^{1/s}}{\Lambda^{1/s}} \cdot \frac{ms+1-n_{h_4}p/2}{n_{h_4}p}$$

The multipliers are

$$\begin{aligned} m &= [n_e-(p+1-n_{h_4})/2] \\ &= 100-(6+1-1)/2 \\ &= 97 \end{aligned}$$

and

$$\begin{aligned} s &= \left(\frac{p^2 n_{h_4}{}^2-4}{p^2+n_{h_4}{}^2-5}\right)^{1/2} \\ &= \left(\frac{6^2(1^2)-4}{6^2+1^2-5}\right)^{1/2} \\ &= 1 \end{aligned}$$

The *F* statistic is

$$\begin{aligned} F &= \frac{1-.973^1}{.973^1} \cdot \frac{97(1)+1-(1)(6)/2}{1(6)} \\ &= .028 \cdot \frac{95}{6} \\ &= .43 \end{aligned}$$

The test statistic is referred to the *F* distribution, with 6 and 95 degrees of freedom. *F* does not exceed the critical value at $\alpha = .05$, and H_0 is accepted.

The six univariate test statistics provide descriptive data concerning the effect upon particular teeth. The univariate statistics are simple ratios of hypothesis to error mean squares. That is,

$$F_k = \frac{[s_{h_4}]_{kk}/n_{h_4}}{[s_e]_{kk}/n_e}$$

For the interaction effect with matrix $\mathbf{S}_{H_4}$,

$$F_1 = \frac{.10/1}{137.90/100} = .07 \quad \text{Right canine}$$

$$F_2 = \frac{1.09/1}{261.87/100} = .42 \quad \text{Right lateral incisor}$$

$$F_3 = \frac{9.74/1}{423.98/100} = 2.30 \quad \text{Right central incisor}$$

$$F_4 = \frac{6.62/1}{619.14/100} = 1.07 \quad \text{Left central incisor}$$

$$F_5 = \frac{1.17/1}{308.62/100} = .38 \quad \text{Left lateral incisor}$$

$$F_6 = \frac{.46/1}{157.90/100} = .29 \quad \text{Left canine}$$

Each F ratio has 1 and 100 degrees of freedom. Although the tests are not independent, no single F statistic exceeds the .05 critical value. The decision to accept H_0 is further supported. There appears to be some trend for the F ratio to be higher for the middle teeth, or those with higher mean calculus scores, and to decrease symmetrically toward the two sides.

Since $\mathbf{\Theta}_{AB}=\mathbf{0}$, we may proceed to test H_0: $\mathbf{\Theta}_A=\mathbf{0}$ in the same order of effects. The hypothesis is equivalently that the vector means for the two years are equal, or H_0: $\boldsymbol{\alpha}_1=\boldsymbol{\alpha}_2$. The hypothesis matrix is $\mathbf{S}_{H_3}$, having one degree of freedom. The likelihood ratio is

$$\Lambda=\frac{|\mathbf{S}_E|}{|\mathbf{S}_E+\mathbf{S}_{H_3}|}=.976$$

The F approximation is $F=.38$, with 6 and 95 degrees of freedom. F does not exceed the critical value, and H_0 is accepted. The agents show no significant difference in effectiveness over years of experimentation, for the six teeth jointly.

Since the years effect is not significant, we may proceed to test the equality of the two control groups, and between active agents and the controls. If years were significant, we would not have valid tests of the preceding effects in this order of elimination. Instead, we would reorder the effects so that "years" is ahead of "agents," and reorthogonalize. We could then obtain tests of the controls and agents, eliminating significant year differences.

Instead, we proceed to test equality of the vector means for the two control groups. The null hypothesis is H_0: $\mathbf{\Theta}_{B*}=\mathbf{0}$, or H_0: $\boldsymbol{\beta}_1=\boldsymbol{\beta}_2$. The hypothesis matrix is $\mathbf{S}_{H_2}$. The likelihood ratio is

$$\Lambda=\frac{|\mathbf{S}_E|}{|\mathbf{S}_E+\mathbf{S}_{H_2}|}=.943$$

The F statistic for all six variates is $F=.96$, with 6 and 95 degrees of freedom. The critical F value is not exceeded; H_0 is supported. The two control groups both appear to have only the base product or unaltered control dentifrice.

Since years, controls, and interaction effects are nonsignificant, we may obtain a valid test of the active agent effects, in this order. The hypothesis is H_0: $\mathbf{\Theta}_B=\mathbf{0}$. The hypothesis matrix is $\mathbf{S}_{H_1}$, with $n_{h_1}=3$ degrees of freedom. The likelihood ratio is

$$\Lambda=\frac{|\mathbf{S}_E|}{|\mathbf{S}_E+\mathbf{S}_{H_1}|}$$

We have determined that $\log_e|\mathbf{S}_E|=29.764$. To obtain $\log_e|\mathbf{S}_E+\mathbf{S}_{H_1}|$, we sum the two matrices and factor according to Cholesky, $(\mathbf{S}_E+\mathbf{S}_{H_1})=\mathbf{T}^*[\mathbf{T}^*]'$. The triangular factor is

$$\mathbf{T}^*=\begin{bmatrix} 12.03 & & & & & \text{(Zero)} \\ 9.55 & 14.27 & & & & \\ 8.55 & 13.05 & 16.20 & & & \\ 10.33 & 14.69 & 13.69 & 13.45 & & \\ 7.08 & 9.20 & 6.78 & 7.12 & 10.46 & \\ 8.08 & 2.82 & 2.01 & .19 & 3.87 & 8.72 \end{bmatrix}$$

Then

$$\log_e|\mathbf{S}_E+\mathbf{S}_{H_1}| = 2\sum_{k=1}^{6}\log_e [t^*]_{kk}$$
$$=30.086$$

The log of the likelihood ratio is

$$\log_e \frac{|\mathbf{S}_E|}{|\mathbf{S}_E+\mathbf{S}_{H_1}|} = 29.764-30.086$$
$$=-.322$$

and

$$\Lambda = e^{-.322} = .725$$

The multipliers for F are

$$m = 100-(6+1-3)/2 = 98$$

and

$$s=\left(\frac{6^2(3^2)-4}{6^2+3^2-5}\right)^{1/2}=2.8284$$

The test statistic requires $1/s = .354$. Then

$$F=\frac{1-.725^{.354}}{.725^{.354}}\cdot\frac{98(2.8284)+1-(3)(6)/2}{3(6)}$$
$$=.121\cdot\frac{269.186}{18}$$
$$=1.80$$

F has 18 and 269.186 degrees of freedom. The distribution may be evaluated by mathematical approximation, as in the MULTIVARIANCE program, or by rounding the degrees of freedom down to the nearest whole number (269). F exceeds the tabled critical value of 1.6, and H_0 is rejected at $\alpha=.05$.

For further information about the teeth most strongly affected, we may inspect the six univariate F ratios. The ratios of hypothesis and error mean squares are

$$F_1=\frac{6.78/3}{137.90/100}=1.64 \quad \text{Right canine}$$

$$F_2=\frac{33.08/3}{261.87/100}=4.21 \quad \text{Right lateral incisor}$$

$$F_3=\frac{81.94/3}{423.98/100}=6.44 \quad \text{Right central incisor}$$

$$F_4=\frac{71.41/3}{619.14/100}=3.84 \quad \text{Left central incisor}$$

$$F_5=\frac{32.18/3}{308.62/100}=3.48 \quad \text{Left lateral incisor}$$

$$F_6=\frac{10.48/3}{157.90/100}=2.21 \quad \text{Left canine}$$

The effect appears strongest for the middle teeth, or those having the greatest overall calculus formation. The four central teeth (incisors) have univariate F ratios that exceed the .05 critical F value, with 3 and 100 degrees of freedom. These, however, are independent and should not be employed as partial tests of the multivariate hypothesis.

The constant term and three active-agent contrasts are all necessary to the model. The appropriate rank of the model for estimation is $c=4$. Best estimates of nonzero effects are obtained by deleting all terms for which H_0 was accepted and determining $\hat{\boldsymbol{\Theta}}$ for those remaining. This is the matrix estimate given on page 282, along with the standard errors in **H**.

Inspection of $\hat{\boldsymbol{\Theta}}_4$ reveals that virtually all contrasts of agents with controls are negative; all agents have produced lower mean calculus scores than the control dentifrice. For comparability across elements of $\hat{\boldsymbol{\Theta}}_4$, each estimated contrast is divided by its respective standard error. The resulting matrix is

$$\hat{\boldsymbol{\Theta}}_{\text{std}} = \begin{bmatrix} 4.82 & 5.66 & 8.61 & 6.98 & 5.69 & 3.49 \\ -1.12 & -2.45 & -2.24 & -2.47 & -2.25 & -1.02 \\ .32 & -1.22 & -1.01 & -1.63 & -1.56 & -1.54 \\ -2.04 & -3.29 & -4.35 & -2.94 & -2.85 & -2.32 \end{bmatrix} \begin{matrix} \mathbf{k}' & \text{Constant} \\ \boldsymbol{\beta}_3' - 1/2(\boldsymbol{\beta}_1' + \boldsymbol{\beta}_2') & \text{Agent 1} \\ \boldsymbol{\beta}_4' - 1/2(\boldsymbol{\beta}_1' + \boldsymbol{\beta}_2') & \text{Agent 2.} \\ \boldsymbol{\beta}_5' - 1/2(\boldsymbol{\beta}_1' + \boldsymbol{\beta}_2') & \text{Agent 3} \end{matrix}$$

Right canine, Right lateral incisor, Right central incisor, Left central incisor, Left lateral incisor, Left canine

The most effective agent is consistently agent 3. The effect is accentuated still further on those teeth showing the highest univariate F ratios—that is, the right central and lateral incisors. By comparison, agent 2 appears to have the smallest effect, and by itself may not differ significantly from the controls. The standardized contrasts for agent 2 may be compared to critical values of the t distribution with 100 degrees of freedom. No single tooth shows a significant improvement. However a multivariate test of the contrast for the six teeth together may suggest otherwise.

The central teeth are known to develop higher calculus concentrations than those further apart. Step-down analysis may be considered as an alternative to Λ for testing agent effectiveness. All significant differences among agents may be "concentrated" in the four central teeth, or in the two central incisors alone. Peripheral teeth may not contribute any additional significant between-group variation.

Let us employ the step-down technique to test H_0: $\boldsymbol{\Theta}_B = \mathbf{0}$, although we might have used the same procedure for all hypotheses. For the step-down analysis, we may reorder the variates according to centrality—that is, right and left central incisors, followed by right and left lateral incisors, and finally the right and left canines. This constitutes a simple reordering of the elements of $\mathbf{S}_E$ and $\mathbf{S}_{H_1}$, but does not affect the values of the elements or the determinants. Λ is unaltered by the reordering. The step-down statistics are specific to the predetermined order of variates, however.

The Cholesky factors of $\mathbf{S}_E$ and $\mathbf{S}_E+\mathbf{S}_{H_1}$, with the modified order of elements, are

$$\underset{\text{(reord.)}}{\mathbf{T}_E} = \begin{bmatrix} 20.59 & & & & & \text{(Zero)} \\ 20.94 & 13.44 & & & & \\ 10.56 & 2.91 & 11.91 & & & \\ 11.78 & 7.61 & 1.69 & 10.44 & & \\ 3.94 & 1.85 & 4.62 & .52 & 9.87 & \\ 5.43 & 1.20 & 3.33 & 4.09 & 5.10 & 8.55 \end{bmatrix}$$

and

$$\underset{\text{(reord.)}}{\mathbf{T}^*} = \begin{bmatrix} 22.49 & & & & & \text{(Zero)} \\ 22.31 & 13.89 & & & & \\ 11.91 & 3.07 & 11.99 & & & \\ 12.91 & 7.83 & 1.76 & 10.47 & & \\ 4.57 & 1.60 & 4.63 & .52 & 9.97 & \\ 6.16 & 1.26 & 3.35 & 4.13 & 4.94 & 8.72 \end{bmatrix}$$

Each diagonal element is the square root of the conditional sum of squares for one variate, eliminating those preceding.

The step-down F ratios are ratios of conditional hypothesis mean squares to conditional error mean squares. That is,

$$F_k^* = \frac{([t^*]_{kk}{}^2 - [t_e]_{kk}{}^2)/n_{h_1}}{[t_e]_{kk}{}^2/(n_e - k + 1)}$$

The six ratios are

$$F_1^* = \frac{(22.49^2 - 20.59^2)/3}{20.59^2/(100-1+1)} = \frac{27.31}{4.24} = 6.44 \quad \text{Right central incisor}$$

$$F_2^* = \frac{(13.89^2 - 13.44^2)/3}{13.44^2/(100-2+1)} = \frac{4.15}{1.82} = 2.28 \quad \text{Left central incisor}$$

$$F_3^* = \frac{(11.99^2 - 11.91^2)/3}{11.91^2/(100-3+1)} = \frac{.63}{1.45} = .43 \quad \text{Right lateral incisor}$$

$$F_4^* = \frac{(10.47^2 - 10.44^2)/3}{10.44^2/(100-4+1)} = \frac{.17}{1.12} = .15 \quad \text{Left lateral incisor}$$

$$F_5^* = \frac{(9.97^2 - 9.87^2)/3}{9.87^2/(100-5+1)} = \frac{.68}{1.01} = .67 \quad \text{Right canine}$$

$$F_6^* = \frac{(8.72^2 - 8.55^2)/3}{8.55^2/(100-6+1)} = \frac{.99}{.77} = 1.28 \quad \text{Left canine}$$

The first step-down F^* statistic is identical to the univariate F ratio for the right central incisor. Each subsequent ratio tests the effect of agents on the particular tooth, eliminating variation attributable to prior teeth. Each has one fewer degree of freedom for error. F_1^* is referred to the F distribution with 3 and 100 degrees of freedom, F_2^* with 3 and 99, and so on.

Table 9.3.2 Analysis of Variance for Anticalculus Agents

Source	Degrees of Freedom	Simultaneous Test Λ	Simultaneous Test *F* (d.f.)	Step-down *F* Statistics R.C.I.*	L.C.I.	R.L.I.	L.L.I.	R.C.	L.C.
Constant	1	—	—	—	—	—	—	—	—
Agents, eliminating constant	$n_{h_1} = 3$	.725	1.80† (18,269)	6.44†	2.28	.43	.15	.67	1.2
Controls, eliminating constant and agents	$n_{h_2} = 1$	.943	.96 (6, 95)	.05	.05	.01	2.99	2.30	.3
Years, eliminating constant, agents, and controls	$n_{h_3} = 1$	.976	.38 (6, 95)	.09	1.50	.30	.01	.41	.0
Agents × years, eliminating all above	$n_{h_4} = 1$	.973	.43 (6, 95)	2.30	.19	.12	.08	.00	.0
				Univariate Mean Squares					
Residual (within)	$n_e = 100$			4.24	6.19	2.62	3.09	1.38	1.5
Total	$N = 107$								

*R.C.I., right central incisor; L.C.I., left central incisor; R.L.I., right lateral incisor; L.L.I., left lateral incisor; R.C., canine; L.C., left canine. Step-down tests conducted in this order.

†Significant at $p < .05$.

Beginning with F_6^* and proceeding backward, there is no significant effect for the left canine, eliminating all others; no significant effect for the right canine, eliminating all incisors; no significant effect for the left lateral incisor, eliminating the central and right lateral incisors; no significant effect for the right lateral incisor, eliminating central incisors; and, at $\alpha = .05$, no significant effect for the left central incisor, eliminating the right. However, F_1^* does exceed the .05 critical *F* value with 1 and 100 degrees of freedom, and H_0 is rejected.

Should some other F^* ratio exceed the critical value, the same hypothesis would be rejected sooner, and testing would stop at that point. However, because of strong interdependencies of the six teeth, it appears that the effectiveness of anticalculus agents may be assessed from only a single tooth, and at most from the two central incisors. We conclude that the agents under study (especially agent 3) are effective in reducing calculus formation.

The descriptive data for the study are the means, variances, correlations, and contrast estimates and their standard errors. In addition, an analysis-of-variance summary table may be useful in conveying the results of the hypothesis testing. A suggested format is given by Table 9.3.2. Especially in the nonorthogonal design, notations to indicate the order of effects are crucial. Should alternate orderings be necessary, the table may become more complex and present only selected results from among several orderings.

Sample Problem 4 – Essay Grading Study

The essay grading data are analyzed by fitting a four-way fixed-effects analysis-of-variance model to the data. The factors of classification are pupil race (*A*), having two levels; pupil sex (*B*), with two levels; pupil ability (*C*), with two levels; and essay pairs (*D*), having four levels. The total number of groups is $J = 32$, with $N = 112$ observations. The cell frequencies vary from 1 to 6 per subclass. All effects are experimental in the sense of assigned and manipulated by the researcher. However, the same model may be employed in any comparative or nonexperimental situation as well. The two dependent variables are scores on essay topics I and II, respectively. Sample means and *N*'s are given in Table 8.4.1.

The complete model has 32 degrees of freedom between groups; this is *l*, the rank of the model for significance testing. The complete reparameterization is represented symbolically in Table 7.4.2. Simple contrasts are used for the race, sex, and ability factors, and deviation contrasts for essay pairs. The first eight basis vectors are presented following Table 8.4.1. Further vectors of **K** are found in the same manner, or may be obtained as term-by-term multiples of the leading columns.

To obtain the orthogonal estimates for the full model, we orthogonalize the complete 32×32 basis, and multiply by the cell sums $[\mathbf{DY.}]$. The resulting estimates are

$$
\mathbf{U} = [\mathbf{K}^*]'\mathbf{DY.} = \begin{bmatrix}
479.35 & 516.20 \\
5.14 & -4.21 \\
6.11 & 37.51 \\
42.69 & 34.39 \\
1.63 & -27.89 \\
-21.02 & 51.26 \\
31.02 & 67.84 \\
-33.20 & -30.74 \\
10.20 & 10.60 \\
7.70 & -13.90 \\
12.13 & 16.79 \\
-6.61 & -6.92 \\
-3.82 & 1.19 \\
8.40 & 9.01 \\
10.15 & 10.73 \\
-15.33 & 7.01 \\
11.44 & -.30 \\
4.14 & -12.48 \\
13.46 & 1.98 \\
-14.40 & -19.62 \\
-7.79 & -15.26 \\
25.97 & 16.32 \\
16.52 & 39.77 \\
11.50 & 7.34 \\
-.36 & 20.73 \\
-15.58 & -15.34 \\
1.86 & 5.01 \\
-12.69 & -23.42 \\
-8.72 & .41 \\
-20.92 & -20.05 \\
22.26 & -5.35 \\
-6.73 & -4.33
\end{bmatrix} = \begin{bmatrix}
\mathbf{u}'_1 \\ \mathbf{u}'_2 \\ \mathbf{u}'_3 \\ \mathbf{u}'_4 \\ \mathbf{u}'_5 \\ \mathbf{u}'_6 \\ \mathbf{u}'_7 \\ \mathbf{u}'_8 \\ \mathbf{u}'_9 \\ \mathbf{u}'_{10} \\ \mathbf{u}'_{11} \\ \mathbf{u}'_{12} \\ \mathbf{u}'_{13} \\ \mathbf{u}'_{14} \\ \mathbf{u}'_{15} \\ \mathbf{u}'_{16} \\ \mathbf{u}'_{17} \\ \mathbf{u}'_{18} \\ \mathbf{u}'_{19} \\ \mathbf{u}'_{20} \\ \mathbf{u}'_{21} \\ \mathbf{u}'_{22} \\ \mathbf{u}'_{23} \\ \mathbf{u}'_{24} \\ \mathbf{u}'_{25} \\ \mathbf{u}'_{26} \\ \mathbf{u}'_{27} \\ \mathbf{u}'_{28} \\ \mathbf{u}'_{29} \\ \mathbf{u}'_{30} \\ \mathbf{u}'_{31} \\ \mathbf{u}'_{32}
\end{bmatrix}
\begin{array}{l}
\text{Constant} \\ \text{Race} \\ \text{Sex} \\ \text{Ability} \\ \text{Essay} \\ \text{Essay} \\ \text{Essay} \\ \text{Race} \times \text{Sex} \\ \text{Race} \times \text{ability} \\ \text{Race} \times \text{essay} \\ \text{Race} \times \text{essay} \\ \text{Race} \times \text{essay} \\ \text{Sex} \times \text{ability} \\ \text{Sex} \times \text{essay} \\ \text{Sex} \times \text{essay} \\ \text{Sex} \times \text{essay} \\ \text{Ability} \times \text{essay} \\ \text{Ability} \times \text{essay} \\ \text{Ability} \times \text{essay} \\ \text{Race} \times \text{sex} \times \text{ability} \\ \text{Race} \times \text{sex} \times \text{essay} \\ \text{Race} \times \text{sex} \times \text{essay} \\ \text{Race} \times \text{sex} \times \text{essay} \\ \text{Race} \times \text{ability} \times \text{essay} \\ \text{Race} \times \text{ability} \times \text{essay} \\ \text{Race} \times \text{ability} \times \text{essay} \\ \text{Sex} \times \text{ability} \times \text{essay} \\ \text{Sex} \times \text{ability} \times \text{essay} \\ \text{Sex} \times \text{ability} \times \text{essay} \\ \text{Race} \times \text{sex} \times \text{ability} \times \text{essay} \\ \text{Race} \times \text{sex} \times \text{ability} \times \text{essay} \\ \text{Race} \times \text{sex} \times \text{ability} \times \text{essay}
\end{array}
$$

Essay topic I   Essay topic II

Each effect is estimated eliminating all preceding effects.

The error sum of products for the two essay topics is the within-group matrix, $\mathbf{S}_E = \mathbf{Y}'\mathbf{Y} - \mathbf{Y}_{\cdot}'\mathbf{D}\mathbf{Y}_{\cdot} = \mathbf{S}_W$. This is given in Section 8.4. That is,

$$\mathbf{S}_E = \begin{bmatrix} 13877.68 & 8475.37 \\ 8475.37 & 17429.10 \end{bmatrix} \begin{matrix} \text{Essay topic I} \\ \text{Essay topic II} \end{matrix}$$
$$\begin{matrix} \text{Essay} & \text{Essay} \\ \text{topic I} & \text{topic II} \end{matrix}$$

$\mathbf{S}_E$ has $N - J = 112 - 32 = 80$ degrees of freedom. The matrix of mean squares and cross products is the within-group variance–covariance matrix

$$\mathbf{M}_E = \hat{\boldsymbol{\Sigma}}$$
$$= \frac{1}{80}\mathbf{S}_E$$
$$= \begin{bmatrix} 173.47 & 105.94 \\ 105.94 & 217.86 \end{bmatrix} \begin{matrix} \text{Essay topic I} \\ \text{Essay topic II} \end{matrix}$$
$$\begin{matrix} \text{Essay} & \text{Essay} \\ \text{topic I} & \text{topic II} \end{matrix}$$

The error mean squares are $\hat{\sigma}_1{}^2 = 173.47$ and $\hat{\sigma}_2{}^2 = 217.86$ for the two topics separately.

To test the fit of the model, we compute the F transform of Λ for each main effect and interaction, in reverse order. There are a total of fifteen hypothesis sums of products, one for each main effect, and one for each interaction of two or more design factors. We shall assume that there is no particular interest in the constant term.

The last effect in the order of elimination is the four-way interaction, eliminating all other effects. The sum of products is

$$\mathbf{S}_{H_{15}} = \sum_{i=30}^{32} \mathbf{u}_i \mathbf{u}'_i$$
$$= \begin{bmatrix} 978.54 & 329.45 \\ 329.45 & 449.22 \end{bmatrix}$$

$\mathbf{S}_{H_{15}}$ has $n_{h_{15}} = 3$ degrees of freedom. The hypothesis is $H_{0_{15}}$: $\boldsymbol{\Theta}_{ABCD} = \mathbf{0}$, where $\boldsymbol{\Theta}_{ABCD}$ is the final three rows of $\boldsymbol{\Theta}$ for the four-way interaction; or else $H_{0_{15}}$: $(\boldsymbol{\alpha\beta\gamma\delta})_{jklm} = \mathbf{0}$. The likelihood ratio is

$$\Lambda = \frac{|\mathbf{S}_E|}{|\mathbf{S}_E + \mathbf{S}_{H_{15}}|} = .904$$

The F transformation with $p = 2$, $m = 80$, and $s = 2$, is

$$F = \frac{1 - \sqrt{.904}}{\sqrt{.904}} \cdot \frac{80(2) + 1 - (3)(2)/2}{3(2)}$$
$$= .052 \cdot \frac{158}{6}$$
$$= 1.36$$

F does not exceed the .05 critical value of the F distribution, with 6 and 158 degrees of freedom; $H_{0_{15}}$ is accepted.

The univariate F statistics for the two essay topics separately, for the four-way interaction, eliminating all other effects, are

$$F_1 = \frac{978.54/3}{173.47} = 1.88 \quad \text{Essay topic I}$$

and

$$F_2 = \frac{449.22/3}{217.86} = .69 \quad \text{Essay topic II}$$

Neither exceeds the critical F value with 3 and 80 degrees of freedom.

Having found the four-way interaction nonsignificant, we proceed with the test of the three-degree-of-freedom sex-by-ability-by-essay interaction, with $\mathbf{S}_{H_{14}} = \mathbf{u}_{27}\mathbf{u}'_{27} + \mathbf{u}_{28}\mathbf{u}'_{28} + \mathbf{u}_{29}\mathbf{u}'_{29}$. The results for this and all other hypotheses, in the specified order of elimination, are given in Table 9.3.3.

Reading from the last hypothesis backward, we see that no significant multivariate test statistic is encountered until we reach the race-by-sex interaction. A single significant univariate F ratio is found for the race-by-sex-by-essays three-way interaction, but the decision to accept $H_{0_{12}}$ is made from the simultaneous test *only*. We may later inspect the data to locate the source of the single significant univariate ratio. Similarly, one univariate F ratio for the essay-pair main effect is not significant. H_{0_4} is rejected, however, based upon the multivariate likelihood ratio criterion of .57. Λ provides information on both stimuli simultaneously, and can be tested independently of the other multivariate tests, with a prespecified type-I error rate.

However, before investigating the essay-pair main effect, we must inspect the significant race-by-sex interaction. Under this ordering of effects, all preceding terms (all main effects) are confounded with race-sex interactions, and the resulting test criteria are not valid.

To understand the interaction, we may inspect means predicted by a rank-8 model, which includes all main effects plus the race-by-sex interaction. These are obtained by letting the rank of model for *estimation* be $c = 8$, and estimating only the leading 8 rows of $\mathbf{\Theta}$. The estimates are combined with the leading columns of $\mathbf{K}$ to predict $\hat{\mathbf{Y}}. = \mathbf{K}_8\hat{\mathbf{\Theta}}_8$. Table 8.4.2 on page 295 has predicted means for all 32 groups.

To investigate the race-by-sex interaction, the means are combined to obtain means for each combination of pupil sex and race. The significant interaction may be interpreted in terms of the teachers having very different reactions to white boys and girls, and about the same expectations for all black children regardless of sex. Or it may be that Negro females are given a score advantage relative to white girls, while Negro males are punished.

Let us consider the other main effects. A significant interaction confounds main effects in two manners. First, although the test of interaction is made eliminating main effects, main-effect tests are confounded with interaction sums of products. Second, for interpretation, the existence of interaction suggests that tests of simple main effects may not be valid.

Table 9.3.3 Analysis of Variance for Four-factor Essay-grading Study

Source	Degrees of Freedom	Simultaneous Test Λ	Simultaneous Test F (d.f.)	Univariate F Statistic: Essay Topic I	Univariate F Statistic: Essay Topic II
Constant	1	—	—	—	—
Race, eliminating constant	$n_{h_1}=1$	.99	.25 (2,79)	.15	.08
Sex, eliminating constant and race	$n_{h_2}=1$	.91	3.79* (2,79)	.22	6.46*
Ability, eliminating constant, race, and sex	$n_{h_3}=1$	.88	5.41* (2,79)	10.50*	5.43*
Essay pairs, eliminating constant, race, sex, and ability	$n_{h_4}=3$	.57	8.61* (6, 158)	2.70	12.25*
Race×sex, eliminating constant and all main effects	$n_{h_5}=1$	.92	3.49* (2,79)	6.36*	4.34*
Race×ability, eliminating all above	$n_{h_6}=1$	.99	.36 (2,79)	.60	.52
Race×essays, eliminating all above	$n_{h_7}=3$	.95	.71 (6,158)	.48	.80
Sex×ability, eliminating all above	$n_{h_8}=3$	1.00–	.08 (2,79)	.08	.01
Sex×essays, eliminating all above	$n_{h_9}=3$	.95	.71 (6,158)	.79	.38
Ability×essays, eliminating all above	$n_{h_{10}}=3$	.95	.65 (6,158)	.63	.24
Race×sex×ability, eliminating all above	$n_{h_{11}}=1$	.98	.97 (2,79)	1.20	1.77
Race×sex×essays, eliminating all above	$n_{h_{12}}=3$	.86	2.00 (6,158)	1.94	3.18*
Race×ability×essays, eliminating all above	$n_{h_{13}}=3$	.94	.86 (6,158)	.72	1.10
Sex×ability×essays, eliminating all above	$n_{h_{14}}=3$	.96	.54 (6,158)	.46	.88
Race×sex×ability×essays, eliminating all else	$n_{h_{15}}=3$	.90	1.36 (6,158)	1.88	.69
				Mean Squares	
Within	$n_e=80$			173.47	217.86
Total	$N=112$				

*Significant at $p<.05$.

For example, overall mean differences across sex groups appear small or inconsistent. When subjects are divided by race, however, sex differences for whites are large and consistent, while those for black pupils are not. We may wish to estimate or test sex differences separately for each racial group. Or, we may wish to compare the ratings for black and white males separately from those for black and white females.

Either approach consists of an alternate reparameterization of the original model. A nested design reparameterization replaces the crossed design, for those factors of concern. For example, to test sex differences separately for the two racial groups, the sex and race-by-sex contrasts are replaced by a sex contrast for Negro pupils and one for whites. That is, Kronecker products $C0 \otimes C1 \otimes$

C0⊗D0 (sex) and C1⊗C1⊗C0⊗D0 (race-by-sex) are replaced by I1⊗C1⊗C0⊗D0 (sex within race 1) and I2⊗C1⊗C0⊗D0 (sex within race 2).

Logically, the race-by-sex interaction does not confound either the ability or essay-pairs main effect. However, because of the nonorthogonality of the design, there remains a mathematical interdependence. The essay-pairs effect is not of particular concern. Mean differences are expected. Since there is no vested interest in these particular stimuli, we shall not be concerned with testing the magnitude or direction of differences.

However, the ability effect is of concern. We may order the race-by-sex interaction ahead of ability and reorthogonalize. First, let us evaluate the degree to which ability is confounded with the race-by-sex interaction. The variance–covariance factors of the estimates are assessed in Section 8.4, as matrix **G**. The covariance of the ability and race-by-sex (fourth and eighth) effects is −.0001, with variances of .03622 and .14738, respectively. The correlation of the two effects is

$$\frac{-.0001}{\sqrt{.03622(.14738)}} = -.0013$$

Making the subjective decision that the confounding is negligible, we proceed directly with a test of the ability effect, without concern for the race-by-sex interaction.

The essay main effect is significant and must be eliminated from ability. We must reorthogonalize the basis with the ability column following all the other main effects. That is, index the leading columns of **K** in the original order, as vectors $\mathbf{k}_1, \mathbf{k}_2, \ldots, \mathbf{k}_7$; $\mathbf{k}_4$ is the ability-effect column. The vectors are reordered to $\mathbf{k}_1$, $\mathbf{k}_2$, $\mathbf{k}_3$, $\mathbf{k}_5$, $\mathbf{k}_6$, $\mathbf{k}_7$, $\mathbf{k}_4$. We may reorthogonalize the leading seven columns of **K** by Gram-Schmidt; all following columns will remain unaltered. The seventh row of **U** now estimates the ability effect, eliminating the constant and the three other main effects.

The *revised* hypothesis sum of products for H_0: $\gamma_1 = \gamma_2$ or H_0: $\mathbf{\Theta}_C = \mathbf{0}$, is

$$\mathbf{S}_{H_C} = \mathbf{u}_7\mathbf{u}'_7 = \begin{bmatrix} 1816.86 & 1284.61 \\ 1284.61 & 908.28 \end{bmatrix}$$

$\mathbf{S}_E$ is defined as previously. Then

$$\Lambda = \frac{|\mathbf{S}_E|}{|\mathbf{S}_E + \mathbf{S}_{H_C}|} = .883$$

The multivariate test statistic is $F = 5.23$, with 2 and 79 degrees of freedom. H_0 is rejected at $\alpha = .05$.

The univariate results for ability, eliminating all other main effects, are

$$F_1 = \frac{1816.86/1}{173.47} = 10.47 \quad \text{Essay topic I}$$

and

$$F_2 = \frac{908.28/1}{217.86} = 4.17 \quad \text{Essay topic II}$$

Table 9.3.4 Estimated Means and Mean Differences for Ratings of Essays When Teachers Have Been Told the Authors Were High-ability and Low-ability Fifth-grade Pupils*

Student Group	*Essay Topic I*†	*Essay Topic II*‡
High ability	49.37	51.96
Low ability	41.25	46.22
Estimated difference	8.12	5.74
Standard error of difference	2.51	2.81

*Range of possible ratings is from 9 to 90 points.
†My favorite school subject.
‡What I think about.

Both exceed the .05 critical F-value with 1 and 80 degrees of freedom. Although none of these results differs dramatically from those of Table 9.3.3, in other situations the reordering may produce large alterations. These multivariate and univariate results should replace those in the table, with appropriate labeling, rather than requiring a second table for the alternate order of effects.

The data may be inspected to determine the source of the significant ability effect. The predicted means of Table 8.4.2 may be combined across groups, to obtain unweighted averages for high and low-ability pupils. These results, together with the estimated difference from $\hat{\mathbf{\Theta}}_8$, and standard errors, are given in Table 9.3.4. When teachers perceived that the essays were written by high-intelligence, high-achievement pupils, their mean ratings were invariably higher than if they thought the authors were of low ability and achievement. The differences are even more pronounced for individual essays (see Table 8.4.1). The expectations held by the teachers for pupils of differing ability and achievement records may be so strong as to pervade their evaluations of the pupils' actual performance. The evaluations, in turn, may play a significant role in shaping the child's own behavior, both in and out of the classroom.

From Table 9.3.3, we see that the eight leading effects in $\mathbf{K}$ and $\mathbf{\Theta}$ describe factors that affect the teachers' ratings. These are all main-effect degrees of freedom, plus the race-by-sex interaction. The other terms do not contribute, and may be eliminated. The model of rank $c=8$ is confirmed for these data. This is the rank assumed for estimation in Section 8.4.

Let us turn briefly to the large univariate race-by-sex-by-essay-pair F ratio. The observed means for race-sex combinations, for the second essay topic have a single mean out of the range of the others. The mean score on topic II, for teachers scoring essay pair 1 who thought the pupils were white females, is low, with value $[10\times1+29.25\times4]/5=25.4$. It is observed in Chapter 8 that subject 88, with the lowest score, did not truly participate in the study. Reanalysis without s_{88} reduces the single three-way interaction to nonsignificance.

Sample Problem 5—Programmed Instruction Effects

The final example is the conditions-by-classes-by-sex design for testing classroom procedures for absenteeism compensation. The fixed effects in the model are experimental conditions (remediation, no remediation, or experimental-control), and sex (male-female). The units of analysis are classroom means; mean achievement has been separately determined for males and females in each class. Classes are considered a random effect, nested within experimental conditions and crossed with sex. There are 19 seventh-grade teachers employing the remediation program, and 18 giving pupils no special remediation when mathematics material is missed. The dependent variables are three measures of cognitive achievement, administered at the end of the school year: the Cooperative Mathematics Test, the Stanford Modern Mathematics Concepts Test, and the (City) Junior High School Mathematics Test.

The mean model is given by Eq. 7.1.34. That is,

$$\mathbf{y}'_{\cdot jkl} = \boldsymbol{\mu}' + \boldsymbol{\alpha}'_j + \boldsymbol{\beta}'_l + (\boldsymbol{\alpha\beta})'_{jl} + \mathbf{c}'_{k(j)} + \boldsymbol{\epsilon}'_{\cdot jkl}$$

$\mathbf{y}_{\cdot jkl}$ is the vector mean for class k, nested within treatment j, for sex group l. $\mathbf{c}_{k(j)}$ is a random class vector, with ($k=1, 2, \ldots, 19$) for the experimental condition, and ($k=1, 2, \ldots, 18$) for the control. $\boldsymbol{\epsilon}_{\cdot jkl}$ is assumed to follow a trivariate normal distribution, with covariance matrix $\boldsymbol{\Sigma}$; $\mathbf{c}_{k(j)}$ is assumed normal with covariance matrix $\boldsymbol{\Sigma}_c$.

For programming purposes, the nested design may be treated as a $2\times19\times2$ crossed design.* In reparameterization to contrasts, effects may be chosen so that the variance among classes is estimated separately for each experimental condition. The symbolic representation of the reparameterization is presented in Section 7.4. There is only one vector observation per subclass (per sex-class combination). Thus we may obtain the sex-by-classes-in-groups interaction as a residual, obtaining orthogonal estimates for only the main effects and conditions-by-sex interaction. The symbolic contrasts and effects in the parameter matrix are

$$\boldsymbol{\Theta} = \left[\begin{array}{l} \boldsymbol{\Theta}_k \;(1\times3) \\ \hdashline \boldsymbol{\Theta}_A \;(1\times3) \\ \hdashline \boldsymbol{\Theta}_C \;(1\times3) \\ \hdashline \boldsymbol{\Theta}_{AC} \;(1\times3) \\ \hdashline \\ \\ \\ \boldsymbol{\Theta}_B \;(35\times3) \\ \\ \\ \\ \\ \end{array}\right] \begin{array}{ll} \text{C0}\otimes\text{D0}\otimes\text{C0} & \text{Constant} \\ \text{C1}\otimes\text{D0}\otimes\text{C0} & \text{Experimental conditions} \\ \text{C0}\otimes\text{D0}\otimes\text{C1} & \text{Sex} \\ \text{C1}\otimes\text{D0}\otimes\text{C1} & \text{Conditions}\times\text{sex} \\ \text{I1}\otimes\text{D1}\otimes\text{C0} & \text{Classes in experimental group} \\ \text{I1}\otimes\text{D2}\otimes\text{C0} & \\ \quad\vdots & \\ \text{I1}\otimes\text{D18}\otimes\text{C0} & \\ \text{I2}\otimes\text{D1}\otimes\text{C0} & \text{Classes in control group} \\ \text{I2}\otimes\text{D2}\otimes\text{C0} & \\ \quad\vdots & \\ \text{I2}\otimes\text{D17}\otimes\text{C0} & \end{array}$$

$\hat{\boldsymbol{\Theta}}$ and $\mathbf{U}$ have $l=39$ rows (the rank of the model for significance testing). For

*This is conditions×classes×sex, or $A\times B\times C$; it is not the order in which factors appear in the model.

obtaining the Kronecker products, the vectors from one-way bases are multiplied in the order conditions-classes-sex. The complete **K** is 76×39; the last two rows are deleted since there are only 18 control classes.

Because of the nested factor and multiple sources of random variation ($\boldsymbol{\Theta}_B$ contains random effects), we must consider the sources of variation and the expected sums of squares and cross products, prior to significance testing. Let us partition the triangular factor of **K**′**DK**, as we did $\boldsymbol{\Theta}$. The upper triangular Cholesky factor is

$$\mathbf{T}' = \begin{bmatrix} \mathbf{T}'_k \ (1\times 39) \\ \hline \mathbf{T}'_A \ (1\times 39) \\ \hline \mathbf{T}'_C \ (1\times 39) \\ \hline \mathbf{T}'_{AC} \ (1\times 39) \\ \hline \mathbf{T}'_B \ (35\times 39) \end{bmatrix}$$

T satisfies $\mathbf{K}'\mathbf{D}\mathbf{K} = \mathbf{T}\mathbf{T}'$.

The entire matrix of orthogonal estimates is $\mathbf{U} = \mathbf{T}'\hat{\boldsymbol{\Theta}} = [\mathbf{K}^*]'\mathbf{D}\mathbf{Y}_{\cdot}$, of order 39×3. The portion of **U** corresponding to any effect is the corresponding section of **T**′ times the entire estimate $\hat{\boldsymbol{\Theta}}$. For example, **U** for the experimental groups effect, is the 1×3 submatrix $\mathbf{U}_A = \mathbf{T}'_A\hat{\boldsymbol{\Theta}}$. Because of the upper triangular nature of **T**′, rows of $\mathbf{U}_B$ are weighted sums of only the rows of $\hat{\boldsymbol{\Theta}}_B$; $\mathbf{U}_{AC}$ is a weighted sum of rows of $\hat{\boldsymbol{\Theta}}_{AC}$ and $\hat{\boldsymbol{\Theta}}_B$; $\mathbf{U}_C$ is a weighted sum of rows of $\hat{\boldsymbol{\Theta}}_C$, $\hat{\boldsymbol{\Theta}}_{AC}$, and $\hat{\boldsymbol{\Theta}}_B$; and so on.

Table 9.3.5 Partition of Sums of Products for Mixed Model, Nested Design

Source	*d.f.*	*Sum of Products*	*Expected Sum of Products*
Fixed effects:			
Constant	1	$\mathbf{U}'_k\mathbf{U}_k$	
Experimental conditions, eliminating constant	$n_{h_1} = 1$	$\mathbf{S}_{H_1} = \mathbf{U}'_A\mathbf{U}_A$	$m_1\boldsymbol{\Sigma} + m_2\boldsymbol{\Sigma}_c + \boldsymbol{\Theta}'\mathbf{T}_A\mathbf{T}'_A\boldsymbol{\Theta}$
Sex, eliminating conditions and constant	$n_{h_2} = 1$	$\mathbf{S}_{H_2} = \mathbf{U}'_C\mathbf{U}_C$	$m_3\boldsymbol{\Sigma} + \boldsymbol{\Theta}'\mathbf{T}_C\mathbf{T}'_C\boldsymbol{\Theta}$
Conditions×sex, eliminating constant, conditions and sex	$n_{h_3} = 1$	$\mathbf{S}_{H_3} = \mathbf{U}'_{AC}\mathbf{U}_{AC}$	$m_3\boldsymbol{\Sigma} + \boldsymbol{\Theta}'\mathbf{T}_{AC}\mathbf{T}'_{AC}\boldsymbol{\Theta}$
Random effects:			
Classes within conditions, eliminating fixed effects	$n_{e_1} = 35$	$\mathbf{S}_{E_1} = \mathbf{U}'_B\mathbf{U}_B$	$m_4\boldsymbol{\Sigma} + m_5\boldsymbol{\Sigma}_c$
Sex×classes within conditions, eliminating all above (Residual)	$n_{e_2} = 35$	$\mathbf{S}_{E_2} = \mathbf{Y}'\mathbf{Y} - \mathbf{U}'\mathbf{U}$	$m_6\boldsymbol{\Sigma}$
Total	$N = 74$	$\mathbf{S}_T = \mathbf{Y}'\mathbf{Y}$	

The partition of sums of products is given in Table 9.3.5. m_1 through m_6 are multipliers which depend upon the number of observations per subclass and the number of levels of the experimental factors. This partition of sums of products may be employed for any such design, with design factors *A* and *C* fixed, and levels of *B* random, nested within *A* and crossed with *C*. There is one unit of analysis per subclass, so that there is no within-group variation. The design arises commonly in educational experimentation when class means are the units of analysis (Glass, 1968; Raths, 1967).

To determine the appropriate tests of hypotheses, we compare the expected sums of products. $\mathbf{S}_{E_1}$ contains all components in $\mathbf{S}_{H_1}$ except the *A* fixed effect. Thus $\mathbf{S}_{E_1}$ will form the correct error sum of products for experimental conditions. $\mathbf{S}_{E_2}$ has only a random $\mathbf{\Sigma}$ component, and is an appropriate error term for $\mathbf{S}_{H_2}$ and $\mathbf{S}_{H_3}$. Each has the $\mathbf{\Sigma}$ component, plus a single fixed effect of concern. Finally, should we wish to test a hypothesis concerning $\mathbf{\Sigma}_c$, a comparison of $\mathbf{S}_{E_1}$ and $\mathbf{S}_{E_2}$ would be appropriate. Since variation among classes is expected, we shall omit a test of this hypothesis.

The sample partition of effects is obtained from the orthogonal estimates. $\mathbf{U}$ has row $\mathbf{u}'_1$ for the constant, $\mathbf{u}'_2$ for experimental conditions, $\mathbf{u}'_3$ for sex, $\mathbf{u}'_4$ for conditions-by-sex, and $\mathbf{u}'_5, \mathbf{u}'_6, \ldots, \mathbf{u}'_{39}$ for classes within conditions. The sums of products are

$$\mathbf{S}_{H_1} = \mathbf{u}_2\mathbf{u}'_2 = \begin{bmatrix} .54 & & \text{(Symm.)} \\ -1.88 & 6.57 & \\ 2.79 & -9.74 & 14.45 \end{bmatrix} \quad \begin{array}{l}\text{Experimental conditions,} \\ \quad \text{eliminating constant}\end{array}$$

$$\mathbf{S}_{H_2} = \mathbf{u}_3\mathbf{u}'_3 = \begin{bmatrix} 12.32 & & \text{(Symm.)} \\ -2.92 & .69 & \\ 1.65 & -.39 & .22 \end{bmatrix} \quad \begin{array}{l}\text{Sex, eliminating conditions} \\ \quad \text{and constant}\end{array}$$

$$\mathbf{S}_{H_3} = \mathbf{u}_4\mathbf{u}'_4 = \begin{bmatrix} 1.73 & & \text{(Symm.)} \\ -.99 & .56 & \\ -1.03 & .59 & .62 \end{bmatrix} \quad \begin{array}{l}\text{Conditions} \times \text{sex,} \\ \quad \text{eliminating constant,} \\ \quad \text{conditions, and sex}\end{array}$$

$$\mathbf{S}_{E_1} = \sum_{i=5}^{39} \mathbf{u}_i\mathbf{u}'_i = \begin{bmatrix} 865.95 & & \text{(Symm.)} \\ 575.90 & 514.97 & \\ 677.25 & 479.62 & 621.88 \end{bmatrix} \quad \begin{array}{l}\text{Classes within conditions,} \\ \quad \text{eliminating fixed effects}\end{array}$$

The residual sum of products is

$$\mathbf{S}_{E_2} = \mathbf{Y}'\mathbf{Y} - \mathbf{U}'\mathbf{U}$$

$$= \begin{bmatrix} 20332.73 & & \text{(Symm.)} \\ 22444.51 & 25275.56 & \\ 16193.22 & 17947.80 & 13054.33 \end{bmatrix} - \begin{bmatrix} 20268.15 & & \text{(Symm.)} \\ 22438.02 & 25188.27 & \\ 16172.53 & 17943.84 & 13016.10 \end{bmatrix}$$

$$= \begin{bmatrix} 64.58 & & \text{(Symm.)} \\ 6.49 & 87.29 & \\ 20.69 & 3.96 & 38.23 \end{bmatrix} \quad \begin{array}{l}\text{Sex} \times \text{classes within conditions,} \\ \quad \text{eliminating all else}\end{array}$$

For all matrices the three variables are in the following order: Cooperative Mathematics Test, Stanford Modern Mathematics Test, and (City) Junior High School Mathematics Test.

The first hypothesis to be tested involves the last fixed effect in the order of elimination—the conditions-by-sex interaction. The hypothesis is H_0: $\mathbf{\Theta}_{AC}=\mathbf{0}$. The hypothesis matrix is $\mathbf{S}_{H_3}$ and the error matrix is $\mathbf{S}_{E_2}$. From these

$$\Lambda=\frac{|\mathbf{S}_{E_2}|}{|\mathbf{S}_{E_2}+\mathbf{S}_{H_3}|}=.926$$

The F statistic, with $p=3$, $n_{h_3}=1$, and $n_{e_2}=35$, is $F=.88$, with 3 and 33 degrees of freedom. F does not exceed the .05 critical value.

The univariate F statistics are

$$F_1=\frac{1.73/1}{64.58/35}=.94 \quad \text{Cooperative test}$$

$$F_2=\frac{.56/1}{87.29/35}=.23 \quad \text{Stanford test}$$

$$F_3=\frac{.62/1}{38.23/35}=.56 \quad \text{City test}$$

None exceeds the .05 critical F value, with 1 and 35 degrees of freedom. We accept the null hypothesis.

The second null hypothesis to be tested is H_0: $\mathbf{\Theta}_C=\mathbf{0}$, for the equality of sex group means. The hypothesis matrix is $\mathbf{S}_{H_2}$ and the error matrix is $\mathbf{S}_{E_2}$.

$$\Lambda=\frac{|\mathbf{S}_{E_2}|}{|\mathbf{S}_{E_2}+\mathbf{S}_{H_2}|}=.820$$

The corresponding F approximation is $F=2.41$, with 3 and 33 degrees of freedom. Although F does not exceed the .05 critical value, it does approach significance. The three univariate test statistics are $F_1=6.67$, $F_2=.28$, and $F_3=.20$, respectively. Each is referred to the F distribution with 1 and 35 degrees of freedom. It appears that there is some sex differentiation on the Cooperative Mathematics Test. However, based upon the simultaneous test statistic, we continue to maintain H_0.

Since neither sex nor conditions-by-sex is significant, we may test experimental conditions in this order. The hypothesis is H_0: $\mathbf{\Theta}_A=\mathbf{0}$, or H_0: $\boldsymbol{\alpha}_1=\boldsymbol{\alpha}_2$. The hypothesis and error matrices are $\mathbf{S}_{H_1}$ and $\mathbf{S}_{E_1}$, respectively. $\mathbf{S}_{E_1}$ is a "special effects" error term, comprised of variation due to the last 35 contrasts coded in $\mathbf{\Theta}$.

The likelihood ratio criterion is

$$\Lambda=\frac{|\mathbf{S}_{E_1}|}{|\mathbf{S}_{E_1}+\mathbf{S}_{H_1}|}=.801$$

The corresponding F statistic is $F=2.74$. F comes very close to but does not exceed the .05 critical value with 3 and 33 degrees of freedom. The three univariate F statistics are $F_1=.02$, $F_2=.45$, and $F_3=.81$. No one measure displays any significant between-group variation. We must again maintain H_0.

Finding none of the experimental effects to be significant, we conclude that the treatment was ineffective. The children were not able to compensate for absenteeism through utilization of the individually programmed materials. However, it is possible that the error sums of products may be inflated by systematic class differences in mean absenteeism. That is, in classes with the highest absenteeism rate it may have been impractical to have the large numbers of returning children operate the technical machinery. Thus we may still employ the technique of *analysis of covariance*, to remove any confounding with the additional measured antecedent, absenteeism rate.

There is little point in our estimating means or mean differences other than the mean of all subjects. Note, however, that in estimating standard errors we must utilize the appropriate error variances for the respective effect. The estimate of $\mathbf{\Sigma}$ for standard errors of experimental-condition effects is $\mathbf{S}_{E_1}/35$, while that for the sex and sex-by-conditions effects is $\mathbf{S}_{E_2}/35$. For example, let the rank of the model for estimation be $c=2$, to estimate the constant and experimental-groups effects. Then

$$\hat{\mathbf{\Theta}}_2=(\mathbf{K}_2'\mathbf{D}\mathbf{K}_2)^{-1}\mathbf{K}_2'\mathbf{D}\mathbf{Y}.$$

$\mathbf{K}_2$ contains the first two columns of the basis. These estimates are

$$\hat{\mathbf{\Theta}}_2=10^{-4}\times\begin{bmatrix}135.23 & -7.31\\ -7.31 & 540.94\end{bmatrix}\mathbf{K}_2'\mathbf{D}\mathbf{Y}.$$

$$=\begin{bmatrix}16.18 & 18.27 & 12.92\\ .17 & -.60 & .88\end{bmatrix}\begin{matrix}\text{Constant}\\ \text{Experimental}-\text{control}\end{matrix}$$

Cooperative test Stanford test City test

The mean of 19 experimental classes on the Cooperative test is 16.27 and the control mean is 16.10. The estimates show that the mean of all classes is 16.18, and the experimental-control difference is +.17 point.

The corresponding standard errors are $\mathbf{H}=\mathbf{g}\mathbf{d}'$, where $\mathbf{g}$ is a two-element column vector of square roots of the diagonals of $(\mathbf{K}_2'\mathbf{D}\mathbf{K}_2)^{-1}$ and $\mathbf{d}'$ is a three-element row vector of variable standard deviations. The first of these is

$$\mathbf{g}=\begin{bmatrix}\sqrt{.0135}\\ \sqrt{.0541}\end{bmatrix}=\begin{bmatrix}.116\\ .233\end{bmatrix}$$

For $\mathbf{d}$ we require the variances of the three measures within experimental groups—that is, across classes. The variance–covariance matrix (mean squares and products) is

$$\mathbf{M}_{E_1} = \mathbf{S}_{E_1}/35$$

$$= \begin{bmatrix} 24.74 & & (\text{Symm.}) \\ 16.45 & 14.71 & \\ 19.35 & 13.70 & 17.77 \end{bmatrix} \begin{matrix} \text{Cooperative test} \\ \text{Stanford test} \\ \text{City test} \end{matrix}$$

Cooperative test, Stanford test, City test

$\mathbf{M}_{E_1}$ may be reduced to correlational form in the usual manner to estimate the test intercorrelations. These are correlations among class means, however, rather than across individual pupils. The results for individuals and classes may be very dissimilar.

d′, the vector of variable standard deviations, is

$$\mathbf{d}' = [\sqrt{24.74} \quad \sqrt{14.71} \quad \sqrt{17.77}] = [4.97 \quad 3.84 \quad 4.22]$$

The standard errors are

$$\mathbf{H} = \begin{bmatrix} .116 \\ .233 \end{bmatrix} [4.97 \quad 3.84 \quad 4.22]$$

$$= \begin{bmatrix} .58 & .45 & .49 \\ 1.16 & .89 & .98 \end{bmatrix} \begin{matrix} \text{Constant} \\ \text{Experimental} - \text{control} \end{matrix}$$

Cooperative test, Stanford test, City test

None of the separate experimental differences is even as large as one standard error, and therefore none is significant.

CHAPTER 10

Analysis of Variance: Additional Topics

10.1 DISCRIMINANT ANALYSIS

Through the method of discriminant analysis, a set of p variates may be linearly transformed to a new set of s ($\leq p$) measures, with properties facilitating the interpretation and analysis of group-mean differences. Namely the transformed variables, or *discriminant variables*, are constructed in such a way that the univariate F ratios (mean square between groups/mean square within) for these variables are maximal. In some instances more than one discriminant variable is computed for a given set of data. A second variable is constructed that has maximum between-group discrimination on a dimension orthogonal to the first. If a third is computed, it describes between-group variation on a dimension orthogonal to the first two, and so on. In total, the number of discriminant variables necessary to describe all between-group variation is the minimum of the between-group degrees of freedom and the number of variates. That is,

$$s = \min (n_h, p) \tag{10.1.1}$$

Suppose, for example, that we have two groups of observations, with each observation measured on three criterion variates, y_1, y_2, and y_3. We may graph the group vector means as points in a three-dimensional Euclidean space. Let the means on the three measures for group one be $\mathbf{y}'_{\cdot 1} = (y_{\cdot 1}^{(1)}\ y_{\cdot 1}^{(2)}\ y_{\cdot 1}^{(3)})$, and for group two be $\mathbf{y}'_{\cdot 2} = (y_{\cdot 2}^{(1)}\ y_{\cdot 2}^{(2)}\ y_{\cdot 2}^{(3)})$. If we utilize the means for each group to give us coordinates on the three axes, we locate the vector means as in Figure 10.1.1.

Regardless of the dimensionality of the representation, all between-group variation is described by a single variable (z), which unlike the y variables, exactly separates points $\mathbf{y}_{\cdot 1}$ and $\mathbf{y}_{\cdot 2}$. The discriminant variable shows greater between-group dispersion than any of the y_k. In turn, z may be expressed as a linear compound of y_1, y_2, and y_3. With z, the location of $\mathbf{y}_{\cdot 1}$ or $\mathbf{y}_{\cdot 2}$ may be expressed in terms of only a single coordinate—that is, the distance from the origin on z. For this situation, $s = \min(2-1, 3) = 1$. It is possible that the number of groups would exceed two, in which case the number of dimensions of between-group variation would increase, up to a maximum of $p = 3$.

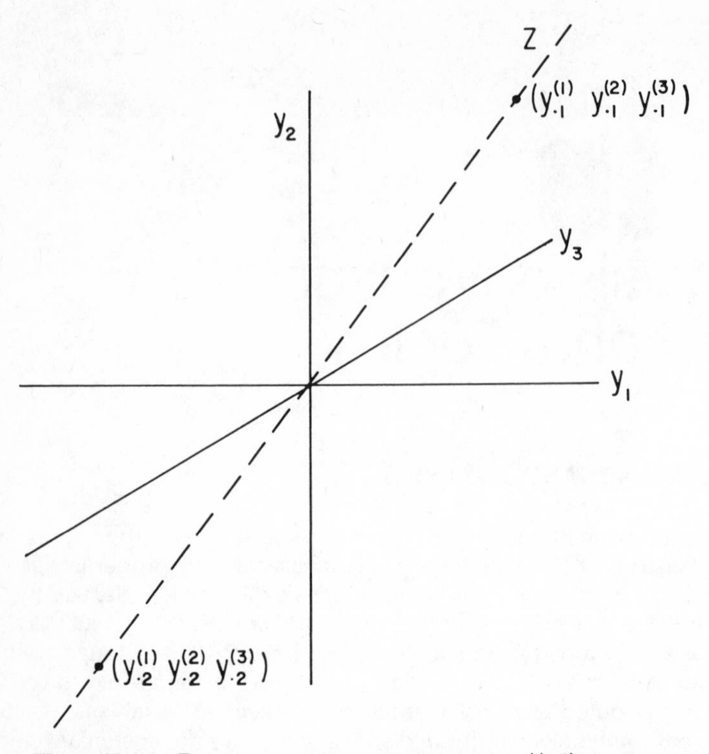

Figure 10.1.1 Two group vector means represented in three-space.

As a second example, consider four groups of observations, each measured on two variates. The group vector means may be represented in terms of y_1 and y_2, as in Figure 10.1.2.

The original vector means may all be located in Figure 10.1.2 by specifying the y_1- and y_2-coordinates. However, a variable different from either of these (z_1) has maximal between-group distance of any line passing through the origin, including the two y_k. Thus z_1 is the first discriminant variable. The points $\mathbf{y}_{\cdot j}$ do not fall exactly on z_1, however. Thus we require a second discriminant variable, to describe between-group variation in a direction orthogonal to z_1. In two-dimensional space, there is only one such additional dimension, represented by z_2. In higher-order spaces z_2 is selected from all dimensions orthogonal to z_1 to maximize group differences on that dimension; z_3 is selected from all dimensions orthogonal to z_1 and z_2, and so on up to z_s.

In Figure 10.1.2, z_1 and z_2 may be expressed as linear combinations of y_1 and y_2. Then $\mathbf{y}_{\cdot 1}$ and $\mathbf{y}_{\cdot 2}$ may be located in terms of their coordinates with respect to the new z axes. Similarly, the estimated mean differences may be expressed in terms of the z rather than y. We refer to the z, or discriminant, variates as *canonical variates*, since they express mean differences in a standard and perhaps simpler form. The least-squares estimates of group mean contrasts may be expressed for the z_i as the *canonical form of the estimated differences*.

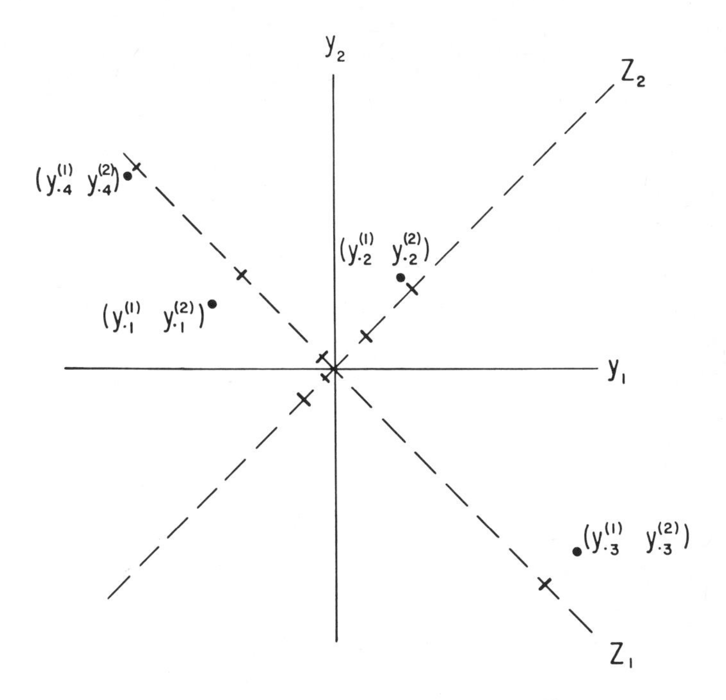

Figure 10.1.2 Four group vector means represented in two-space.

In Figure 10.1.2, $s = \min(4-1, 2) = 2$. Whenever s is greater than unity, we may test whether between-group differences on one, two, or all of the discriminant measures are significant. It is possible, for example, that all significant between-group variation is described by the single dimension z_1. Deviations from the z_1 line on z_2 may represent not population mean deviations, but only random error. Intuitively, we can see that a test of between-group differences on *all s* canonical variates, must yield identical results to the overall test in terms of the y_k—that is, the test of H_0: $\boldsymbol{\mu}_1 = \boldsymbol{\mu}_2 = \boldsymbol{\mu}_3 = \boldsymbol{\mu}_4$. This is exactly the case; group mean differences are neither increased nor decreased in transforming to canonical variates, but merely expressed in terms of new axes.

Technically, the discriminant problem is one of determining weights to apply to the y_k to form z variates that have the properties illustrated above. If we let $\boldsymbol{\alpha}_i$ $(i = 1, 2, \ldots, s)$ be a vector of weights, then

$$z_i = \boldsymbol{\alpha}_i'\mathbf{y} \tag{10.1.2}$$

is the ith discriminant variable. We would like to choose $\boldsymbol{\alpha}_i$ so as to maximize the between-group-to-within-group variance ratio for z_i. Elements α_{ki} are the *discriminant function coefficients*.

Let us assume that we have a $p \times p$ sum-of-products matrix $\mathbf{S}_H$, for any between-group hypothesis, with n_h degrees of freedom $(n_h \geqslant 1)$. Also, $\mathbf{S}_E$ is the error sum of products, with n_e degrees of freedom. The between-group sum of squares for z_i is $\boldsymbol{\alpha}_i'\mathbf{S}_H\boldsymbol{\alpha}_i$. Likewise, the within-group sum of squares for z_i is $\boldsymbol{\alpha}_i'\mathbf{S}_E\boldsymbol{\alpha}_i$.

The variance ratio to be maximized to obtain the first discriminant function is

$$\lambda_1 = \frac{\boldsymbol{\alpha}_1' \mathbf{S}_H \boldsymbol{\alpha}_1}{\boldsymbol{\alpha}_1' \mathbf{S}_E \boldsymbol{\alpha}_1} \tag{10.1.3a}$$

It is necessary to restrict Eq. 10.1.3a so that it will have only a single solution. A convenient side condition is to require the error variance of z_i to be unity. That is,

$$\frac{1}{n_e} \boldsymbol{\alpha}_i' \mathbf{S}_E \boldsymbol{\alpha}_i = 1 \tag{10.1.4}$$

As a result, λ_i is only a measure of between-group variation on z_i, and is called the *canonical variance*. Larger values of λ_i indicate more disparate group mean vectors on the discriminant variable.

If a second discriminant function is required, λ_2 is maximized, where

$$\lambda_2 = \frac{\boldsymbol{\alpha}_2' \mathbf{S}_H \boldsymbol{\alpha}_2}{\boldsymbol{\alpha}_2' \mathbf{S}_E \boldsymbol{\alpha}_2} \tag{10.1.3b}$$

The condition of Eq. 10.1.4 is maintained for $\boldsymbol{\alpha}_2$. In addition, $\boldsymbol{\alpha}_2$ is constrained to be orthogonal to $\boldsymbol{\alpha}_1$ in the error metric. That is,

$$\boldsymbol{\alpha}_2' \mathbf{S}_E \boldsymbol{\alpha}_1 = 0 \tag{10.1.5}$$

As a result, sample values for $z_1 = \boldsymbol{\alpha}_1' \mathbf{y}$ and $z_2 = \boldsymbol{\alpha}_2' \mathbf{y}$ are always uncorrelated.

If further discriminant functions are necessary (that is, $s > 2$), each λ_i maximizes an expression such as Eq. 10.1.3a or b, subject to the constraints of unit within-group variances (Eq. 10.1.4), and orthogonality with all prior functions (Eq. 10.1.5). These properties can be described in terms of matrices. Let $\mathbf{A}$ be a $p \times s$ matrix having column vectors $\boldsymbol{\alpha}_i$. Let $\boldsymbol{\Lambda}$ be an $s \times s$ diagonal matrix of canonical variances λ_i, ordered from largest (λ_1) to smallest (λ_s). The conditions of Eqs. 10.1.3–10.1.5 are

$$\frac{1}{n_e} \mathbf{A}' \mathbf{S}_E \mathbf{A} = \mathbf{I} \tag{10.1.6}$$

and

$$\mathbf{A}' \mathbf{S}_H \mathbf{A} = \boldsymbol{\Lambda} \tag{10.1.7}$$

Maximum values for λ_i and associated vectors $\boldsymbol{\alpha}_i$ are the solutions of the homogeneous equations

$$\left(\mathbf{S}_H - \frac{\lambda_i}{n_e} \mathbf{S}_E \right) \boldsymbol{\alpha}_i = \mathbf{0} \tag{10.1.8}$$

where λ_i satisfies

$$\left| \mathbf{S}_H - \frac{\lambda_i}{n_e} \mathbf{S}_E \right| = 0 \tag{10.1.9}$$

Estimates of λ_i and $\boldsymbol{\alpha}_i$ are obtained by substituting sample hypothesis and error matrices in Eq. 10.1.8. The solutions are the characteristic roots and vectors of $\mathbf{S}_H$, in the metric $(1/n_e)\mathbf{S}_E$. The characteristic roots and vectors may be computed in a number of ways (for example, Jacobi and Householder-Ortega-Wilkinson). The computations are heavy even for small problems, however, and computer routines are essential (Bock and Repp, 1970). For some computational ease, the equations may be transformed to a one-matrix characteristic equation problem, as in Chapter 2, and in Chapter 6 for the estimation of canonical correlations.

Let $\hat{\lambda}_i$ and $\hat{\boldsymbol{\alpha}}_i$ be the estimates of λ_i and $\boldsymbol{\alpha}_i$, respectively, comprising matrix estimates $\hat{\boldsymbol{\Lambda}}$ and $\hat{\mathbf{A}}$. $\mathbf{A}$ may be estimated in raw form or in a form applicable to standardized measures y_k. This is accomplished by multiplying each estimated weight $\hat{\alpha}_{ki}$ by the corresponding y standard deviation $\hat{\sigma}_k$. In matrix representation, let

$$\mathbf{D}_E = \text{diag}\left(\frac{\mathbf{S}_E}{n_e}\right) = \text{diag}\,(\hat{\boldsymbol{\Sigma}}) \tag{10.1.10}$$

where $\mathbf{D}_E$ is the $p \times p$ matrix of variances of the y variates. The matrix of standardized coefficients is

$$\hat{\mathbf{A}} = \mathbf{D}_E^{1/2}\hat{\mathbf{A}} \tag{10.1.11}$$

Care must be exercised in the interpretation of the weight values, for they do *not* merely reflect the relative contribution of the y variates to between-group discrimination. The magnitudes of the weights are functions of the scaling of the criterion measures as well as their intercorrelations. That is, addition or deletion of a single measure may have a major effect upon coefficients for remaining variables. Standardization, as in Eq. 10.1.11, removes scaling effects. The interdependencies are not so easily removed, however. Instead of the examination of discriminant weights, either the univariate or step-down test statistics should be used for locating the sources of group discrimination. For example, the largest of p *univariate* test statistics is obtained for the maximally discriminating measure. The estimates of group-mean differences and their standard errors for particular y variables reveal the magnitude, direction, and precision of the effect. These results are directly interpretable in terms of the original and better-understood outcome measures. Results from the discriminant functions are likely to be both more complex and more tenuous.

Means and mean contrasts may be transformed to the discriminant metric to aid in interpretation. If group j in the analysis-of-variance design has mean vector $\mathbf{y}_{\cdot j}$, then the mean for the group on z_i is

$$z_{\cdot ji} = \hat{\boldsymbol{\alpha}}_i' \mathbf{y}_{\cdot j} \tag{10.1.12}$$

The n_h contrasts for the between-group effect in $\mathbf{S}_H$ is an $n_h \times p$ submatrix of $\hat{\boldsymbol{\Theta}}$—that is, $\hat{\boldsymbol{\Theta}}_h$. Values of the same contrasts for the discriminant variables z_i $(i = 1, 2, \ldots, s)$ are given by the $n_h \times s$ matrix

$$\hat{\boldsymbol{\Theta}}_z = \hat{\boldsymbol{\Theta}}_h \hat{\mathbf{A}} \tag{10.1.13}$$

Contrasts are all expressed in within-group standard deviation units, because of the restriction of Eq. 10.1.4. That is, each mean difference is the number of within-group standard deviations separating the means on the discriminant variable. The n_h discriminant contrasts may be represented graphically to illustrate the separation of groups.

The proportion of between-group variation attributable to each discriminant function is estimated by

$$P_i = \frac{\hat{\lambda}_i}{\sum_{i=1}^{s} \hat{\lambda}_i} = \frac{\hat{\lambda}_i}{\text{tr}\,(\hat{\boldsymbol{\Lambda}})} \tag{10.1.14}$$

The measure is converted to a percentage by multiplying by 100. Multiple proportions may be inspected to determine if all between-group variability is concentrated in one or several discriminant dimensions.

Several methods are available for testing the nullity of true between-group variation on one or more of the discriminant functions. The overall hypothesis is the same as H_0: $\boldsymbol{\Theta}_h = \mathbf{0}$ of Eq. 9.2.1. In terms of the discriminant measures, H_0 is

$$H_0: \boldsymbol{\Theta}_z = \mathbf{0} \tag{10.1.15}$$

$\boldsymbol{\Theta}_z$ can be null if and only if $\boldsymbol{\Theta}_h$ is null, since $\boldsymbol{\alpha}_i$ are non-null solutions of Eq. 10.1.8. An equivalent form of hypothesis 10.1.15 is H_0: $\lambda_i = 0$ ($i = 1, 2, \ldots, s$), or that there is no between-group variation on the discriminant measure.

Roy's largest root criterion for testing Eq. 10.1.15 is sensitive to departure from H_0 in a single dimension. The test statistic is

$$\phi = \frac{\hat{\lambda}_1}{\hat{\lambda}_1 + 1} \tag{10.1.16}$$

ϕ is referred to the tables in Heck (1960), and Pillai (1960, 1964, 1965, 1967). The arguments for ϕ are s and

$$m = (|p - n_h| - 1)/2 \tag{10.1.17}$$

$$n = (n_e - p - 1)/2 \tag{10.1.18}$$

Roy's criterion may be applied to smaller roots $\lambda_2, \lambda_3, \ldots, \lambda_s$, reducing n_e and n_h by one for each prior (larger) function removed.

Hotelling's trace criterion provides a test of H_0 for all dimensions simultaneously. The test statistic is

$$\begin{aligned} \operatorname{tr}(\mathbf{S}_E^{-1}\mathbf{S}_H) &= \operatorname{tr}(\hat{\boldsymbol{\Lambda}}) \\ &= \sum_{i=1}^{s} \hat{\lambda}_i \end{aligned} \tag{10.1.19}$$

Hotelling's criterion is referred to the Heck (1960) and Pillai tables (1960, 1964, 1965, 1967), with arguments identical to those for ϕ (that is, s, m, and n).

Test of H_0 may be made for all discriminant functions simultaneously, all minus the largest, all minus the largest two, and so on to just the smallest dimension. Through successive tests, it may be found that a subset of discriminant functions depicts all population mean differences, and remaining smaller functions reflect only random variation. To test H_0 for all functions jointly, we may employ the likelihood ratio statistic, as in the analysis-of-variance model. The likelihood ratio is

$$\begin{aligned} \Lambda_1 &= \frac{|\mathbf{S}_E|}{|\mathbf{S}_E + \mathbf{S}_H|} \\ &= \prod_{i=1}^{s} \left(\frac{1}{1 + \hat{\lambda}_i} \right) \end{aligned} \tag{10.1.20a}$$

Λ_1 may be transformed to either the χ^2 or F statistic. The test statistic for all discriminant functions is identical to the multivariate test of equality of mean vectors, in Chapter 9.

A test of H_0, removing λ_1, is obtained through likelihood ratio procedures, with ratio

$$\Lambda_2 = \prod_{i=2}^{s} \left(\frac{1}{1+\hat{\lambda}_i} \right) \tag{10.1.20b}$$

For computing degrees of freedom for the χ^2 statistic for Λ_2, $p-1$ and n_h-1 substitute for p and n_h, respectively.

In general, the test of H_0 for roots j through s has the likelihood ratio

$$\Lambda_j = \prod_{i=j}^{s} \left(\frac{1}{1+\hat{\lambda}_i} \right) \tag{10.1.21}$$

The χ^2 transformation is

$$\chi^2 = -\left(n_e + n_h - \frac{n_h+p+1}{2} \right) \log_e \Lambda_j \tag{10.1.22}$$

χ^2 is referred to tables of the χ^2 distribution with $(p-j+1)(n_h-j+1)$ degrees of freedom. If the test statistic drops to below the critical value after removing the largest $j-1$ functions, it may be concluded that between-group variation resides in only the first $j-1$ z-dimensions.

If the *first* discriminant function is found to contain all significant between-group variation, λ_1 may be used to construct p-variate confidence bounds on $\mathbf{\Theta}_h$. Let $\mathbf{H}_h$ be the $n_h \times p$ submatrix of sample standard errors of $\hat{\mathbf{\Theta}}_h$, from $\mathbf{H}$ in Eq. 8.2.19. From the Heck or Pillai tables, we can obtain ϕ_α, the 100α percent critical value of ϕ. Then the $1-\alpha$ confidence bounds on $\mathbf{\Theta}_h$ are

$$\mathbf{\Theta}_h\text{:}\ \hat{\mathbf{\Theta}}_h \pm \sqrt{n_e \lambda_\alpha}\, \mathbf{H}_h \tag{10.1.23}$$

where $\lambda_\alpha = \phi_\alpha/(1-\phi_\alpha)$. Hummel and Sligo (1971) suggest that this approach yields intervals for particular effects that are too conservative for most behavioral science purposes. Thus, specialization to a single contrast and/or single criterion measure, as in Eqs. 8.2.20 and 8.2.21, is recommended.

Sample Problem 3 – Dental Calculus Reduction

The toothpaste data of Sample Problem 3 comprise a 2×5 factorial arrangement, with six measures for each observation. The effects in the model are given in Section 9.3. These are

1. B, differences between active agents and the control groups (3 d.f.)
2. B^*, differences between the two control groups (1 d.f.)
3. A, differences between the two years of experimentation (1 d.f.)
4. AB, interaction of years and treatments ($3-2=1$ d.f.)

The hypothesis cross-products matrices are $\mathbf{S}_{H_1}$ through $\mathbf{S}_{H_4}$, on pages 336–337, and error matrix $\mathbf{S}_E$, on page 337. Assuming no interaction, let us examine differences between the two years of experimentation through a discriminant approach. The hypothesis matrix is $\mathbf{S}_{H_3}$, with $n_{h_3} = 1$ degree of freedom.

The number of discriminant functions for the hypothesis is $s = \min(1, 6) = 1$.

For this hypothesis, Eq. 10.1.8 becomes

$$\left(\mathbf{S}_{H_3} - \frac{\hat{\lambda}}{100}\mathbf{S}_E\right)\hat{\boldsymbol{\alpha}} = \mathbf{0}$$

Solving the determinantal equation (10.1.9) for $\hat{\lambda}$ and then substituting to find $\hat{\boldsymbol{\alpha}}$, we have

$$\hat{\lambda} = .0242$$

and

$$\hat{\boldsymbol{\alpha}}' = [-.33 \quad .48 \quad -.59 \quad .53 \quad .04 \quad -.19]$$

Before interpreting the function, we may wish to test H_0: $\boldsymbol{\Theta}_A = \mathbf{0}'$, or H_0: $\boldsymbol{\Theta}_A\boldsymbol{\alpha} = 0$. Since there is only a single discriminant function, $\hat{\lambda}$ accounts for 100 percent of variation between year 1 and year 2 results. The need to test multiple discriminant functions is obviated. The likelihood ratio is

$$\Lambda = \frac{1}{1+.0242} = .98$$

This is identical to Λ for the analysis-of-variance test. The χ^2 transformation of Λ is

$$\chi^2 = -\left(100+1-\frac{1+6+1}{2}\right)\log_e .98$$

$$= 2.32$$

χ^2 has 6(1) = 6 degrees of freedom. H_0 is not rejected. The discriminant function appears to reflect only random variation among group means, and is not worthy of interpretation.

Having accepted H_0: $\boldsymbol{\Theta}_A = \mathbf{0}'$, we may move on to test H_0: $\boldsymbol{\Theta}_{B*} = \mathbf{0}'$, with no reordering of effects. Solving Eq. 10.1.8 for the single root and vector, with $\mathbf{S}_{H_2}$ and $\mathbf{S}_E$, we find

$$\hat{\lambda} = .0607$$

$$\hat{\boldsymbol{\alpha}}' = [-.49 \quad .39 \quad -.02 \quad .25 \quad -.54 \quad -.30]$$

The likelihood ratio is

$$\Lambda = \frac{1}{1+.0607} = .94$$

The χ^2 transformation is

$$\chi^2 = -\left(100+1-\frac{1+6+1}{2}\right)\log_e .94$$

$$= 5.72$$

Again, H_0 is accepted. There is no significant variation between vector means for the two control groups.

Finding both $\boldsymbol{\Theta}_A$ and $\boldsymbol{\Theta}_{B*}$ to be null, we may proceed to test H_0: $\boldsymbol{\Theta}_B = \mathbf{0}$, with the same order of effects. Should either $\boldsymbol{\Theta}_A$ or $\boldsymbol{\Theta}_{B*}$ have been nonzero, the significant effect(s) would need to be reordered to precede the B effects, and the design basis reorthogonalized before testing $\mathbf{\Theta}_B$ (due to the lack of orthogonality).

$\mathbf{S}_{H_1}$ is the three-degree-of-freedom sum of products for comparing the three experimental agents with the two control groups. The number of discriminant functions is $s = \min(3, 6) = 3$. Substituting $\mathbf{S}_{H_1}$ and $\mathbf{S}_E$ in Eq. 10.1.8, with $n_{h_1} = 3$, the three characteristic roots are $\hat{\lambda}_1 = .2273$, $\hat{\lambda}_2 = .0920$, and $\hat{\lambda}_3 = .0294$. These are the between-group variances of the three discriminant variables. The corresponding raw weight vectors are

$$\hat{\mathbf{A}} = \begin{bmatrix} .20 & .74 & -.56 \\ .09 & -.31 & -.27 \\ .66 & .51 & .33 \\ -.37 & -.53 & -.21 \\ .17 & .10 & -.24 \\ -.11 & -.57 & .91 \end{bmatrix} \begin{matrix} \text{Right canine} \\ \text{Right lateral incisor} \\ \text{Right central incisor} \\ \text{Left central incisor} \\ \text{Left lateral incisor} \\ \text{Left canine} \end{matrix}$$

First function Second function Third function

Before attempting to interpret the discriminant functions, let us test H_0: $\mathbf{\Theta}_B = \mathbf{0}$ or, equivalently, H_0: $\lambda_i = 0$ $(i = 1, 2, 3)$. The sum of the $\hat{\lambda}_i$ is $\text{tr}(\hat{\mathbf{\Lambda}}) = .3487$. The percent of between-group variation attributable to each of the functions is

$$P_1 = \frac{100(.2273)}{.3487} = 65.18 \quad \text{First function}$$

$$P_2 = \frac{100(.0920)}{.3487} = 26.38 \quad \text{Second function}$$

$$P_3 = \frac{100(.0294)}{.3487} = 8.44 \quad \text{Third function}$$

It appears that most between-group variance is attributable to a single linear combination of the tooth measures. A second function may also account for some of the variation of the experimental agents from the control group. We shall apply formal test criteria to determine if *any* of this variation is significant.

Roy's largest-root statistic may be used to test H_0: $\lambda_1 = 0$. We find

$$\phi = \frac{.2273}{1 + .2273} = .1852$$

with

$$m = (|6-3|-1)/2$$
$$= 1$$

and

$$n = (100-6-1)/2$$
$$= 46.5$$

Comparison to the Pillai tables, with $s=3$, reveals that ϕ just exceeds the .05 critical value of .18 (obtained by interpolation).

For H_0: $\lambda_2=0$, n_h and n_e are each reduced by one. The test statistic is

$$\phi=\frac{.0920}{1+.0920}=.0843$$

with

$$\begin{aligned} m &= (|6-2|-1)/2 \\ &= 1.5 \end{aligned}$$

and

$$\begin{aligned} n &= (99-6-1)/2 \\ &= 46 \end{aligned}$$

ϕ does not exceed the .05 critical value and H_0 is accepted. All significant variation between the experimental and control groups can be attributed to a single linear function of the six variates. Although it is no longer necessary to test H_0: $\lambda_3=0$, we would find that the hypothesis is not rejected. Here $\phi=.0286$, with $m=2$ and $n=45.5$.

If we chose to test H_0: $\mathbf{\Theta}_B=\mathbf{0}$ by means of Hotelling's trace criterion, the test statistic is

$$\text{tr}\,(\hat{\mathbf{\Lambda}})=.3487$$

The .05 critical value for $s=3$, $m=1$, and $n=46.5$, is .32. H_0 is again rejected at $\alpha=.05$ (but not at $\alpha=.01$).

Finally let us test H_0 through successive likelihood ratio tests. For all three roots, the ratio is

$$\begin{aligned} \Lambda_1 &= \left(\frac{1}{1+.2273}\right)\left(\frac{1}{1+.0920}\right)\left(\frac{1}{1+.0294}\right) \\ &= .72 \end{aligned}$$

This is *exactly* the likelihood ratio obtained in Chapter 9 for the test of equality of mean vectors. The χ^2 transformation is

$$\begin{aligned} \chi^2 &= -\left(100+3-\frac{3+6+1}{2}\right)\log_e .72 \\ &= -98(-.322) \\ &= 31.54 \end{aligned}$$

χ^2 has $6(3)=18$ degrees of freedom. The tabled .05 critical value of $\chi_{18}{}^2$ is 28.87. This value is exceeded, and H_0 is rejected.

We can also obtain a likelihood ratio for the two smaller roots alone. That is,

$$\begin{aligned} \Lambda_2 &= \left(\frac{1}{1+.0920}\right)\left(\frac{1}{1+.0294}\right) \\ &= .89 \end{aligned}$$

The test statistic is

$$\begin{aligned} \chi^2 &= -98\,(\log_e .89) \\ &= 11.47 \end{aligned}$$

χ^2 from Λ_2 has $(6-1)(3-1)=10$ degrees of freedom. $\chi_{10,.05}{}^2=18.31$ is not exceeded. When the largest canonical variate is excluded, no significant variation between experimental and control groups remains. All significant between-group variation is concentrated in the first discriminant dimension.

The third function alone has

$$\Lambda_3 = \frac{1}{1+.0294}$$
$$= .97$$

The test statistic is

$$\chi^2 = -98(\log_e .97)$$
$$= 2.84$$

χ^2 from Λ_3 has $(6-2)(3-2)=4$ degrees of freedom. Since Λ_2 did not exceed the critical value, Λ_3 will also show no significant effect.

In this case, all three test criteria have yielded the same conclusion. Let us examine the first discriminant function more closely. The discriminant weights are the first column of $\hat{\mathbf{A}}$. That is,

$$\hat{\boldsymbol{\alpha}}_1 = \begin{bmatrix} .20 \\ .09 \\ .66 \\ -.37 \\ .17 \\ -.11 \end{bmatrix}$$

Since the variances of the six teeth measures are disparate, we may wish to standardize $\hat{\boldsymbol{\alpha}}_1$ for inspection. The diagonal matrix of within-group standard deviations is given in previous chapters.

$$\mathbf{D}_E{}^{1/2} = \text{diag}\,(1.17, \quad 1.62, \quad 2.06, \quad 2.49, \quad 1.76, \quad 1.26)$$

The standardized weights are

$$\hat{\mathbf{a}}_1 = \mathbf{D}_E{}^{1/2}\hat{\boldsymbol{\alpha}}_1$$

$$= \begin{bmatrix} .23 \\ .15 \\ 1.36 \\ -.91 \\ .30 \\ -.14 \end{bmatrix} \begin{matrix} \text{Right canine} \\ \text{Right lateral incisor} \\ \text{Right central incisor} \\ \text{Left central incisor} \\ \text{Left lateral incisor} \\ \text{Left canine} \end{matrix}$$

Although the weights are interdependent, the function is largely influenced by calculus formation on the two central teeth. These teeth have the highest mean calculus formation of the six. The *difference between them* appears to be the strongest discriminator of the control groups from those utilizing the experimental additives. The differences favor (lower means) the right side in the control groups and the left side in the experimental groups.

To evaluate the effectiveness of the experimental agents, let us transform the three contrasts to the metric of the first discriminant function. The estimate $\hat{\boldsymbol{\Theta}}$ is given in Section 8.4. The contrasts of the three experimental groups with the controls (groups 1 and 2), are

$$\hat{\boldsymbol{\Theta}}_B = \begin{bmatrix} -.31 & -.93 & -1.07 & -1.43 & -.92 & -.30 \\ .18 & -.93 & -.98 & -1.91 & -1.29 & -.91 \\ -.59 & -1.31 & -2.21 & -1.80 & -1.24 & -.72 \end{bmatrix} \begin{matrix} \boldsymbol{\beta}_3' - 1/2(\boldsymbol{\beta}_1' + \boldsymbol{\beta}_2') & \text{Agent 1} \\ \boldsymbol{\beta}_4' - 1/2(\boldsymbol{\beta}_1' + \boldsymbol{\beta}_2') & \text{Agent 2} \\ \boldsymbol{\beta}_5' - 1/2(\boldsymbol{\beta}_1' + \boldsymbol{\beta}_2') & \text{Agent 3} \end{matrix}$$

Right canine, Right lateral incisor, Right central incisor, Left central incisor, Left lateral incisor, Left canine

For the first discriminant variable the differences are

$$\hat{\boldsymbol{\Theta}}_z = \hat{\boldsymbol{\Theta}}_B \hat{\boldsymbol{\alpha}}_1$$

$$= \begin{bmatrix} -.451 \\ -.112 \\ -1.161 \end{bmatrix} \begin{matrix} \text{Agent 1} \\ \text{Agent 2} \\ \text{Agent 3} \end{matrix}$$

The mean of the first experimental group is about half a standard deviation below the controls, on the discriminant variable; the second experimental group is one tenth of a within-group standard deviation below the controls; the third experimental group is more than one standard deviation below the mean of the controls. The third active agent appears to be the *most effective* of the three in reducing dental calculus. This effect may be detected, but with less clarity, by inspecting the subclass means or mean differences for the six separate teeth.

The contrasts may be graphed to depict the effect. The control-group mean forms the origin of the graph. Graphing procedures are likely to be more useful, however, when more than a single discriminant variable is significant. The results can be plotted with two or three discriminant variables as orthogonal axes. In this example, the discriminant analysis effectively isolates and simplifies the effect of major interest in the study.

10.2 ANALYSIS OF COVARIANCE

The Models

Analysis of covariance was introduced by Fisher (1932) as a means for reducing error variation and increasing the sensitivity of an experimental analysis to mean differences. The method depends upon identifying one or more measured independent variables, which are related to the response measures but not to the experimental treatment conditions. In a multiple regression analysis, these variables are termed *predictor variables*. When the same variables are used for additional control in an experiment, they are termed *concomitant vari-*

ables or *covariates*. The corresponding statistical model is the *analysis-of-covariance* model. By including concomitant measures in the model, residual variation can be reduced to the extent that it is attributable to the covariates—that is, to the extent that the criteria and covariates are linearly intercorrelated.

The analysis-of-covariance model may also be viewed from a different perspective. When the independent variables are defined by membership in experimental or naturally occurring groups, we compare means through the analysis-of-variance model. When the independent variables are *measured* predictor variables, we test their association to the criteria through the multiple regression model. Both of these cases are different applications of the same general linear model—identical in computation and in statistical tests, but for differently scaled independent variables.

The analysis-of-covariance model is the same general linear model. It is appropriate when we have *both* measured and group-membership independent variables, and one or more criteria. We may test hypotheses about group differences on the criteria, holding constant or eliminating the covariates. These tests alone are usually referred to as analysis-of-covariance tests. We may also test the regression of the criteria upon the covariates, removing group mean differences. These tests are a simple modification of the regression tests of Chapter 5, and are also conducted under the analysis-of-covariance model.

A third statistical test is also of interest—the test of *homogeneity of regression.* Before adjusting error variation for covariates, it is necessary to determine whether a single adjustment will suffice or whether the covariate adjustment must be different for each group of observations. This is equivalent to testing that the regression weights are the same for all groups in the experimental design. The homogeneity test may also be of experimental interest in itself—for example, in the comparison of teaching approaches. A researcher may wish to test whether the dependence of achievement on verbal capacity is different (lower) when nonverbal media are emphasized in teaching. Verbal and nonverbal approaches are tested with independent groups of subjects. The regression weights of final achievement upon prior verbal IQ scores may be compared across groups, even with multiple measures of each trait.

The inclusion of covariance controls in an experimental design is an efficient procedure. As in regression analysis, each measured independent variable requires only a single degree of freedom. However, *no* reasonable number of covariates can equate experimental groups in the sense that randomization can. An unjudicious choice of covariates can introduce sufficient error into the estimation of between-group effects to render them uninterpretable. The careful selection of a small number of covariates is best accomplished through reference to an explicit psychological model of the behavior under investigation.

As an example, assume that we have a two-way fixed analysis-of-variance model, with p dependent measures taken from each subject. The analysis-of-variance model for observation i in subclass jk is

$$\mathbf{y}'_{ijk} = \boldsymbol{\mu}' + \boldsymbol{\alpha}'_j + \boldsymbol{\beta}'_k + \boldsymbol{\gamma}'_{jk} + \boldsymbol{\epsilon}'_{ijk} \tag{10.2.1}$$

All terms are $1 \times p$ vectors, with

$$\mathbf{y}'_{ijk} = [y_{ijk}{}^{(1)} \quad y_{ijk}{}^{(2)} \quad \cdots \quad y_{ijk}{}^{(p)}] \tag{10.2.1a}$$

Assume further that we postulate that q additional variables are related to the criteria. Scores on these covariates are collected prior to the introduction of the experimental conditions. Let the q scores for observation i in subclass jk comprise the $1\times q$ vector,

$$\mathbf{x}'_{ijk} = [x_{ijk}^{(1)} \quad x_{ijk}^{(2)} \quad \cdots \quad x_{ijk}^{(q)}] \tag{10.2.2}$$

Adding these independent variables to Eq. 10.2.1, we have the covariance model,

$$\mathbf{y}'_{ijk} = \boldsymbol{\mu}' + \boldsymbol{\alpha}'_j + \boldsymbol{\beta}'_k + \boldsymbol{\gamma}'_{jk} + (\mathbf{x}_{ijk} - \mathbf{x}_{\cdot\cdot\cdot})'\mathbf{B} + (\boldsymbol{\epsilon}^*_{ijk})' \tag{10.2.3}$$

$\mathbf{B}$ is the $q\times p$ matrix of partial regression coefficients of $\mathbf{y}$ on $\mathbf{x}$. $\mathbf{x}_{\cdot\cdot\cdot}$ is the vector mean for the concomitant variables for all $N = \Sigma N_{jk}$ observations,

$$\mathbf{x}_{\cdot\cdot\cdot} = \frac{1}{N} \Sigma_i \Sigma_j \Sigma_k \mathbf{x}_{ijk} \tag{10.2.4}$$

$\boldsymbol{\epsilon}^*_{ijk}$ is the p-element vector of *reduced* or *adjusted* random errors. Error vectors are assumed identically and independently distributed in p-variate normal fashion, with expectation $\mathbf{0}$ and covariance matrix $\boldsymbol{\Sigma}^*$. That is,

$$\boldsymbol{\epsilon}^*_{ijk} \sim \mathcal{N}_p(\mathbf{0}, \boldsymbol{\Sigma}^*) \tag{10.2.5}$$

The analysis-of-covariance model may also be written for subclass means. Let N_{jk} be the number of observations in cell jk of the sampling design. Then subclass mean vectors are

$$\mathbf{y}_{\cdot jk} = \frac{1}{N_{jk}} \Sigma_i \mathbf{y}_{ijk} \tag{10.2.6a}$$

and

$$\mathbf{x}_{\cdot jk} = \frac{1}{N_{jk}} \Sigma_i \mathbf{x}_{ijk} \tag{10.2.6b}$$

The mean model is

$$\mathbf{y}'_{\cdot jk} = \boldsymbol{\mu}' + \boldsymbol{\alpha}'_j + \boldsymbol{\beta}'_k + \boldsymbol{\gamma}'_{jk} + (\mathbf{x}_{\cdot jk} - \mathbf{x}_{\cdot\cdot\cdot})'\mathbf{B} + (\boldsymbol{\epsilon}^*_{\cdot jk})' \tag{10.2.7}$$

with

$$\boldsymbol{\epsilon}^*_{\cdot jk} = \frac{1}{N_{jk}} \sum_i \boldsymbol{\epsilon}^*_{ijk}$$

Error vectors are independently normally distributed with expectation $\mathbf{0}$ and covariance matrix $(1/N_{jk})\boldsymbol{\Sigma}^*$. That is,

$$\boldsymbol{\epsilon}^*_{\cdot jk} \sim \mathcal{N}_p\left(\mathbf{0}, \frac{1}{N_{jk}} \boldsymbol{\Sigma}^*\right) \tag{10.2.8}$$

Mean models for all J cells of the sampling design may be juxtaposed and written as the sum of matrix products. For a 2×2 design, the total number of groups is $J = 4$. The models are

$$\begin{bmatrix} \mathbf{y}'_{\cdot 11} \\ \mathbf{y}'_{\cdot 12} \\ \mathbf{y}'_{\cdot 21} \\ \mathbf{y}'_{\cdot 22} \end{bmatrix} = \begin{bmatrix} 1 & 1 & 0 & 1 & 0 & 1 & 0 & 0 & 0 \\ 1 & 1 & 0 & 0 & 1 & 0 & 1 & 0 & 0 \\ 1 & 0 & 1 & 1 & 0 & 0 & 0 & 1 & 0 \\ 1 & 0 & 1 & 0 & 1 & 0 & 0 & 0 & 1 \end{bmatrix} \begin{bmatrix} \boldsymbol{\mu}' \\ \boldsymbol{\alpha}'_1 \\ \boldsymbol{\alpha}'_2 \\ \boldsymbol{\beta}'_1 \\ \boldsymbol{\beta}'_2 \\ \boldsymbol{\gamma}'_{11} \\ \boldsymbol{\gamma}'_{12} \\ \boldsymbol{\gamma}'_{21} \\ \boldsymbol{\gamma}'_{22} \end{bmatrix} + \begin{bmatrix} \mathbf{x}'_{\cdot 11} - \mathbf{x}'_{\cdot\cdot\cdot} \\ \mathbf{x}'_{\cdot 12} - \mathbf{x}'_{\cdot\cdot\cdot} \\ \mathbf{x}'_{\cdot 21} - \mathbf{x}'_{\cdot\cdot\cdot} \\ \mathbf{x}'_{\cdot 22} - \mathbf{x}'_{\cdot\cdot\cdot} \end{bmatrix} \mathbf{B} + \begin{bmatrix} (\boldsymbol{\epsilon}^*_{\cdot 11})' \\ (\boldsymbol{\epsilon}^*_{\cdot 12})' \\ (\boldsymbol{\epsilon}^*_{\cdot 21})' \\ (\boldsymbol{\epsilon}^*_{\cdot 22})' \end{bmatrix} \tag{10.2.9}$$

or

$$\mathbf{Y}_{\cdot} = \mathbf{A}\boldsymbol{\Theta}^* + (\mathbf{X}_{\cdot} - \mathbf{1}\mathbf{x}'_{\cdot\cdot\cdot})\mathbf{B} + \mathbf{E}^*_{\cdot} \tag{10.2.9a}$$

$\mathbf{Y}_{\cdot}$ is the $J \times p$ matrix with rows $\mathbf{y}'_{\cdot jk}$. $\mathbf{X}_{\cdot}$ is the $J \times q$ matrix of subclass means for the covariates, having rows $\mathbf{x}'_{\cdot jk}$. $\mathbf{1}$ is a J-element unit vector, so the matrix $[\mathbf{1}\mathbf{x}'_{\cdot\cdot\cdot}]$ has identical rows $[\mathbf{x}'_{\cdot\cdot\cdot}]$. $\mathbf{A}$ is the $J \times m$ analysis-of-variance model matrix, and $\boldsymbol{\Theta}^*$ the $m \times p$ matrix of fixed parameters, as in Chapter 7. $\mathbf{B}$ is the $q \times p$ matrix of regression coefficients of $\mathbf{y}$ on $\mathbf{x}$. Unlike $\mathbf{B}$ for the regression model, it does not contain a constant term; the $\mathbf{y}$ scaling factor is absorbed by the first column of model matrix $\mathbf{A}$. The $\mathbf{x}$ scaling factor is zero for mean-deviation scores.

$\mathbf{E}^*_{\cdot}$ is $J \times p$ and contains the mean residuals for all J groups. Rows of $\mathbf{E}^*_{\cdot}$ have independent p-variate normal distributions as in Eq. 10.2.8. Together their distribution is

$$\mathbf{E}^*_{\cdot} \sim \mathcal{N}_{Jp}(\mathbf{0},\ \mathbf{D}^{-1} \otimes \boldsymbol{\Sigma}^*) \tag{10.2.10}$$

$\mathbf{D}$ is the diagonal matrix of subclass frequencies $(N_{11}, N_{12}, N_{21}, N_{22})$. $\mathbf{0}$ is a $J \times p$ null matrix.

The steps in covariance analysis begin with the reparameterization from $\boldsymbol{\Theta}^*$ to contrasts $\boldsymbol{\Theta}$, as in the analysis-of-variance model. Estimates of the terms in $\boldsymbol{\Theta}$ are obtained, *eliminating* the covariates in $\mathbf{X}$. The estimate of $\mathbf{B}$ is found, *eliminating* group effects in $\mathbf{A}$. $\boldsymbol{\Theta}$ and $\mathbf{B}$ may be estimated simultaneously in a single least-squares solution, or separately. The latter approach is taken here; the estimation of $\mathbf{B}$ is presented first. Then $\boldsymbol{\Theta}$ is estimated for the y measures and adjusted for the effects of the covariates. Finally $\boldsymbol{\Sigma}^*$ is estimated, eliminating both regression and group-membership effects.

The test for parallelism of regression planes (homogeneity of regression) indicates whether a single estimate of $\mathbf{B}$ is satisfactory for all groups, or whether the regressions differ from one group of subjects to another. Tests of significance are made on sections or all of $\mathbf{B}$, to decide whether there is nonzero regression of $\mathbf{y}$ on $\mathbf{x}$. Finally tests may be conducted on sections or all of covariate-adjusted $\boldsymbol{\Theta}$. These provide tests of means and mean differences, after the effects of the covariates are eliminated. The tests of significance all follow directly from regression and analysis-of-variance tests, as described in the preceding chapters.

We may begin by reparameterizing $\mathbf{A}\boldsymbol{\Theta}^*$ to $\mathbf{K}\boldsymbol{\Theta}$ in the two-way example. A 2×2 fixed model is described in detail and reparameterized to contrasts in

Chapters 7 and 8. The rank of **A** in Eq. 10.2.9 is $l=4$, while the column order is $m=9$. The four effects in the reparameterized model are the constant term, the contrast between $\boldsymbol{\alpha}_j$'s, the contrast between $\boldsymbol{\beta}_k$'s, and an interaction contrast. The rows of the contrast matrix **L** must be linear combinations of rows of **A** ($\mathbf{a}'_i$). Thus **L** is

$$\mathbf{L}=\begin{bmatrix} 1 & .5 & .5 & .5 & .5 & .25 & .25 & .25 & .25 \\ 0 & 1 & -1 & 0 & 0 & .5 & .5 & -.5 & -.5 \\ 0 & 0 & 0 & 1 & -1 & .5 & -.5 & .5 & -.5 \\ 0 & 0 & 0 & 0 & 0 & 1 & -1 & -1 & 1 \end{bmatrix} \begin{matrix} 1/4\sum_i \mathbf{a}'_i \\ 1/2(\mathbf{a}'_1+\mathbf{a}'_2)-1/2(\mathbf{a}'_3+\mathbf{a}'_4) \\ 1/2(\mathbf{a}'_1+\mathbf{a}'_3)-1/2(\mathbf{a}'_2+\mathbf{a}'_4) \\ (\mathbf{a}'_1+\mathbf{a}'_4)-(\mathbf{a}'_2+\mathbf{a}'_3) \end{matrix} \tag{10.2.11}$$

The substitute parameter matrix is

$$\boldsymbol{\Theta}=\mathbf{L}\boldsymbol{\Theta}^*$$
$$=\begin{bmatrix} \boldsymbol{\mu}'+\boldsymbol{\alpha}'_.+\boldsymbol{\beta}'_.+\boldsymbol{\gamma}'_{..} \\ (\boldsymbol{\alpha}_1-\boldsymbol{\alpha}_2)'+(\boldsymbol{\gamma}_{1.}-\boldsymbol{\gamma}_{2.})' \\ (\boldsymbol{\beta}_1-\boldsymbol{\beta}_2)'+(\boldsymbol{\gamma}_{.1}-\boldsymbol{\gamma}_{.2})' \\ (\boldsymbol{\gamma}_{11}-\boldsymbol{\gamma}_{12})'-(\boldsymbol{\gamma}_{21}-\boldsymbol{\gamma}_{22})' \end{bmatrix} \begin{matrix} \text{Constant} \\ A \text{ main effect} \\ B \text{ main effect} \\ AB \text{ interaction} \end{matrix} \tag{10.2.12}$$

The basis, or reparameterized model matrix, is the $J\times l$ matrix,

$$\mathbf{K}=\mathbf{AL}'(\mathbf{LL}')^{-1}$$
$$=\begin{bmatrix} 1 & .5 & .5 & .25 \\ 1 & .5 & -.5 & -.25 \\ 1 & -.5 & .5 & -.25 \\ 1 & -.5 & -.5 & .25 \end{bmatrix} \tag{10.2.13}$$
$$\begin{matrix}\text{Constant} & A & B & AB\end{matrix}$$

The product $\mathbf{K}\boldsymbol{\Theta}$ substitutes for $\mathbf{A}\boldsymbol{\Theta}^*$ in Eq. 10.2.9a. Assuming **X** to be of full rank q, the entire model is now of full rank $l+q$; least-squares estimates of $\boldsymbol{\Theta}$ and $\mathbf{B}$ may be derived. The rank condition requires that there be as many subjects as degrees of freedom in the complete model, $N\geq l+q$. Additional observations are necessary to estimate residual variation and to conduct tests of significance on $\boldsymbol{\Theta}$ and $\mathbf{B}$. For **X** to be of full rank, no covariate can be a direct linear combination of other concomitant measures.

Estimating $\boldsymbol{\Theta}$ and $\mathbf{B}$

The reparameterized form of the model of Eq. 10.2.9a is

$$\mathbf{Y}_.=\mathbf{K}\boldsymbol{\Theta}+(\mathbf{X}_.-\mathbf{1x}'_{..})\mathbf{B}+\mathbf{E}^*_. \tag{10.2.14}$$

$\boldsymbol{\Theta}$ and $\mathbf{B}$ may be estimated so that the sum of squared weighted residuals, $\text{tr}([\hat{\mathbf{E}}^*_.]'\mathbf{D}\hat{\mathbf{E}}^*_.)$, will be minimal in the sample. Two sets of normal equations are obtained, each containing both $\boldsymbol{\Theta}$ and $\mathbf{B}$. The two may be solved simultaneously to obtain the respective least-squares estimates.

An alternative approach to estimation follows from regression analysis in Chapter 4. Let $\mathbf{v}_{ij}$ be the $(p+q)$-element vector for observation i in subclass

j, having all p y-measures *and* all q x-measures. That is,

$$\begin{aligned}\mathbf{v}'_{ij} &= [\mathbf{y}'_{ij} \;,\; \mathbf{x}'_{ij}] \\ &= [y_{ij}^{(1)} \quad y_{ij}^{(2)} \quad \cdots \quad y_{ij}^{(p)} \mid x_{ij}^{(1)} \quad x_{ij}^{(2)} \quad \cdots \quad x_{ij}^{(q)}]\end{aligned} \tag{10.2.15}$$

We use only a single group index (j) although the groups may be cells in a two-way or higher-order design. $\mathbf{V}$ is the $N\times(p+q)$ total data matrix for all observations, with rows $\mathbf{v}'_{ij}$. $\mathbf{V}$ is formed by augmenting the $N\times p$ outcome matrix $\mathbf{Y}$, by the $N\times q$ matrix of covariate values $\mathbf{X}$. That is,

$$\mathbf{V} = [\mathbf{Y}, \mathbf{X}] \tag{10.2.16}$$

The matrix of subclass means for all groups on $p+q$ measures is

$$\mathbf{V}. = [\mathbf{Y}., \mathbf{X}.] \tag{10.2.17}$$

$\mathbf{V}.$ has J rows and $p+q$ columns.

As a first step, between-group effects are estimated for *both* the criterion measures and the covariates. Assume that $\boldsymbol{\Theta}$ is of order $l\times(p+q)$, and is represented as $\boldsymbol{\Theta}_v$. The matrix may be partitioned for y and x variables. That is,

$$\boldsymbol{\Theta}_v = [\boldsymbol{\Theta}_y, \quad \boldsymbol{\Theta}_x] \tag{10.2.18}$$

$\boldsymbol{\Theta}_y$ ($l\times p$) are the contrasts among groups on the criterion variables, and will ultimately be "adjusted" for the covariates. $\boldsymbol{\Theta}_x$ ($l\times q$) are mean differences for the concomitant measures.

We may estimate $\boldsymbol{\Theta}_v$ for all measures, assuming analysis-of-variance model

$$\mathbf{V}. = \mathbf{K}\boldsymbol{\Theta}_v + \mathbf{E}. \tag{10.2.19}$$

The least-squares estimate is the usual one, according to Eq. 8.1.2. That is,

$$\begin{aligned}\hat{\boldsymbol{\Theta}}_v &= (\mathbf{K}'\mathbf{D}\mathbf{K})^{-1}\mathbf{K}'\mathbf{D}\mathbf{V}. \\ &= (\mathbf{K}'\mathbf{D}\mathbf{K})^{-1}\mathbf{K}'\mathbf{D}[\mathbf{Y}., \mathbf{X}.] \\ &= [\hat{\boldsymbol{\Theta}}_y, \quad \hat{\boldsymbol{\Theta}}_x]\end{aligned} \tag{10.2.20}$$

Since columns of $\boldsymbol{\Theta}_v$ are estimated separately from one another, inclusion of x variables in the matrix does not effect $\hat{\boldsymbol{\Theta}}_y$.

From $\hat{\boldsymbol{\Theta}}_v$ we may obtain the error sums of squares and products for all variables, eliminating group-mean effects. This is the matrix $\mathbf{S}_E$ of the analysis-of-variance model, but including the two sets of variates. The residual sum of products is $(p+q)$-square and symmetric.

$$\mathbf{S}_E = (\mathbf{V}'\mathbf{V} - \hat{\boldsymbol{\Theta}}'_v\mathbf{K}'\mathbf{D}\mathbf{K}\hat{\boldsymbol{\Theta}}_v) \tag{10.2.21}$$

$\mathbf{S}_E$ has $n_e = N-l$ degrees of freedom.

If the model includes all possible between-group effects ($l=J$), $\mathbf{K}$ is square and $\mathbf{S}_E$ is the within-groups sum of products for all $p+q$ measures. In this case,

$$\begin{aligned}\mathbf{S}_E &= (\mathbf{V}'\mathbf{V} - \mathbf{V}'.\mathbf{D}\mathbf{V}.) \\ &= \mathbf{S}_W\end{aligned} \tag{10.2.22}$$

The degrees of freedom are $n_e = N-J$. This is the form in all common factorial analysis-of-variance designs with replications (see Eqs. 8.2.7–8.2.10).

In either case, since **V** and **V.** have y and x components, $\mathbf{S}_E$ may be partitioned like the residual matrix ($\mathbf{S}_w$) in the regression model. Let $\mathbf{S}_E$ be partitioned into $\mathbf{S}_E^{(yy)}$ for the criterion measures, $\mathbf{S}_E^{(xx)}$ for the covariates, and $\mathbf{S}_E^{(yx)} = [\mathbf{S}_E^{(xy)}]'$ for the cross products of the two. That is,

$$\mathbf{S}_E = \left[\begin{array}{c|c} \mathbf{S}_E^{(yy)} & \mathbf{S}_E^{(yx)} \\ \hline \mathbf{S}_E^{(xy)} & \mathbf{S}_E^{(xx)} \end{array}\right] \begin{array}{l} p \text{ rows} \\ q \text{ rows} \end{array} \tag{10.2.23}$$

p columns $\quad q$ columns

The estimate of $\mathbf{B}$ may be obtained directly from the partitions of $\mathbf{S}_E$, as in the regression model. Unlike the regression model, $\mathbf{B}$ is estimated after eliminating group-mean differences (in Eq. 10.2.21). The estimate is

$$\hat{\mathbf{B}} = [\mathbf{S}_E^{(xx)}]^{-1}\mathbf{S}_E^{(xy)} \tag{10.2.24}$$

The expectation of $\hat{\mathbf{B}}$ is $\mathbf{B}$, and the covariance matrix is $[\mathbf{S}_E^{(xx)}]^{-1} \otimes \mathbf{\Sigma}^*$. Once the estimate of $\mathbf{\Sigma}^*$ is found, standardized regression coefficients, confidence intervals, and test statistics may be computed for $\mathbf{B}$ exactly as in the multiple regression model.

$\hat{\mathbf{B}}$ is used to adjust the mean differences in $\hat{\mathbf{\Theta}}_y$ for covariates. The estimate of $\mathbf{\Theta}$ in Eq. 10.2.14, eliminating the covariates, is the $l \times p$ matrix,

$$\hat{\mathbf{\Theta}} = \hat{\mathbf{\Theta}}_y - \hat{\mathbf{\Theta}}_x \hat{\mathbf{B}} \tag{10.2.25}$$

The resulting estimates will be very different from the unadjusted $\hat{\mathbf{\Theta}}_y$ if the regression is strong ($\hat{\mathbf{B}}$ elements large). $\hat{\mathbf{\Theta}}$ and $\hat{\mathbf{\Theta}}_y$ are generally similar if there is little or no regression of **y** on **x**. $\hat{\mathbf{\Theta}}$ is an unbiased estimate of $\mathbf{\Theta}$ in Eq. 10.2.14.

Estimating Dispersions

To draw intervals and conduct tests on the adjusted mean differences, we require the variance–covariance matrix of $\hat{\mathbf{\Theta}}$. Two properties of the covariance model are necessary: (1) **X** and thus $\hat{\mathbf{\Theta}}_x$ are fixed constants and (2) $\hat{\mathbf{\Theta}}_y$ and $\hat{\mathbf{\Theta}}_x\hat{\mathbf{B}}$ are linearly independent. Property (1) is true by definition; property (2) is easily demonstrated. Then

$$\begin{aligned} \mathscr{V}(\hat{\mathbf{\Theta}}) &= \mathscr{V}(\hat{\mathbf{\Theta}}_y - \hat{\mathbf{\Theta}}_x\hat{\mathbf{B}}) \\ &= \mathscr{V}(\hat{\mathbf{\Theta}}_y) + \mathscr{V}(\hat{\mathbf{\Theta}}_x\hat{\mathbf{B}}) \\ &= (\mathbf{K}'\mathbf{D}\mathbf{K})^{-1} \otimes \mathbf{\Sigma}^* + \hat{\mathbf{\Theta}}_x \mathscr{V}(\hat{\mathbf{B}}) \hat{\mathbf{\Theta}}_x' \\ &= [(\mathbf{K}'\mathbf{D}\mathbf{K})^{-1} + \hat{\mathbf{\Theta}}_x (\mathbf{S}_E^{(xx)})^{-1} \hat{\mathbf{\Theta}}_x'] \otimes \mathbf{\Sigma}^* \\ &= \mathbf{G} \otimes \mathbf{\Sigma}^* \end{aligned} \tag{10.2.26}$$

The standard errors of the $[\hat{\theta}_{ik}]$ are the square roots of the diagonal elements of Eq. 10.2.26. The standard error of adjusted contrast i for variate y_k is

$$\sigma_{\hat{\theta}_{ik}} = \sqrt{g_{ii}}\,\sigma_k^* \tag{10.2.27}$$

To estimate $\sigma_{\hat{\theta}_{ik}}$ and to draw intervals on θ_{ik}, we require an estimate of $\mathbf{\Sigma}^*$.

The residual variance–covariance matrix is estimated after eliminating *both* group membership and regression effects. $\mathbf{S}_E$ is the sum-of-products matrix removing the group-mean differences. The effects of the predictors may be removed as in regression analysis. Assume $\mathbf{S}_E$ to be partitioned as in Eq. 10.2.23. The residual sum of products, given both sets of independent variables, is

$$\begin{aligned}\mathbf{S}_E^* &= \mathbf{S}_E^{(yy)} - \mathbf{S}_E^{(yx)}\hat{\mathbf{B}} \\ &= \mathbf{S}_E^{(yy)} - \mathbf{S}_E^{(yx)}[\mathbf{S}_E^{(xx)}]^{-1}\mathbf{S}_E^{(xy)}\end{aligned} \tag{10.2.28}$$

$\mathbf{S}_E^*$ has degrees of freedom

$$\begin{aligned}n_e^* &= n_e - q \\ &= N - I - q\end{aligned} \tag{10.2.29}$$

Thus the estimate of $\mathbf{\Sigma}^*$ is

$$\begin{aligned}\hat{\mathbf{\Sigma}}^* &= \frac{1}{n_e^*}\mathbf{S}_E^* \\ &= \mathbf{V}_E^*\end{aligned} \tag{10.2.30}$$

The diagonal elements of $\mathbf{V}_E^*$ are the *reduced error variances* or *reduced error mean squares*; their square roots are the reduced variable standard deviations, $\hat{\sigma}_k^*$.

The estimates may be used in drawing intervals on the elements of $\mathbf{B}$, and substituted in Eqs. 10.2.26 and 10.2.27 to obtain $\hat{\sigma}_{\hat{\theta}_{ik}}$; $(\hat{\theta}_{ik} - \theta_{ik})/\hat{\sigma}_{\hat{\theta}_{ik}}$ follows a t distribution, with n_e^* degrees of freedom.

Prediction

Frequently social science research poses the conditional question, "What would the group means have been if all subjects had scored alike on the covariates?" The covariate-adjusted means for all groups are a function of the estimate $\hat{\mathbf{\Theta}}_v$.

The predicted means for all groups on both the criterion and covariate meaures are found by substitution in Eq. 10.2.19. The predicted matrix is $\hat{\mathbf{V}}.$ of order $J \times (p+q)$. That is,

$$\begin{aligned}\hat{\mathbf{V}}. &= \mathbf{K}\hat{\mathbf{\Theta}}_v \\ &= \mathbf{K}[\hat{\mathbf{\Theta}}_y, \quad \hat{\mathbf{\Theta}}_x] \\ &= [\hat{\mathbf{Y}}., \quad \hat{\mathbf{X}}.]\end{aligned} \tag{10.2.31}$$

$\hat{\mathbf{V}}.$ comprises two sets of predicted means, for the y and x variables, respectively. $\hat{\mathbf{Y}}.$ is $J \times p$, and $\hat{\mathbf{X}}.$ is $J \times q$. We note that if all between-group degrees of freedom are included in the model ($I = J$), these are equivalent to the observed means $\mathbf{V}.$.

The submatrix $\hat{\mathbf{Y}}.$ may be adjusted for covariates in the following manner. Let $\hat{\mathbf{x}}'._j$ be the vector of covariate means for subclass j. $\hat{\mathbf{x}}'._j$ is one row of $\hat{\mathbf{X}}.$. The vector of grand means, or the mean of rows of $\hat{\mathbf{X}}.$, is

$$\begin{aligned}\hat{\mathbf{x}}'.. &= \frac{1}{J}\sum_j \hat{\mathbf{x}}'._j \\ &= \frac{1}{J}\mathbf{1}'\hat{\mathbf{X}}.\end{aligned} \tag{10.2.32}$$

where $\mathbf{1}'$ is a $1 \times J$ unit vector.

The $J \times p$ matrix of adjusted means for all groups is

$$\mathbf{Y}^*_{\cdot} = \hat{\mathbf{Y}}_{\cdot} - (\hat{\mathbf{X}}_{\cdot} - \mathbf{1}\hat{\mathbf{x}}'_{\cdot\cdot})\hat{\mathbf{B}} \tag{10.2.33}$$

Rows of $\mathbf{Y}^*_{\cdot}$ may be averaged, without differential weighting, to provide adjusted row, column, and interaction means for combined subgroups of observations. If $l = J$ and $\mathbf{K}$ is square, $\hat{\mathbf{Y}}_{\cdot}$ is equal to the observed means $\mathbf{Y}_{\cdot}$. Then $\mathbf{Y}^*_{\cdot}$ is the matrix of covariate-adjusted observed means. These are commonly referred to as *adjusted treatment means*.

It may be useful to obtain predicted means under the covariance model 10.2.14. It is especially informative to compare predicted means with and without covariates, to examine the improvement in prediction when they are added to the model. The *adjusted predicted means* are

$$\begin{aligned}\hat{\mathbf{Y}}^*_{\cdot} &= \mathbf{K}\hat{\mathbf{\Theta}} + (\mathbf{X}_{\cdot} - \mathbf{1}\mathbf{x}'_{\cdot\cdot})\hat{\mathbf{B}} \\ &= \mathbf{Y}^*_{\cdot} + (\mathbf{X}_{\cdot} - \mathbf{1}\mathbf{x}'_{\cdot\cdot})\hat{\mathbf{B}}\end{aligned} \tag{10.2.34}$$

$\mathbf{X}_{\cdot}$ contains the *observed* covariate values and $\mathbf{x}'_{\cdot\cdot}$ is the simple average of rows of $\mathbf{X}_{\cdot}$. That is,

$$\mathbf{x}'_{\cdot\cdot} = \frac{1}{J}\mathbf{1}'\mathbf{X}_{\cdot} \tag{10.2.35}$$

The mean residuals are the differences between observed criterion means $\mathbf{Y}_{\cdot}$ and those predicted under the covariance model. That is,

$$\hat{\mathbf{E}}^*_{\cdot} = \mathbf{Y}_{\cdot} - \hat{\mathbf{Y}}^*_{\cdot} \tag{10.2.36}$$

These may be inspected for outliers and for trends in the data not reflected in the model. The comparison of $\hat{\mathbf{E}}^*_{\cdot}$ and the difference $\mathbf{Y}_{\cdot} - \hat{\mathbf{Y}}_{\cdot}$ will give an indication of the predictive power gained through covariate adjustment.

Tests of Hypotheses

Parallelism: The primary statistical tests conducted under Eq. 10.2.14 are the tests of whether there is nonzero regression of the criteria upon the covariates and whether there are significant group mean differences after making the covariate adjustment. Prior to conducting these tests, it is necessary to decide whether a common regression matrix is appropriate to all groups of observations or whether the matrices differ significantly from one group to another. Let $\mathbf{B}_j$ be the $q \times p$ matrix of regression coefficients for group j in the sampling design. The total number of groups in the complete design is J. The null hypothesis for the test of homogeneity, or *parallelism of regression planes* is

$$H_0: \ \mathbf{B}_1 = \mathbf{B}_2 = \cdots = \mathbf{B}_J = \mathbf{B} \tag{10.2.37}$$

If H_0 is rejected, it may be necessary to make separate and distinct covariate adjustments for each group of subjects. The discussion on preceding pages assumes that the matrices are homogeneous, so that only a single estimate is necessary.

To test for regression parallelism, the covariate adjustment is made to the sum of products for each group of observations. These results are pooled and then compared with the adjusted common within-group sum of products. Comparison of the two results reveal the extent to which the J separate regression estimates reduce criterion variation more than a single common estimate.

To make the covariance adjustment for a single group of observations, let $\mathbf{v}_{ij}$ be the vector observation for subject i in subclass j. $\mathbf{v}_{ij}$ has the p criterion scores plus q predictor variable values for the individual,

$$\mathbf{v}'_{ij} = [\mathbf{y}'_{ij}, \quad \mathbf{x}'_{ij}] \tag{10.2.38}$$

The vector mean of all observations in subclass j is

$$\mathbf{v}'_{\cdot j} = \frac{1}{N_j} \sum_i \mathbf{v}'_{ij} \tag{10.2.39}$$

where N_j is the number of observations in the group. The sum of products of mean deviations for one group is

$$\begin{aligned} \mathbf{S}_{w_j} &= \sum_i (\mathbf{v}_{ij} - \mathbf{v}_{\cdot j})(\mathbf{v}_{ij} - \mathbf{v}_{\cdot j})' \\ &= \sum_i \mathbf{v}_{ij}\mathbf{v}'_{ij} - N_j \mathbf{v}_{\cdot j}\mathbf{v}'_{\cdot j} \end{aligned} \tag{10.2.40}$$

$\mathbf{S}_{w_j}$ may be partitioned into sections, as in Eq. 10.2.23. $\mathbf{S}_{w_j}{}^{(yy)}$ is the criterion sum of products, $\mathbf{S}_{w_j}{}^{(xx)}$ the covariate sum of products, and $\mathbf{S}_{w_j}{}^{(yx)} = [\mathbf{S}_{w_j}{}^{(xy)}]'$ is the cross-product matrix of the two sets. That is,

$$\mathbf{S}_{w_j} = \left[\begin{array}{c|c} \mathbf{S}_{w_j}{}^{(yy)} & \mathbf{S}_{w_j}{}^{(yx)} \\ \hline \mathbf{S}_{w_j}{}^{(xy)} & \mathbf{S}_{w_j}{}^{(xx)} \end{array}\right] \begin{array}{l} p \text{ rows} \\ q \text{ rows} \end{array} \tag{10.2.41}$$

$$p \text{ columns} \quad q \text{ columns}$$

To make the covariate adjustment for one group, we follow Eq. 10.2.28. The $p \times p$ adjusted matrix for one group is

$$\begin{aligned} \mathbf{S}^*_{w_j} &= \mathbf{S}_{w_j}{}^{(yy)} - \mathbf{S}_{w_j}{}^{(yx)}[\mathbf{S}_{w_j}{}^{(xx)}]^{-1}\mathbf{S}_{w_j}{}^{(xy)} \\ &= \mathbf{S}_{w_j}{}^{(yy)} - \mathbf{S}_{w_j}{}^{(yx)}\hat{\mathbf{B}}_j \end{aligned} \tag{10.2.42}$$

$\mathbf{S}^*_{w_j}$ has $N_j - 1 - q$ degrees of freedom.

$\mathbf{S}^*_{w_j}$ is computed for all J groups and the results are summed to provide the error matrix for the parallelism test. That is,

$$\mathbf{S} = \sum_j \mathbf{S}^*_{w_j} \tag{10.2.43}$$

$\mathbf{S}$ has degrees of freedom

$$\begin{aligned} n^* &= \sum_j (N_j - 1 - q) \\ &= N - J - qJ \end{aligned} \tag{10.2.44}$$

The adjusted common within-group sum of products is the hypothesis-plus-error matrix for the test. Let

$$\begin{aligned} \mathbf{S}_E &= \sum_j \mathbf{S}_{w_j} \\ &= \mathbf{V}'\mathbf{V} - \mathbf{V}'_{\cdot}\mathbf{D}\mathbf{V}_{\cdot} \end{aligned} \tag{10.2.45}$$

Then the adjusted matrix is $\mathbf{S}_E^*$, as defined by Eq. 10.2.28, with $N-J-q$ degrees of freedom.

$$\mathbf{S}_E^* = \mathbf{S}_E^{(yy)} - \mathbf{S}_E^{(yx)}[\mathbf{S}_E^{(xx)}]^{-1}\mathbf{S}_E^{(xy)} \tag{10.2.46}$$

The difference of $\mathbf{S}_E^*$ and $\mathbf{S}$ represents the additional reduction attributable to making separate covariate adjustments. The hypothesis matrix for the parallelism test is

$$\mathbf{S}_H = \mathbf{S}_E^* - \mathbf{S} \tag{10.2.46a}$$

The degrees of freedom for $\mathbf{S}_H$ are

$$\begin{aligned} n_h &= (N-J-q)-(N-J-qJ) \\ &= q(J-1) \end{aligned} \tag{10.2.47}$$

All of the univariate and multivariate test criteria may be applied. The p univariate F ratios are

$$F_k = \frac{[s_h]_{kk}/n_h}{s_{kk}/n^*} \tag{10.2.48}$$

F_k may be referred to the F distribution, with n_h and n^* degrees of freedom. Step-down test statistics may be computed, with $\mathbf{S}_H$ and $\mathbf{S}$ as the hypothesis and error matrices, respectively.

The likelihood ratio may be used to provide a simultaneous parallelism test for the p criterion measures. The ratio is

$$\Lambda = \frac{|\mathbf{S}|}{|\mathbf{S}_E^*|} \tag{10.2.49}$$

Λ can be transformed either to the χ^2 or F approximation, with n_h degrees of freedom for hypothesis. The F transform is

$$F = \frac{1-\Lambda^{1/s}}{\Lambda^{1/s}} \cdot \frac{ms+1-n_hp/2}{n_hp} \tag{10.2.50}$$

The multipliers are

$$m = [n^*-(p+1-n_h)/2] \tag{10.2.51}$$

and

$$s = \left(\frac{p^2n_h^2-4}{p^2+n_h^2-5}\right)^{1/2} \tag{10.2.52}$$

F is referred to percentage points of the F distribution, with n_hp and $ms+1-n_hp/2$ degrees of freedom. H_0 is rejected if the critical F value is exceeded; a single common covariate adjustment will not suffice. If H_0 is maintained, a common $\mathbf{B}$ is assumed for the remainder of the analysis-of-variance testing. The set of regression weights is not significantly different from one group to another, and the regression planes are parallel.

Covariance tests: The first set of covariance tests is for determining the extent to which the criterion variables depend upon the values of the covariates. These are the tests of *regression* of the y on the x measures. The estimate of the regression coefficient matrix depends upon the $(p+q)$-square matrix $\mathbf{S}_E$, and is given by Eq. 10.2.24. The error sum of products is $\mathbf{S}_E^*$, given by Eq. 10.2.28, with $n_e^* = N-I-q$ degrees of freedom. The sum of products for regression for all covariates is

$$\begin{aligned}\mathbf{S}_R &= \mathbf{S}_E^{(yx)}\hat{\mathbf{B}} \\ &= \mathbf{S}_E^{(yx)}[\mathbf{S}_E^{(xx)}]^{-1}\mathbf{S}_E^{(xy)} \qquad (10.2.53)\end{aligned}$$

$\mathbf{S}_R$ has q degrees of freedom.

All regression estimates and tests discussed in Chapters 4 and 5 can be obtained from $\hat{\mathbf{B}}$, $\mathbf{S}_E^*$, and $\mathbf{S}_R$. $\hat{\mathbf{B}}$ may be standardized, and confidence intervals constructed. $\mathbf{S}_E^*$ may be converted to a matrix of reduced variances and covariances, or to the partial correlation form. Univariate, multivariate, and canonical tests of all or parts of $\mathbf{B}$ follow the previous forms, and are not repeated here. The only unique aspect of regression analysis within the covariance model is that the error matrix $\mathbf{S}_E^*$ has been adjusted for J group mean vectors, instead of a single "overall" vector of means. Likewise the error degrees of freedom (n_e^*) are smaller than in a regression model for a single group of observations. $\mathbf{S}_E^*$ and n_e^* can be directly substituted for $\mathbf{S}_E$ and n_e in Chapters 4 and 5.

The second covariance test is that mean vectors are equal, after covariate adjustments have been made. That is, we wish to test that sections or all of $\boldsymbol{\Theta}$ are null, eliminating regression effects in $\mathbf{B}$. For these tests, $\mathbf{S}_E^*$ and n_e^* are the error sum of products and degrees of freedom, respectively.

To obtain hypothesis sums of products for mean differences, orthogonal estimates are first computed from $\hat{\boldsymbol{\Theta}}_v$ for all criterion measures *and* concomitant variables. The orthogonal estimates comprise a reparameterization of Eq. 10.2.19, exactly as presented in Chapter 9 for analysis-of-variance models. The basis matrix $\mathbf{K}$ is factored into an orthonormal basis $\mathbf{K}^*$ and an upper triangular matrix $\mathbf{T}'$, such that

$$\mathbf{K}^*\mathbf{T}' = \mathbf{K} \qquad (10.2.54)$$

and

$$[\mathbf{K}^*]'\mathbf{D}\mathbf{K}^* = \mathbf{I} \qquad (10.2.55)$$

Then Eq. 10.2.19 becomes

$$\mathbf{V}. = \mathbf{K}^*\mathbf{T}'\boldsymbol{\Theta}_v + \mathbf{E}. \qquad (10.2.56)$$

The least-squares estimates of orthogonal effects $\mathbf{T}'\boldsymbol{\Theta}_v$ are

$$\begin{aligned}\mathbf{U}_v &= \mathbf{T}'\hat{\boldsymbol{\Theta}}_v \qquad (10.2.57)\\ &= ([\mathbf{K}^*]'\mathbf{D}\mathbf{K}^*)^{-1}[\mathbf{K}^*]'\mathbf{D}\mathbf{V}. \\ &= [\mathbf{K}^*]'\mathbf{D}\mathbf{V}. \qquad (10.2.57a)\end{aligned}$$

$\mathbf{U}_v$ is the $I\times(p+q)$ matrix of semipartial regression coefficients. $\mathbf{U}_v$ has a single row for each effect in the analysis-of-variance model, *eliminating all preceding effects*. $\mathbf{U}_v$ may be determined either from Eq. 10.2.57 or 10.2.57a, since $\mathbf{T}'$ is also the upper triangular Cholesky factor of $(\mathbf{K}'\mathbf{D}\mathbf{K})$; that is,

$$\begin{aligned}(\mathbf{K}'\mathbf{D}\mathbf{K}) &= \mathbf{T}[\mathbf{K}^*]'\mathbf{D}\mathbf{K}^*\mathbf{T}' \\ &= \mathbf{T}\mathbf{T}' \qquad (10.2.58)\end{aligned}$$

In completely orthogonal designs (equal cell frequencies, orthogonal contrast parameters), $\mathbf{K}'\mathbf{DK}$ and $\mathbf{T}$ will be diagonal. The resulting orthogonal estimates are then a simple rescaling of rows of $\hat{\mathbf{\Theta}}_v$. In any case $\mathbf{U}_v$ estimates the same effects as $\hat{\mathbf{\Theta}}_v$, except that the basis has been columnwise orthonormalized before estimation. Thus each estimate obtained is the effect that is not confounded with preceding terms in the model.

Let us represent the ith row of $\mathbf{U}$ as $\mathbf{u}'_i$. For the 2×2 design, the matrix has four rows:

$$\mathbf{U}_v = \begin{bmatrix} \mathbf{u}'_1 \\ \mathbf{u}'_2 \\ \mathbf{u}'_3 \\ \mathbf{u}'_4 \end{bmatrix} \begin{matrix} \text{Constant} \\ A\text{, eliminating constant} \\ B\text{, eliminating constant and } A \\ AB\text{, eliminating constant, } A\text{, and } B \end{matrix} \tag{10.2.59}$$

Each row has $p+q$ elements. In designs with more than two levels of any factor, $\mathbf{U}$ will have more than a single row for the corresponding main effect and interactions.

From each row of $\mathbf{U}_v$, a between-group sum-of-products matrix of order $(p+q)\times(p+q)$ is constructed. For the constant term, the matrix is $\mathbf{S}_{H_1} = \mathbf{u}_1\mathbf{u}'_1$; for A, eliminating the constant, $\mathbf{S}_{H_2} = \mathbf{u}_2\mathbf{u}'_2$; for B, eliminating A and the constant, $\mathbf{S}_{H_3} = \mathbf{u}_3\mathbf{u}'_3$; and for interaction, eliminating all else, $\mathbf{S}_{H_4} = \mathbf{u}_4\mathbf{u}'_4$. Consecutive matrices $\mathbf{u}_i\mathbf{u}'_i$ may be pooled to provide multiple-degree-of-freedom tests as necessary (see the example that follows). Each row of $\mathbf{U}$ represents a single degree of freedom.

Each matrix $\mathbf{S}_{H_j}$ is adjusted for covariates in the following manner. First, add the $(p+q)$-square unadjusted error matrix $\mathbf{S}_E$ (Eq. 10.2.21) to the hypothesis matrix $\mathbf{S}_{H_j}$. The result is the sum

$$\mathbf{S}_{T_j} = \mathbf{S}_{H_j} + \mathbf{S}_E \tag{10.2.60}$$

This "total" matrix for the hypothesis may be partitioned like $\mathbf{S}_E$ in Eq. 10.2.23. That is,

$$\mathbf{S}_{T_j} = \left[\begin{array}{c|c} \mathbf{S}_{T_j}{}^{(yy)} & \mathbf{S}_{T_j}{}^{(yx)} \\ \hline \mathbf{S}_{T_j}{}^{(xy)} & \mathbf{S}_{T_j}{}^{(xx)} \end{array}\right] \begin{matrix} p \text{ rows} \\ q \text{ rows} \end{matrix} \tag{10.2.61}$$

p columns q columns

Second, adjust $\mathbf{S}_{T_j}$ for covariates. Represent the matrix of adjusted sums of products for the criteria as $\mathbf{S}^*_{T_j}$. Then

$$\mathbf{S}^*_{T_j} = \mathbf{S}_{T_j}{}^{(yy)} - \mathbf{S}_{T_j}{}^{(yx)}[\mathbf{S}_{T_j}{}^{(xx)}]^{-1}\mathbf{S}_{T_j}{}^{(xy)} \tag{10.2.62}$$

Having an adjusted hypothesis-plus-error matrix, and the adjusted error matrix $\mathbf{S}^*_E$, the adjusted hypothesis matrix $\mathbf{S}^*_{H_j}$ is found by subtraction. That is,

$$\mathbf{S}^*_{H_j} = \mathbf{S}^*_{T_j} - \mathbf{S}^*_E \tag{10.2.63}$$

$\mathbf{S}^*_{H_j}$ has the same degrees of freedom as $\mathbf{S}_{H_j}$ – that is, the number of rows of $\mathbf{U}$ from which it was formed (n_{h_j}). In the 2×2 example all $\mathbf{S}_{H_j}$ have a single degree of freedom (all $n_{h_j} = 1$). The sums of products for the 2×2 crossed analysis-of-covariance design are given in Table 10.2.1.

Table 10.2.1 Sums of Cross Products for a 2×2 Analysis-of-covariance Model

Source	*Degrees of Freedom*	*Sum of Cross Products*
Constant	$n_{h_1}=1$	$\mathbf{S}^*_{H_1}=\mathbf{S}^*_{T_1}-\mathbf{S}^*_E$
A, eliminating constant and **X**	$n_{h_2}=1$	$\mathbf{S}^*_{H_2}=\mathbf{S}^*_{T_2}-\mathbf{S}^*_E$
B, eliminating constant, A, and **X**	$n_{h_3}=1$	$\mathbf{S}^*_{H_3}=\mathbf{S}^*_{T_3}-\mathbf{S}^*_E$
AB, eliminating constant A, B, and **X**	$n_{h_4}=1$	$\mathbf{S}^*_{H_4}=\mathbf{S}^*_{T_4}-\mathbf{S}^*_E$
Covariates **X**, eliminating design effects	q	$\mathbf{S}_R=\mathbf{S}_E^{(yx)}[\mathbf{S}_E^{(xx)}]^{-1}\mathbf{S}_E^{(xy)}$
Residual	$n^*_e=n_e-q$ $=N-4-q$	$\mathbf{S}^*_E=\mathbf{S}_E^{(yy)}-\mathbf{S}_R$

All analysis-of-variance test criteria may be employed in analysis of covariance, with hypothesis matrix $\mathbf{S}^*_{H_j}$ and error matrix $\mathbf{S}^*_E$. The null hypothesis for any one matrix is

$$H_0\colon \mathbf{\Theta}_h=\mathbf{0} \tag{10.2.64}$$

where $\mathbf{\Theta}_h$ is an $n_{h_j}\times p$ submatrix of $\mathbf{\Theta}$, containing n_{h_j} rows, or degrees of freedom. $\mathbf{\Theta}$ is estimated under the covariance model in Eq. 10.2.25 and has been "adjusted" for covariate effects.

For example, to test for interaction in the 2×2 design, the null hypothesis is $H_0\colon \mathbf{\Theta}_{AB}=\mathbf{0}'$, where $\mathbf{\Theta}_{AB}$ is the last $1\times p$ row of $\mathbf{\Theta}$. The hypothesis sum-of-products matrix is $\mathbf{S}^*_{H_4}$, with $n_{h_4}=(a-1)(b-1)=1$ degree of freedom. The error matrix is $\mathbf{S}^*_E$, with $n^*_e=n_e-q$ degrees of freedom. If interaction is nonsignificant, we may test for the B main effect, with $H_0\colon \mathbf{\Theta}_B=\mathbf{0}'$ or $H_0\colon \boldsymbol{\mu}_{\cdot 1}=\boldsymbol{\mu}_{\cdot 2}$. $\mathbf{\Theta}_B$ is the third $1\times p$ row of $\mathbf{\Theta}$, and the hypothesis matrix is $\mathbf{S}^*_{H_3}$. If H_0 is not rejected, we may test $H_0\colon \mathbf{\Theta}_A=\mathbf{0}'$, or $H_0\colon \boldsymbol{\mu}_{1\cdot}=\boldsymbol{\mu}_{2\cdot}$, with $\mathbf{S}^*_{H_2}$ and $\mathbf{S}^*_E$. If $\mathbf{\Theta}_B$ is nonzero (H_0 rejected), the second and third columns of **K** must be interchanged and the basis reorthonormalized to estimate the A contrast, eliminating B. The A row of **U** will then be the third row, and the adjusted hypothesis matrix for A must be totally reconstructed by Eqs. 10.2.60–10.2.63 before the test can be conducted.

Any of the hypotheses may be tested for all p variates jointly, for each of the p criterion measures, and for each measure holding constant preceding measures in a specified order. To test H_0 for all criterion variables, eliminating the effects of the covariate(s), the likelihood ratio criterion is

$$\Lambda=\frac{|\mathbf{S}^*_E|}{|\mathbf{S}^*_E+\mathbf{S}^*_{H_j}|} \tag{10.2.65}$$

Λ may be referred to either the chi-square or F distribution. If N is large, the chi-square approximation will have sufficient accuracy.

$$\chi^2=-m\log_e\Lambda \tag{10.2.66}$$

with

$$m=[n^*_e-(p+1-n_{h_j})/2] \tag{10.2.67}$$

χ^2 is referred to a table of the χ^2 distribution, with $n_{h_j}p$ degrees of freedom. H_0 is rejected with confidence $1-\alpha$ if the 100α upper percentage point is exceeded.

A more accurate approximation is the F transform, with

$$F=\frac{1-\Lambda^{1/s}}{\Lambda^{1/s}}\cdot\frac{ms+1-n_{h_j}p/2}{n_{h_j}p} \qquad (10.2.68)$$

and

$$s=\left(\frac{p^2n_{h_j}{}^2-4}{p^2+n_{h_j}{}^2-5}\right)^{1/2} \qquad (10.2.69)$$

where m is defined by Eq. 10.2.67. F is compared to critical values of the F distribution, with $n_{h_j}p$ and $ms+1-n_{h_j}p/2$ degrees of freedom. In the case of s indeterminate ($n_{h_j}p=2$), setting s to unity will provide an appropriate statistic.

Discriminant functions may be computed for covariance-adjusted effects, substituting $\mathbf{S}^*_{H_j}$ and $\mathbf{S}^*_E$ for $\mathbf{S}_{H_j}$ and $\mathbf{S}_E$ in Section 10.1. Roy's largest-root criterion, Hotelling's trace criterion, and likelihood ratio tests of successive canonical variates provide additional multivariate test criteria for H_0. All reflect departure from H_0 in terms of the maximally discriminating canonical or discriminant variables. The simultaneous test of all discriminant functions is identical to the results of testing Λ in Eq. 10.2.65.

Univariate covariance tests for the dependent variables are obtained from the diagonal elements of $\mathbf{S}^*_{H_j}$ and $\mathbf{S}^*_E$. The ratio for criterion measure y_k ($k=1, 2, \ldots, p$) is

$$F_k=\frac{[s^*_{h_j}]_{kk}/n_{h_j}}{[s^*_e]_{kk}/n^*_e} \qquad (10.2.70)$$

F_k may be referred to tables of the F distribution, with n_{h_j} and n^*_e degrees of freedom. Multiple univariate F ratios for one hypothesis are not independent of one another and should not be used to decide whether or not H_0 is supported. They do provide useful descriptive data, however, to compare the relative effects of the experimental treatments upon the various outcome measures.

Step-down tests for H_0, which depend upon an ordering of the y variables, may be conducted exactly as in analysis-of-variance models. Successive conditional standard deviations are the diagonal elements of the Cholesky factors of $\mathbf{S}^*_E$ and $\mathbf{S}^*_{T_j}$, as defined by Eq. 10.2.62. Represent the factorizations as

$$\mathbf{S}^*_E=\mathbf{T}_E\mathbf{T}'_E \qquad (10.2.71a)$$

and

$$\mathbf{S}^*_{T_j}=\mathbf{T}^*[\mathbf{T}^*]' \qquad (10.2.71b)$$

$[t_e]_{kk}$ and $[t^*]_{kk}$ are the diagonal elements of $\mathbf{T}_E$ and $\mathbf{T}^*$ respectively. The step-down statistic for criterion y_k, eliminating y_1 through y_{k-1}, is

$$F^*_k=\frac{[t^*]_{kk}{}^2-[t_e]_{kk}{}^2}{[t_e]_{kk}{}^2}\cdot\frac{n^*_e-k+1}{n_{h_j}} \qquad (10.2.72)$$

F^*_k is referred to tables of the F distribution, with n_{h_j} and n^*_e-k+1 degrees of freedom. Unlike all other test criteria, the step-down statistics are not invariant under permutation of the criterion variables. Testing begins with F^*_p and proceeds in a backward direction. If a significant F^* ratio is encountered, no earlier statistic may be validly interpreted under this ordering of variables. Hypothesis 10.2.64 is accepted if and only if none of the step-down F^* ratios exceeds its respective critical value. If no logical ordering of variates exists, the step-down tests are of little value and H_0 should be tested using the other multivariate criteria.

Sample Problem 2 – Word Memory Experiment

The model fit to the word memory example is a one-way bivariate analysis-of-variance model, with four experimental conditions. The matrix representation is $\mathbf{Y.} = \mathbf{A}\mathbf{\Theta}^* + \mathbf{E.}$, with

$$\mathbf{A} = \begin{bmatrix} 1 & 1 & 0 & 0 & 0 \\ 1 & 0 & 1 & 0 & 0 \\ 1 & 0 & 0 & 1 & 0 \\ 1 & 0 & 0 & 0 & 1 \end{bmatrix} \qquad \mathbf{\Theta}^* = \begin{bmatrix} \boldsymbol{\mu}' \\ \boldsymbol{\alpha}_1' \\ \boldsymbol{\alpha}_2' \\ \boldsymbol{\alpha}_3' \\ \boldsymbol{\alpha}_4' \end{bmatrix}$$

$\mathbf{Y.}$ and $\mathbf{E.}$ are 4×2 matrices. The reparameterization of the model has contrast matrix

$$\mathbf{L} = \begin{bmatrix} 1 & .25 & .25 & .25 & .25 \\ 0 & 1 & -1 & 0 & 0 \\ 0 & 0 & 1 & -1 & 0 \\ 0 & 0 & 0 & 1 & -1 \end{bmatrix} \begin{matrix} \text{L0} \\ \text{L1} \\ \text{L2} \\ \text{L3} \end{matrix}$$

The matrix of contrast parameters is

$$\mathbf{\Theta} = \begin{bmatrix} \boldsymbol{\mu}' + 1/4 \sum_j \boldsymbol{\alpha}_j' \\ \boldsymbol{\alpha}_1' - \boldsymbol{\alpha}_2' \\ \boldsymbol{\alpha}_2' - \boldsymbol{\alpha}_3' \\ \boldsymbol{\alpha}_3' - \boldsymbol{\alpha}_4' \end{bmatrix} \begin{matrix} \text{L0} \\ \text{L1} \\ \text{L2} \\ \text{L3} \end{matrix}$$

The basis matrix for $\mathbf{\Theta}$ is

$$\mathbf{K} = \begin{bmatrix} 1.00 & .75 & .50 & .25 \\ 1.00 & -.25 & .50 & .25 \\ 1.00 & -.25 & -.50 & .25 \\ 1.00 & -.25 & -.50 & -.75 \end{bmatrix}$$
$$\begin{matrix} \text{L0} & \quad\text{L1} & \quad\text{L2} & \quad\text{L3} \end{matrix}$$

In addition to the two outcome measures, three recordings were made of the time taken by the subjects in completing the task, on each of three earlier trials. Since individual differences in time may be related to task proficiency, an analysis of covariance, with time measures as the covariates, is performed.

The analysis-of-covariance model is given by Eq. 10.2.14. $\mathbf{X.}$ is 4×3, with subclass means on the three concomitant measures; $\mathbf{x}'_{..}$ is 1×3. The purposes of the analysis are:

1. To estimate the regression weights of learning on time for each of the four groups, and to test whether they are the same.
2. To test whether there is any regression of the two outcome variables on the three time measures, eliminating between-group differences.
3. To test whether there are significant differences among groups' means on the two outcomes, eliminating the effects of time.

The complete matrix of means for criteria and covariates (time in seconds) is

$$\mathbf{V}. = [\mathbf{Y}., \mathbf{X}.]$$

$$= \left[\begin{array}{cc|ccc} 39.83 & .97 & 155.58 & 116.00 & 106.92 \\ 42.17 & .94 & 151.75 & 153.67 & 130.75 \\ 40.00 & 1.00 & 117.92 & 106.00 & 95.25 \\ 36.25 & .97 & 100.00 & 110.42 & 103.92 \end{array}\right] \begin{array}{l} \text{Condition 1} \\ \text{Condition 2} \\ \text{Condition 3} \\ \text{Condition 4} \end{array}$$

$$\begin{array}{ccccc} \text{Words} & \text{Categories} & \text{Time trial 2} & \text{Time trial 4} & \text{Time trial 6} \end{array}$$

There are twelve subjects under each experimental condition.

The within-group sum of products for one subclass is

$$\mathbf{S}_{w_j} = \sum_i \mathbf{v}_{ij}\mathbf{v}'_{ij} - N_j \mathbf{v}._j \mathbf{v}'._j$$

$\mathbf{v}'._j$ is row j of $\mathbf{V}.$. $\mathbf{S}_{w_j}$ is partitioned into sections for criteria, covariates, and the cross products of the two sets. That is,

$$\mathbf{S}_{w_j} = \left[\begin{array}{c|c} \mathbf{S}_{w_j}^{(yy)} & \mathbf{S}_{w_j}^{(yx)} \\ \hline \mathbf{S}_{w_j}^{(xy)} & \mathbf{S}_{w_j}^{(xx)} \end{array}\right] \begin{array}{l} \text{2 criteria} \\ \text{3 time measures} \end{array}$$

$$\begin{array}{cc} \text{2 criteria} & \text{3 time measures} \end{array}$$

The 2×2 matrices for criteria only, for the four groups, are presented in Chapter 8. For the covariance analysis these previous matrices become $\mathbf{S}_{w_j}^{(yy)}$ of the extended sums of products. The complete 5×5 matrices are

$$\mathbf{S}_{w_1} = \left[\begin{array}{cc|ccc} 547.67 & & & & \text{(Symmetric)} \\ 2.94 & .02 & & & \\ \hline -1939.83 & -17.07 & 46522.92 & & \\ -555.01 & -4.70 & 9513.00 & 9336.00 & \\ -180.17 & -1.63 & 6232.58 & 4021.00 & 6128.91 \end{array}\right]$$

$$\mathbf{S}_{w_2} = \left[\begin{array}{cc|ccc} 505.67 & & & & \text{(Symmetric)} \\ 6.62 & .13 & & & \\ \hline 239.50 & 8.72 & 43322.25 & & \\ -334.33 & 3.27 & 38758.00 & 39642.67 & \\ -359.50 & -3.87 & 17178.25 & 16516.00 & 10714.25 \end{array}\right]$$

$$\mathbf{S}_{w_3} = \left[\begin{array}{cc|ccc} 222.00 & & & & \text{(Symmetric)} \\ 0 & 0 & & & \\ \hline -180.00 & 0 & 7478.92 & & \\ 205.00 & 0 & 9399.00 & 17030.00 & \\ 261.00 & 0 & 6637.25 & 12683.00 & 10018.25 \end{array}\right]$$

$$\mathbf{S}_{w_4} = \left[\begin{array}{cc|ccc} 210.25 & & & & \text{(Symmetric)} \\ 2.30 & .07 & & & \\ \hline 464.00 & -.20 & 4662.00 & & \\ 238.75 & 3.57 & 2850.00 & 9168.92 & \\ -73.75 & -6.03 & 3162.00 & 4325.42 & 6176.92 \end{array}\right]$$

The pooled within-group sum of products is the unadjusted error matrix

$$\mathbf{S}_E = \textstyle\sum_j \mathbf{S}_{w_j}$$

$$= \left[\begin{array}{c|c} \mathbf{S}_E^{(yy)} & \mathbf{S}_E^{(yx)} \\ \hline \mathbf{S}_E^{(xy)} & \mathbf{S}_E^{(xx)} \end{array}\right]$$

$$= \left[\begin{array}{cc|ccc} 1485.58 & & & & \text{(Symmetric)} \\ 11.85 & .22 & & & \\ \hline -1416.33 & -8.54 & 101986.08 & & \\ -445.58 & 2.13 & 60520.00 & 75177.58 & \\ -352.42 & -11.54 & 38210.08 & 37545.42 & 33038.33 \end{array}\right]$$

Prior to adjusting means and mean differences for covariates, we shall test the hypothesis

$$H_0\colon\ \mathbf{B}_1 = \mathbf{B}_2 = \mathbf{B}_3 = \mathbf{B}_4 = \mathbf{B}$$

that the 3×2 matrices of coefficients do not differ from one group to another, or that regression planes are parallel.

Let us first make a single common regression adjustment to $\mathbf{S}_E$. The common estimate $\hat{\mathbf{B}}$ is

$$\hat{\mathbf{B}} = [\mathbf{S}_E^{(xx)}]^{-1}\mathbf{S}_E^{(xy)}$$

$$= \begin{bmatrix} 101986.08 & & \text{(Symmetric)} \\ 60520.00 & 75177.58 & \\ 33210.08 & 37545.42 & 33038.33 \end{bmatrix}^{-1} \begin{bmatrix} -1416.33 & -8.54 \\ -445.58 & 2.13 \\ -352.42 & -11.54 \end{bmatrix}$$

$$= 10^{-4} \times \begin{bmatrix} -195.75 & -1.45 \\ 123.29 & 5.71 \\ -50.01 & -8.52 \end{bmatrix} \begin{matrix} \text{Time 2} \\ \text{Time 4} \\ \text{Time 6} \end{matrix}$$

$$\qquad\qquad \text{Words} \quad \text{Categories}$$

The regression sum of products is

$$\mathbf{S}_R = \mathbf{S}_E^{(yx)}[\mathbf{S}_E^{(xx)}]^{-1}\mathbf{S}_E^{(xy)}$$

$$= \mathbf{S}_E^{(yx)}\hat{\mathbf{B}}$$

$$= 10^{-4} \times \begin{bmatrix} -1416.33 & -455.58 & -352.42 \\ -8.54 & 2.13 & -11.54 \end{bmatrix} \begin{bmatrix} -195.75 & -1.45 \\ 123.29 & 5.71 \\ -50.01 & -8.52 \end{bmatrix}$$

$$= \begin{bmatrix} 23.99 & .25 \\ .25 & .01 \end{bmatrix}$$

The covariate-adjusted error sum of products is

$$\mathbf{S}_E^* = \mathbf{S}_E^{(yy)} - \mathbf{S}_R$$

$$= \begin{bmatrix} 1485.58 & 11.85 \\ 11.85 & .22 \end{bmatrix} - \begin{bmatrix} 23.99 & .25 \\ .25 & .01 \end{bmatrix}$$

$$= \begin{bmatrix} 1461.59 & 11.60 \\ 11.60 & .21 \end{bmatrix} \begin{matrix} \text{Words} \\ \text{Categories} \end{matrix}$$

Words Categories

The degrees of freedom for $\mathbf{S}_E^*$ are $n_e^* = 48-4-3 = 41$.

The adjusted variance–covariance matrix is

$$\hat{\mathbf{\Sigma}}^* = \frac{1}{41}\mathbf{S}_E^*$$

$$= \begin{bmatrix} 35.65 & .280 \\ .28 & .005 \end{bmatrix} \begin{matrix} \text{Words} \\ \text{Categories} \end{matrix}$$

Words Categories

The adjusted error mean squares are the diagonal elements of $\hat{\mathbf{\Sigma}}^*$. The standard deviations of the criteria, holding constant the three time measures, are the respective square roots:

$$\hat{\sigma}_1^* = \sqrt{35.65} = 5.97 \quad \text{Words}$$

$$\hat{\sigma}_2^* = \sqrt{.005} = .07 \quad \text{Categories}$$

(The unadjusted value of $\hat{\sigma}_1 = 5.81$ is smaller than the adjusted value of 5.97. In this instance the adjustment is negligible and the sum-of-square reduction is relatively smaller than the three-degree-of-freedom loss.)

In contrast to $\mathbf{S}_E^*$, we may make separate covariate adjustments to each group's matrix, and pool the results. For each group the adjusted matrix is $\mathbf{S}_{w_j}^*$, given by Eq. 10.2.42. For example, for the first group of observations,

$$\mathbf{S}_{w_1}^* = \begin{bmatrix} 547.67 & 2.94 \\ 2.94 & .02 \end{bmatrix}$$

$$- \begin{bmatrix} -1939.83 & -555.01 & -180.17 \\ -17.07 & -4.70 & -1.63 \end{bmatrix} \begin{bmatrix} 46522.92 & 9513.00 & 6232.58 \\ 9513.00 & 9336.00 & 4021.00 \\ 6232.58 & 4021.00 & 6128.91 \end{bmatrix}^{-1}$$

$$\times \begin{bmatrix} -1939.83 & -17.07 \\ -555.01 & -4.70 \\ -180.17 & -1.63 \end{bmatrix} = \begin{bmatrix} 458.90 & 2.16 \\ 2.16 & .02 \end{bmatrix}$$

For the other groups,

$$\mathbf{S}_{w_2}^* = \begin{bmatrix} 414.23 & 5.50 \\ 5.50 & .11 \end{bmatrix} \quad \mathbf{S}_{w_3}^* = \begin{bmatrix} 174.59 & .00 \\ .00 & .00 \end{bmatrix} \quad \mathbf{S}_{w_4}^* = \begin{bmatrix} 120.91 & 1.53 \\ 1.53 & .05 \end{bmatrix}$$

The pooled adjusted matrices are

$$\mathbf{S} = \sum_j \mathbf{S}^*_{w_j}$$

$$= \begin{bmatrix} 1168.63 & 9.19 \\ 9.19 & .18 \end{bmatrix}$$

$\mathbf{S}$ has $n^* = 48 - 4 - 12 = 32$ degrees of freedom.

The hypothesis matrix for the parallelism test is

$$\mathbf{S}_H = \begin{bmatrix} 1461.59 & 11.60 \\ 11.60 & .21 \end{bmatrix} - \begin{bmatrix} 1168.63 & 9.19 \\ 9.19 & .18 \end{bmatrix}$$

$$= \begin{bmatrix} 292.96 & 2.41 \\ 2.41 & .03 \end{bmatrix}$$

$\mathbf{S}_H$ has $n_h = 41 - 32 = 9$ degrees of freedom.

The likelihood ratio criterion for H_0 is

$$\Lambda = \frac{|\mathbf{S}|}{|\mathbf{S}^*_E|}$$

$$= \frac{127.88}{172.40}$$

$$= .741$$

The multiplier is $m = [32 - (2+1-9)/2] = 35$, and

$$s = \left(\frac{2^2(9^2) - 4}{2^2 + 9^2 - 5}\right)^{1/2}$$

$$= 2$$

The F transformation is thus

$$F = \frac{1 - \sqrt{.741}}{\sqrt{.741}} \cdot \frac{35(2) + 1 - (9)(2)/2}{9(2)}$$

$$= \frac{.14}{.86} \cdot \frac{62}{18}$$

$$= .56$$

F does not exceed the .05 critical F value, with 18 and 62 degrees of freedom. We accept H_0; the regression planes are parallel and a single common regression estimate will suffice. The dependence of the learning measures upon time is the same for all four groups of subjects.

We may also conduct univariate parallelism tests for each dependent variable. These reproduce the results that would have been obtained if only one criterion measure had been included in the model. The univariate F statistics are

$$F_1 = \frac{292.96/9}{1168.63/32} = .89 \quad \text{Words}$$

and

$$F_2 = \frac{.03/9}{.18/32} = .56 \qquad \text{Categories}$$

Neither exceeds the critical F value, with 9 and 32 degrees of freedom. Although F_1 and F_2 are not independent test statistics, H_0 does receive support from either measure individually.

Accepting that all regression planes are parallel, we may next test for nonzero slope, or nonzero regression of two y variates on the three covariates. The hypothesis is

$$H_0: \mathbf{B} = \mathbf{0}$$

Complete tests of H_0 are discussed in the earlier regression chapters. Here we shall obtain the single likelihood ratio statistic for all three predictors.

The hypothesis matrix for regression is $\mathbf{S}_R$, with q degrees of freedom; the error matrix is $\mathbf{S}_E^*$, with n_e^* degrees of freedom. The likelihood ratio is

$$\begin{aligned}\Lambda &= \frac{|\mathbf{S}_E^*|}{|\mathbf{S}_R + \mathbf{S}_E^*|} \\ &= \frac{172.40}{190.12} \\ &= .908\end{aligned}$$

The F transformation has $m = [41 - (2+1-3)/2] = 41$ and

$$\begin{aligned}s &= \left(\frac{2^2(3^2)-4}{2^2+3^2-5}\right)^{1/2} \\ &= 2\end{aligned}$$

Then

$$\begin{aligned}F &= \frac{1-\sqrt{.908}}{\sqrt{.908}} \cdot \frac{41(2)+1-(3)(2)/2}{3(2)} \\ &= \frac{.05}{.95} \cdot \frac{80}{6} \\ &= .66\end{aligned}$$

F does not exceed the .05 critical value, with 6 and 80 degrees of freedom, and H_0 is maintained. We must conclude that there is no significant relationship of learning scores with time taken to complete the task. We may decide to exclude the covariates on this basis, for residual variation is not significantly reduced by continuing to carry them in the model. Or we may decide that the covariates are of logical importance and continue to maintain them on theoretical grounds (although the theory appears to be challenged). For exemplary purposes, we shall take the latter approach and maintain the covariates.

In nonexperimental studies we may wish to see if significant mean differences become smaller or disappear when the covariate adjustment is made. That is, even if error variation is not reduced, the covariates may account for observed group-mean differences on the criteria.

The model matrix after reparameterization **K**, and the means **V.** provide the estimate of mean contrasts for all five measures. The covariance factors (also in Section 8.4) are

$$(\mathbf{K}'\mathbf{D}\mathbf{K})^{-1} = \begin{bmatrix} .0208 & & & \text{(Symmetric)} \\ 0 & .1667 & & \\ 0 & -.0833 & .1667 & \\ 0 & 0 & -.0833 & .1667 \end{bmatrix}$$

Then

$$\begin{aligned}\hat{\boldsymbol{\Theta}}_v &= (\mathbf{K}'\mathbf{D}\mathbf{K})^{-1}\mathbf{K}'\mathbf{D}\mathbf{V}. \\ &= [\hat{\boldsymbol{\Theta}}_y, \hat{\boldsymbol{\Theta}}_x] \\ &= \left[\begin{array}{rr|rrr} 39.56 & .97 & 131.31 & 121.52 & 109.21 \\ -2.33 & .03 & 3.83 & -37.67 & -23.83 \\ 2.17 & -.06 & 33.83 & 47.67 & 35.50 \\ 3.75 & .03 & 17.92 & -4.42 & -8.67 \end{array}\right] \begin{array}{l} \boldsymbol{\mu}' + 1/4 \sum_j \boldsymbol{\alpha}_j' \\ \boldsymbol{\alpha}_1' - \boldsymbol{\alpha}_2' \\ \boldsymbol{\alpha}_2' - \boldsymbol{\alpha}_3' \\ \boldsymbol{\alpha}_3' - \boldsymbol{\alpha}_4' \end{array}\end{aligned}$$

Words Categories Time 2 Time 4 Time 6

$\hat{\boldsymbol{\Theta}}_y$ is reproduced from the analysis-of-variance estimates of Chapter 8. The estimate of $\boldsymbol{\Theta}$, eliminating the three time covariates, is

$$\begin{aligned}\hat{\boldsymbol{\Theta}} &= \hat{\boldsymbol{\Theta}}_y - \hat{\boldsymbol{\Theta}}_x\hat{\mathbf{B}} \\ &= \begin{bmatrix} 39.56 & .97 \\ -2.33 & .03 \\ 2.17 & -.06 \\ 3.75 & .03 \end{bmatrix} - 10^{-4} \times \begin{bmatrix} 131.31 & 121.52 & 109.21 \\ 3.83 & -37.67 & -23.83 \\ 33.83 & 47.67 & 35.50 \\ 17.92 & -4.42 & -8.67 \end{bmatrix} \begin{bmatrix} -195.74 & -1.45 \\ 123.29 & 5.71 \\ -50.01 & -8.52 \end{bmatrix} \\ &= \begin{bmatrix} 39.56 & .97 \\ -1.91 & .03 \\ 2.42 & -.05 \\ 4.11 & .03 \end{bmatrix} \begin{array}{l} \boldsymbol{\mu}' + 1/4 \sum_j \boldsymbol{\alpha}_j' \\ \boldsymbol{\alpha}_1' - \boldsymbol{\alpha}_2' \\ \boldsymbol{\alpha}_2' - \boldsymbol{\alpha}_3' \\ \boldsymbol{\alpha}_3' - \boldsymbol{\alpha}_4' \end{array}\end{aligned}$$

Words Categories

The adjusted variance–covariance factors are

$$\begin{aligned}\mathbf{G} &= (\mathbf{K}'\mathbf{D}\mathbf{K})^{-1} + \hat{\boldsymbol{\Theta}}_x[\mathbf{S}_E^{(xx)}]^{-1}\hat{\boldsymbol{\Theta}}_x' \\ &= \begin{bmatrix} .3924 & & & \text{(Symmetric)} \\ -.0623 & .2108 & & \\ .1137 & -.1160 & .2074 & \\ -.0190 & .0197 & -.0944 & .1797 \end{bmatrix}\end{aligned}$$

Rather than computing the entire variance–covariance matrix of the eight elements in $\hat{\boldsymbol{\Theta}}$, we shall obtain just the standard errors of each. The adjusted standard deviations comprise vector **d**, where

$$\mathbf{d}' = [\hat{\sigma}_1^* \quad \hat{\sigma}_2^*] = [5.97 \quad .07]$$

The factors that multiply **d** to provide the standard errors are the square roots of the variance factors, or diagonal elements of **G**. Let

$$\mathbf{g} = \begin{bmatrix} \sqrt{.3924} \\ \sqrt{.2108} \\ \sqrt{.2074} \\ \sqrt{.1797} \end{bmatrix} = \begin{bmatrix} .626 \\ .459 \\ .455 \\ .424 \end{bmatrix}$$

The matrix of adjusted standard errors is

$$\mathbf{H} = \mathbf{g}\mathbf{d}'$$

$$= \begin{bmatrix} 3.74 & .04 \\ 2.74 & .03 \\ 2.72 & .03 \\ 2.53 & .03 \end{bmatrix} \begin{matrix} \boldsymbol{\mu}' + 1/4 \sum_j \boldsymbol{\alpha}_j' \\ \boldsymbol{\alpha}_1' - \boldsymbol{\alpha}_2' \\ \boldsymbol{\alpha}_2' - \boldsymbol{\alpha}_3' \\ \boldsymbol{\alpha}_3' - \boldsymbol{\alpha}_4' \end{matrix}$$

Words Categories

Confidence intervals may be drawn on any element or row of $\boldsymbol{\Theta}$ using the corresponding standard errors $[h_{ik}]$. Under the assumption of normal **y**, $(\hat{\theta}_{ik} - \theta_{ik})/h_{ik}$ follows a t distribution with $n_e^* = 41$ degrees of freedom. The critical t value may be used to test that one contrast is null for a single variable (words or categories), holding constant the three time covariates.

Adjusted treatment means are obtained from the predicted means $\hat{\mathbf{V}}.$ by Eq. 10.2.31. In the word memory experiment we assume a model including the constant and all three mean contrasts. Thus $I = J = 4$, and the matrix of predicted means $[\hat{\mathbf{Y}}., \hat{\mathbf{X}}.]$ is the same as those observed, or $[\mathbf{Y}., \mathbf{X}.]$. The adjusted treatment means are given by Eq. 10.2.33; they are

$$\mathbf{Y}_.^* = \begin{bmatrix} 40.37 & .97 \\ 42.28 & .94 \\ 39.86 & 1.00- \\ 35.75 & .96 \end{bmatrix} \begin{matrix} \text{Condition 1} \\ \text{Condition 2} \\ \text{Condition 3} \\ \text{Condition 4} \end{matrix}$$

Words Categories

In this case they are not systematically or greatly different from the observed matrix **Y**.. Predicted means under the analysis-of-covariance model are here identical to **Y.** since $\hat{\mathbf{Y}}. = \mathbf{Y}.$ and $\hat{\mathbf{X}}. = \mathbf{X}.$ (see Eqs. 10.2.33 and 10.2.34). Adjusted mean residuals are identically zero.

To test equality of the four experimental effects under the covariance model, the hypothesis is

$$H_0: \boldsymbol{\alpha}_1 = \boldsymbol{\alpha}_2 = \boldsymbol{\alpha}_3 = \boldsymbol{\alpha}_4$$

Orthogonal estimates are required for all five measures. H_0 is equivalently H_0: $\boldsymbol{\Theta}_A = \mathbf{0}$, where $\boldsymbol{\Theta}_A$ is the last three rows of $\boldsymbol{\Theta}$—that is, the three between-group contrasts for both criterion variables. $\mathbf{0}$ is a 3×2 null matrix.

The orthogonal estimates are $\mathbf{U}_v = [\mathbf{K}^*]'\mathbf{D}\mathbf{V}_{..}$ $\mathbf{K}^*$ is the orthonormalized basis matrix, and was obtained in Chapter 9 for the analysis of variance. That is,

$$\mathbf{K}^* = \begin{bmatrix} .144 & .250 & 0 & 0 \\ .144 & -.083 & .236 & 0 \\ .144 & -.083 & -.118 & .204 \\ .144 & -.083 & -.118 & -.204 \end{bmatrix}$$

and

$$\mathbf{D} = \text{diag}\,(12, 12, 12, 12)$$

Then

$$\mathbf{U}_v = [\mathbf{U}_y, \mathbf{U}_x]$$

$$= \left[\begin{array}{rr|rrr} 274.10 & 6.71 & 909.76 & 841.92 & 756.62 \\ 1.08 & -.01 & 97.08 & -22.08 & -9.17 \\ 11.43 & -.12 & 121.03 & 128.58 & 88.15 \\ 9.19 & .08 & 43.89 & -10.82 & -21.23 \end{array}\right] \begin{array}{l} \mathbf{u}'_1 \\ \mathbf{u}'_2 \\ \mathbf{u}'_3 \\ \mathbf{u}'_4 \end{array}$$

Words Categories Time 2 Time 4 Time 6

Rows of $\mathbf{U}_v$ estimate the same effects as those of $\hat{\mathbf{\Theta}}_v$, but in a stepwise fashion. Each contrast is estimated after eliminating any correlation with preceding effects.

There is no particular interest in the constant term, and a corresponding sum of products $\mathbf{u}_1\mathbf{u}'_1$ is unnecessary. To test H_0: $\mathbf{\Theta}_A = \mathbf{0}$, we pool the sums of products for the three independent effects. The hypothesis matrix is

$$\mathbf{S}_H = \mathbf{u}_2\mathbf{u}'_2 + \mathbf{u}_3\mathbf{u}'_3 + \mathbf{u}_4\mathbf{u}'_4$$

$$= \left[\begin{array}{rr|rrr} 216.23 & & & & \text{(Symmetric)} \\ -.61 & .02 & & & \\ \hline 1891.90 & -11.49 & 26000.23 & & \\ 1346.52 & -15.85 & 12943.19 & 17136.40 & \\ 802.79 & -12.05 & 8847.79 & 11766.37 & 8305.58 \end{array}\right]$$

This is the same as $\mathbf{S}_H$ for analysis of variance, but with the three additional covariate measures. $\mathbf{S}_H^{(yy)}$ is identical to $\mathbf{S}_H$ in Section 9.3. Hypothesis degrees of freedom are $n_h = 3$. (Since there is only a single hypothesis in the particular study, the subscript on $\mathbf{S}_H$, $\mathbf{S}_T$, and n_h is omitted.)

To adjust $\mathbf{S}_H$ for covariates, form

$$\mathbf{S}_T = \mathbf{S}_H + \mathbf{S}_E$$

$$= \left[\begin{array}{c|c} \mathbf{S}_T^{(yy)} & \mathbf{S}_T^{(yx)} \\ \hline \mathbf{S}_T^{(xy)} & \mathbf{S}_T^{(xx)} \end{array}\right]$$

$$= \left[\begin{array}{rr|rrr} 1701.81 & & & & \text{(Symmetric)} \\ 11.24 & .24 & & & \\ \hline 475.57 & -20.03 & 127986.31 & & \\ 900.94 & -13.72 & 73463.19 & 92313.98 & \\ 450.37 & -23.59 & 42057.87 & 49311.79 & 41343.91 \end{array}\right]$$

The adjusted hypothesis-plus-error matrix is

$$\mathbf{S}_T^* = \begin{bmatrix} 1701.81 & 11.24 \\ 11.24 & .24 \end{bmatrix} - \begin{bmatrix} 475.57 & 900.94 & 450.37 \\ -20.03 & -13.72 & -23.59 \end{bmatrix} \begin{bmatrix} 127986.31 & 73463.19 & 42057.87 \\ 73463.19 & 92313.98 & 49311.79 \\ 42057.87 & 49311.79 & 41343.91 \end{bmatrix}^{-1}$$

$$\times \begin{bmatrix} 475.57 & -20.03 \\ 900.94 & -13.72 \\ 450.37 & -23.59 \end{bmatrix} = \begin{bmatrix} 1692.15 & 11.32 \\ 11.32 & .22 \end{bmatrix}$$

The adjusted hypothesis matrix is

$$\mathbf{S}_H^* = \mathbf{S}_T^* - \mathbf{S}_E^*$$

$$= \begin{bmatrix} 1692.15 & 11.32 \\ 11.32 & .22 \end{bmatrix} - \begin{bmatrix} 1461.59 & 11.60 \\ 11.60 & .21 \end{bmatrix}$$

$$= \begin{bmatrix} 230.56 & -.28 \\ -.28 & .01 \end{bmatrix} \begin{matrix} \text{Words} \\ \text{Categories} \end{matrix}$$

Words Categories

Had there been more than a single hypothesis matrix ($\mathbf{S}_H$ or $\mathbf{S}_{H_j}$), each would have been separately pooled with $\mathbf{S}_E$ and adjusted to obtain $\mathbf{S}_{H_j}^*$.

Let us use the likelihood ratio criterion to test H_0. That is,

$$\Lambda = \frac{|\mathbf{S}_E^*|}{|\mathbf{S}_E^* + \mathbf{S}_H^*|} = \frac{172.40}{249.14} = .694$$

The F transform has multipliers $m = [41-(2+1-3)/2] = 41$ and

$$s = \left(\frac{2^2(3^2)-4}{2^2+3^2-5} \right)^{1/2} = 2$$

Then

$$F = \frac{1-\sqrt{.694}}{\sqrt{.694}} \cdot \frac{41(2)+1-(3)(2)/2}{3(2)} = \frac{.17}{.83} \cdot \frac{80}{6} = 2.68$$

F has 6 and 80 degrees of freedom. The .05 critical value is exceeded, and H_0 is rejected. We note that H_0 was rejected also without the covariates (analysis-of-variance $F = 3.29$ with 6 and 86 degrees of freedom). Consistent with the

Table 10.2.2 Analysis of Covariance for Word Memory Experiment

Source	d.f.	Mean Products: Words	Mean Products: Categories	Multivariate F (d.f.)	Univariate F: Words	Univariate F: Categories
Constant	1	$\mathbf{u}_1\mathbf{u}'_1$		—	—	—
Between groups, eliminating covariates	3	$\begin{bmatrix} 76.85 & -.090 \\ -.09 & .004 \end{bmatrix}$		2.68* (6, 80)	2.16	.83
Covariates, eliminating design effects	3	$\begin{bmatrix} 8.00 & .080 \\ .08 & .003 \end{bmatrix}$		.66 (6, 80)	.22	.80
Within groups, eliminating covariates	41	$\begin{bmatrix} 35.65 & .280 \\ .28 & .005 \end{bmatrix}$				
Total	48					

*Significant at $p < .05$.

findings of the regression analysis, the covariates do not account for any sizable portion of error variation in the outcome measures. Had the covariates been more influential in the learning outcomes, we might have discovered that mean differences were significant only with the covariates in the model.

Univariate F ratios may also be computed for the separate criterion measures, for the adjusted mean differences. The ratios are

$$F_1 = \frac{230.56/3}{1461.59/41} = \frac{76.85}{35.65} = 2.16 \quad \text{Words}$$

and

$$F_2 = \frac{.01/3}{.21/41} = \frac{.004}{.005} = .83 \quad \text{Categories}$$

The numerators and denominators are adjusted hypothesis and error mean squares respectively. Each F ratio has 3 and 41 degrees of freedom; neither exceeds the .05 critical F value.

The covariance results may be summarized as in Table 10.2.2, and may be compared with the analysis-of-variance results of Table 9.3.1.

Appendix A

ANSWERS TO MATRIX ALGEBRA EXERCISES (SECTION 2.7)

1. $a_{22}=-1 \qquad \mathbf{c}_2=\begin{bmatrix} 0 \\ 30 \\ 32 \end{bmatrix}$

2. $\mathbf{I}_3=\begin{bmatrix} 1 & 0 & 0 \\ 0 & 1 & 0 \\ 0 & 0 & 1 \end{bmatrix} \qquad \mathbf{1}_3=\begin{bmatrix} 1 \\ 1 \\ 1 \end{bmatrix}$

3. $\mathbf{A}'=\begin{bmatrix} 1 & 3 & 0 & 1 \\ 2 & -1 & 2 & 0 \\ 1 & -1 & 3 & 0 \end{bmatrix} \qquad \mathbf{e}'=[1.0 \quad 1.5 \quad 1.0 \quad 2.5] \qquad \mathbf{H}'=\mathbf{H}$

4. $\mathbf{C}+\mathbf{T}=\begin{bmatrix} 26 & 0 & -3 \\ 4 & 31 & 32 \\ 3 & 31 & 43 \end{bmatrix} \qquad (\mathbf{e}+\mathbf{v})'=[-1.0 \quad .5 \quad 2.0 \quad 3.5]$

$$\mathbf{D}-\mathbf{H}=\begin{bmatrix} -1 & -4 & 2 & -2 \\ -4 & -6 & 2 & -4 \\ 2 & 2 & -13 & 1 \\ -2 & -4 & 1 & -1 \end{bmatrix}$$

5. $\frac{1}{10}\mathbf{A}=\begin{bmatrix} .1 & .2 & .1 \\ .3 & -.1 & -.1 \\ 0 & .2 & .3 \\ .1 & 0 & 0 \end{bmatrix} \qquad 4\mathbf{v}=\begin{bmatrix} -8 \\ -4 \\ 4 \\ 4 \end{bmatrix}$

6. $\mathbf{e}'\mathbf{v}=\mathbf{v}'\mathbf{e}=0$ **e** and **v** are orthogonal

$\mathbf{ef}'=\begin{bmatrix} 28 & 44 & 10 \\ 42 & 66 & 15 \\ 28 & 44 & 10 \\ 70 & 110 & 25 \end{bmatrix}$ $\mathbf{e}'\mathbf{f}$ not defined (not conformable)

$\mathbf{1}'\mathbf{v}=[1 \quad 1 \quad 1 \quad 1]\mathbf{v}=-1$

$\mathbf{1}_4'\mathbf{1}_4=4 \qquad \mathbf{e}'\mathbf{e}=10.5 \qquad \mathbf{v}'\mathbf{v}=7$ The sum of squared elements

$|\mathbf{e}|=\sqrt{10.5}=3.24 \qquad |\mathbf{v}|=\sqrt{7}=2.65$

$\mathbf{v}^*=\frac{1}{\sqrt{7}}\begin{bmatrix} -2 \\ -1 \\ 1 \\ 1 \end{bmatrix}=\begin{bmatrix} -.756 \\ -.378 \\ .378 \\ .378 \end{bmatrix} \qquad |\mathbf{v}^*|=1$

7. $\mathbf{AI} = \mathbf{IA} = \mathbf{A}$

$$\mathbf{AB} = \begin{bmatrix} 0 & 2 & 5 & 3 \\ 4 & 3 & 1 & 2 \\ -3 & -1 & 4 & 2 \\ 1 & 1 & 1 & 1 \end{bmatrix}$$

$\mathbf{A'B}$, $\mathbf{B'A}$ not defined (not conformable)

$$\mathbf{B'A'} = \begin{bmatrix} 0 & 4 & -3 & 1 \\ 2 & 3 & -1 & 1 \\ 5 & 1 & 4 & 1 \\ 3 & 2 & 2 & 1 \end{bmatrix}$$

$$\mathbf{DA} = \begin{bmatrix} 3 & 6 & 3 \\ 6 & -2 & -2 \\ 0 & 8 & 12 \\ 2 & 0 & 0 \end{bmatrix} \qquad \mathbf{BD} = \begin{bmatrix} 3 & 2 & 4 & 2 \\ 0 & 2 & 8 & 2 \\ -3 & -2 & 0 & 0 \end{bmatrix}$$

Premultiplication by **D** rescales rows of **A**. Postmultiplication rescales columns of **B**.

$$\mathbf{T+U} = \begin{bmatrix} 3.5 & 0 & 0 \\ 5.0 & 2.0 & 0 \\ 5.0 & 1.0 & 4.0 \end{bmatrix} \qquad \mathbf{TU} = \begin{bmatrix} 1.5 & 0 & 0 \\ 3.0 & 1.0 & 0 \\ 0 & 3.0 & 4.0 \end{bmatrix}$$

Both results are (lower) triangular matrices.

$$\mathbf{KK'} = \mathbf{K'K} = \begin{bmatrix} 1 & 0 & 0 \\ 0 & 1 & 0 \\ 0 & 0 & 1 \end{bmatrix}$$

K is orthonormal by rows and columns

$$\mathbf{A'A} = \begin{bmatrix} 11 & -1 & -2 \\ -1 & 9 & 9 \\ -2 & 9 & 11 \end{bmatrix} \qquad \mathbf{AA'} = \begin{bmatrix} 6 & 0 & 7 & 1 \\ 0 & 11 & -5 & 3 \\ 7 & -5 & 13 & 0 \\ 1 & 3 & 0 & 1 \end{bmatrix}$$

$$\mathbf{B'B} = \begin{bmatrix} 2 & 2 & 1 & 1 \\ 2 & 3 & 3 & 2 \\ 1 & 3 & 5 & 3 \\ 1 & 2 & 3 & 2 \end{bmatrix} \qquad \mathbf{BB'} = \begin{bmatrix} 4 & 4 & -2 \\ 4 & 6 & -1 \\ -2 & -1 & 2 \end{bmatrix}$$

$$\mathbf{A'DA} = \begin{bmatrix} 23 & 0 & -3 \\ 0 & 30 & 32 \\ -3 & 32 & 41 \end{bmatrix} \qquad \mathbf{BHB'} = \begin{bmatrix} 42 & 46 & -22 \\ 46 & 75 & -10 \\ -22 & -10 & 20 \end{bmatrix}$$

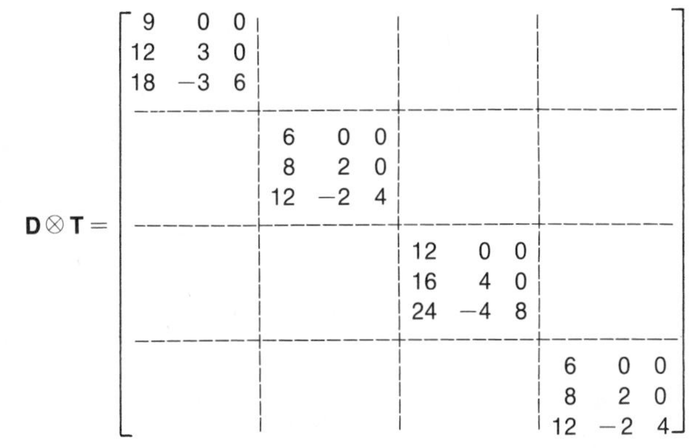

$$\mathbf{D} \otimes \mathbf{T} = \left[\begin{array}{ccc|ccc|ccc|ccc} 9 & 0 & 0 & & & & & & & & & \\ 12 & 3 & 0 & & & & & & & & & \\ 18 & -3 & 6 & & & & & & & & & \\ \hline & & & 6 & 0 & 0 & & & & & & \\ & & & 8 & 2 & 0 & & & & & & \\ & & & 12 & -2 & 4 & & & & & & \\ \hline & & & & & & 12 & 0 & 0 & & & \\ & & & & & & 16 & 4 & 0 & & & \\ & & & & & & 24 & -4 & 8 & & & \\ \hline & & & & & & & & & 6 & 0 & 0 \\ & & & & & & & & & 8 & 2 & 0 \\ & & & & & & & & & 12 & -2 & 4 \end{array}\right] \qquad \mathbf{f} \otimes \mathbf{v} = \begin{bmatrix} -56 \\ -28 \\ 28 \\ 28 \\ -88 \\ -44 \\ 44 \\ 44 \\ -20 \\ -10 \\ 10 \\ 10 \end{bmatrix}$$

(All missing elements zero)

$$e. = \frac{1}{4}(6) = 1.5 \qquad \mathbf{e} - e.\mathbf{1} = \begin{bmatrix} 1.0 \\ 1.5 \\ 1.0 \\ 2.5 \end{bmatrix} - \begin{bmatrix} 1.5 \\ 1.5 \\ 1.5 \\ 1.5 \end{bmatrix} = \begin{bmatrix} -.5 \\ 0 \\ -.5 \\ 1.0 \end{bmatrix}$$

Mean of elements Vector of mean deviations

$$\mathbf{GA} = \begin{bmatrix} 1 & 2 & 1 \\ 1 & 0 & 0 \\ 0 & 2 & 3 \\ 3 & -1 & -1 \end{bmatrix}$$ Rows of **A** rearranged

8. $$\mathbf{W} = \begin{bmatrix} 4.796 & 0 & 0 \\ 0 & 5.477 & 0 \\ -.626 & 5.843 & 2.543 \end{bmatrix}$$

$|\mathbf{W}| = 4.796\,(5.477)(2.543) = 66.80 \qquad |\mathbf{C}| = 66.80^2 = 4462.08$

$$\mathbf{W}^{-1} = \begin{bmatrix} .209 & 0 & 0 \\ 0 & .183 & 0 \\ .051 & -.420 & .393 \end{bmatrix} \qquad |\mathbf{W}^{-1}| = \frac{1}{66.80} = .0150$$

$$\mathbf{C}^{-1} = \begin{bmatrix} .046 & -.022 & .020 \\ -.022 & .210 & -.165 \\ .020 & -.165 & .154 \end{bmatrix} \qquad |\mathbf{C}^{-1}| = \frac{1}{4462.08} = .0002$$

$$\mathbf{A}^* = \begin{bmatrix} .209 & .365 & .395 \\ .626 & -.183 & .179 \\ 0 & .365 & .341 \\ .209 & 0 & .051 \end{bmatrix} \qquad \mathbf{R} = \begin{bmatrix} 4.796 & 0 & 0 \\ 0 & 5.477 & 0 \\ -.626 & 5.843 & 2.543 \end{bmatrix} \qquad \mathbf{A}(\mathbf{R}^{-1})' = \mathbf{A}^*$$

9. $r(\mathbf{A}) = r(\mathbf{A}'\mathbf{A}) = r(\mathbf{AA}') = 3 \qquad r(\mathbf{D}) = 4$
$|\mathbf{A}'\mathbf{A}| = 187 \qquad |\mathbf{AA}'| = 0 \qquad |\mathbf{D}| = 48 \qquad |\mathbf{AA}'\mathbf{D}| = 0$
$|\mathbf{G}| = -1 \qquad |\mathbf{GD}| = -48$

10. $\mathrm{tr}(\mathbf{TT}') = 67$

Appendix B

PROGRAM USER'S GUIDE

The following pages describe the input data to the computer program *MULTIVARIANCE: Univariate and multivariate analysis of variance, covariance, and regression—Version V (March, 1972)* (Finn, 1972d). MULTIVARIANCE is a FORTRAN IV program which performs the analyses discussed in this text. The MULTIVARIANCE program package and *User's Guide* are distributed by National Educational Resources, Inc., 215 Kenwood Avenue, Ann Arbor, Michigan 48103.

The five sample problems described in the text have been run with MULTIVARIANCE Version V. The input/output listings are contained in Appendix C. The description that follows is intended as a guide for reading the data listings. Parameters and options not directly germane to the analysis are omitted (for example, spacing, data screening, and punching codes). Control cards and parameters that are necessary to all runs are starred (*).

For analysis-of-variance designs, coded "Symbolic Contrast Vectors" substitute for the Kronecker product codes of Chapter 8. These utilize the same conventions as given in Chapter 8, but the Kronecker operator $\otimes$ is replaced by commas (,) for keypunching. Several additional examples of contrast coding are provided.

Key: b = blank column
0 = numeric zero
Ø = alphabetic "oh"

Phase 1—Input†

1. Title Cards*
   Card 1* Columns 1–60 Alphameric problem title
   Card 2* Columns 1–60 Alphameric problem title (continued)

2. Input Description Card*
   Cols. 1–4* Number of measured variables in input set. No distinction is made between dependent variables and covariates.

†Adapted from Chapters 2, 3, and 5 of *User's Guide—MULTIVARIANCE: Univariate and multivariate analysis of variance, covariance and regression—Version V (March, 1972)*; ©1972 by National Educational Resources, Inc. Used by permission of National Educational Resources, Inc., Ann Arbor, Mich.

Cols. 7–8* Number of factors (ways of classification) in analysis-of-variance design. For regression only, set to 1.

Col. 12* Data form code
- 1 = raw unsorted data, each observation with its own cell identification information
- 2 = raw data sorted by cells, each cell with its own header card
- 3 = raw data sorted by cells, no header cards
- 4 = within-group variance–covariance matrix and mean-frequency summary data
- 5 = raw unsorted data to be read from an independently prepared binary tape
- 6 = raw data grouped by subclasses to be read from an independently prepared binary tape
- 7 = within-group correlation matrix and mean-frequency summary data

Col. 16* Number of Variable Format Cards

Col. 20 Transformation code
- 1 = transformations
- b or 0 = no transformations

Cols. 21–24 Number of variables remaining after input variable transformations have have been performed (if different from columns 1–4).

Col. 28 Transformation matrix code
- 1 = read transformation matrix
- 2 = generate transformation matrix with Symbolic Contrast Vectors
- 3 = generate transformation matrix and orthonormalize leading rows
- 4 = read transformation matrix and orthonormalize leading rows
- b or 0 = no transformation matrix

Cols. 29–32 Number of variables remaining after transformation matrix has been applied (if different from columns 21–24).

Col. 40 Punched output code
- 1 = punch summary data (summary data will be printed whether or not this option is chosen)
- 2 = punch all scores after transformations (see Variable Format Cards)
- 3 = punch summary data and all scores after transformations
- b or 0 = do *not* punch summary data or scores after transformations

Col. 52 Data list code
- 1 = list all data before and after transformations
- b or 0 = list only first observation

Col. 64 Optional output code
- 1 = optional printed output requested throughout problem run
- b or 0 = normal printed output throughout problem run

3. Factor Identification Card(s)*
   Six-character factor names followed by four digits giving the number of levels for that factor. For regression analysis only, punch 1 in column 10.

4. Comments Cards
   Cols. 1–80 Comments, maximum of 300 cards

5. End-of-Comments Card*
   Cols. 1–6* FINISH

6. Variable Format Card(s)*
   Input: For data form 1 include format for observation and cell identification
   For data form 2 or 3 include format for dependent variables and covariates only

Output: If column 40 of the Input Description Card is 2 or 3, then the user must include a Variable Format Card describing the punched transformed scores.

7. Transformation Cards
   Cols. 1–4 Location of resultant variable
   Cols. 7–8 Transformation code (list in complete manual)
   Cols. 9–12 First variable to be transformed
   Cols. 13–16 Second variable to be transformed
   Cols. 17–20 Third variable to be transformed
   Cols. 21–30 Constant to be used in transformation

8. End-of-transformation Card
   Cols. 1–80 Blank; to be used only if Transformation Cards are used

9. Variable Label Cards*
   Six-column alphameric labels, 13 to a card, as many labels as variables after all transformations

10. Data*
    The data form code is punched in column 12 of the Input Description Card. For regression only, all observations are entered into cell "1."

    Data Form 1:
    Raw unsorted data, each observation with its own cell identification information

    Each observation is contained on one or more cards. The dependent variables and covariates are preceded by numbers identifying to which level the observation belongs on each factor of the design.

    For a 2×3 design (say sex by social class) a data card might be punched as follows:

    010306.211.5

    The identification vector (0103) indicates that this observation is of the first sex and the third social class. The scores on the two dependent variables of this observation are 6.2 and 11.5.

    The observations do not have to be sorted, and cell frequencies are accumulated automatically. The user does not have to account for missing cells. The Variable Format Card must contain Fixed Point fields describing the level identifying numbers and Floating Point fields for the other variables to be read.

    The last card(s) is one completely blank observation (i.e., the data are ended with as many blank cards as cards in any one observation).

    Data Form 2:
    Raw data sorted by cells, each cell with its own header card
    For each cell,
    (a) Header Card
        Cols. 1–6 Number of observations in the cell (NØBS)
        Cols. 7–10 Level on first factor named on Factor Identification Card
        Cols. 11–14 Level on second factor
        Cols. 15–18 Level on third factor
        .
        .
        .
        etc.
    (b) Observations for that cell (exactly NØBS observations)
    Last data card—*one blank card* following the observations of the last cell

    Data Form 3:
    Raw data sorted by cells, no header cards

(a) Vector of cell frequencies
(b) All data cards grouped by cells, in the same order as the vector of frequencies, no header cards

Data Form 4:
Within-group variance–covariance matrix and mean-frequency summary data
(a) Matrix of cell means one row at a time
(b) Vector of cell frequencies
(c) One Variable Format Card describing the within-cell variance–covariance matrix
(d) Pooled within-cell variance–covariance matrix

Data Form 5:
Raw unsorted data to be read from an independently prepared binary tape

Data Form 6:
Raw data grouped by subclasses to be read from an independently prepared binary tape

Data Form 7:
Within-group correlation matrix and mean-frequency summary data. Same as Data Form 4 except that the within-cell correlation matrix with standard deviations in diagonal positions replaces the variance–covariance matrix (d).

11. Transformation Matrix
If column 28 of the Input Description Card is 1 or 4:
(a) Variable Format Card describing one row of the matrix
(b) Matrix one row at a time
If column 28 of the Input Description Card is 2 or 3:
(a) Design Card
Cols. 1–4 Number of factors in design on dependent variables (within-subject factors)
Col. 8 Number of factors for arbitrary contrasts
Col. 12 Number of factors for orthogonal polynomials
Col. 16 1 = construct transformation matrix from contrast vectors
b or 0 = construct transformation matrix from basis vectors
(b) Factor Card for within-subject factors
Six-character within-subject factor names, followed by four digits giving the number of levels for that factor
(c) Arbitrary contrasts for transformation matrix
(d) Orthogonal polynomials for transformation matrix
(e) As many Symbolic Contrast Vectors as number of variables after transformation matrix

Phase II – Estimation

12. Estimation Specification Card*
Cols. 1–4* Rank of analysis-of-variance model for significance testing (l in Chapter 7). Total degrees of freedom for all between-cell hypotheses, including one for the grand mean. Set to zero for regression analysis only. May not exceed the number of nonempty cells in the design. Symbolic Contrast Vectors, each symbolizing a single-degree-of-freedom source of variation are entered at a later point in the input data deck.
Cols. 5–8 Rank of the model for estimation. Number of effects of which least-

squares estimates and their standard errors will be calculated and printed. Also number of effects to be included in model for predicting means and obtaining mean residuals (*c* in Chapter 8).

May not exceed rank of the model for significance testing. It may be set to zero if contrast estimates are not required. Estimated subclass and row and column means will be based on fitting a model of rank *c*. The residuals, if calculated, will be the remainder after a model of this rank has been fit to the data.

The rank of the model for significance testing (*l*) corresponds to between-cell contrasts that will be tested for significant contribution to criterion variation. At this point, the magnitude of the *c* leading contrasts and their standard errors may be calculated and printed.

Col. 12* Error term code (error term to be used in the analysis of variance)
b or 0 = Pooled within-group variance–covariance matrix
1 = Residual variance–covariance matrix, after variation corresponding to all degrees of freedom in the model for significance testing has been removed from the total variance–covariance matrix.
2 = Special effects, contrasts included in the model are used to obtain an error estimate. See columns 13–16.

Cols. 13–16 Degrees of freedom for error if special effects are used (if column 12 = 2). The *last* effects in the first order of the model for significance testing will be summed to form the error sum of products and variance–covariance matrix.

Cols. 17–20 Number of alternative orders of effects (contrasts) to be established, other than the first

Cols. 23–24 Number of factors in the analysis-of-variance design for which arbitrary contrasts will be used

Cols. 27–28 Number of factors in the design for which orthogonal polynomials will be used

Col. 32 Cell means and residuals code
1 = calculate and print estimated cell means and residuals
b or 0 = do not calculate and print estimated cell means and residuals

Col. 44 Combined means code
1 = print combined observed means and *N*'s
2 = print combined estimated means
3 = print both observed and estimated combined means
b or 0 = no combined means
(If option 1, 2 or 3 is selected, the following card must be a Means Key.)

Col. 48 Orthogonal analysis code
1 = completely orthogonal analysis
b or 0 = general nonorthogonal analysis

13. Means Key

If column 44 of the Estimation Specification Card is 1, 2 or 3, a Means Key is entered at this point, to determine which observed and/or estimated combinations of subclass means are to be computed.

The Means Key treats the factors in the order in which they appear on the Factor Identification Card. For example, if that card were

SEXbbbbbb2MAJØRbbbb5TRTMTbbbb3

then SEX would be considered factor 1, MAJØR factor 2, and TRTMT factor 3. To obtain means on all criterion variables for both levels of the sex factor, across all other factors, the Means Key is

1. MEANS KEY

This would produce a table of means for all males and another for all females.

To obtain means for each combination of levels of certain factors, an asterisk (*) is interposed between the numbers of the factors. For example, the Means Key to obtain means for each combination of the levels of sex and treatment would be

1*3. MEANS KEY

The Means Key to print overall means for all subjects, for each treatment level, for each treatment level of each sex group, and for each treatment level of each major, is

0, 3, 1*3, 2*3. MEANS KEY

Requests are separated by commas, and ended with a period. Comments may fill the remainder of the card.

14. Arbitrary Contrast Matrices
If program's "standard" contrasts are not applicable
   (a) Factor Name Card; columns 1–6 contain factor name as it appears on the Factor Identification Card
   (b) Variable Format Card describing one row of contrast matrix
   (c) Contrast matrix one row at a time
15. Orthogonal Polynomials
   (a) Factor Name Card; columns 1–6 contain factor name exactly as it appears on the Factor identification Card; column 10 equals 1 for user-supplied metric, blank or 0 for evenly spaced metric
   (b) Arbitrary metric for orthogonal polynomials, if col. 10 of preceding card is 1
16. Symbolic Contrast Vectors (SCV's)*
There are as many Symbolic Contrast Vectors as indicated in columns 1–4 of the Estimation Specification Card (rank of model for significance testing). Each SCV defines either the general mean or one contrast to be made among the cells of the design. Each SCV, which corresponds to one between-cell degree of freedom, is punched on one Symbolic Contrast Vector card. *Each SCV causes the program's basis generator to produce one column of a basis for the model.* The order in which these cards are entered is the original order of effects in the model for significance testing.

Four types of contrasts are allowed by the program plus a nesting vector, and an option for using arbitrary contrasts of the user's own construction:
   (a) "C" or simple contrasts, in which all levels but one of a given factor are contrasted with the one omitted. For a three-level factor, the contrasts might compare the first level with the second level and the third level with the second level, respectively.
   (b) "D" or deviation contrasts, in which all but the last level of a given factor are compared to the mean of all levels of the factor.
   (c) "H" or Helmert contrasts, in which cells 1 through $a-1$ are compared with the cells following, where a is the total number of levels of the factor. In a four-level factor, the H contrasts would compare cell 1 to the average of cells 2 through 4, cell 2 to the average of cells 3 and 4, and cell 3 with cell 4, respectively.
   (d) "I" or a column of an identity matrix used in constructing a basis for nested designs.

(e) "L" or optional contrasts, entered by the user
(f) "P" or orthogonal polynomials

Accompanying each contrast code is a number indicating which of the contrasts is desired. Zero indicates grand mean, or constant term, of the model.
For example:

H1, would indicate the first possible Helmert contrast, which would be cell 1 contrasted with the average of all the remaining levels of that factor.
D3, would indicate cell 3 contrasted with the mean of all cells for that factor.
C0, would indicate grand mean and that simple contrasts will be used.

Rules of thumb:

(a) If indicating a list of "C" contrasts, say C1, C2, and C4, the number omitted will be the cell to which the others will be compared (in this case, the third).
(b) In "H" or "D" contrasts, the number to be omitted must be the last; e.g. for a four-level factor, the D contrasts would be D1, D2, D3.
(c) In "L" or "P" contrasts, the number indicates the row of the respective contrast matrix to be used.
(d) In all cases, the letter-number combination signifies an entire *contrast vector* for one factor of the design. (Thus it represents more than a single group number or weight.)
(e) To estimate common anova parameters (μ, α_j, β_k, etc.), deviation (D) contrasts are required.

Every indicated contrast is followed by a comma (as shown in the examples). The *l*th comma indicates the end of that part of the contrast pertaining to the *l*th factor of the design. The comma replaces the Kronecker operator $\otimes$ of Chapter 8. Comments may fill unused card columns.

Example 1
For a one-way (one factor) design with five levels, for which it is desired to compare the first (say, control group) to all others, the SCV's would be:

```
C0,   GRAND MEAN
 2,   LEVEL 2—LEVEL 1 (CØNTRØL)
 3,   LEVEL 3—LEVEL 1 (CØNTRØL)
 4,   LEVEL 4—LEVEL 1 (CØNTRØL)
 5,   LEVEL 5—LEVEL 1 (CØNTRØL)
```

Unless it is desired to change contrast types (for a given factor), the alphabetic contrast code can be omitted from all but the first SCV.

Example 2
Consider a 2×3 ($A \times B$) crossed design in which it is desired to contrast the two *A* groups with each other and to contrast the first with the second and third, and the second with the third level, on the three-level factor. The SCV's would read:

```
C0, H0,   GRAND MEAN ØF BØTH FACTØRS                  (I)
 1,  0,   A1–A2, GRAND MEAN ØF B                      (II)
          [levels of B all weighted equally for this contrast]
 0,  1,   GRAND MEAN ØF A, B1—(B2+B3)/2               (III)
 0,  2,   GRAND MEAN ØF A, B2—B3                      (IV)
 1,  1,   INTERACTIØN ØF II AND III                   (V)
 1,  2,   INTERACTIØN ØF II AND IV                    (VI)
```

The contrast to the left of the first comma pertains to the first factor on the Factor Identification Card, that to the left of the second comma to the second factor, etc.

Note how this compares to a "traditional" anova table:

Source	Degrees of Freedom	Corresponding SCV's
Grand Mean	1	I
A	$a-1$ (=1)	II
B	$b-1$ (=2)	III, IV
$A\times B$	$(a-1)(b-1)$ (=2)	V, VI

Example 3

Consider a 2×3×3 three-way design for which orthogonal polynomials have bee entered to find the linear and quadratic trends of the second factor. This is th example given on page 238, and in Table 7.4.1. The SCV's are:

Symbolic Vector	**Comment**
C0, P0, C0,	GENERAL MEAN
1, 0, 0,	A1–A2
0, 1, 0,	LINEAR B
0, 2, 0,	QUADRATIC B
0, 0, 1,	C1–C3
0, 0, 2,	C2–C3
1, 1, 0,	LINEAR A B INTERACTIØN
1, 2, 0,	QUADRATIC A B INTERACTIØN
1, 0, 1,	A×C INTERACTIØN
1, 0, 2,	A×C INTERACTIØN
0, 1, 1,	B×C INTERACTIØN
0, 1, 2,	B×C INTERACTIØN
0, 2, 1,	B×C INTERACTIØN
0, 2, 2,	B×C INTERACTIØN
1, 1, 1,	A×B×C INTERACTIØN
1, 1, 2,	A×B×C INTERACTIØN
1, 2, 1,	A×B×C INTERACTIØN
1, 2, 2,	A×B×C INTERACTIØN

Example 4

The basis of a *nested* sampling design with the structure:

A_1					A_2								
B_1			B_2		B_3			B_4		B_5			
C_1	C_2	C_3	C_4	C_5	C_6	C_7	C_8	C_9	C_{10}	C_{11}	C_{12}	C_{13}	C_{14}

could be generated symbolically by:

Symbolic Vector	**Comment**
C0, D0, D0,	GENERAL MEAN
1, 0, 0,	A1–A2
I1, 1, 0,	B CØNTRAST IN A1
2, 1, 0,	B CØNTRAST IN A2 (1)
2, 2, 0,	B CØNTRAST IN A2 (2)
1, I1, 1,	C CØNTRAST IN B1 IN A1 (1)
1, 1, 2,	C CØNTRAST IN B1 IN A1 (2)
1, 2, 1,	C CØNTRAST IN B2 IN A1

Symbolic Vector			Comment
2,	1,	1,	C CØNTRAST IN B3 IN A2 (1)
2,	1,	2,	C CØNTRAST IN B3 IN A2 (2)
2,	2,	1,	C CØNTRAST IN B4 IN A2
2,	3,	1,	C CØNTRAST IN B5 IN A2 (1)
2,	3,	2,	C CØNTRAST IN B5 IN A2 (2)
2,	3,	3,	C CØNTRAST IN B5 IN A2 (3)

This design is regarded as an incomplete 2×3×4 design with non-empty cells as follows:

A_1												A_2											
B_1				B_2				-				B_3				B_4				B_5			
C_1	C_2	C_3	-	C_4	C_5	-	-	-	-	-	-	C_6	C_7	C_8	-	C_9	C_{10}	-	-	C_{11}	C_{12}	C_{13}	C_{14}

The grand mean is almost always included as a first SCV, unlike tables shown in most statistics texts.

There are always as many symbolic codes (grand mean or otherwise) indicated on each SCV as there are factors in the design. When indicating a main-effect contrast for one factor, the other factors may be set to zero, indicating "grand mean" for those factors, i.e., "not involved" in the contrast.

Spacing. The SCV's may be punched one to a card in columns 1 through 74. Any number of embedded blanks is allowed. The columns following the last comma should be used to provide a description of the contrast, as in the examples.

Repeat Code. MULTIVARIANCE provides a "repeat code" which reduces the number of SCV cards that must be prepared. The convention which has been adopted is a code of the form

$$nCm,$$

which will represent Symbolic Vectors

$$\begin{array}{l} Cm, \\ C(m+1), \\ C(m+2), \\ \vdots \\ C(m+n-1), \end{array}$$

For example, 6I2, would represent

I2,
I3,
I4,
I5,
I6,
I7,

The number preceding the alphabetic contrast-type code determines the number of vectors to be generated. The first such vector will contain the contrast of that card, i.e. *Cm*,. Each of the $n-1$ remaining vectors assumes the same letter code and a number code increased by one.

The repeat code may be used for designs with more than a single factor. For example

C0, 3C0, H1,

would generate the Symbolic Vectors

C0, C0, H1,
C0, C1, H1,
C0, C2, H1,

17. Contrast Reordering Keys
    As many keys as indicated in columns 17–20 of the Estimation Specification Card. Each key may contain no more elements than the rank of the model for significance testing (number of contrasts) and begins on a new card. The key contains the desired new order of the basis vectors (i.e., the vector to be ordered first has its subscript first, the second vector in the new order has its subscript second, etc.). The original order is the order in which the SCV cards are entered in the input data deck. The reordering numbers are separated by commas and ended with a period. The format of the card is completely free.

    For example, a key to reorder the *B* factor first in the two-way SCV example would read:

    1, 3, 4, 2, 5, 6. REØRDER

    Since the interaction terms will not be altered by interchanging the preceding effects they may be ignored in the alternate orders. Therefore, a Contrast Reordering Key containing all effects of interest in the second order would be

    1, 3, 4, 2. REØRDER

    Thus fewer columns are orthogonalized in the alternate order.

Phase III – Analysis

The following set of cards (Analysis Selection Card, Variable Select Key, Covariate Grouping Key, and Hypothesis Test Cards) may be repeated any number of times.

18. Analysis Selection Card*

Cols. 1–4*	Number of dependent variables to be selected from the input set (p).
Cols. 5–8	Number of covariates for analysis of covariance, or predictor variables for regression (q). Rank of regression model.
Col. 12	Variable selection code. 1=variables are to be deleted or rearranged to obtain the desired sets. b or 0=variables are in correct sets and order as entered in Phase I. (Covariates must follow dependent variables in Phase III.)
Cols. 13–16	Number of alternative contrast orders to be run with this set of variables – other than the first.
Col. 20	Principal components code. 1 = principal components of correlation matrix 2 = principal components of covariance matrix b or 0 = no principal components
Col. 24	Discriminant function analysis code. 1 = perform discriminant analysis b or 0 = do not perform discriminant analysis
Col. 32	Canonical correlation code. 1 = perform canonical correlation analysis if there are covariates (predictors) b or 0 = do not perform canonical correlation analysis
Col. 36	Covariate grouping code. 1 = covariates (predictors) are to be entered into regression by user's key b or 0 = covariates (predictors) are to be entered one-at-a-time (all $q_{h_j} = 1$) Ignore if no covariates.

Col. 40 Parallelism code.
1 = perform test of parallelism of regression planes
b or 0 = do not perform test of parallelism of regression planes

19. Variable Select Key
If column 12 of the Analysis Selection Card is 1, then this key is prepared with $p+q$ elements indicating the variable order and placed in the input data deck at this point. Elements are separated by commas, and ended with a period.

For example, if it is desired to select the tenth, eleventh, and fourteenth of the original input variables as dependent and the second as a covariate, the key would read:

10, 11, 14, 2. VAR SELECT

20. Covariate (Predictor) Grouping Key
If column 36 of the Analysis Selection Card is 1, then this key is prepared with elements (q_{h_j}) indicating the numbers of covariates to be added to the regression equation, and placed in the input data deck at this point. Covariates are taken successively in the order in which they have been selected by the Variable Select Key or by their order when input to the program. Elements separated by commas, ended with a period.

For example, if five predictors were chosen, and we wish to test the joint contribution of the first four, and then the additional contribution of the fifth, the key would read

4, 1.

21. Hypothesis Test Card(s)*
At this point, the contrasts (corresponding to degrees of freedom) may be grouped and tested by analysis of variance or covariance. There should be one Hypothesis Test Card for the original contrast order plus one for each alternative order indicated in columns 13–16 of the Analysis Selection Card.

These numbers are the n_{h_j} values of Chapter 9, and determine the number of rows of **U** which form the hypothesis matrix.

The grouping of effects will begin with the first Symbolic Contrast Vector entered into the program and will proceed in the order in which the SCV's follow one another. Effects may be tested for significance individually or may be combined to test the significance of main effects, interactions, or parts of them. Each group of degrees of freedom to be tested is separated by commas and ended with a period.

If the "degrees of freedom" number is negative, tests of those contrasts will be skipped. If no degrees of freedom are given and only a period is punched, only the regression analysis of the dependent variables on the covariates will be performed.

Example
In the 2×3 crossed design the Hypothesis Test Card might read:

−1, 1, 2, 2. FIRST ØRDER

The −1 indicates skipping the significance test for the general mean (corresponding to the first SCV). The 1 indicates a one-degree-of-freedom test of the two-level factor (corresponding to the second SCV). The first 2 indicates a two-degree-of-freedom test of the three-level factor (corresponding to the third and fourth SCV's), and the second 2 indicates the test of the interaction.

Note that the numbers in this case correspond to the degrees of freedom in the traditional analysis-of-variance table. If, however, one-degree-of-freedom tests of the two *B* contrasts are desired, the card would read:

−1, 1, 1, 1, 2. 1-DF TESTS

If effects *B* and *A* had been reversed in order, a second Hypothesis Test Card corresponding to testing the effects in the second order might read:

−1, 2, 1, 2. REØRDER A AND B

22. End-of-job Card*
This is the last card of the problem deck and is blank except for columns 60 ff. The format of the End-of-job Card is as follows:

Cols. 60–67 CØNTINUE If data and program control cards for another problem run follow immediately

or

Cols. 60–63 STØP If this is the end of the last (or only) problem run

In case an error is encountered during the run, MULTIVARIANCE will ignore all cards until the End-of-job Card is encountered. If CØNTINUE has been punched, the next problem will be attempted. Any number of problem decks may be stacked.

Appendix C*

INPUT–OUTPUT LISTINGS FOR FIVE SAMPLE PROBLEMS*

The following pages contain printouts of the input decks, including all data cards, for the five sample problems discussed in the text. Each deck has been prepared for the MULTIVARIANCE program, as specified in Appendix B. The design and control card setup is described in the Comments section of the data deck. Following the input listing, the output which results from running the data with the MULTIVARIANCE program is reproduced. The analysis and results correspond to the presentations of Chapters 1 through 10.

Sample Problem	Beginning page	
	Input listing	Output listing
1. Creativity and achievement	C. 1	C. 5
2. Word memory experiment	C. 22	C. 26
3. Dental calculus reduction	C. 56	C. 61
4. Essay grading study	C. 107	C. 112
5. Programmed instruction effects	C. 147	C. 151

*From *Listing of Sample Problem Output-MULTIVARIANCE: Univariate and multivariate analysis of variance, covariance, and regression—Version V (March 1972).* (Ann Arbor, Mich.: National Educational Resources, Inc., 1972). Used by permission of National Educational Resources, Inc.